Microcomputer Design and Construction

Building Your Own System
with the Motorola 6800

Microcomputer Design and Construction

Building Your Own System with the Motorola 6800

Alan Clements
Teesside Polytechnic,
England

Prentice/Hall  International

Englewood Cliffs, New Jersey · London · New Delhi
Sydney · Toronto · Tokyo · Singapore · Wellington

Library of Congress Cataloging in Publication Data

Clements, Alan, 1948–
Microcomputer design and construction.

Bibliography: p.
Includes index.
1. Microcomputers—Amateurs' manuals.
2. MC6800 (Computer) I. Title.
TK9969.C56 621.3819'58 81-15835
ISBN 0-13-580738-7 AACR2

British Library Cataloguing in Publication Data

Clements, Alan
Microcomputer design and construction.
1. Microcomputers—Design and construction—
Amateurs' manuals
I. Title
621.3819'5835 TK9969

ISBN 0-13-580738-7

ISBN 0-13-580738-7

PRENTICE-HALL INTERNATIONAL, INC., *London*
PRENTICE-HALL OF AUSTRALIA PTY., LTD., *Sydney*
PRENTICE-HALL CANADA, INC., *Toronto*
PRENTICE-HALL OF INDIA PRIVATE LIMITED, *New Delhi*
PRENTICE-HALL OF JAPAN, INC., *Tokyo*
PRENTICE-HALL OF SOUTHEAST ASIA PTE., LTD., *Singapore*
PRENTICE-HALL, INC., *Englewood Cliffs, New Jersey*
WHITEHALL BOOKS LIMITED, *Wellington, New Zealand*

Printed in the United States of America

10 9 8 7 6 5 4 3 2

To
Sue,
my parents,
Heinz, Margarete,
Klaus, Gabi and little Anne

Contents

List of Main Circuit Diagrams

Figure	*Page*	
2.5	26	The TS1 power supply
3.17	48	The clock generator and control circuit of the TS1
4.15	76-77	The TS1 bus interface
4.18	80-81	The TS1 clock generator and bus interface
5.42	158-59	RAM module circuit diagram
6.5	175	The PIC on the CPU module
6.11	186-87	The PIA on the CPU module
6.14	201	The ACIA on the CPU module
6.19	211	The PTM on the CPU module
6.42	258-59	Memory-mapped display
6.46	266-67	A VDT using the Thomson-Efcis CRT controller
6.53	276-77	The bus extender circuit
6.54	281	The TS1 bus terminator network
6.61	292-93	A dual channel D/A convertor
6.70	305	The interface between the TS1 microprocessor system and the ADC0817 A/D convertor
6.71	308-309	An example of the use of an A/D convertor and D/A convertor as a signal processor
6.91	354-55	The address decoder and bus interface circuits of the special interface module
6.92	358-59	The EPROM, RAM, and PIA on the special interface module
6.93	360-61	The multiplier and APU sections of the special interface module
6.95	364-65	The complete circuit diagram of the special interface module
7.13	388-89	The slave-processor module

Preface

This book is different. It has not been written to compete with the proliferation of other works on the operation of microprocessors, but to complement them. In at least one sense, this book is autobiographical because it mirrors my own experience with microprocessors. When I first started building microprocessor systems in 1975, practical information was difficult to come by. Apart from the standard books on digital design and computer architecture, there were only manufacturers' data sheets to help the designer. This book is designed to bridge the gap between textbooks and data sheets. In short, it tells the reader how to go about building a microprocessor system.

Books are written for people to read, which is rather a mixed blessing. On the one hand, people buy books, which helps the author a little (and the publisher a lot); on the other hand it is difficult to pitch the level of a book at that of some hypothetical standard reader. Some readers are electrical engineering graduates who wish to build a microprocessor system to control a motor, while other readers are computer science graduates who want to implement a database on a microprocessor. I have tried to compromise between these two extremes and have assumed that the reader has some knowledge of basic electronics, digital circuitry, microprocessor fundamentals and programming. For those who need to brush up on any of these topics, the bibliography provides some suitable references.

My approach to writing this book is to deal with each of the component parts of a microprocessor system in general, and then to choose a particular arrangement as part of the microprocessor system (the TS1—derived from "Teesside One") which unfolds throughout this book. This is in contrast with the typical magazine article which, although excellent, often presents the circuit diagram of a microprocessor system as a *fait accompli,* leaving the poor reader to puzzle out the details. By the time the reader has gone through this book he should be able to design a microprocessor system to his own specifications.

It is difficult to know where to begin and where to end when writing a practical guide to microprocessor system design. I have attempted to deal with the design of a microprocessor system from the power supply to the VDT. Some more advanced topics—multiple microprocessor systems, analog-to-digital conversion, and external processing have been included to broaden the scope of the book.

Chapter 1 gives a brief résumé of the microprocessor revolution and defines the object of the book.

Chapter 2 discusses the overall structure of the TS1 microprocessor system. In this chapter the bus used by the TS1 is defined, and the construction of a suitable power supply described. Power supplies may seem out of place here, but I have tried to deal with as many of the practical aspects of a microprocessor system as time and space allow.

Chapter 3 deals with the clock circuit which generates the timing signals required to synchronize the microprocessor system. Various ways of modifying the operation of the clock generator to deal with slow memories and direct memory-access systems are described. At the end of this chapter, the clock pulse generator circuit and its interface to the microprocessor is provided.

Chapter 4 is concerned with the electrical characteristics of the data highways, or buses, which link together the various modules, or subsystems, of the TS1 microprocessor system. This chapter concludes with the circuit diagram of the system bus interface and its control circuits found on the CPU module of TS1.

Chapter 5 begins with a general introduction to the properties of semiconductor memories found in microprocessor systems and includes a discussion of the timing diagrams of memory components and how they must be matched to the CPU's own timing diagrams. The principal part of this chapter is concerned with the way in which memory devices are connected to the system address bus. This topic is called address decoding. This chapter ends with a description of the memory components found on TS1's CPU module, and the circuit diagram of a 24K-byte memory module with facilities for write-protecting each 4K block of memory.

Chapter 6 deals with the broad subject of input and output techniques, and is subdivided into nine parts. Section 6.1 looks at the subject of interrupt handling. Section 6.2 describes the properties of three of the most popular interface chips found in microprocessor systems—parallel interfaces, serial interfaces, and counter-timers.

Sections 6.3 and 6.4 describe the operation of the popular ASCII-encoded keyboard and the serial data link between the keyboard and the computer. Section 6.5 is unusual as it both describes the operation of, and gives the circuit of, two VDTs. This section is included because the VDT is often an intimate part of the microprocessor system rather than an add-on peripheral. Section 6.6 describes the bus extender module. This allows the TS1 microprocessor system to be extended to an external memory module. Sections 6.7 and 6.8 deal, respectively, with the ways in which digital signals are converted into analog form and vice versa. This topic is important because it enables the microprocessor to read an analog quantity (temperature, pressure, etc.), process it digitally and then to output an analog quantity (a control signal). Section 6.9 shows how the power of a microprocessor may be augmented by adding external arithmetic processors to the system on a "subcontracting" basis. Two devices considered are the multiplier chip which forms the product of two numbers by means of combinatorial logic, and the arithmetic processor unit, which is able to execute floating-point arithmetic operations.

Chapter 7 has been included to give the reader an insight into, and an overview of, multiple processor systems. As the price of the microprocessor chip continues to tumble, it becomes more and more attractive to use several microprocessors in the same system. This arrangement enables the cheap but powerful microprocessors to share expensive peripherals. One of the purposes of this chapter is to describe a single-board microcomputer which may be operated as a slave processor by coupling it to TS1's CPU module. This single-board computer may, of course, be operated on its own, independently of the TS1 microprocessor system. One of the purposes of including this slave processor module is to provide a design example of a basic microprocessor system in contrast with the more sophisticated TS1.

Chapter 8 considers the software requirements of a small microprocessor system. In the first part of this chapter the requirements of a typical microprocessor monitor are described. The design of a monitor, "TS1BUG", enabling programs to be entered into the system memory, modified and then executed, is given. Considerable emphasis is placed on the way in which the monitor deals with input and output operations. This chapter ends with an assembled listing of TS1BUG with comments.

Chapter 9 takes a brief look at the way in which the TS1 microprocessor system is constructed and provides the user with some hints for debugging the system.

There are four appendices presenting background information which would be out of place in the main text. Appendix A1 considers, in some detail, the factors which affect the design of a power supply. Appendix A2 gives part of the data sheet of the 6800 CPU, while Appendix A3 gives some details of two widely used interface devices found on RS232C serial data links. Appendix A4 provides a program for controlling the memory-mapped VDT presented in Section 6.5.

As I have set out to show the reader how a microprocessor system may be designed I have been forced to choose a particular microprocessor. The whole point of this book is to get away from the generalizations found in other texts and to consider the design of a microprocessor system in detail. I have chosen the 6800 microprocessor system for several reasons, but principally because it is easy to work with and its assembly language is easy to learn and use. I feel that this book (parts of which are processor independent in any case) will still be of value to the designers of systems on other CPUs.

At this point it is appropriate to give the reader a comment and a word of warning. This book is not a "Heathkit" construction manual. Such manuals are provided with the kits produced by Heath Electonics and are renowned for their great clarity and step-by-step approach to kit construction. If I had resorted to this approach my book would have been a failure and the reader would have learned little by blindly copying my example. It is my sincere hope that the reader will be able to build a better microprocessor system than the TS1. He should be able to tailor his computer to his own specific needs, cutting out any unnecessary frills that I have provided. Furthermore, the reader has this book to help him. I had no such book. If I were to start again my next computer would be very different from the

TS1. As time passes, techniques change and new components are introduced, forcing changes in system design by providing more cost-effective solutions to design problems.

Now for the warning. Never trust no-one! This book does not replace thought—it only augments it. I designed the circuits of the TS1, built them, tested them and, where necessary, modified them. These circuits were then incorporated into my text. This text was then re-drawn by professional draftsmen. It is possible that errors may have crept into this chain of events. For example, pin 7 of an integrated circuit may end up labelled as pin 1, with unfortunate consequences to the reader who constructs things blindly. Be skeptical—cross check all information wherever possible.

ACKNOWLEDGEMENTS

The greatest source of help in writing this book has been my wife, Sue, who has carefully read through successive drafts and provided many helpful suggestions in matters of style. Without her encouragement and prodding I might never have finished this book. I would also like to thank the typists at Teesside Polytechnic who prepared the manuscript, and Dr John Darby, my Head of Department, who provided me with some of the facilities for the construction of the TS1, and who spared me so much of the administrative aggro involved in teaching while I was working on this project.

Technical data relating to the MC6800 and other associated products described in this publication is reproduced by kind permission of Motorola Semiconductors.

Motorola reserves the right to make any changes to any products herein to improve reliability, function or design. Motorola does not assume any liability arising out of the application or use of any product or circuit described herein; neither does it convey any license under its patent rights nor the rights of others.

Finally, I should like to thank many of the companies who gave me varying amounts of help and sometimes even free samples!

Microcomputer Design and Construction

Building Your Own System
with the Motorola 6800

1

Introduction

1.1 THE MICROPROCESSOR REVOLUTION

A few years ago the word "microprocessor" was known only to a small group of engineers. Today the microprocessor is discussed in television programs; the financial pages of newspapers chart the growth of the microprocessor industry; union leaders worry about its devastating impact on their members; and government ministers suddenly find themselves confronted by an explosion of high technology.

Everybody has heard about the computer revolution. In fact there has been no revolution—computer science and technology have advanced at an accelerating pace leading to a rapid evolution which has been confused with a revolution. Mechanized computation has a long history of successive developments resulting from a marriage of technology and the desire for improved computational power. Some of the early mechanical calculating machines were a product of the industrial revolution and the need to produce the accurate mathematical tables required by navigators in an age of expansion. Early electronic computers used valves to perform the complex calculations required to get shells from point A to point B, a process necessitated by the Second World War. After the war computers were applied to data processing (as opposed to purely mathematical computation), and the age of the final demand for $0.00 from the electricity company had begun.

In the 1950s the thermionic valve, with its high power dissipation and unreliability, began to be replaced by the germanium transistor and later by the silicon transistor. Transistors occupy a much smaller volume than valves, and dissipate a tiny fraction of the power consumed by them. This led to smaller computers with increased computational power and reliability. In the 1960s semiconductor manufacturers began to fabricate several transistors on a single piece of silicon (chip) to produce a circuit which could be used as a building block in a system. As time passed, manufacturers were able to put more and more transistors on a single chip of silicon, and the building blocks grew from simple logic functions to subsystems such as arithmetic logic units. By 1969 Intel, using metal oxide semiconductor technology (MOS), succeeded in producing the 8008, a single component having the same basic structure as a general-purpose digital computer.

Since then a large number of manufacturers have created a rapid proliferation of microprocessor chips and their support components. Because the manufacture of silicon chips is highly automated, the cost of the chips is falling rapidly. At the same time improvements in the photolithography used in the production of chips has led to a new generation of components capable of operating at ever-increasing clock rates. Although semiconductor technology has advanced to a state where tens of thousands of transistors can now be placed on one chip, there has been no corresponding great leap forward in the architecture of microprocessors. The basic structure, or architecture, of the microprocessor is that of the von Neumann machine which was proposed in the 1940s. Perhaps a true computer revolution will occur when today's semiconductor technology is applied to a radically new computer architecture.

The low cost of microprocessors has enabled computer power to be brought to the simplest and most mundane devices, from automated petrol pumps to robots used in undersea exploration. An executive of a company manufacturing microprocessors once told an engineer that a microprocessor with the computational power of one of today's large mainframe computers would soon be available, and inquired what the engineer would do with such a powerful device. The engineer replied that he would put it in a washing machine. The astonished executive asked why. "I'd make the washing machine understand the spoken command", said the engineer.

1.2 OBJECTIVE

Now that the microprocessor is being used in such a wide range of applications a number of books have been written explaining the operation of the microprocessor, and comparing the various microprocessors available today. Unfortunately, very few books give the designer or engineer any idea how he may go about designing a complete system. The design of any system is always a compromise between the various options open to the designer. It is hoped that this book will provide the reader with an insight into some of the ways in which components may be combined together to build a system.

The design of any system should begin with a formulation of its precise aims and objectives. Clearly, the system cannot be optimized until the designer knows exactly what its function is to be. For the purpose of this book a general-purpose microprocessor system will be considered. Such a system may be used as a home computer by the enthusiast, as a vehicle for the study and teaching of microprocessor systems, or as a microprocessor-development system. The overall objective is to produce a versatile system which may readily be expanded at a later date to suit the requirements of the user. To avoid continual references to "the microprocessor system" this will be referred to throughout the book as the TS1.

2

The TS1

In this chapter four aspects of the TS1 microprocessor system are dealt with. As the nature of a microprocessor system is so heavily affected by the particular microprocessor at its heart, we begin with a description of the actual microprocessor chosen for the TS1. This is followed by an outline of the TS1 microprocessor system and the functions of the various modules making up the TS1. Because the way in which the modules of the TS1 communicate with each other is of great importance in both defining the physical construction of the system and some of its electrical properties, the third part of this section is concerned with the design of a bus, or backplane, linking all modules together. The final part of this section deals with the power supply. A power supply is vital to the operation of any microprocessor system, and it is essential that the designer is familiar with its operation and characteristics.

2.1 THE CHOICE OF THE MICROPROCESSOR

A major step in the design of any microprocessor system is the selection of the microprocessor itself. This choice is not effortless, but it is not quite as difficult as the bewildering array of currently available chips would suggest. The importance of selecting the best chip for any given application lies in the fact that the microprocessor chip has a profound effect on some aspects of the microprocessor system. The use of the word "best" in the above sentence is somewhat unscientific as there is no simple figure of merit which can be applied to a microprocessor chip. The importance of choosing an adequate microprocessor can be seen from the following example. When putting together a Hi-Fi system the buyer knows that he can always improve its performance by substituting a better loudspeaker or amplifier at some later date. This type of action is not open to the microprocessor systems designer. He cannot choose an 8-bit microprocessor today, and then improve the accuracy of its computations by swapping if for a 16-bit processor later.

The microprocessor is the heart of the TS1 and determines the nature of the entire system. Great care must be exercised in the choice of a microprocessor. Some of the criteria by which this choice may be made are given below.

Cost This factor has been included not to demonstrate the importance of the microprocessor's cost in the development of a general-purpose microprocessor system, but rather to indicate the irrelevance of cost as a factor. To illustrate this point consider the following examples. A washing-machine manufacturer selects microprocessor *A* rather than microprocessor *B*, if *A* costs $5 less than *B*. This is because the electronic system found in a washing machine is fairly simple and $5 is a relatively large fraction of the overall cost. Furthermore, as washing machines are manufactured in large quantities, the total saving made by selecting microprocessor *A* may be very large indeed. When a microprocessor is to be selected for a general-purpose digital computer things are very different. Now, the cost of the microprocessor chip itself represents only a tiny fraction of the cost of the whole system, especially if a large quantity of memory is needed. There are some very low-cost microprocessors available which are well-suited to the role of an intelligent controller. These microprocessors should not be used to produce a "poor man's minicomputer".

Architecture The architecture of a microprocessor is its internal structure. It is the architecture of a microprocessor that determines what it can do and how its operations are carried out. Most currently available microprocessors, suitable for use in a general-purpose microprocessor system, have either 8-bit or 16-bit architectures. Some devices have an internal 16-bit architecture but interface with external components through an 8-bit data bus. Such an arrangement gives the engineer the computational power of the 16-bit machine while allowing the use of low-cost 8-bit data buses and peripherals. This book does not deal with 16-bit microprocessors as their cost and complexity requires a larger and more expensive system than is described here.

The most popular 8-bit microprocessors which are well-suited to the general-purpose digital computer are the 8080A, 8085, Z80, 6800, 6809 and 6502. All these microprocessors have broadly similar architectures and may be regarded as mainstream devices. There are, of course, important differences between them: the nature of the instruction set, the addressing modes, the number of on-chip registers, the way in which interrupts are handled, etc. The significance of these differences is, unfortunately, not always apparent, and it is difficult to make a meaningful comparison of one device with another. Sometimes comparisons are made between competing devices in terms of "benchmarks"—sample programs which may be run on several different machines so that their execution times may be compared. However, the man who said, "There are lies, damned lies and statistics", would have re-phrased this expression if he had ever come across benchmarks. Often only by writing programs or by getting "hands-on-experience" of a particular microprocessor can a designer get to know the quirks of any one device. Only those who have programmed a 6800 can appreciate the frustrations caused by the lack of a "Push X register onto the stack" instruction. Before any microprocessor is considered for an application, the designer should carefully examine the instruction set to see if it contains the type of instructions relevant to his application, and to look for any omissions which might lead to difficulties in its implementation.

Development systems A development system is a microprocessor system whose purpose is to aid the design of other microprocessor systems. A typical microprocessor-development system allows software to be produced, debugged and then run to see how the system being designed would behave. Some development systems permit the system being designed to be operated while monitoring its operation. The availability of a microprocessor-development system may substantially aid the design and testing of any microprocessor system.

Second sourcing A microprocessor is said to be second sourced when it is produced by more than one manufacturer. For example, the 8080A was designed and first produced by Intel, but is now also manufactured by Texas Instruments (and several other manufacturers). There are two types of second source. In the first type, the second manufacturer produces a microprocessor to their own design which is functionally equivalent to the original. In the second type, the original manufacturer provides the second-source manufacturer with the masks from which the chip is produced. Clearly, the first type of second source produces "functionally equivalent" copies of a microprocessor, while the second type produces an identical copy, sometimes called a true second source. The availabilty of one or more second sources implies that a microprocessor is popular, is in demand, and is likely to be supported over a long period of time.

Availability of information Each manufacturer supports his product by providing information about it. This information may vary from a rather sparse data sheet giving a little more than the functions of the chip's pins, a definition of the instruction set, and a few cursory timing diagrams, to a highly detailed data sheet with actual examples of circuits using the microprocessor. Some manufacturers provide a considerable amount of information in the form of application reports. Many of the books now published on microprocessors choose the most popular microprocessors as their models. An additional, and often unbiased, source of information is found in the many journals devoted to microprocessors. By choosing a microprocessor which is well-documented, the design time may be reduced and (often) pitfalls may be avoided.

Software While the microprocessor user may wish to write software for his own specific application, he would not normally care to write a BASIC interpreter, a PASCAL compiler, or an editor/assembler. There exists today a wealth of software associated with the most popular microprocessors. An 8K BASIC interpreter with full floating-point facilities and trigonometric functions can be bought for $10, while compilers for FORTRAN, ALGOL, and PASCAL are available for a few tens of dollars. Popular microprocessor journals give the listing of programs, ranging from computer games to compilers. If, however, a relatively obscure microprocessor is purchased, the user may find it impossible to find suitable software at a reasonable price.

The Choice of a Microprocessor for the TS1

The Motorola M6800 has been chosen for the TS1. This does not imply that the 6800 is especially suited to the microprocessor system described in this book. Indeed any of the other popular 8-bit microprocessors (8080A, 8085, Z80, 6502) would, almost certainly, be just as good a choice as the 6800. The three factors which have led to the choice of the 6800 are:

(1) The 6800 is a popular microprocessor and has a wealth of literature and software associated with it.
(2) It is relatively easy to interface the 6800 with memory and peripheral components.
(3) It has a compact, easy-to-learn assembly language.

Three important disadvantages of the 6800 are its poor indexing arrangement (the single X register cannot be pushed onto the stack, and arithmetic operations cannot be carried out on it), the lack of any wait state enabling the microprocessor to be halted in mid-operation, and the lack of an interrupt-acknowledge mechanism.

Since beginning this project, Motorola have introduced the 6809, which is an enhanced version of the 6800 just as the Z80 is regarded as an enhanced version of the 8080A. While the 8080A and the Z80 are compatible at the object-code level (the machine code of the Z80 is a superset of that of the 8080A) the 6800 and the 6809 do not share this compatibility. There is a large measure of compatibility between the source codes (assembly language) of the 6800 and the 6809. An assembly-language program for the 6800 can be re-assembled to produce suitable code for the 6809. The most fundamental improvement in the 6809 over the 6800 is the introduction of a host of new addressing modes making the manipulation of data much easier. More specifically, the 6809 has two index registers and two stack pointers while the 6800 has only one of each. The 6809 is one of the few 8-bit microprocessors to include multiplication as one of its operations. Electrically, the 6800 and 6809 are very similar so that it is not difficult to modify a 6800-based microprocessor system to operate with a 6809 microprocessor.

2.2 THE 6800 MICROPROCESSOR

It is not the purpose of this book to examine the operation of microprocessors in general, or the 6800 in particular. The reader is assumed to have some knowledge of microprocessors which may be augmented by referring to the material listed in the bibliography. However, as an appreciation of the operation of the 6800 is so crucial to this book, the section of the manufacturer's data sheet dealing with those aspects of the 6800 concerned with interfacing and timing are given in Appendix A2. This appendix serves as a useful reference to those wishing to learn more about the 6800, and relates to the following chapters which are concerned with the interfacing of a 6800 to a general-purpose microprocessor system.

The data sheet of the 6800 given (in part) in Appendix A2 is a particularly good example of a data sheet, giving the full electrical characteristics of the 6800 and the timing diagrams (and therefore the interface requirements). In this book we are mainly concerned with the functions of the pins of the 6800 and the way in which they facilitate (or otherwise) the design of a microprocessor system.

2.3 THE STRUCTURE OF THE TS1

This book is concerned with the way in which a microprocessor system may be designed. In order to illustrate the various aspects of the design of a microprocessor system, an example of a complete system is given. In effect, many of the chapters of this book consist of a discussion of the factors affecting some aspect of a microprocessor system followed by a worked example. These "worked examples" gradually build up a microprocessor system called the TS1. All aspects of the design of a microprocessor system, ranging from the power supply to the monitor (a program which controls the operation of the system) are dealt with. The concluding chapter deals, briefly, with the actual construction of the TS1.

It must be stated here that the TS1 has been designed to illustrate the various topics dealt with in this book. Consequently, the TS1 should be regarded as an example rather than as a target machine worthy of emulation. It is unlikely that any reader would ever wish to build a carbon copy of the TS1, simply because it has far more features than are normally required in any given application. It is hoped that the reader will be able to design his own microprocessor system to his own specifications by the time he has finished this book. Although only one microprocessor is dealt with, the reader will find many of the points raised applicable to any other microprocessor.

The reader may be interested in the pedigree of the TS1. In 1974 as microprocessors were first beginning to appear at a reasonable price, the author obtained a Motorola MEK 6800D1 microprocessor development kit. Since there was no access to a Video Display Terminal (VDT—a CRT terminal) or a printer, a VDT also had to be built before the kit could be fully tested. When completed the MEK 6800D1 and the VDT worked first time—much to the author's surprise. This surprise is explained by the author's earlier experience of analog circuitry. Digital circuits (generally) function correctly as long as no blunders have been made in the design or construction of the circuit. As digital systems operate on signals in one of two distinct ranges ($0-0.8$ V and $2.0-5.0$ V), errors due to extraneous signals (noise and cross-talk) are rare. Possibly, the greatest potential source of trouble in a digital system stems from timing arrangements. That is, it is not only necessary to have a signal at the right point, it must also be there at the right time. This aspect of digital systems recurs several times throughout this book.

In contrast, analog circuits operate with signals having wide dynamic ranges, often from the microvolt to the tens-of-volts range in a single circuit. It is normally a requirement that the analog signals must be processed linearly so that waveforms are not distorted. Furthermore, the designer is often interested in second-, third-, or even higher-order effects in analog devices. Consider the following example. At the very low frequencies found in audio amplifiers the electrical characteristics of a transistor may change cyclically as the junction is periodically heated and cooled, in sympathy with the signal. The unfortunate designer must now find some way of removing this source of distortion.

The MEK 6800D1 kit, while demonstrating the operation and programming of a small microprocessor system, soon proved inadequate from both hardware and software points of view. The amount of memory provided was too little to run even modest programs, and the monitor (MIKBUG) was too inflexible. The author then decided to build his own system based on experience gained from operating the MEK 6800D1 kit. This system proved to be an adequate general-purpose microprocessor system. It is from this system that the TS1 is derived. Of course, the TS1 is no "ultimate" microprocessor system. Each cycle of design, construction, and testing yields information and experience leading to further improvements in the next generation.

The TS1 is designed as a modular microprocessor system, each module (a single 20 cm × 20 cm (8 in × 8 in) card) being a single entity. Apart from the central processor module itself, the TS1 can be operated independently of any module. This facilitates testing and enables faults to be speedily localized to a module. A block diagram of the basic microprocessor system is given in Fig. 2.1, and Fig. 2.2 indicates some of the additional facilities which may be added to the TS1. The current version of the TS1 includes the following nine modules.

(1) The power-supply module which provides the low-voltage direct current required by each of the other modules.
(2) The CPU module itself, plus control and interface circuits, permitting it to communicate with other modules.
(3) The keyboard module from which the system receives its commands. This module is provided with its own housing and is physically separate from the rest of the system.
(4) The stand-alone VDT module which allows the CPU module to display alphanumeric characters on a domestic television. This module is called "stand-alone" because it may be operated independently of the CPU module, if desired. That is, the CPU does not, directly, control the operation of this module.
(5) The memory-mapped display module. This module displays the contents of part of the CPU's memory space on a television in the form of alphanumeric characters. This arrangement differs from that of module 4 in that the display is entirely controlled by a program executed by the CPU module.
(6) A random-access memory (RAM) module which holds programs and data.
(7) A special interface module which contains an eight bit multiplier and an arithmetic unit capable of handling floating point arithmetic, independently of the CPU.
(8) A bus terminator module which terminates the system bus and provides buffers so that the bus may be extended to another system.
(9) A slave processor module. This is essentially a single board computer which may be operated independently of the TS1 system. It is connected to the main processor module by means of a serial data link and may be operated in parallel with the main processor.

At the heart of the TS1 lies the processor module with its 6800 CPU. This is a single-board computer to the extent that it can operate independently of all other modules

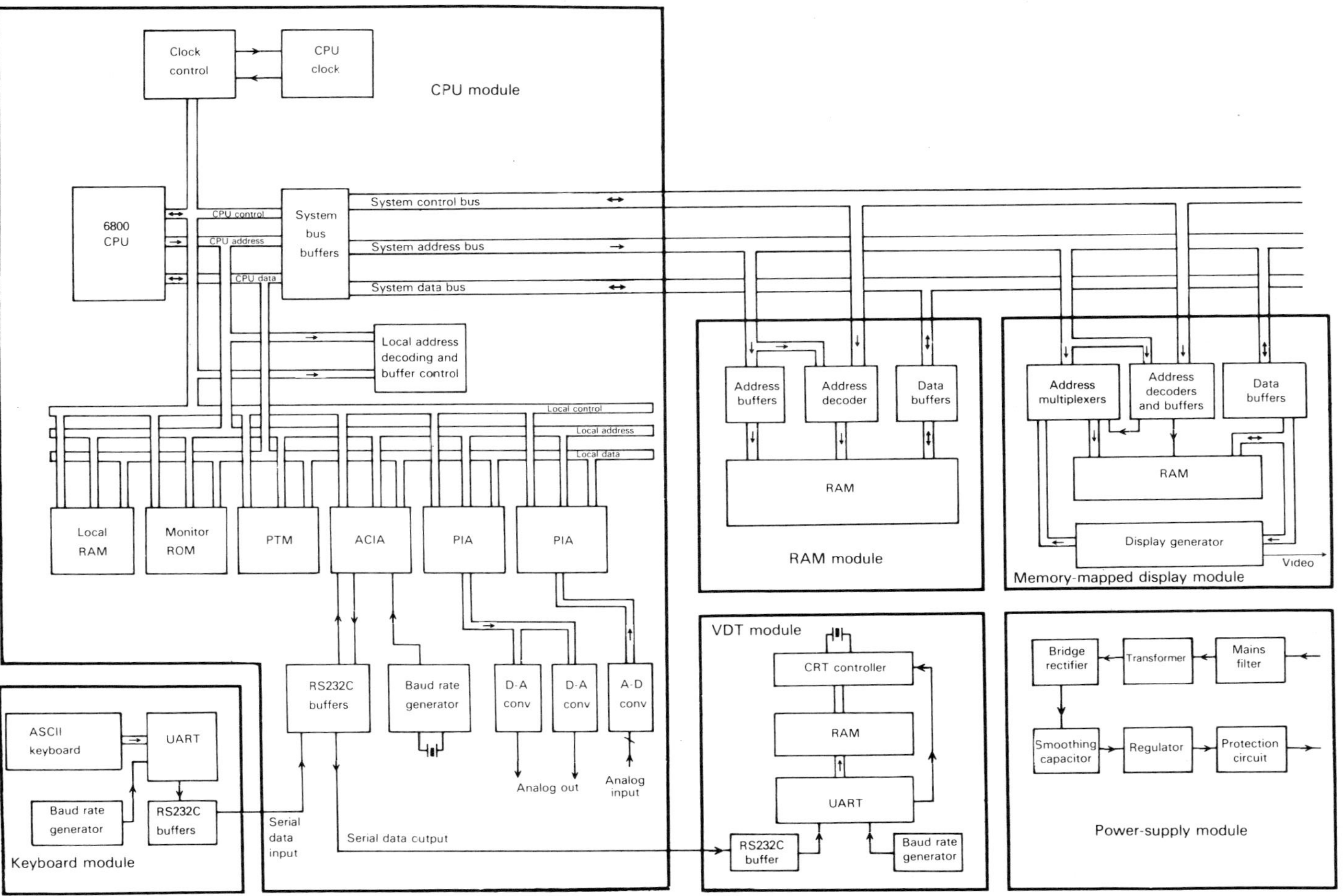

Figure 2.1 ***Block diagram at the basic microprocessor system***

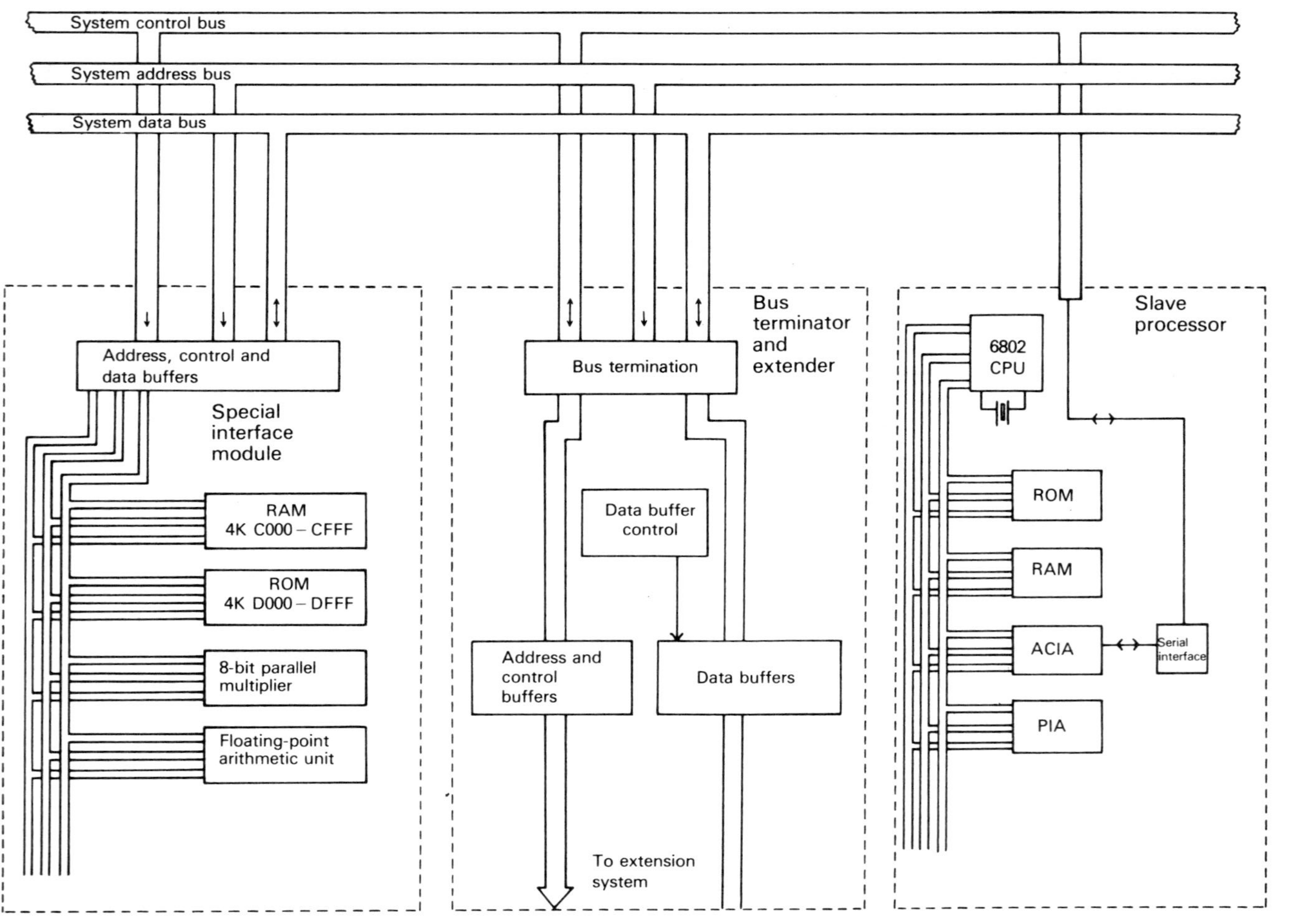

Figure 2.2 Three modules of the TS1

(apart from the power supply). This module communicates with all the other modules through its control, address and data buses which are buffered where necessary (see Chapter 4). The most important features of this module are:

(a) A versatile clock generator providing facilities for direct memory access (DMA) whereby other modules may take control of the system bus (see Section 3).
(b) A small quantity of on-board RAM, situated in the regions A000 – A3FF, and E000 – E3FF is included for three reasons. Firstly, some on-board RAM is necessary if the module is to be tested independently of the other modules (remember that RAM is required to hold the system stack and temporary data needed by the monitor). Secondly, the RAM at A000 is included to make the TS1 compatible with much of the software written for some commercially available 6800-based systems because they place the stack in this region. Thirdly, some 6800-based systems locate their monitor between E000 and E3FF so that by putting RAM in this region a monitor may be loaded to make TS1 "look like" one of the popular microprocessor systems.
(c) A programmable timer module (PTM) (see Section 6.2.3) is incorporated to provide facilities for frequency measurement, event counting, interval measurement, square-wave generation, and single pulses of a predetermined duration. All these facilities operate under software control.
(d) The CPU module includes circuits capable of converting digital quantities into analog signals and vice versa (see Sections 6.7 and 6.8). Two channels of digital-to-analog conversion and 16 channels of analog-to-digital conversion are provided by three integrated circuits. This facility permits the system to read an analog signal, process it digitally and then output a new analog signal. Such an operation is known as digital filtering. The analog-to-digital and digital-to-analog converters have been located on the CPU module simply because there was space available for them.
(e) Two serial interfaces are provided. One communicates with a VDT or teletype and constitutes the console input. The second serial input/output port allows the programmer to communicate with an auxiliary device (e.g. cassette interface). In the TS1 this second serial port forms the link to a second, slave, processor.

The keyboard module is built around a commonly available ASCII-encoded keyboard which generates a seven-bit code for each key pressed together with a strobe indicating the presence of a new character. This seven-bit code is transformed into a serial stream of bits by means of a UART (see Section 6.3). The serial data is fed by a two-wire link to the CPU's serial input port. A serial data link avoids the necessity for long lengths of expensive ribbon cable. Furthermore, by providing a serial data link between the CPU and the keyboard module a high level of versatility and interchangeability is achieved, a major objective of the design of the TS1.

The stand-alone VDT module provides an inexpensive method of displaying ASCII-encoded alphanumeric characters and the symbols +, *, %, etc on a standard, unmodified domestic television. A serial data link connects the VDT module to the CPU module (as in the case of the keyboard) so that compatibility with existing VDTs and teletypes is achieved. A major feature of this module is the use of a single-chip CRT controller, greatly simplifying the design and reducing the cost.

The memory-mapped display module is so called because part of the CPU's own memory space is "mapped" onto a screen. That is, a block of RAM is shared between the CPU and the VDT. When the CPU is not actually accessing (writing to or reading from) this common memory, a display generator steps through successive memory locations and displays the contents of each location as the appropriate alphanumeric character or, if required, as a graphic symbol on a raster scan display (television). Unlike the stand-alone VDT module, the memory-mapped display is intimately controlled by software. The CPU may, therefore, change a character in only a few microseconds. This allows the display to be rapidly modified and so permits a limited amount of animation.

The RAM module expands the amount of memory available for programs and data. In the current version of the TS1 up to 24K bytes of memory may readily be accommodated on this module. A useful feature of this module is the ability to "write-protect" any 4K block of RAM. When the memory is write-protected it appears to the CPU as read-only memory (ROM) because its contents can no longer be modified. In this way important code may be protected from corruption if a program runs wild (crashes).

The special interface module has been designed to accommodate two important devices: the multiplier chip and the ALU chip. These devices enable the programmer to perform eight-bit multiplication and floating-point arithmetic operations, respectively, at a much greater rate than could be executed by the 6800 CPU itself. Without these devices the programmer must resort to slow and cumbersome software routines to perform all but the most basic arithmetic operations. This module also contains 4K of read/write memory and 4K of ROM.

The bus terminator module has a dual function. Firstly, it helps to remove some noise from the system bus by providing a termination to the bus lines (see Section 6.6). Secondly, it provides a buffered interface to the system bus. This interface permits the system bus to be expanded beyond the basic system, enabling additional modules and memory to be catered for.

A significant feature of the TS1 is the total absence of any form of front panel. Some microprocessor systems and minicomputers (particularly older models) have a front panel which allows the operator to enter data directly into RAM by means of toggle switches mounted on the front panel. Other features of a typical front panel are rows of light-emitting diodes (LEDs) enabling the contents of memory locations to be examined or the system status to be displayed. A single-step facility whereby a program may be executed one instruction at a time is often included.

All the above front-panel facilities have been omitted from the TS1 because the entry of addresses and data from toggle switches is both tedious and prone to error. Likewise, reading data from 24 or more LEDs is not a task to be recommended. All the functions performed by a front panel can readily be undertaken by a keyboard and video display under the control of a monitor program. This approach permits data to be entered, modified, and read in the form best suited to the needs of the programmer.

2.3.1 An Introduction to the System Bus

In order to achieve the maximum amount of versatility, many microprocessor systems have a bus common to all the modules making up the system. Such an arrangement allows new modules to be added without modifications being made to the structure of the system. The bus often takes the form of a motherboard, that is a printed-circuit board with a number of parallel copper tracks joining corresponding pins of the connectors into which each module will be plugged.

In the TS1 each module is built on a 20 cm (8 in) square card which plugs into edge connectors mounted at the back of a cardframe. The electrical details of a bus are dealt with in Chapter 4, along with the arrangements needed to control the orderly flow of data along a bus. The system bus is described at this early point in the book simply because it is so important to the understanding of what follows. After the choice of the microprocessor itself, the design of a system bus is possibly the second most important consideration facing the designer of a microprocessor system.

The design of a system bus is a difficult task. Indeed, it would be unfair to compare the effort of designing a bus structure with such simple jobs as putting a man on the moon, or curing the common cold. If this somewhat extravagant statement surprises the reader, he need only look at the readers' letters pages of some of the popular microprocessor magazines. This difficulty springs from the need of the designer to please all of the people all of the time by providing every function required by every user. Furthermore, he has to please people in the future by providing facilities today for the functions of tomorrow.

If a bus is designed to suit a given microprocessor, what happens when the microprocessor manufacturers produce the Mark 2 version of their machine with a new control line? The users must then decide whether to forego the advantages of the new machine; buy a new bus system; modify the present bus; or sell up and go into antiques where the state-of-the-art does not change from day to day. One of the basic problems of bus design, getting it right first time, is neatly summed up by Lesea and Zaks in their book *Microprocessor Interfacing Techniques,* where they write, "A standard can always be improved: but it won't be—this is why it is a standard!".

The origin of the difficulties experienced by the designer of a backplane is the conflict between the economic, mechanical, electrical, functional, and universality requirements of a system bus. These conflicting requirements are:

Economic It is no good designing the perfect bus if the result is too expensive to build, or if the finished product cannot be sold. In general, the OEM or high-volume manufacturer will put considerable effort into reducing the cost of the bus because the money saved over a large number of systems will be greater than the design costs, while the enthusiast or the one-off designer will either use a ready-made bus, or build one using off-the-shelf components. The bus in the TS1 uses readily available boards and connectors, in an international standard cardframe.

Mechanical The bus must be physically strong enough to withstand the repeated insertion and removal of modules without distorting, cracking or damaging the tracks. I have encountered one commercially made motherboard which required four hands to remove a module—two to hold the module, and two to hold the motherboard down to stop it snapping. Other mechanical factors include the ease of manufacturing the backplane and connectors, and the tolerances in the dimensions of the backplane and connectors.

Electrical The copper tracks forming the electrical paths along the motherboard have electrical properties of resistance, inductance and capacitance, which affect the propagation of signals along the bus. In particular, the signals are attenuated, and suffer from time-dispersion effects which appear as increased rise-and-fall times and ringing. The effect of attenuation is normally quite small and shows up as a reduction in the noise immunity of the signals. One of the most serious problems experienced in systems with a common bus structure is that of cross talk between adjacent tracks, which reduces the noise immunity of wanted signals at best, and causes spurious errors at worst. Because the tracks forming the bus behave as transmission lines, reflections occur on the bus unless it is terminated by an impedance equal to its own characteristic impedance. Fortunately, reflections should not be troublesome on buses shorter than about a metre. From an electrical point of view, the bus should consist of wide tracks, well separated from each other, with an earth plane between adjacent tracks. The ground and power supply tracks must have a low series resistance and inductance if a high noise immunity is to be maintained. In the majority of systems several tracks are normally connected together in parallel to serve as the common ground.

Functional The functional specification of a bus defines the functions of the signals which use it. The various signals which use the bus may be grouped as follows:

(1) The ground to which all logic levels are referenced, and the power supply lines.
(2) The address bus used by the CPU to specify the memory location currently being accessed. Provision is normally made to enable devices, other than the CPU, to control the address bus themselves in order to make peripheral-to-memory data transfers (DMA).
(3) The data bus, which transfers data between the CPU and memory. The data bus uses bidirectional lines which enable data to be moved to or from the CPU, depending on whether the CPU is executing a read or write cycle. As with the address bus, the data bus can be externally controlled during DMA operations.
(4) The control bus, which carries three types of signal.
   (a) System signals, e.g. clock, $\overline{\text{RESET}}$.
   (b) Control signals from the CPU, e.g. READ/$\overline{\text{WRITE}}$, valid memory address (VMA), bus available (BA).

(c) Control signals to the CPU from peripherals, e.g. $\overline{\text{INTERRUPT REQUEST (IRQ)}}$, $\overline{\text{HALT}}$.

It is often the control bus which determines the flexibility of the system. For example, the S100 bus owes much of its popularity to the wide range of control functions provided, while the SS50 is limited to the most basic functions necessary for the operation of the system.

Universality With the wide range of microprocessors currently available, it is sensible to design the bus to be compatible with more than one type of microprocessor. Such an approach would probably have economic advantages. A bus capable of supporting several different microprocessors would be attractive to independent manufacturers of memory and peripheral boards because of the potentially large volume of sales. Unfortunately, we are unlikely to see any really universal bus. While the architectures of all microprocessors have very little variation, the details of their interface requirements are so diverse that the idea of a common bus is on the difficult side of impossible. Each particular microprocessor has a set of pins with which it communicates with the outside world, and these pins have their own unique timing and functional peculiarities. It is possible to design buses for "similar" microprocessors (Z80 – 8080, 6800 – 6502). Occasionally, and with much ingenuity, a 6800 (say) can be adapted for a 8080-based (e.g. S100) bus, but a full measure of compatibility is not possible.

It is a great pity that the semi-conductor manufacturers have never got together and decided on a common bus structure for their microprocessors. It would be an excellent idea to wall up designers from Intel, Motorola, TI and others in a small room (with little or no food) until white smoke rises from the chimney signifying *"habemus omnibus"*.

A limited measure of universality can be attained by allowing some room for expansion or later developments. Obvious candidates for this treatment are an extended address bus (say 20 or more bits), a 16-bit data bus, and facilities for multiprocessor operation.

2.3.2 A System Bus for the TS1

The physical format of TS1's bus and backplane is determined by the selection of 203.2 × 203.2 mm Vero cards with a 77-way edge connector. Note that the connector has 78 pins but as one of the pins forms an index and is not used there are *effectively* 77 pins. The actual details of the construction of the TS1 are given in Chapter 9. Having chosen a 77-way bus it is necessary to decide how the pins should be arranged. It is not the purpose of this book to define a new bus standard or to present an existing standard, but to illustrate how the pins may be grouped.

There is now a range of buses for microprocessors. Unfortunately, as mentioned previously, there is no universal standard. Worse still, the buses tend to be dedicated to a particular microprocessor so that, for example, the S100 bus is found almost exclusively in 8080 or Z80-based systems while the SS50 bus is exclusive to the 6800. It is possible to adapt a particular microprocessor to operate with a bus not designed to operate with it. For example, the $\overline{\text{read}}$ and $\overline{\text{write}}$ strobes of the S100 bus may be generated from $\overline{\phi_2.\text{VMA}.\text{R}/\overline{\text{W}}}$ and $\phi_2.\text{VMA}.\overline{\text{R}/\overline{\text{W}}}$ signals from the 6800. In practice there are further problems arising from data and address hold times for 6800-type components differing from those of their 8080-type brothers. This solution is neither elegant nor universal because the functions found on one microprocessor may not exist on another—the 6800 has both an $\overline{\text{NMI}}$ and $\overline{\text{IRQ}}$ input but no interrupt-acknowledge output, while the 8080 has a single interrupt-request input and an interrupt-acknowledge output.

The bus chosen for the TS1 has not been modelled on any existing system and it is certainly not designed as a standard. The TS1 bus uses 56 of the 77 pins available on the edge connectors. These 56 pins have the functions listed in Table 2.1.

Table 2.1

Pin	*Function*	*Notes*
1	ground	Power rail
2	ground	Power rail
3	SDMS	Serial data (RS232C) from the master to the slave
4	SDSM	Serial data (RS232C) from the slave to the master
5		
6		
7		
8		
9		
10		
11		
12		
13		
14		
15		
16		
17		
18		
19		
20		
21		
22		
23	D_7	The system data bus. The data is positive true, unlike the SS50 data bus. This bus is driven by tristate buffers on the module currently controlling the data bus.
24	D_6	
25	D_5	
26	D_4	
27	D_3	
28	D_2	
29	D_1	
30	D_0	

Pin	*Function*	*Notes*
31	$\overline{\text{MEMORY DISABLE}}$	An active-low input to the CPU module which when active disables the ROM on the CPU module.
32		
33	$\overline{\text{MEMORY CONTROL}}$	An active-low output from the CPU module which when active indicates that the contents of the address bus have a different meaning to their normal meaning.
34	A_{15}	The system address bus. The address is normally supplied by tristate buffers on the CPU module. Whenever BA or DMA GRANT is active this bus is floated (placed in a high-impedence state) at the CPU module.
35	A_{14}	
36	A_{13}	
37	A_{12}	
38	A_{11}	
39	A_{10}	
40	A_9	
41	A_8	
42	A_7	
43	A_6	
44	A_5	
45	A_4	
46	A_3	
47	A_2	
48	A_1	
49	A_0	
50		
51		
52	DMA GRANT	An active-high signal which when active indicates that the clock has been frozen in the ϕ_1 high state. This signal is a handshake as a result of a $\overline{\text{DMA REQUEST}}$.
53	$\overline{\text{DMA REQUEST}}$	An active-low input to the CPU module which, when active, requests a direct memory-access operation. This signal is used to stretch the ϕ_1 high clock pulse to permit a module (other than the CPU module) to take control of the system bus.
54	MEMORY READY	An input to the clock control circuit on the CPU module. When MEMORY READY is pulled low, the ϕ_2 high phase of the clock is stretched until MEMORY READY goes high. This line is normally used by slow peripherals or memory.
55	$2f_c$	A clock signal at twice the frequency of the system clock.
56	MEMORY CLOCK	A system clock in phase with ϕ_2 but which is not frozen by $\overline{\text{DMA REQUEST}}$.
57	ϕ_2 TTL	The main source of timing from the CPU module. ϕ_2 TTL (normally referred to simply as ϕ_2) is in phase with the NMOS ϕ_2 clock. Most peripherals use this signal for internal timing operations.
58	$\overline{\text{VMA E}}$	This is an active-low input to the CPU module and is used to control the state of the VMA line during a DMA cycle.

Table 2.1 *(continued)*

Pin	*Function*	*Notes*
59	VMA	This is an active-high "Valid Memory Address" output from the CPU module which, when active, indicates that the contents of the address bus represent a valid address.
60	R/$\overline{\text{W}}$ E	This is an input to the CPU module and is used to indicate whether a memory-read cycle or a memory-write cycle is required during a DMA operation.
61	R/$\overline{\text{W}}$	This is a signal from the CPU module which indicates whether the CPU is executing a read cycle or a write cycle. When the CPU is performing neither cycle, the R/$\overline{\text{W}}$ line assumes a high state to avoid a spurious write cycle.
62	BA	An active-high signal from the CPU module which, when active, indicates that the CPU is in the halt (idle) state and that the system bus is now available for DMA operations.
63	$\overline{\text{NMI}}$	A negative-edge sensitive input to the CPU module which when active forces a non-maskable interrupt. This line is pulled up to +5 V on the CPU module.
64	$\overline{\text{IRQ}}$	A level-sensitive, active-low input to the CPU module which when active signals an interrupt request. This line is pulled up to +5 V on the CPU module.
65	$\overline{\text{IRQ1}}$	$\overline{\text{IRQ1}}$ to $\overline{\text{IRQ4}}$ are four level-sensitive, active-low inputs to the CPU module which when active signal an interrupt request. These lines are connected to an MC6828 priority interrupt request controller.
66	$\overline{\text{IRQ2}}$	
67	$\overline{\text{IRQ3}}$	
68	$\overline{\text{IRQ4}}$	
69	$\overline{\text{HALT}}$	A level sensitive, active-low input to the CPU module used by peripherals to halt the CPU, and free the system bus for DMA operations. The $\overline{\text{HALT}}$ line may become active at any time, but the CPU does not halt until the end of the current instruction.
70	$\overline{\text{RESET}}$	This active-low output from the CPU module is used to put certain peripherals in a known state on power up, or after a reset request.
71	$\overline{\text{RESET REQUEST}}$	An active-low input to the CPU module which resets the CPU, and any peripherals connected to the $\overline{\text{RESET}}$ line. This line is pulled up to +5 V by a resistor on the CPU module.
72	INDEX	This line is not used.
73	+12 V	Pins 73−78 contain three power supply lines at +12 V −12 V and +5 V. A ground line is used to separate power supplies to reduce the danger of one power line directly touching another.
74	ground	
75	−12 V	
76	ground	
77	+5 V	
78	+5 V	

Timing Requirements of the TS1 Bus

A system bus cannot be completely specified without defining the timing requirements of the signals on the bus. For our purposes it is convenient to divide the lines into groups according to their source. That is, there are four classes of timing requirement as follows:

(1) lines connected to the 6800 CPU;
(2) lines connected to the 6875 clock generator;
(3) lines connected to the 6828 priority-interrupt controller;
(4) the lines not included in 1 to 3 above.

The lines belonging to these four classes are:

(1) address, data, R/$\overline{\text{W}}$, VMA, $\overline{\text{HALT}}$, $\overline{\text{IRQ}}$, $\overline{\text{NMI}}$, BA;
(2) $\overline{\text{MEMORY READY (MR)}}$, $2f_C$, MEMORY CLOCK (MCLK), ϕ_2TTL; $\overline{\text{DMA REQUEST (DMAREQ)}}$, DMA GRANT (DMAG);
(3) $\overline{\text{IRQ1}}$, $\overline{\text{IRQ2}}$, $\overline{\text{IRQ3}}$, $\overline{\text{IRQ4}}$;
(4) $\overline{\text{MEMORY DISABLE (MD)}}$, $\overline{\text{MEMORY CONTROL (MC)}}$, $\overline{\text{RESET}}$; $\overline{\text{RESET REQUEST (RSREQ)}}$, R/$\overline{\text{W}}$ E, $\overline{\text{VMA E}}$.

I do not intend to cover timing diagrams in any detail here, as they are dealt with in some detail in Section 5.2. The above groupings have been chosen on a device rather than a functional basis because their timing requirements are determined by the operation of the component to which they are connected. The first class of lines, those connected to the CPU, behave as specified in the 6800's data sheet (Appendix A2). Of course, as many of these lines are buffered on the CPU module, a change of state at one of the CPU's pins will not appear on the system bus until a few nanoseconds later. Normally, this is of little consequence.

The bus lines connected to the 6875 clock generator are dealt with in Chapter 3, where Fig. 3.12 gives the timing diagram for the CPU clock, $2f_C$, MEMORY CLOCK, and ϕ_2TTL, Fig. 3.13 gives the timing diagram for the $\overline{\text{MEMORY READY}}$ input, and Fig. 3.16 gives the timing diagram of the $\overline{\text{DMA REQUEST}}$ input and the DMA GRANT output.

The third group of lines consists of four interrupt request lines ($\overline{\text{IRQ1}}$ to $\overline{\text{IRQ4}}$) to the 6828 priority interrupt controller. Briefly, the 6828 is able to expand the 6800's (maskable) interrupt-handling facility beyond the single $\overline{\text{IRQ}}$ line provided by the CPU. A negative transition at one of the inputs $\overline{\text{IRQ1}}$ to $\overline{\text{IRQ4}}$ has the effect of forcing $\overline{\text{IRQ}}$ low (subject to the prioritization requirements of the 6828). Section 6.1 deals with the operation of the PIC and Fig. 6.4 gives its timing diagram.

The final group of lines represents functions peculiar to the TS1 (apart from $\overline{\text{RESET}}$). The $\overline{\text{MEMORY DISABLE}}$ and $\overline{\text{MEMORY CONTROL}}$ functions act very much like special-purpose address lines. When $\overline{\text{MD}}$ is active low it switches off the monitor ROM on the CPU module, enabling its memory space to be taken by some other memory device. Similarly, $\overline{\text{MC}}$, when low, allows the user to give the current contents of the address bus a "special" meaning. Consequently the timing requirements of these two inputs to the CPU are the same as those of any other address line—they must be stable within t_{AD} (270 ns) of the start of a memory-access cycle and remain valid for t_{AH} (30 ns) after the end of the cycle.

The $\overline{\text{RESET}}$ line is the logical OR (in terms of negative logic) of three signals: the $\overline{\text{POWER-ON-RESET}}$ output of the clock generator, the output of a manual push-to-reset switch, and an external $\overline{\text{RESET REQUEST}}$ line. $\overline{\text{RESET}}$ is an input to the CPU and to any other devices requiring to be set in a given state after the application of power. This input to the CPU is asynchronous and need not be synchronized with any external event. In fact, apart from the initial power-on-reset, the only time that this line is activated is when control of the CPU has been lost following a system crash. The sole timing requirement of the $\overline{\text{RESET}}$ line (and therefore of $\overline{\text{RESET REQUEST}}$) is that it is held active low for at least eight clock cycles.

In normal operation the information on the system data/address, R/$\overline{\text{W}}$, and VMA buses is determined by the CPU. It is, however, possible to enter a mode known as DMA by either halting the CPU ($\overline{\text{HALT}}$ = 0) or by freezing the system clock ($\overline{\text{DMA REQEST}}$ = 0). These events result in acknowledgements (BA = 1 or DMA GRANT = 1) which have the effect of putting the address and data buses into a high-impedance state (see Section 4.1). This allows some device other than the CPU to read from or write to memory. During the time for which the CPU has relinquished control of the bus, the R/$\overline{\text{W}}$ and VMA signals must be provided by the DMA controller. In the TS1 a DMA operation is acknowledged by either BA or DMAG going high, and when this happens a multiplexer switches the system bus lines R/$\overline{\text{W}}$ and VMA from the CPU to the R/$\overline{\text{W}}$ E and $\overline{\text{VMA E}}$ lines. Thus during a DMA cycle the system R/$\overline{\text{W}}$ and VMA lines are fed from the DMA controller via the R/$\overline{\text{W}}$ E and $\overline{\text{VMA E}}$ buses.

The timing diagram of the halt sequence is given in Appendix A2, and is repeated in Fig. 2.3 (with modifications) to illustrate how DMA may take place. There are no particularly stringent timing requirements for DMA. Once BA is high the DMA controller simply applies an address to the address bus, puts a R/$\overline{\text{W}}$ signal on R/$\overline{\text{W}}$ E, and a VMA signal on $\overline{\text{VMA E}}$. The controller then either writes data to or reads data from memory. This operation may be repeated as rapidly as the memory will allow. Once the requisite number of memory accesses have been completed, the DMA controller allows $\overline{\text{HALT}}$ to go high and the CPU once more takes control of the bus.

In Fig. 2.3 I have made the DMA read/write cycles occur synchronously with the system clock as, in practice, many systems based on the 6800 employ ϕ_2 as a memory enable input, forcing memory accesses to take place only when ϕ_2 is high. The details for a DMA operation by forcing $\overline{\text{DMA REQUEST}}$ low are similar to the above case (see Fig. 3.16 for the timing requirements of $\overline{\text{DMA REQUEST}}$). The only real difference between DMA by halting the processor and DMA by stretching the system clock is that the former allows unlimited memory access while

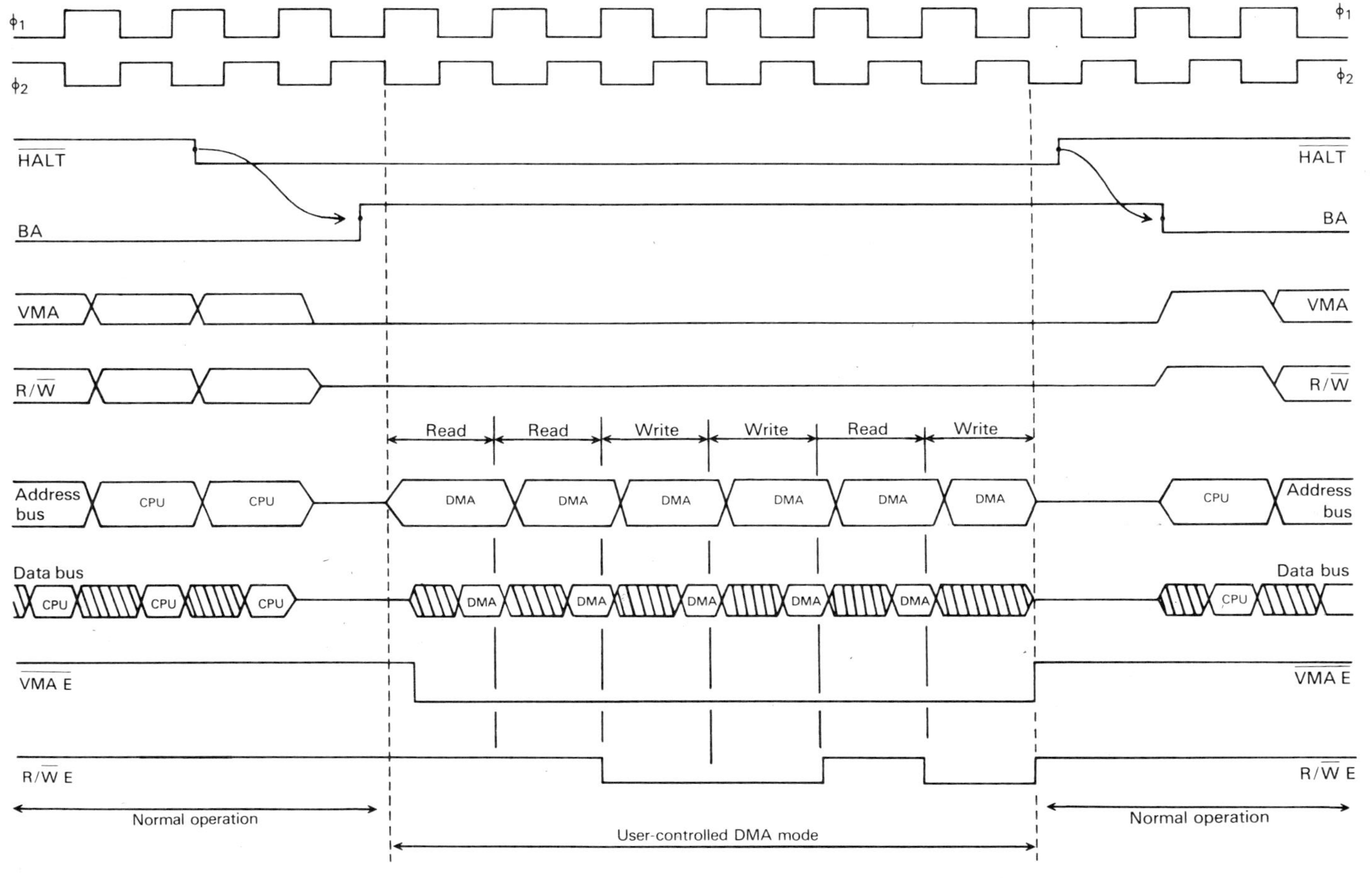

***Figure 2.3** The timing diagram for $\overline{VMA\ E}$ and R/$\overline{W}$ E during a DMA operation*

the latter must not be extended for longer than 10 μs. The CPU is a dynamic device and its clock may not be stopped for any extended period (see Chapter 3).

2.4 THE POWER SUPPLY

A section devoted to power supplies in a book on microprocessors may, at first sight, appear odd. After all, a power supply is often dismissed as nothing more than a black box with its input terminals connected to the public electricity supply. However, this black box has the physical characteristics of volume, mass, power dissipation, regulation, reliability, and cost. In this section a brief description of the operation and characteristics of power supplies is given. The aim is to make the designer of a microprocessor system aware of the power supply, and in particular of the penalties which must be paid if it is inadequate.

All microprocessors require a source of current at a constant voltage to provide them with the power without which they cannot function. The vast majority of microprocessors, their MOS peripherals and bipolar support chips have a single 5 V supply. Some devices, notably EPROMs and dynamic RAMs, require additional sources of current at 12 V, −12 V or −5 V. Fortunately, the trend is to design new ICs needing only a single 5 V supply.

It is often thought that the provision of a power supply for a microprocessor system is a trivial matter. This is not so. In the last few years the power consumed by active devices has fallen dramatically, from the watts dissipated by valves, to the milliwatts dissipated by discrete transistors, and now to the microwatts dissipated by active devices on silicon chips. However, as the power consumed per active devices has fallen, the total number of active devices per system has risen from tens to millions. Today, sophisticated multiple-microprocessor systems can be found with power-supply buses carrying 120 A.

The primary function of a power supply is the production of an adequate current at a constant voltage. A secondary function of a power supply is the protection of the circuit being supplied with power from line-borne transients, or from the failure of some part of the power supply itself. The total power required by a microprocessor system is often largely dependent on the size of the memory used in the system. A small system with only 1024 bytes of RAM has a power consumption mainly determined by the microprocessor and its associated control circuitry. A large system with 64K bytes of static RAM tends to have a power consumption which is almost entirely dominated by the RAM. The actual power consumed by the memory of a microprocessor system is very much a function of the actual RAM chips which make up the memory. In general, the power consumption per bit falls as the number of bits per chip increases. The power consumption of memory chips is also a function of the access time of the chip, the faster the chip the greater the power consumption (and the price). The relationship between power, access time and size of five memory components is given in Table 2.2, although it should be remembered that advances in technology are constantly improving these parameters.

Table 2.2

Memory component	*Access time (ns)*	*Average dissipation (mW)*	*Average power/1K bits (mW)*
TMS4016-25 (16 384 bits)	250	495	31
TMS4044-45 (4096 bits)	450	275	69
TMS4044-15 (4096 bits)	150	440	110
2102AL-4 (1024 bits)	450	174	174
2120AL-2 (1024 bits)	250	225	225

Note that the power consumption of dynamic RAMs is a function of the rate at which the memory is accessed. The above figures corresponḋ to static RAMs which have an essentially constant power dissipation.

A power supply consisting of several circuits connected together in tandem is illustrated in Fig. 2.4. The line filter is used to keep line-borne high-frequency noise and transients out of the system. The transformer performs two functions: it converts the high-voltage line input into a much lower voltage with very little loss of energy, and it provides a means of physically isolating the system from the line. The rectifier and smoothing capacitor convert the alternating current from the transformer into a direct current at an approximately constant voltage. The

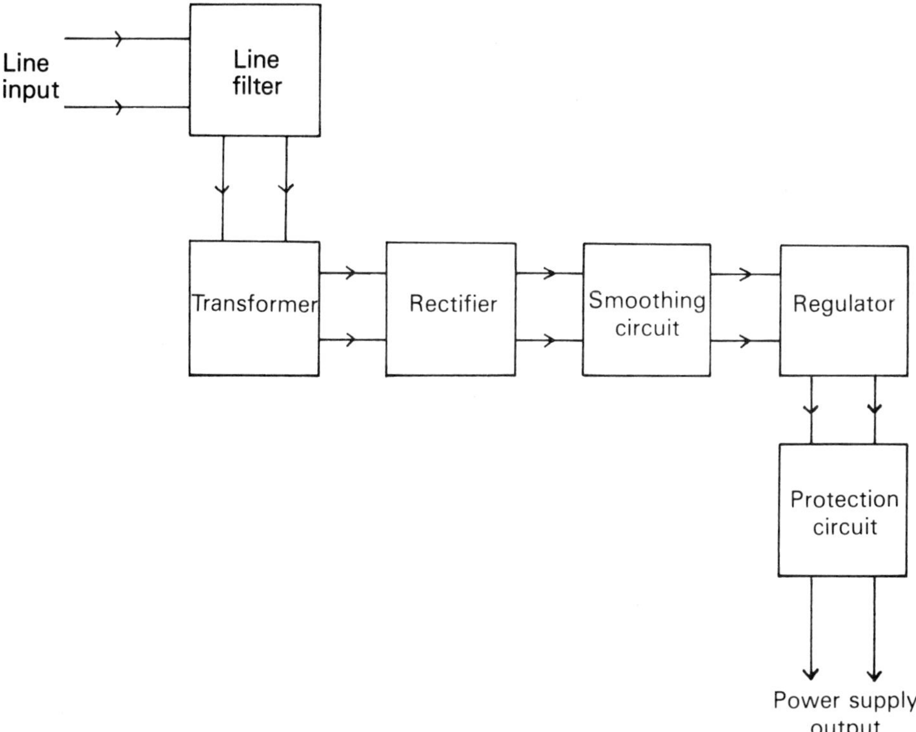

Figure 2.4 The structure of a power supply

regulator converts the approximately constant voltage into the precisely constant voltage required by the microprocessor system. The protection circuit plays a passive role, and isolates the microprocessor system in the event of a dangerous rise in the output voltage from the regulator. The protection circuit is often included in the regulator.

The characteristics of each of the components found in a power supply are discussed in some detail in Appendix A1.

2.4.1 A Power-supply Module for the TS1

The TS1 system bus includes three power-supply rails plus a common ground rail. These power rails furnish all the modules to which they are connected with power at three voltage levels: − 12 V, + 12 V and + 5 V. Unlike the popular S100 and SS50 buses, the TS1 puts its power-supply regulators in the power-supply module, and not on the individual circuit modules of the TS1. By not putting the regulators on the logic circuit boards, the reliability of the system is enhanced. If a regulator increases the temperature of a module by 10°C, the average failure rate of components in the vicinity of the regulator will double.

Before beginning to design a power supply it is necessary to calculate the maximum current demand of the system. As the TS1 is an open-ended project, the actual design being modified to meet the specification of the user, it is difficult to calculate an exact value for its power-supply requirements. If we assume a maximum memory size of 32K, built with 450 μs, 4K-bit static RAM chips, the current consumed by the memory is approximately 3 A. Allowing a further 3 A for the CPU and VDT modules, the total current demand is approximately 6 A.

The design of a power supply is often complicated by the lack of suitable components. For example, a digital system can be constructed from a wide range of commonly available building blocks, while the line transformer used in a power supply must be selected from the often very limited range in a manufacturer's catalog. Of course it is possible to order a transformer wound to a given specification, but this is not cost-effective unless several systems are being made. A suitable transformer is a 9 V, 5.5 A transformer, with the secondary winding arranged as two separate 4.5 V windings which must be connected in series. Unfortunately, this transformer has a secondary winding with a rating of only 5.5 A, which in a bridge-rectifier configuration amounts to a d.c. output of $0.62 \times 5.5 = 3.41$ A. As this current is insufficient to supply the estimated needs of the TS1, it is necessary to connect the secondary windings of two such transformers in parallel, to provide a d.c. output of approximately 6.8 A. When connecting the secondary windings of two transformers in parallel, it is vital that the windings are connected in phase. If the two transformers are identical no problem should arise if the start of the primary winding of the first transformer is connected to the start of the primary winding of the second transformer, and the finish of the primary winding is treated similarly. The secondary windings must also be connected in the same way so that the output voltages across both secondaries are in phase.

When constructing the power supply it is advisable to make a simple test before the secondary windings of the two transformers are finally connected in parallel. Solder the start of the two secondaries together and connect an a.c. voltmeter between the, as yet, unconnected terminals of the two secondaries.

Apply a.c. power to the primaries of the two transformers. If the transformers have been connected together correctly, the meter should show a very low reading—the difference between the nominally identical secondary voltages. If, however, the windings have been incorrectly connected, the voltmeter reads twice the r.m.s. voltage of one winding, and the connection between the secondaries must be reversed.

The peak voltage at the output of the transformer secondary is $9 \times \sqrt{2} = 12.7$ V. The silicon bridge rectifier selected for use in this power supply has an unusually low forward voltage drop of 1.25 V, which leaves approximately 11.4 V across the terminals of the smoothing capacitor. If we allow a maximum peak to peak ripple of 2.5 V under full-load conditions, the minimum voltage across the smoothing capacitor is 8.4 V.

The value of the smoothing capacitor is given by

$$C = \frac{i}{\mathrm{d}v/\mathrm{d}t} = \frac{6.8}{300} = 0.0227 \text{ F} \triangleq 22\,000\ \mu\text{F}.$$

The maximum working voltage of the capacitor must be greater than the peak voltage across the transformer secondary plus a margin to allow for variations in the mains input. A suitable capacitor is a 'computer grade capacitor' with a value of 22 000 μF, a voltage rating of 25 V, and a maximum ripple current (V_R) rating of 14 A at 65°C. Note that the tolerance in the value of an electrolytic capacitor is usually in the range +80% to −20% of the nominal capacitance. The maximum ripple current through a capacitor is given by $267\,V_R C$, which in this case amounts to $267 \times 2.5 \times 0.022 = 14.6$ A. This value is slightly greater than the rated ripple current of the capacitor. The maximum ripple current rating of a capacitor is strongly temperature dependent, a 14 A rating at 65°C corresponding to a 20 A rating at 25°C. As long as the temperature within the power-supply module is kept below 40 – 50°C no problems should arise.

The only other critical component in the power supply is the bridge rectifier. The rectifier chosen is a 25 A silicon bridge rectifier with a peak inverse voltage of 50 V, and a forward voltage drop of 1.2 V at a current of 12.5 A. If this rectifier is to be operated at its full rated current of 25 A, it is necessary to mount the rectifier on a heat sink with a thermal resistance of 0.8°C/W. When operating at an average load current of 7 A, the rectifier can function comfortably at a case temperature of 100°C. Bolting the rectifier to the chassis of the power supply should provide sufficient thermal dissipation. The peak forward current rating of the rectifier is 300 A, which is 44 times the average maximum load of the TS1 power supply, and provides an ample safety margin in this application. This value is also large enough to deal with the initial current inrush into the capacitor when power is first applied.

The circuit diagram of the TS1 power supply is given in Fig. 2.5. A generous measure of transient prevention is applied to the main 8 V supply. Six transient suppression devices are fitted as follows:

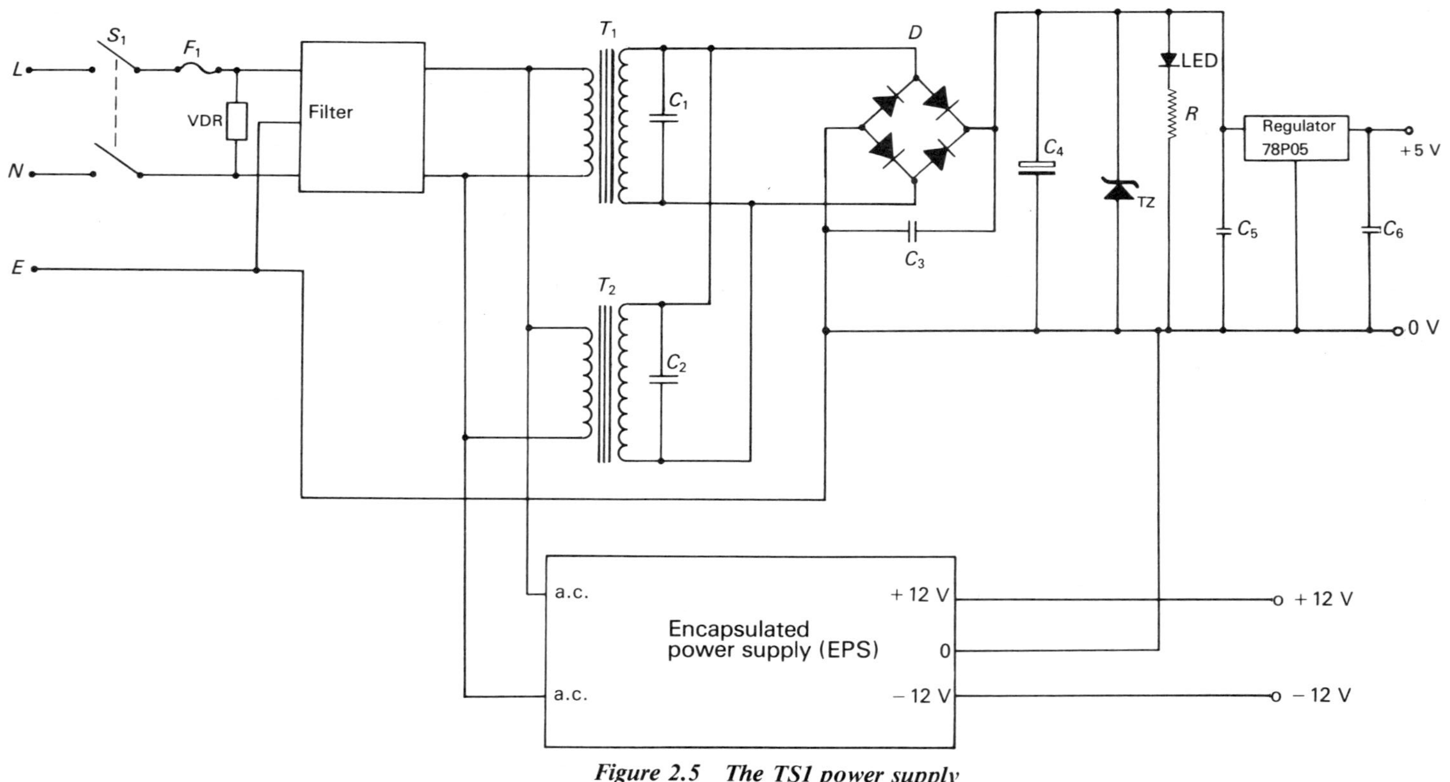

Figure 2.5 The TS1 power supply

(1) A zinc oxide voltage-dependent resistor is connected across the line input of the power supply.
(2) A filter network between the line input and the transformers provides 35 dB of attenuation to frequencies between 150 kHz and 30 MHz.
(3) Small capacitors of 0.1 μF are connected across the secondary windings of the transformers, and across the output terminals of the bridge rectifier.
(4) A TransZorb is connected across the output terminals of the 8 V power supply. The rating of the TransZorb must be greater than the maximum voltage which normally occurs across the output. This is the maximum no-load voltage of 11.4 plus 10% to allow for line variations, i.e. 12.6 V. The TransZorb which has the closest stand-off voltage above this value is the MPTE15 which has a clamp voltage of 20.6 V at a forward current of 10 A.

In the TS1 power supply no additional protection in the form of current limiting or crowbar overvoltage protection is used on the 8 V supply. Any additional protection may be implemented by choosing a monolithic 5 V regulator, with suitable characteristics.

The regulator selected for the TS1's power supply is a Fairchild A78P05, a 5 V 10 A hybrid device in a standard TO-3 package. This regulator has the following characteristics:

(1) internal thermal overload protection;
(2) internal short-circuit current limitation;
(3) 70 W power dissipation at a 25°C case temperature.

At a nominal 8.5 V input the regulator dissipates $(8.5-5.0) \times 6.8 = 23.80$ W full load. From the A78P05's data sheet it can be seen that the regulator can dissipate 30 W at a case temperature of 100°C. If we assume an ambient temperature of 25°C, the maximum temperature differential between the regulator case and the ambient air is 75°C. The thermal resistance between the case and the air is therefore 75°/25 W = 3°C/W. As the maximum value of case to ambient thermal resistance is quoted as 30°C/W, the regulator must be mounted on a heat sink with a thermal resistance of less than 3°C/W.

From Fig. 2.5 it can be seen that a 1 μF solid tantalum capacitor is connected between the regulator's input and ground to improve its transient response.

It must be admitted that although the monolithic regulator is widely employed in microprocessor power supplies, some authorities avoid them like the plague. The monolithic regulator normally has a tolerance of ±4%. To this tolerance must be added the effect of any voltage drop between the regulator's output terminal and the various IC's V_{cc} terminals plus the droop in the regulator's output at full load (typically 50 mV at 25°C and 250 mV at 150°C for a 10 A load). Clearly, unless the regulator is selected from a batch (expensive) problems may arise. Another disdavantage of this type of regulator is its lower reliability than that of regulators constructed from discrete components. A failure rate of 5% in monolithic regulators operating at high currents (but within their operating limits) has been reported.

Table 2.3 Components used in the TS1 Power Supply

Component	*Description*		*RS component part number*
F_1	Fuse holder 20 mm		412 – 879
	Fuse 1A		412 – 144
VDR	Zinc oxide VDR, rms working voltage = 245 (UK)		238 – 457
	rms working voltage = 120 (USA)		238 – 491
Filter	Line filter		238 – 435
T_1, T_2	Transformer secondary = 50 VA, 4.5 V @ 5.5 A twice		207 – 239
$C_1, C_2, C_3,$	Capacitor 0.1 μF, 600 V		112 – 563
C_4	Electrolytic capacitor 22 000 μF, 25 V, T_{ripple} = 14 A		102 – 617
C_5	Capacitor 1 μF, 35 V solid tantalum		101 – 771
C_6	Capacitor 0.1 μF disk ceramic		124 – 178
D	Bridge rectifier 25 A, V_{RRM} = 50 V, I_{FSM} = 300 A		262 – 309
TZ	TransZorb MPTE – 15		
R	Resistor 560 Ω $\frac{1}{4}$ W		
LED	Red light-emitting diode, I_F typically 15 mA		586 – 835
S_1	Subminiature switch DPST		
EPS	Encapsulated power supply ± 12 V @ 250 mA	240 V (UK)	591 – 102
		110 V (USA)	591 – 540
RG	10 A voltage regulator Fairchild A78P05		

The requirements of the + 12 V and – 12 V power supplies are very modest. The TS1 system is designed to use, as far as possible, components requiring only a single + 5 V supply. An exception to this is the RS232C drivers which require a + 12 V and a – 12 V supply at approximately 20 mA. To simplify the design of the + 12 V and – 12 V supplies, an encapsulated power supply is used. This power supply, a single component, is able to supply both the + 12 V and – 12 V rails with a current of up to 250 mA. The specified encapsulated power supply has internal protection against the effects of short circuits.

Although the operation of a power supply is simple in principle, the accurate (as opposed to rule-of-thumb) design of a power supply is a very complex procedure. Unless driven by poverty, the microprocessor systems designer would be better off buying a ready-made power supply from a reputable dealer.

SUMMARY

We have seen that there are many criteria by which a microprocessor may be chosen, from the nature of its internal architecture to the ease with which information may be obtained about it. The 6800 has been chosen for the TS1 for a number of reasons, chiefly its simplicity and ease of programming at the assembly language level. I have assumed that the reader is either familiar with the 6800 or will take the trouble to read some of the many works devoted to this processor.

The TS1 is a microprocessor system whose design unfolds as this book progresses. This system has been created to demonstrate many of the design aspects of a small computer, from the clock and bus-driver circuits to the software necessary to control it. To broaden the scope of the book, the TS1 includes a module containing its own arithmetic processor and one which includes a separate, single-board slave processor.

At this early stage in the book the idea of a system bus and its design has been introduced. The bus is an electronic highway over which the modules of a system communicate with each other. The design of a bus must take account not only of the functional specifications of the bus but also its physical, electrical, and timing requirements. A specification for the bus chosen by the TS1 is given together with its timing requirements.

The final item in this section is the design of a power supply for the TS1. This seemingly out of place subject has been included more to demonstrate the importance of a power supply than to provide a "template" design. Most microprocessor systems designers will, after all, buy their power supply ready-made. To avoid cluttering up this section with the intimate details of the power supply the basis of power supply design has been relegated to Appendix A1.

PROBLEMS

1 I once asked an engineer why his company had selected the 6800 for use in their products. He told me that it was because his manager had, purely by chance, attended a course given by Motorola. Find people who are using microprocessors in their products and determine how they chose their particular chip. Was it for well-argued technical reasons or did chance and coincidence (as above) play a large part in its selection?

2 Examine the instruction set of the 6800. If you had been on the design team and could have modified this instruction set, what improvements would you have made?

3 The designer of a microprocessor instruction set has (normally) only eight bits with which to specify an operation, an accumulator, and an addressing mode. Discuss how you would construct an instruction set and how the trade-off between the number of different instructions, types of addressing mode, and number of addressable accumulators is affected by the intended role of the microprocessor (word processing, number crunching, control systems).

4 The system bus of the TS1 has been designed specifically for the 6800 CPU. Examine the electrical and logical requirements of another CPU and try to specify a bus which may be used by both CPUs (e.g. 6800 and Z80). Can such a bus be designed or is it necessary to have three groups of lines: common to both processors, 6800-only lines, and Z80-only lines?

5 Carry out a worst-case design analysis of the power supply in this section. Will it operate when the line voltage is reduced by 10% and the transformer output drops by 9% at full load? Furthermore, if the line voltage is increased by 10% and the transformer's output is 10% too high, will the power dissipated in the regulator damage it?

3

The System Clock

We are now going to look at the circuits which generate the stream of pulses required by the microprocessor to control its internal and external operations. This section begins with an explanation of why such circuits, called clocks, are necessary in digital systems and continues with examples of clock circuits suitable for use in a microprocessor system based on the 6800. In addition to the basic clock circuits, the arrangements needed to control the clock-pulse generator to cater for slow memory components and DMA are dealt with. At the end of this section the circuit diagram of the clock-pulse generator of the TS1 and its associated components is presented.

3.1 The Need for a Clock

Because all digital computers perform their various operations at discrete points in time, there lies at the heart of each computer a pulse generator producing a stream of (normally) equally spaced electrical pulses. These pulses, commonly referred to as clock pulses, initiate all operations throughout the computer. Any system which operates in this fashion is called synchronous, from the Greek words *syn* = together and *chronos* = time. Not all digital systems operate synchronously, under the control of a clock. Some operate asynchronously (Greek *a* = not) with the next operation commencing as soon as the current operation has ended.

Figure 3.1 illustrates the necessity of a clock in a sequential digital system. Two

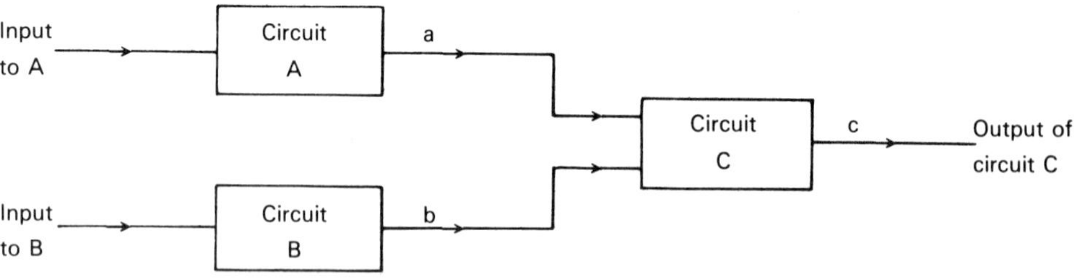

Figure 3.1 The output of circuit C is a function of circuits A and B

circuits A and B produce outputs a and b which are functions of their respective inputs. The outputs of A and B are fed into circuit C to produce an output c which is a function of both a and b. If circuits A, B and C were ideal in the sense that they responded instantly to a change at their inputs, timing problems would not occur, provided that the inputs to A and B were applied simultaneously. Unfortunately, in any real system the times taken by circuits A and B to respond to changes at their inputs are not identical. Furthermore, the inputs to A and B do not arrive simultaneously because these inputs themselves are the outputs of other circuits.

The timing diagram corresponding to the arrangement of Fig. 3.1 is given in Fig. 3.2. From this diagram it can be seen that the desired output from C is valid for

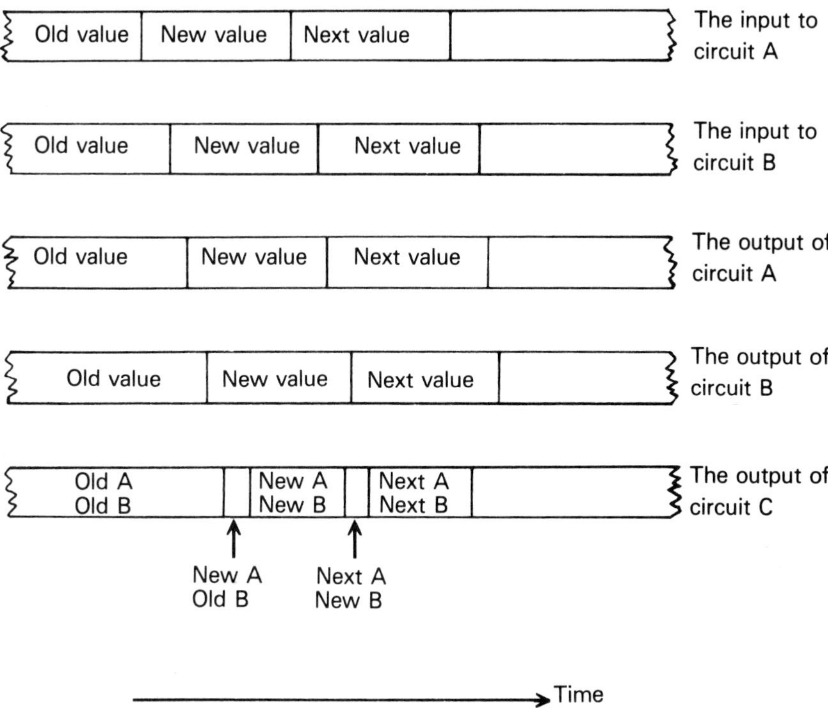

Figure 3.2 The timing diagram for the circuit of Figure 3.1

a relatively short time. Moreover, some way must be devised to distinguish between the wanted output and the spurious outputs which precede and follow it. Transforming the asynchronous circuit of Fig. 3.1 into a synchronous form in Fig. 3.3 solves this problem. Only a clock pulse generator and some latches to hold the values of inputs and outputs constant are needed. When a latch is triggered by a clock pulse the data at its input is copied to its output and then held constant until the latch is clocked again. Between clock pulses, any further change at the input to a latch is ignored.

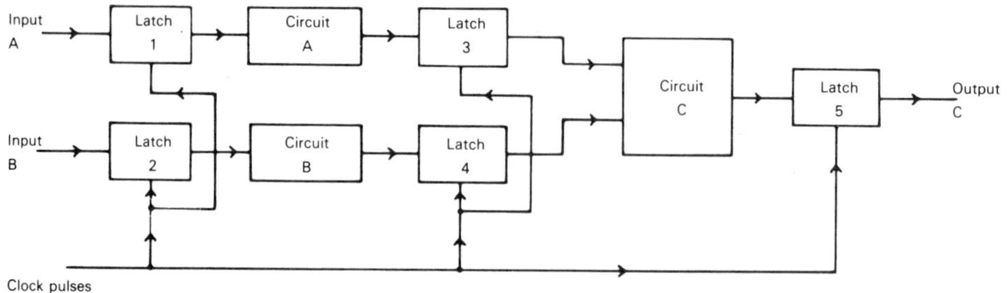

Figure 3.3 The use of a clock and latches to solve a timing problem

Consider now the operation of the scheme given in Fig. 3.3. After the first clock pulse, the inputs to circuits A and B are held constant in latches 1 and 2. On the second clock pulse the outputs of A and B are held in latches 3 and 4, and on the third clock pulse the required output of circuit C is deposited in latch 5.

It should be clear from Fig. 3.3 that the spacing between the clock pulses must allow for the longest circuit delay expected. This is the fundamental disadvantage of a clocked, or synchronous, system. For a microprocessor the maximum clock rate is determined by two factors: the complexity of the microprocessor's circuit, which defines the number of gates in series through which a pulse may ripple; and the technology employed to fabricate the chip, which determines the speed at which a pulse is propagated through a gate. It is interesting to note that many microprocessors not only have a specified maximum rate at which they may be clocked but also a specified minimum clock rate. The 6800 data sheet gives a maximum clock pulse repetition rate of 1 MHz, and a minimum clock pulse repetition rate of 100 kHz. This lower bound to the clock rate is due to the dynamic circuitry inside the 6800. To achieve the greatest circuit complexity for a given number of active devices on a chip, Motorola have resorted to dynamic-storage techniques whereby data within the 6800 is held in the form of a charge on the inter-electrode capacitance of a MOSFET. If data stored in this way is not periodically refreshed (rewritten) the charge on the capacitor discharges and the data is irreversibly lost after a few microseconds. Motorola specify the maximum time between clock-pulse transitions as 9500 ns, after which the integrity of data stored within the chip cannot be guaranteed. The practical disadvantages of having a minimum clock-pulse repetition rate are twofold. Firstly, the CPU cannot be operated in a single-step mode, whereby instructions are executed cycle by cycle each time a button is pushed, simply by slowing down the clock. Secondly, by having the ability to freeze the clock in a fixed state it is possible to hand over control of the system bus to a device other than the CPU. In this way data can be written directly into memory from a (say) floppy disk controller. The 6800 can, in fact, freeze its clock and allow another device to control the bus for no more than approximately 9.5 μs.

Clock Requirements of the 6800

The 6800 requires an externally generated two-phase clock. Figure 3.4 illustrates the relationship between the ϕ_1 clock and the ϕ_2 clock waveforms required by the 6800. The parameters of these clocks are given in Table 3.1. At first sight it may appear that ϕ_2 is simply the complement of ϕ_1 with $\phi_2 = \overline{\phi_1}$. This is not so because ϕ_1 and ϕ_2 are never in a logical one (high) state simultaneously. To comply with this restriction ϕ_2 must make its high-to-low transition before ϕ_1 makes its low-to-high transition. Similarly, the trailing edge of ϕ_1 must occur before the rising edge of ϕ_2. Microprocessors introduced later than the 6800 do not normally have such stringent clock requirements. In Chapter 7 the 6802, which is virtually a 6800 with an internal clock generator, is described. The relationship between the 6800's clock pulses and its address, data and control buses may be seen in Figs. 2 and 3 in Appendix A2. From these diagrams it is clear that during the ϕ_1 high phase of a clock cycle the CPU generates an address, VMA, and an R/$\overline{\text{W}}$ signal which appear at the 6800's pins approximately 270 ns after the rising edge of ϕ_1. However, it is not until approximately 220 ns after ϕ_2 has made its low-to-high transition that data is available in a write cycle* or until approximately 100 ns before the end of a ϕ_2 high clock pulse that data is required in a read cycle. All operations performed by the 6800 are made up of a series of these basic cycles. Many other microprocessors have very much more complex clocking arrangements—the Intel 8080A executes an

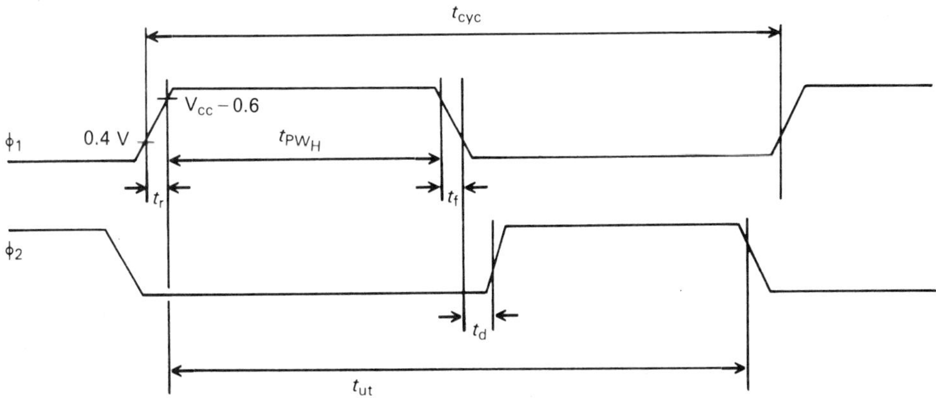

Figure 3.4 The relationship between clock phases ϕ_1 and ϕ_2

* This statement is not strictly true. In a write cycle data becomes available approximately 220 ns after a low-to-high transition at the CPU's data bus enable (DBE) input. However, in many 6800-based systems DBE is connected directly to ϕ_2, so that data becomes available approximately 220 ns after ϕ_2 has gone high.

instruction as a sequence of machine cycles where each machine cycle may be subdivided into 3 – 5 clock pulses. A complex timing arrangement is not necessarily a bad thing as, in the case of the 8080A, the CPU can put out information about its internal status during one of these "special-purpose" machine cycles. The 6800 cannot do this.

One possible way of looking at a clock cycle of a 6800 is to regard it as being divided into three portions:

(1) An initial quiescent period when the CPU is busy generating an address, $R/\overline{W}$, and a VMA output. This phase occurs at the first part of the ϕ_1 high clock.
(2) A second period when the above signals are valid but when data is available neither from the CPU in a write cycle nor from memory in a read cycle. This period straddles the end of the ϕ_1 high clock phase and the beginning of the ϕ_2 high clock phase.
(3) A final period when the contents of the data bus are valid. This occurs towards the end of a ϕ_2 high phase.

Table 3.1 The Characteristics of the Clock Inputs of the 6800

Characteristic	*Symbol*	*Value**	
		Minimum	*Maximum*
Clock cycle time	t_{cyc}	1.0 μs	10.0 μs
Clock pulse width	t_{PWH}	400 ns	9500 ns
Total ϕ_1 and ϕ_2 up time	t_{ut}	900 ns	—
Rise and fall times	t_r, t_f	—	100 ns
Clock separation	t_d	0	9100 ns
Input high voltage	V_{IHC}	$V_{CC}-0.6=4.4$ V	$V_{CC}+0.3=5.3$ V
Input low voltage	V_{ILC}	$V_{SS}-0.3=-0.3$ V	$V_{SS}+0.4=0.4$ V
Input leakage current	I_{in}	—	100 μA
Capacitance ($V_{in}=0, I_A=25°C, f=1$ MHz)	C_{in}	—	70 pF

* $V_{cc}=+5$ V, $V_{ss}=0$ V

This somewhat pedantic description of a clock cycle is included because of its implications. As the CPU does not actually need the system bus during the ϕ_1 high phase of the clock there is no reason why some other device may not "borrow" the system bus when ϕ_1 is high.

The electrical characteristics of the 6800's ϕ_1 and ϕ_2 clock inputs are not TTL compatible. The maximum voltage at the clock input if a logical zero state is to be guaranteed is 0.4 V. For a TTL device the corresponding value is 0.8 V. Similarly, the clock inputs require that the minimum input voltage for a logical one state be 4.4 V as opposed to 2.0 V for a TTL device. Furthermore, the clock inputs of the 6800 are highly capacitive — up to 70 pF for ϕ_2 and 35 pF for ϕ_1. The early versions of the 6800 were fabricated with enhancement-mode MOSFETS and these chips required logic-zero voltages below 0.3 V and logic-one voltages above 4.7 V, which is an even worse situation than the above figures for the current version of the chip with its depletion-mode MOSFETS. Because of these stringent requirements on the logic levels at the 6800's clock inputs it is not advisable to attempt to drive the CPU with standard TTL devices. Consequently, Motorola have produced a number of special-purpose clock-driver chips.

3.2 CLOCK DRIVERS FOR THE 6800

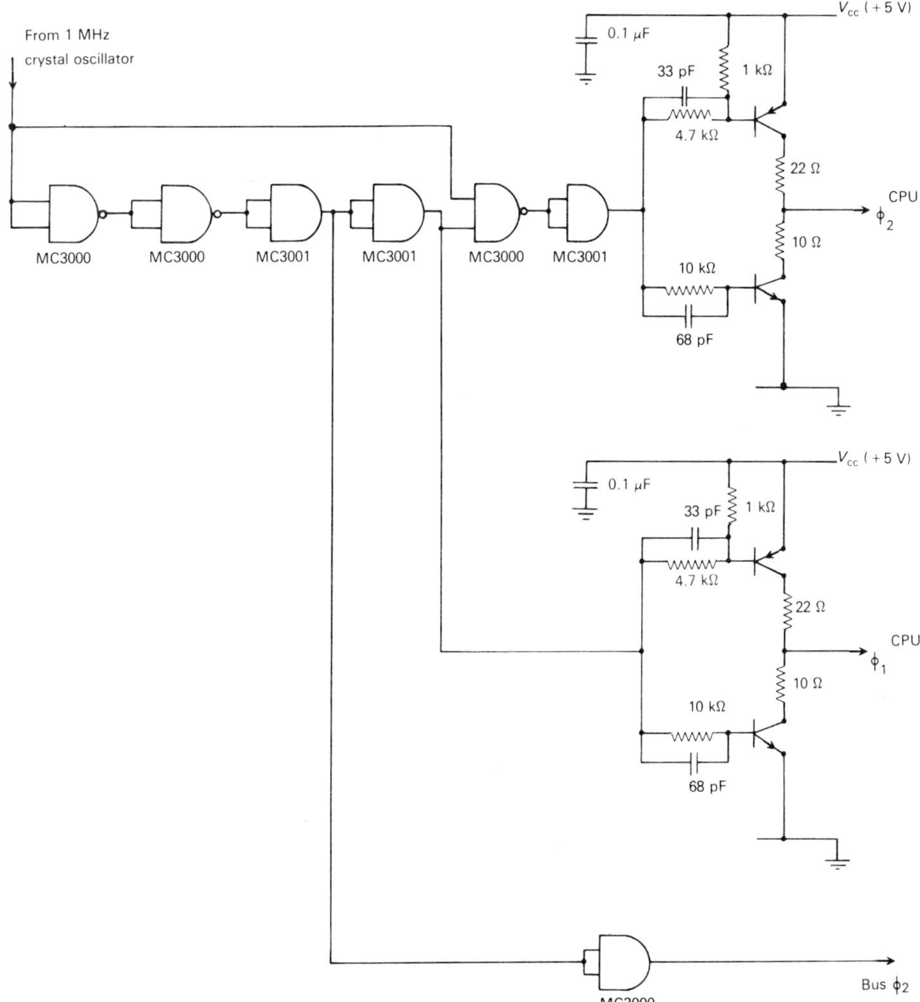

Figure 3.5 A clock driver for the MC6800 using discrete circuitry
(of historical interest only)

Discrete Component Clock Drivers

When the 6800 was first put on the market, no suitable single-chip clock driver existed and the designer was forced to construct his own clock driver from discrete components. This action led to the anomalous situation of a chip containing thousands of transistors being wired up to four transistors, several TTL packages and a handful of resistors and capacitors. Such a clock circuit takes up more room in a system than the CPU itself. The circuit diagram of this type of clock driver is given in Fig. 3.5. This circuit is provided to show just how bad things were in the early days of the microprocessor. The objections to clocks (or any other circuit) built from discrete components are the amount of space taken up by the circuit, the time taken to construct the circuit, and the difficulty in mounting discrete components on boards designed to hold DIL packages. Apart from the circuit of Fig. 3.5 a number of other clock circuits have been devised for the 6800, although some of these have operated outside the specifications provided by Motorola, which means that their reliable operation cannot always be guaranteed. Fortunately the days of the discrete component clock driver are now past.

The 6871A Clock Generator

Motorola produce three clock modules in the MC6870 range. Each module consists of a thick film hybrid circuit together with a quartz crystal hermetically sealed in a metal and ceramic package designed to plug into a 24-pin DIL socket. Unfortunately, the MC6870 series of clock generators are rather expensive, costing more than three times as much as the CPU chip itself. The three clock generators in the MC6870 series are the 6870A which provides only the basic clock functions of ϕ_1 and ϕ_2 at NMOS-compatible levels, plus a separate ϕ_2 system clock at TTL signal levels, and the 6871A and 6871B which have logic circuits built into them to furnish additional facilities.

The most useful clock generator in the MC6870 range is the MC6871A, whose internal structure is illustrated in Fig. 3.6. In addition to the NMOS-compatible ϕ_1 and ϕ_2 clocks, a ϕ_2-TTL clock, a memory clock and a clock at twice the basic clock frequency are provided. The memory clock is a signal in phase with ϕ_2 but not stretched by the chip's $\overline{\text{HOLD}}$ facility (to be explained shortly). This output is provided for memory components which must have a continuous, uninterrupted

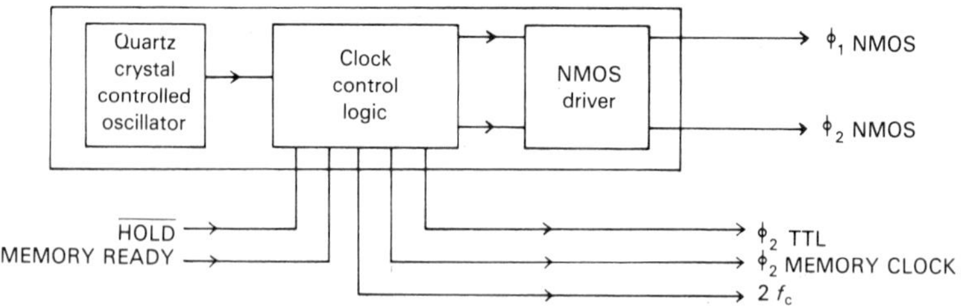

Figure 3.6 Block diagram of the MC6871A hybrid clock module

clock. The relationship between the outputs of the MC6871A is illustrated in Fig. 3.7. According to Motorola's data sheet for the MC6871A, the TTL-compatible outputs lead the ϕ_2 NMOS clock "so that additional system device delays can be accommodated". However, the most recent clock generator from Motorola (the 6875) has its ϕ_2 TTL clock trailing the ϕ_2 NMOS clock. Could it be that some of the new TTL components have negative propagation delays? The MC6871A has two control inputs, MEMORY READY (MR) and $\overline{\text{HOLD}}$, which serve to stretch the ϕ_2 and the ϕ_1 active-high clock phases, respectively. The MR input to the 6871A enables the CPU to work with memory components whose response is too slow to allow an access to take place during the normal memory cycle time. To activate the MR input it must be forced into a low state by a memory controller before the start of the ϕ_2 high waveform which is to be stretched. The ϕ_1, ϕ_2 NMOS compatible clocks and the ϕ_2TTL and MEMORY CLOCK outputs are all stretched as long as MR remains low.

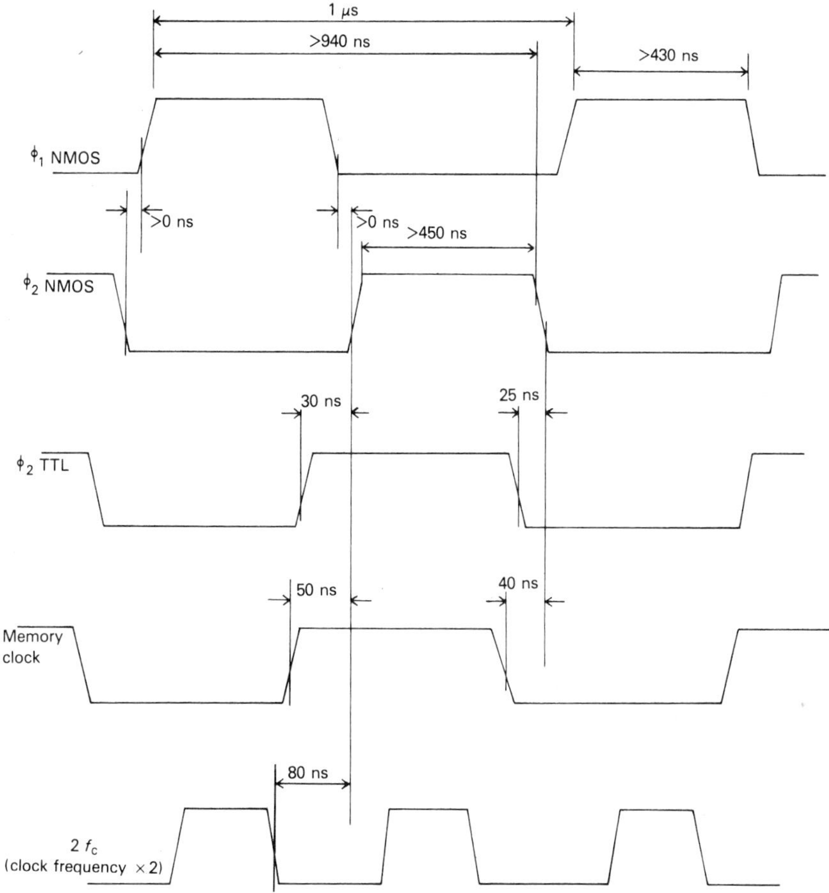

Figure 3.7 Timing diagram of the MC6871A outputs

The ϕ_2 output of the MC6871A remains high for an integral number of half cycles until the first falling edge of the $2f_c$ clock after the MR input has returned to its high state. The action of the MR input and its effect on the outputs of this clock generator are given in Fig. 3.8.

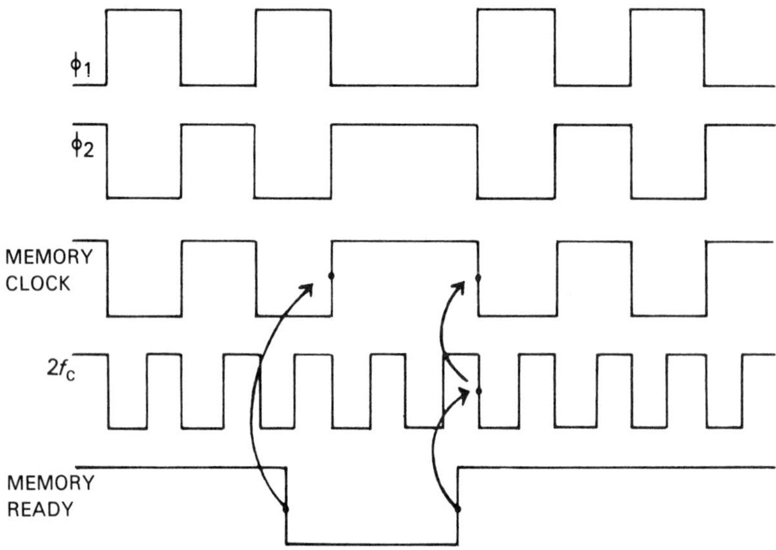

Figure 3.8 The operation of the 6871A's MEMORY READY input

A possible application of the MR input of the MC6871A is described in Fig. 3.9. The address decoder detects a memory reference to a block of slow memory during the ϕ_1 high part of a cycle. The high-to-low transition at the output of the address decoder triggers a monostable circuit which produces an active-low pulse. The width of the pulse is determined by the monostable's CR constant which must be tailored to the particular application. Fortunately, the vast majority of currently available memory components have access times sufficiently short to render the stretching of the ϕ_2 high clock unnecessary. In Section 6.9 a peripheral requiring the use of the clock generator's $\overline{\text{MEMORY READY}}$ facility is described.

The second control input, $\overline{\text{HOLD}}$, to the MC6871A serves to stretch the ϕ_1 active-high phase of the clock cycle. It has already been stated that during the beginning of the ϕ_1 high part of a cycle the CPU is busy generating values of the address, VMA, and $R/\overline{W}$, which do not become valid until approximately 270 ns after the start of a cycle. Any data transfers between the CPU and memory components or peripherals take place only during the ϕ_2 high part of the clock cycle. Consequently, the address and data buses are not required by the CPU when ϕ_1 is high. This statement requires a little qualification. Some peripherals must be selected before ϕ_2 goes high, which means that the contents of the address bus, VMA, $R/\overline{W}$, must be valid before the end of the ϕ_1 high cycle. This restriction is of

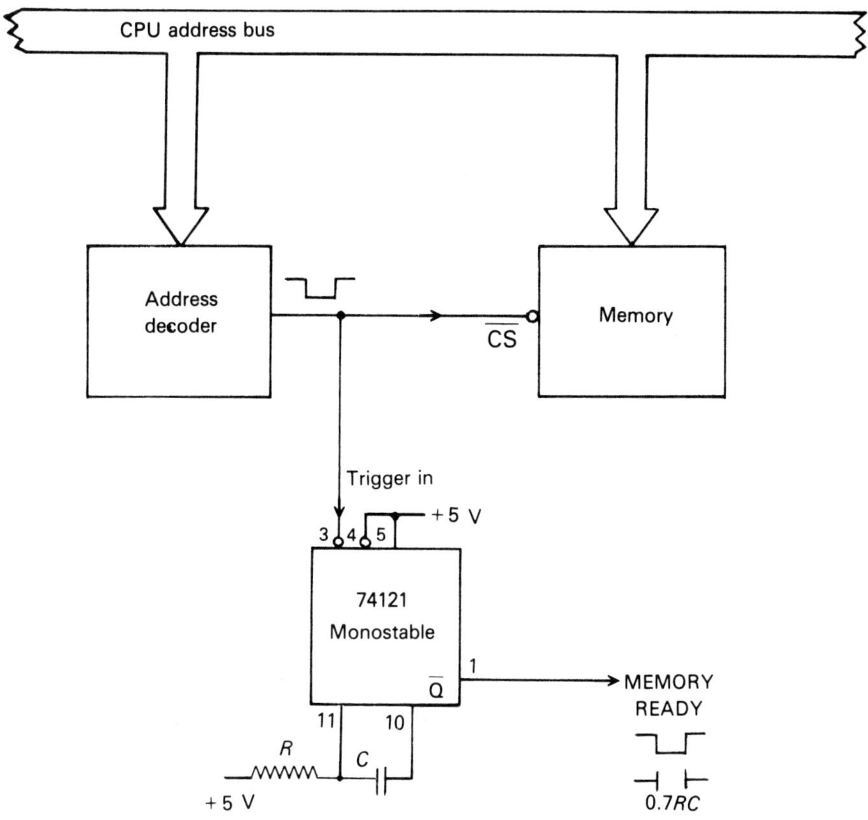

Figure 3.9 The control of the MEMORY READY input

no practical importance because the early part of each and every ϕ_1 high clock cycle is redundant as far as the system is concerned. The corollary of this statement is that when ϕ_1 is high, the system bus may be taken over by other devices. Because the ϕ_1 high clock phase lasts for a nominal 430 ns, any device accessing the memory must perform its operation in 430 ns and the memory itself must have an access time of 350 ns—allowing for time lost in address decoding and buffering. Moreover, unless really high-speed memories are used, only one memory access may take place during this period.

By stretching the ϕ_1 high phase of the clock cycle, sufficient time may be gained to enable one or more memory access cycles to be made by a device other than the CPU. This stretching is, of course, subject to a maximum limit of 9500 ns set by the dynamic nature of the CPU. There are three circumstances in which control of the system bus may be relinquished by the CPU:

Dual Processor Systems

One way of increasing the power of a microprocessor system is to allow two microprocessors to operate simultaneously. If the ϕ_1 clock of one CPU is made the ϕ_2

clock of the other CPU (and vice versa) it is possible to allow the CPUs to share the system bus as both CPUs never require the data bus simultaneously. This topic is treated more fully in Chapter 7.

Direct Memory Access (DMA)

DMA is an arrangement whereby data may be directly written into (or read from) memory by peripherals. This allows, for example, a floppy disk system to move data between itself and the RAM with virtually no CPU overhead. This action requires a DMA controller which stretches the ϕ_1 high waveform, provides an address as a source or destination of the data together with an $R/\overline{W}$ and a VMA signal, and either gets data from, or gives data to, the peripheral. Clearly, providing a microprocessor system with a DMA facility is no mean task.

Dynamic Memory Refresh

Dynamic memory, like the 6800, holds data in the form of a charge. This data is lost unless it is periodically refreshed. Typical dynamic (16K) memories require that a dummy read cycle is made to each of 128 row addresses at least once every 2 ms. In practice, this means that $A_0 - A_6$ must cycle through all possible combinations. The operation of dynamic memory refresh may be thought of as a special case of DMA, except that no actual data transfer is made. At least one microprocessor, the Z80, periodically puts out a refresh address, removing the necessity for a DMA controller. In systems where both DMA and dynamic memory refresh operations take place, a priority controller is needed to give a dynamic memory refresh cycle the highest priority.

In order to stretch the ϕ_1 high phase of a clock cycle the $\overline{\text{HOLD}}$ input of the MC6871A must be brought low. An important criterion of the control of the $\overline{\text{HOLD}}$ signal is that it must not be forced low until the NMOS ϕ_1 signal is in the high state. To fulfil this requirement some additional logic is needed to synchronize the active transition of the $\overline{\text{HOLD}}$ input with the ϕ_1 clock. A DMA request or a memory-refresh request is normally asynchronous in nature, and the circuit diagram of Fig. 3.10 may be employed to achieve the necessary synchronization.

The status of the asynchronous, active low, $\overline{\text{DMA REQUEST}}$ input is sampled on the rising edge of the $2f_c$ clock. This allows the clock output to be stretched in increments of a clock period. Once the $\overline{\text{DMA REQUEST}}$ signal returns to its logical one state, the $\overline{\text{HOLD}}$ input to the clock generator goes high following the rising edge of the next $2f_c$ pulse, and the ϕ_1 clock makes a high-to-low transition at the following edge of this $2f_c$ clock pulse. Note that while ϕ_1 is stretched the $2f_c$ and MEMORY clocks are not affected.

The MC6875

The MC6875 is Motorola's most sophisticated clock generator. This device is available in a standard 16-pin DIL package, and provides all the functions of the MC6871A plus internal sychronization of the $\overline{\text{DMA REQUEST}}$ input and an

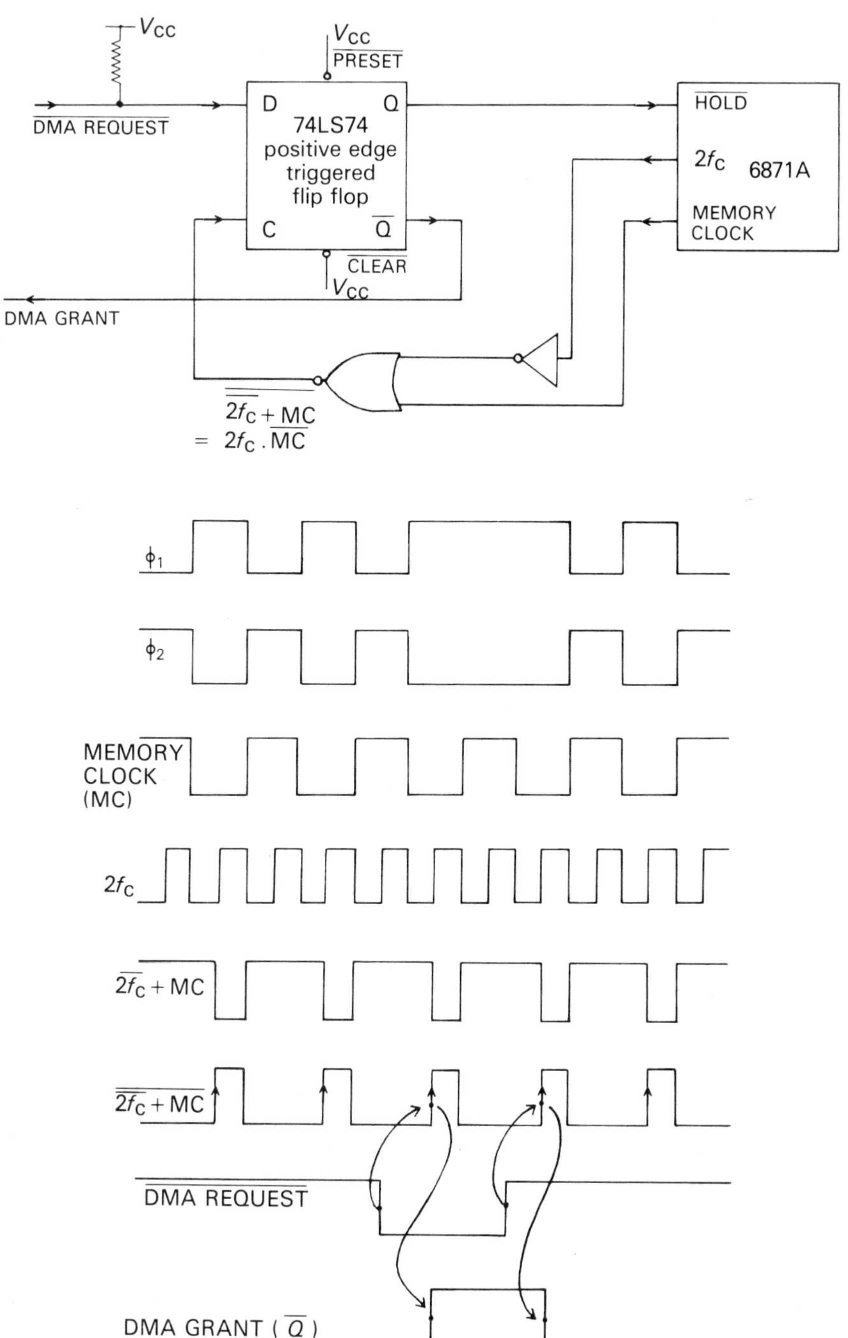

Figure 3.10 Synchronizing the $\overline{HOLD}$ input of the M66871

automatic power-on-reset circuit. Figure 3.11 shows how the 6875 clock generator is interfaced to a 6800 CPU. A quartz crystal connected between ground and pins 1 and 2 of the 6875 provides an accurate source of timing. An external oscillator may be used to provide the timing by connecting the oscillator to pin 3, grounding pin 2, and leaving pin 1 unconnected.

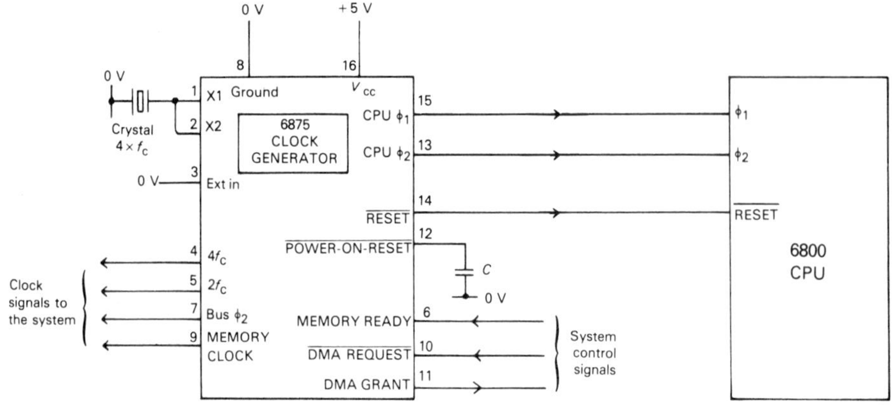

Figure 3.11 The connection of a 6875 clock generator to a 6800 CPU

The clock outputs of the 6875 are illustrated in Fig. 3.12 together with the relationships between them. The basic characteristics of these outputs are as follows:

(1)	$4f_c$	A free-running (continuous) clock at four times the CPU clock rate.
(2)	$2f_c$	A free-running clock at twice the CPU clock rate.
(3)	CPU ϕ_1	An NMOS-compatible clock capable of driving the clock input on two 6800s.
(4)	CPU ϕ_2	An NMOS-compatible clock capable of driving the clock input on two 6800s.
(5)	Bus ϕ_2	A TTL compatible clock output in phase with the CPU ϕ_2 output. Bus ϕ_2 or ϕ_2 TTL provides the principal system timing signal.
(6)	MEMORY CLOCK	The memory clock output is a clock output in phase with the CPU ϕ_2 output, but which operates (is not frozen) during a DMA request operation when the ϕ_2 TTL clock is held in a low state.

The 6875, like the 6871A, has two clock-control inputs: a MEMORY READY (MR) input which serves to freeze the CPU clock in the ϕ_2 high state, and a $\overline{\text{DMA REQUEST}}$ input which can freeze the CPU clock in the ϕ_1 high state. The $\overline{\text{DMA REQUEST}}$ input is asynchronous, unlike the corresponding input ($\overline{\text{HALT}}$) to the 6871A.

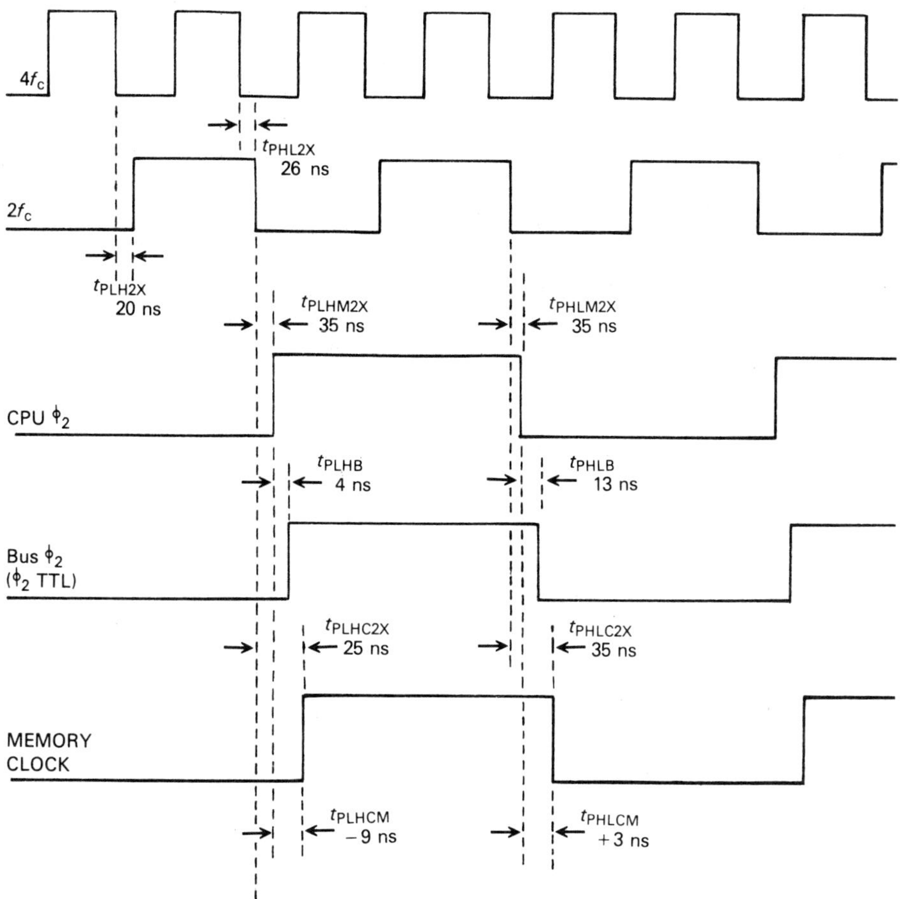

Figure 3.12 The relationship between the clock inputs of a 6875 clock generator (Note: All timing values are typical)

The MR input of the 6875 operates asynchronously and, when low, holds the ϕ_2 clock phase high to enable slow memory components to respond to a read or write cycle. This input is sampled internally on the falling edge of the $2f_c$ clock and if a high-to-low transition on this input is to be recognized, it must occur at least 27 ns (the set-up time) before the falling edge of $2f_c$. As the falling edge of $2f_c$ occurs typically 35 ns before the rising edge of ϕ_2, the MR input must be pulled low at least 62 ns before the rising edge of the ϕ_2 high clock phase to be stretched. Fortunately the contents of the address bus become valid well before the rising edge of ϕ_2, allowing ample time for an address decoder to recognize an access to a block of slow memory and pull MR low. To stretch ϕ_2 high for a minimum of an additional half cycle, MR must return to its high state at least 20 ns before the falling edge of the next $2f_c$ clock pulse. Figure 3.13 shows the operation of the MR input.

An example of the application of the MR input is given in Fig. 3.14 and a timing diagram of this circuit is given in Fig. 3.15. When the block of slow memory is accessed, the active-low chip select ($\overline{CS}$) output from the address decoder releases the $\overline{PRESET}$ input to the 7474 D flip-flop, allowing the next $2f_c \cdot 4f_c$ pulse from the AND gate to clock the current value of ϕ_2 TTL onto the MR line. This arrangement stretches ϕ_2 high for a single half cycle.

The $\overline{\text{DMA REQUEST}}$ of the 6875 operates asynchronously without any additional logic. The $\overline{\text{DMA REQUEST}}$ input is sampled internally on the rising edge of the $2f_c$ clock, and an active-low state is recognized provided the minimum set-up and hold times are met. Once a $\overline{\text{DMA REQUEST}}$ has been recognized, the

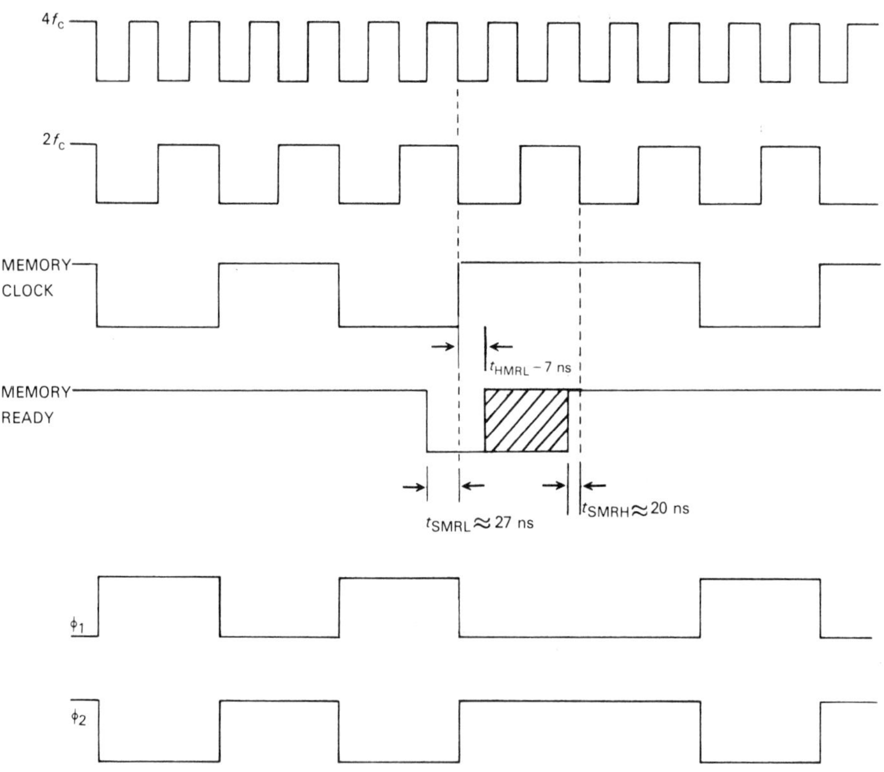

t_{SMRL} = memory ready set-up time
t_{HMRL} = memory ready hold time

Figure 3.13 The operation of the MR input of a 6875 clock generator

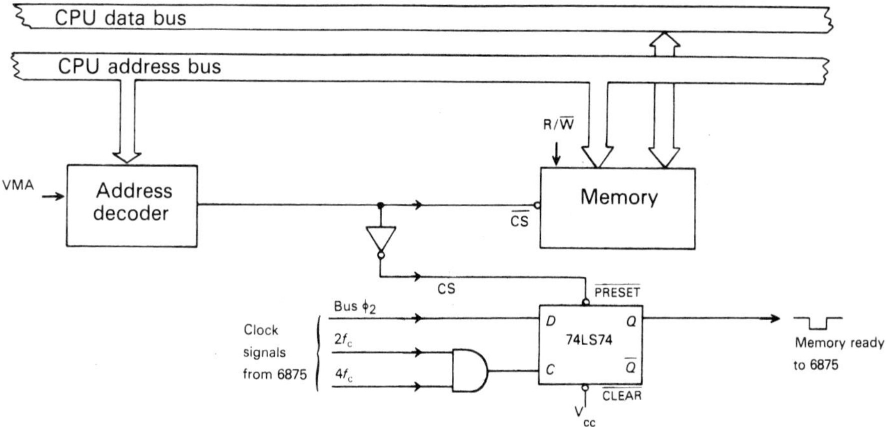

Figure 3.14 A possible control circuit for the MR imput of the 6875 clock generator

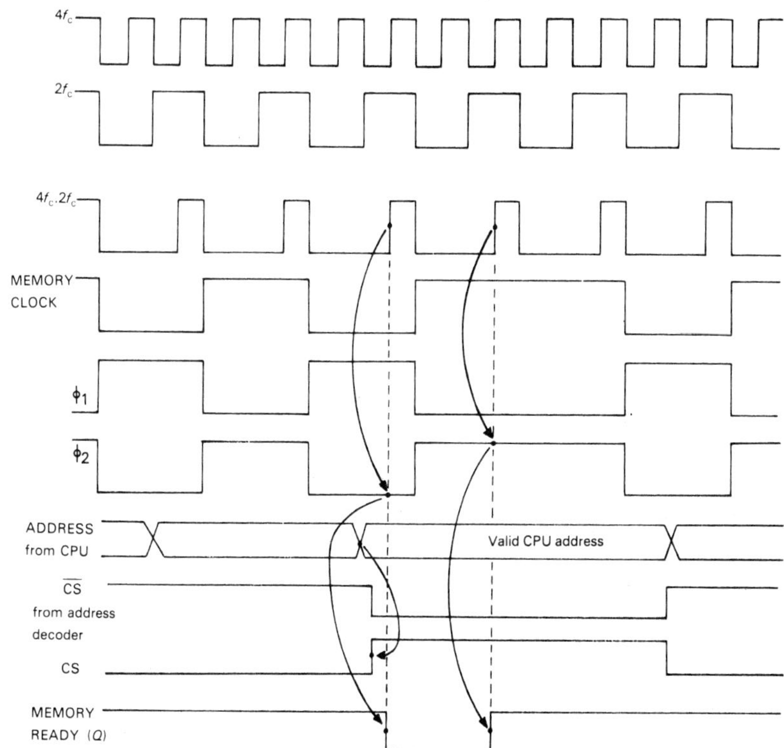

Figure 3.15 Operation of the circuit of Figure 3.14

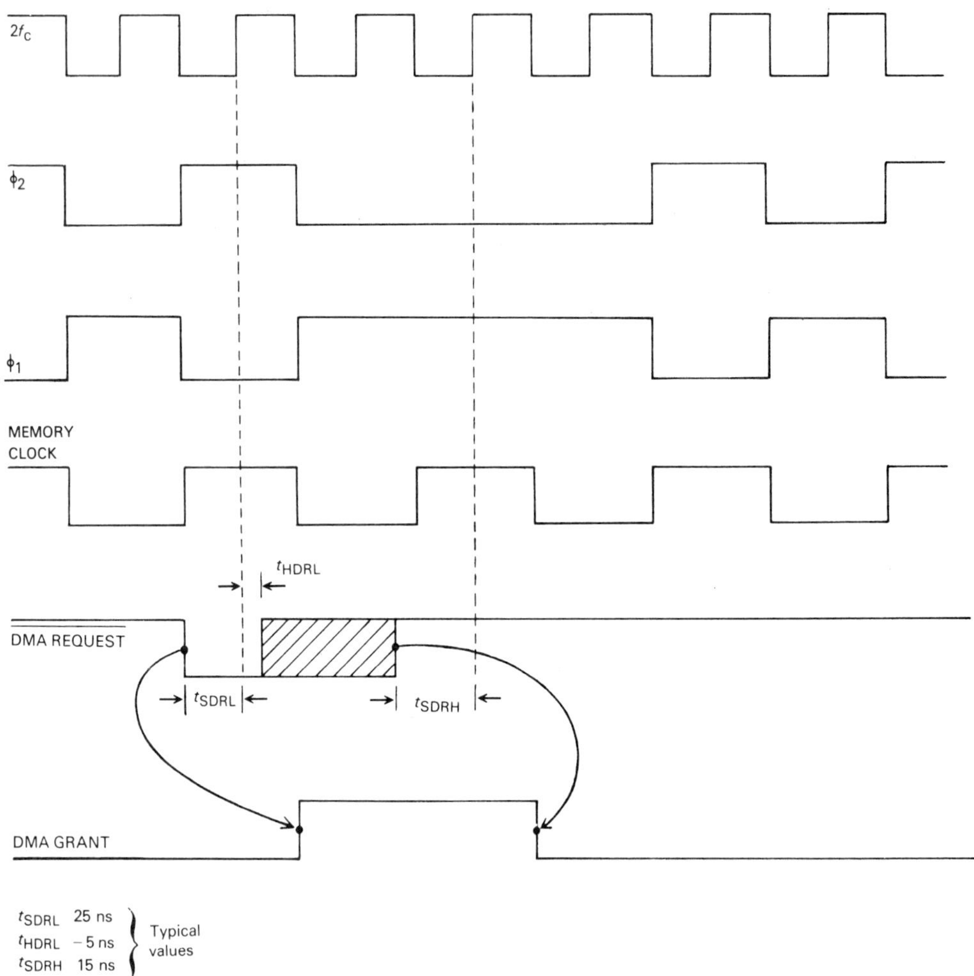

Figure 3.16 The operation of the 6875 $\overline{\text{DMA REQUEST}}$ input

following ϕ_1 high clock phase will be stretched for a full CPU cycle beyond its normal duration, provided that $\overline{\text{DMA REQUEST}}$ returns to its high state prior to the minimum set-up time preceding the next leading edge of the $2f_c$ clock. Figure 3.16 illustrates the behavior of this input.

The 6875 has a DMA GRANT output which, when active-high, indicates that a DMA request has been accepted and that the clock has now been frozen in the ϕ_1 high state. If a DMA controller wishes to make a DMA it first asserts $\overline{\text{DMA REQUEST}}$. When the clock generator has acted on this request it in turn asserts DMA GRANT indicating to the controller that the system is ready for a DMA cycle.

An additional facility of the 6875 clock generator is the ability to reset the CPU (and the rest of the system) automatically after the initial application of power.

Without this facility the poor engineer must resort either to manual reset by means of a push button or to automatic power-on-reset with a circuit requiring a number of discrete components. The 6875 has a $\overline{\text{POWER-ON-RESET}}$ input which is a Schmitt trigger and a $\overline{\text{RESET}}$ output which may be connected to the CPU's $\overline{\text{RESET}}$ input. In normal operation a capacitor is wired between the $\overline{\text{POWER-ON-RESET}}$ input and ground so that when power is initially applied to the system the $\overline{\text{POWER-ON-RESET}}$ input is held low until the capacitor charges up to the positive-going Schmitt threshold (+2.8 V) through an internal 50 kΩ resistor.

The TTL-compatible outputs of the 6875 are able to drive up to five standard TTL inputs without additional buffering. Consequently, the outputs of the clock generator are not buffered on TS1's CPU module but are buffered onto the system bus. The NMOS-compatible outputs of the 6875 drive the 6800 CPU clock input directly. According to the 6875's data sheet the NMOS compatible outputs have a maximum logic zero state value of 0.4 V and a minimum logic one state value of 4.4 V. From these figures it can be seen that there is no noise immunity between the clock generator's output and the CPU's clock inputs. For this reason care must be taken in the interconnection of these two devices. According to Motorola the following precautions should be taken:

(1) The 6875 should be located as close to the 6800 as possible—not more than 5 cm (2 in) away.
(2) The V_{cc} pin of the 6875 should be bypassed to ground at the package with a 0.1 μF capacitor.
(3) A large ground strip with a low impedance should be used to connect the 6875, 6800 and the V_{ss} supply together. This is necessary to prevent a voltage drop in the ground-return path, caused by driving highly capacitive loads.
(4) Series resistors in the range 10 – 30 Ω should be inserted in the ϕ_1 and ϕ_2 clock lines between the 6875 and the CPU. These resistors help to reduce overshoots and reflections on the clock pulses.
(5) The crystal should be located as near as possible to the 6875. The crystal itself should have an internal impedance of 35 – 60 Ω at its series resonant frequency.

3.2.1 The TS1 Clock Circuit and Interface

The circuit diagram of the clock circuit of the TS1 is given in Fig. 3.17. Included in this diagram are the reset arrangements of the TS1 and the interface between the clock circuit and the system bus. The operation of the clock generator, its connection to the CPU and the system bus require no further explanation. However, the control of the CPU's $\overline{\text{RESET}}$ input and part of the CPU's bus interface control need some explanation.

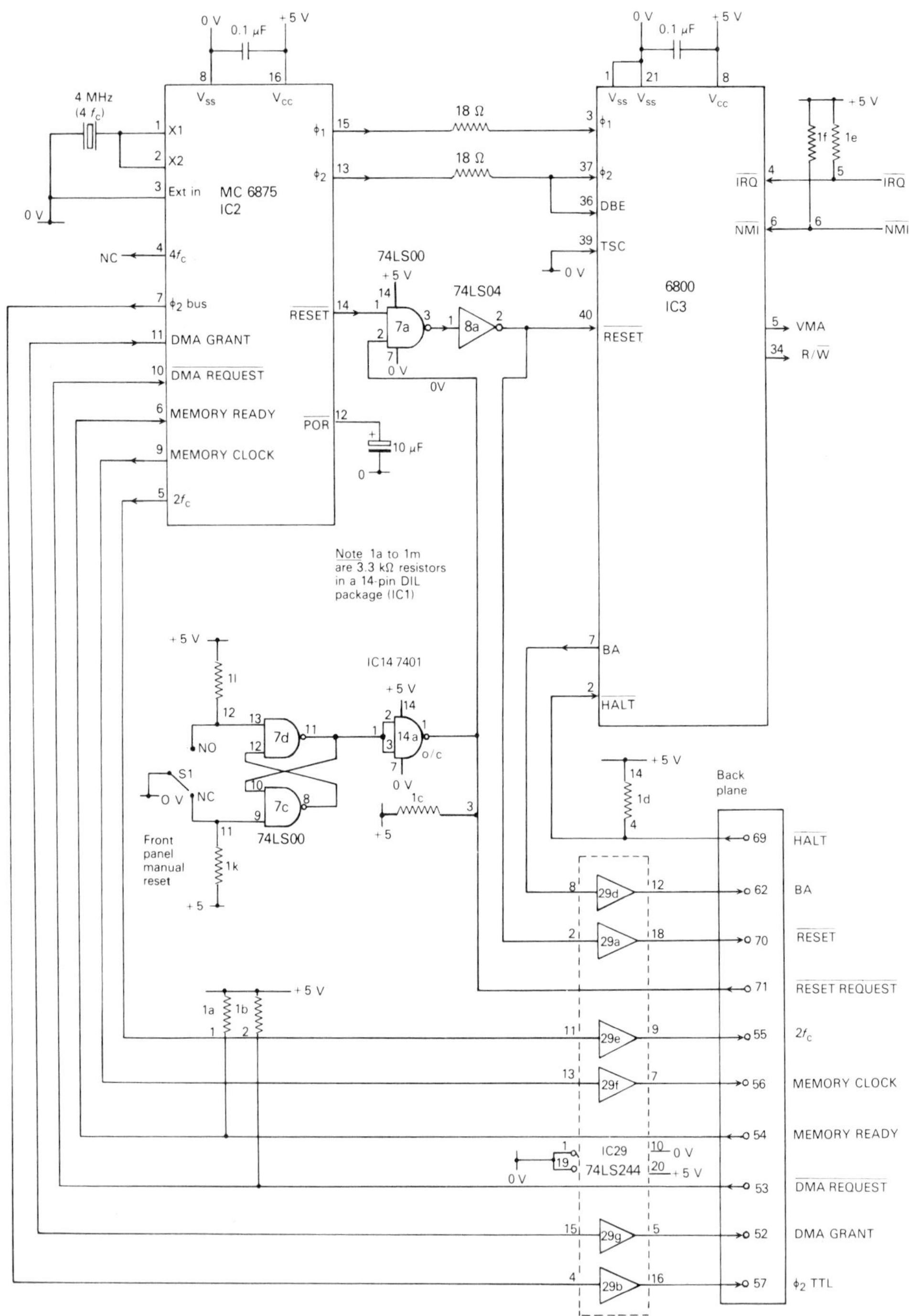

Figure 3.17 The clock generator and control circuit of the TS1

Reset Control

There are two situations in which the CPU needs to be reset, that is, started up in a known mode: first, on the initial application of power, and second, to abort a program which cannot be terminated in any other way (usually because an endless loop has been entered). The 6875 clock generator provides the necessary power-on-reset but according to its data sheet does not allow a reset at any other time. It is, in fact, possible to generate a reset pulse from the 6875 at any time simply by grounding its $\overline{\text{POWER-ON-RESET}}$ input pin. Motorola do not recommend this because grounding this input defeats the clock generator's MR and $\overline{\text{DMA REQUEST}}$ facilities. In Fig. 3.17 the $\overline{\text{RESET REQUEST}}$ line on the system bus is ANDed with the 6875's $\overline{\text{RESET}}$ output. If either input to the AND gate (in practice a NAND gate followed by an invertor) goes low, its output goes low resetting the CPU. A manual reset from a push-button on the front panel is provided by a debounced switch. Switch S1 has its output debounced (i.e. the logic level on the $\overline{\text{RESET}}$ line generates a clean pulse each time the switch is pushed) by the cross-coupled NAND gates IC7c and IC7d. The output of the debouncer is connected to the $\overline{\text{RESET REQUEST}}$ line by means of a gate with an open collector output (IC14a). When the input of IC14a is low, the output of the gate is left floating and is pulled up to a logical-one state by R1c. If the reset button is pushed,the input to IC14a rises and its output is forced into a low state, resetting the CPU. The subject of open-collector gates is dealt with in Chapter 4.

Control of DBE and TSC

The TSC (three-state-control) input of the 6800 causes the address bus drivers to be floated when this input is in a high state. That is, when the TSC = 1 the address bus may be used by another active device in a DMA operation. It is shown, in Chapter 4, that the CPU's address bus must be buffered onto the system bus. Consequently, it is not the CPU's own internal address bus drivers that must be floated in a DMA cycle but the system address bus buffers. The TSC input may therefore be grounded and forgotten about.

The operation of the DBE (data bus enable) input is not quite as simple as the TSC input. The DBE input is a three-state control signal for the CPU's data bus. This input enables the data bus drivers during a CPU write cycle. In a CPU read cycle the data bus drivers are automatically disabled internally. Like the corresponding TSC input, the DBE line may be used to free the data bus for a DMA operation. (*Note:* the active level of the DBE line is opposite to that of the TSC line.) Unfortunately it is not possible to wire DBE to a logical one level and ignore it. DBE must go low for a minimum of 150 ns during the time the ϕ_1 clock is in a logical one state. Very many 6800-based microprocessor systems strap the DBE input to the ϕ_2 clock input. This ensures that DBE goes low every time ϕ_1 is high. The TS1 adopts this approach to the control of the DBE input. Once more it should be stressed that the DBE input is not required for DMA operations as the system data bus (like the address bus) is buffered by external bus drivers which are controlled by the DMA GRANT output of the clock generator (see Section 4.3).

It is interesting to note that in the 6802 and 6809 Motorola has abandoned both the TSC and DBE control inputs as they are largely irrelevant. In some 6800-based systems the DBE input is not connected directly to the ϕ_2 clock for two reasons, both of which are concerned with the time for which the data on the data bus is valid. During a CPU write cycle the data from the CPU becomes valid no later than 225 ns after the positive transition at the DBE input. When DBE $= \phi_2$ the data is not valid until approximately halfway through a ϕ_2 high cycle. Figure 3.18 illustrates this effect. For many memory devices and certainly all those produced by Motorola, the time for which the data is valid (275 ns) exceeds by a wide margin the data set-up time required by the memory device. Some memory devices, notably those intended for operation with 8080A-based systems, require that the data in a CPU write cycle should be valid much earlier in the cycle.

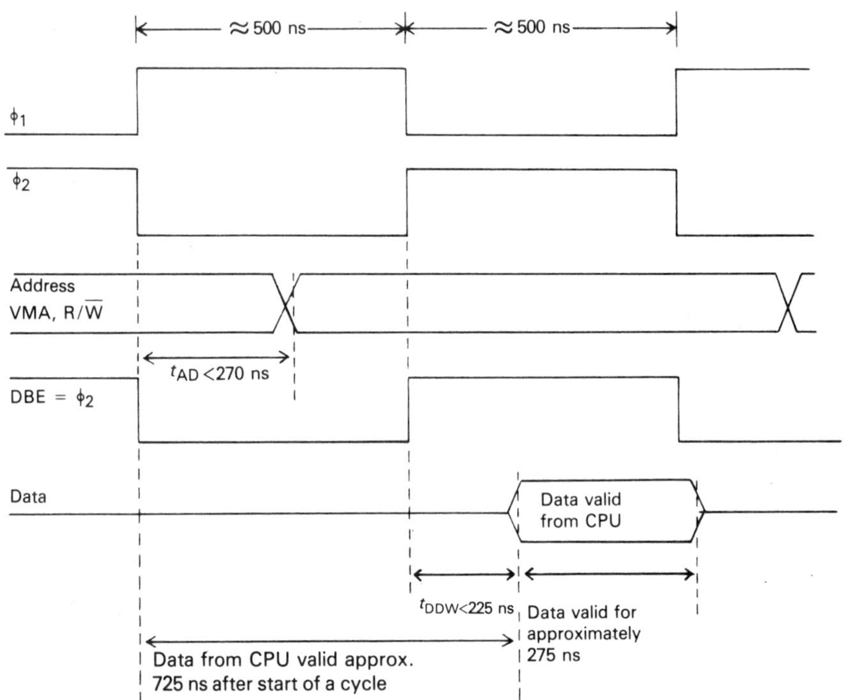

Figure 3.18 The CPU write cycle of a 6800 when DBE $= \phi_2$

To put the data on the data bus early in a cycle, DBE must have a short down time. According to the 6800 data sheet DBE must make its positive transition no earlier than 150 ns after the start of the cycle. The effect of this is illustrated in Fig. 3.19. If DBE is low for its minimum specified time of 150 ns, the data will be valid for at least 625 ns. There are several ways of reducing the down time of the

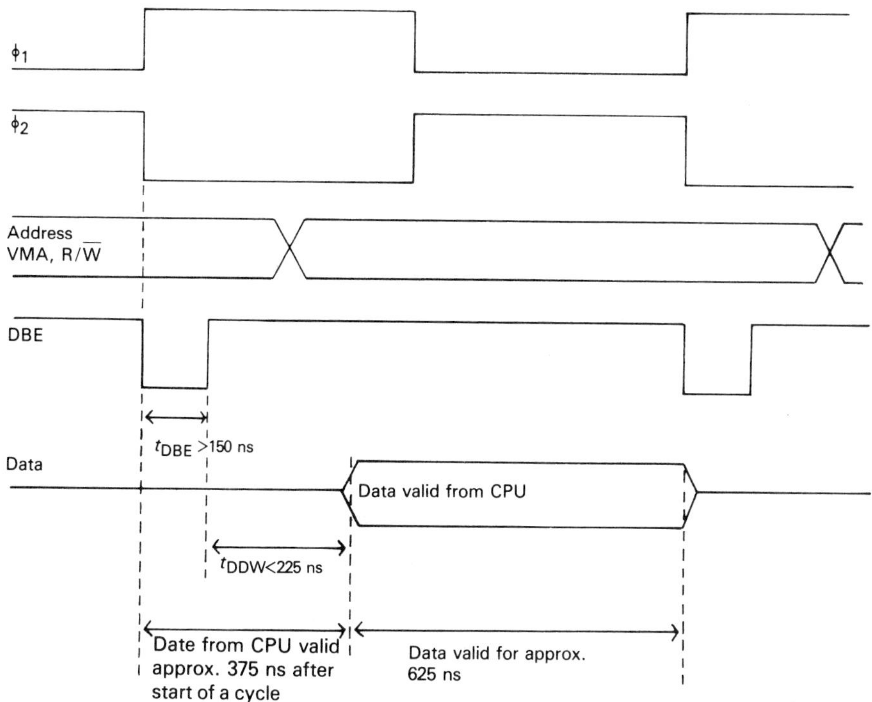

Figure 3.19 The CPU write cycle of a 6800 when DBE $\neq \phi_2$

DBE input—one is to trigger a monostable on the rising edge of the ϕ_1 clock and arrange its negative-going pulse to be approximately 150 ns and act as DBE. Another solution is to form DBE from ϕ_2 and $2f_c$ so that DBE is low when ϕ_2 and $2f_c$ are low. This gives a down time of approximately 250 ns.

Sometimes it is necessary to stretch the time for which DBE is high beyond the falling edge of the ϕ_2 clock pulse. In normal operation when DBE $= \phi_2$ the data from the CPU in a write cycle remains valid for no less than 10 ns after the falling edge of the ϕ_2 clock. This 10 ns is called the data-hold time and is sufficient for most memory components. There are some memory components which require that the data be valid for up to 100 ns after they have been deselected. Figure 3.20 illustrates the effect of stretching DBE beyond the falling edge of ϕ_2. There are many ways of stretching DBE and one such way taken from Motorola's Application Note AN-771 is given in Fig. 3.21. Although facilities for stretching DBE are not provided in the TS1, any module containing memory components with a data-hold time greater than 10 ns may solve the problem by latching the data in a set of eight flip-flops to hold it after a deselect.

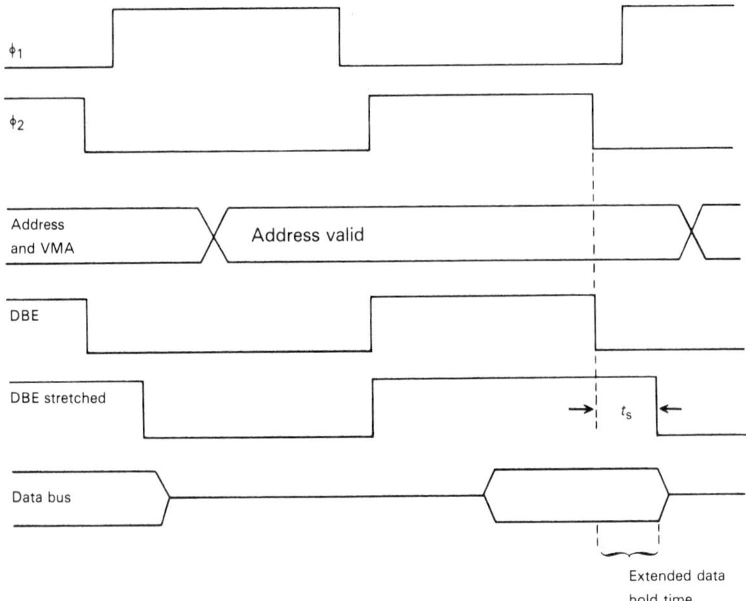

Figure 3.20 The effect of stretching DBE to increase the data hold time

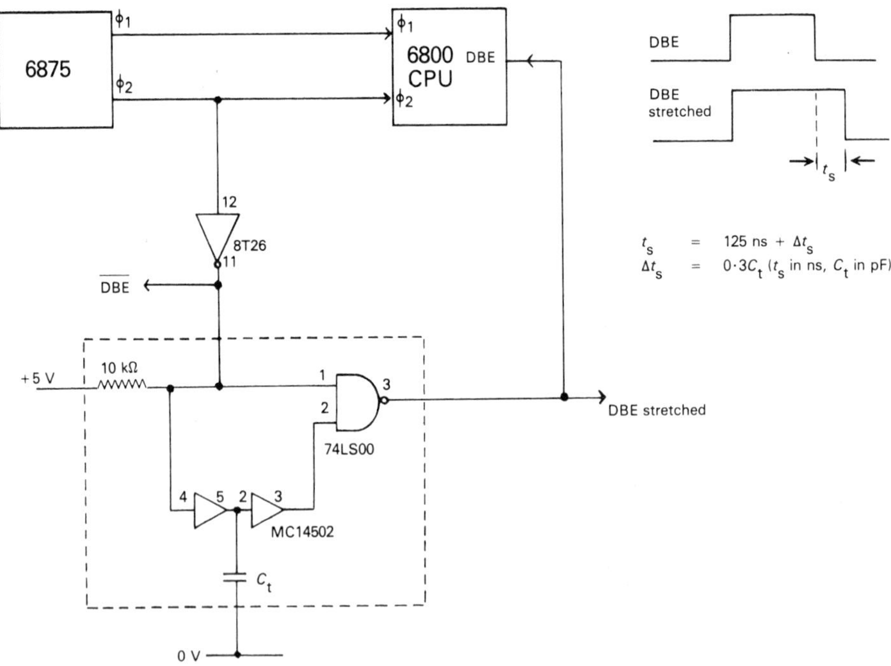

Figure 3.21 A possible DBE stretch circuit

Control of the $\overline{\text{HALT}}$ Input

The $\overline{\text{HALT}}$ input, when pulled low, puts the CPU in an idle state enabling the system address and data buses to be taken over by some other active device. While the CPU is halted its BA (bus available) output is asserted, telling the DMA controller the bus is now free. The advantage of halting the CPU for a DMA operation is that a million cycles of DMA may take place per second as the CPU may be halted indefinitely—internal refresh operations take place normally while the CPU is halted. Of course, halting the CPU stops all computation while DMA is taking place.

When BA is high the CPU's address bus, data bus, and R/$\overline{\text{W}}$ line are floated and VMA is forced low. All these lines are buffered by three-state drivers and Section 4.3 deals with the control of these lines. Some literature on the 6800 provides a rather confusing account of the nature of the $\overline{\text{HALT}}$ input to the CPU. It is sometimes implied that the $\overline{\text{HALT}}$ input must be synchronized with the ϕ_1 clock. This is not so. If the active transition of $\overline{\text{HALT}}$ occurs t_{pcs} (200 ns) before the trailing edge of ϕ_1 of the last cycle of an instruction, then the CPU will be halted at the end of the current instruction. Should $\overline{\text{HALT}}$ not go low within this time the CPU will not be halted until after the next instruction.

Apart from DMA operations, one of the main uses of the $\overline{\text{HALT}}$ input in a 6800 system is to provide a single-step facility. As the 6800 cannot be single-stepped through instructions merely by slowing down the system clock, the execution of a single instruction at a time must be done by holding $\overline{\text{HALT}}$ low and raising it just long enough to allow a single instruction to be executed. If the $\overline{\text{HALT}}$ line is raised to a logical one state within 100 ns of the rising edge of ϕ_1, and then returned to a low state after one clock cycle, a single instruction is executed.

SUMMARY

This chapter has examined the heart of a CPU module—its clock. The clock is not only responsible for controlling the rate at which the processor executes instructions, but often must also be able to deal with slow memory components and to handle DMA operations. The characteristics of the 6800 clock have been defined and several possible arrangements of clock generator have been discussed. Towards the end of this chapter the first part of the TS1 CPU module has been presented plus the clock circuit and some of the control circuits of the 6800.

PROBLEMS

1 The circuit diagram of Fig. 3.9 is designed to generate a MEMORY READY pulse whenever a particular block of slow memory is accessed. If a simple address decoder were used, the possibility of the generation of a spurious trigger pulse exists because during the time in which the address lines are changing from one state to another they may pass through the value chosen to trigger the monostable. Devise a circuit which would overcome this problem, bearing in mind that the address bus of the 6800 is not guaranteed to be stable before VMA is active.

2 If the 6875 were not available, how could an effectively equivalent clock generator be constructed from standard TTL parts? What advantages (or otherwise) would there be in building such a circuit rather than buying the 6875?

3 In the prototype TS1 the power-on-reset circuit of the 6875 does not always function as it should, leaving the operator to push the manual reset button. Devise some system whereby a reset would be forced if the CPU were not operating as intended.

4 Using the information about the timing requirements of the $\overline{\text{HALT}}$ input in Appendix A2, design a circuit capable of stepping the CPU through a program, an operation at a time, whenever a button is pushed.

5 Devise a simple DMA controller using TTL circuits to halt the CPU, to provide an address, R/$\overline{\text{W}}$ E and $\overline{\text{VMA}}$ E signals to the system bus, and to move a byte of data from an external input to the CPU's memory space. This question should not be attempted until the concepts of tri-state logic and bus drivers have been studied (Chapter 4).

4

The Electrical Characteristics of a Bus

A bus is a highway composed of one or more paths which transfer information and electrical power between the various components of a digital system. The concept of a common bus, carrying data from one part of a system to another, is so obvious that it is difficult to imagine a complex digital system without one.

To many microprocessor users the bus structure of their system is as important as the microprocessor chip itself. This is because engineers do not always wish to design an entire microprocessor system, and would rather couple their own processor module to, say, a commercially available memory board. Clearly, manufacturers produce bus-compatible peripherals and memories only if the bus is a standard bus, guaranteeing high sales to many different users.

One of the most famous buses is the UNIBUS found in the DEC PDP-11 system. This is a well-designed bus whose principal feature is its asynchronous operation, allowing peripherals of various speeds to share the same bus. Microprocessor buses have developed on a rather *ad hoc* basis. For example, the ubiquitous S100 bus was originally introduced by MITS Inc in their Altair microprocessor kit, and has become a *de facto* standard in the 8080 and Z80 hobby computer market. The IEEE has now produced a draft of a formal standard for this bus.

The lines, or information highways, which form a microprocessor bus may be characterized in four ways:

(1) The function of the highway: for example, address lines, data lines, VMA, $R/\overline{W}$.
(2) The direction of data transfer—to the CPU, from the CPU, bidirectional.
(3) The protocol observed by the lines. This includes the sequence of events which must take place for data to be moved on the bus.
(4) The electrical specification of the signals on the bus: for example, the guaranteed electrical levels representing the logical one and zero states.

In this section we are concerned largely with the electrical characteristics of a bus. It is often this aspect of a microprocessor system that causes the inexperienced microprocessor systems designer most trouble. This is not because the electrical characteristics of a bus are difficult to understand, they are often simply forgotten about.

4.1 THE THREE TYPES OF BUS LINES

From an electrical point of view, the various lines forming a system bus may be divided into three groups: unidirectional lines with one transmitter and many receivers, unidirectional lines with one receiver and many transmitters, and bidirectional lines. Here, the term "transmitter" refers to a device which can put data onto the bus, and "receiver" refers to a device which can read data from it. Sometimes transmitters are called "talkers", and receivers are called "listeners". Figure 4.1 shows how the bus lines of the TS1 microprocessor system may be grouped according to the above classification.

4.1.1 Unidirectional Lines with One Transmitter

A typical example of the unidirectional line with one transmitter and many receivers is an address line. The 6800 microprocessor puts out an address on its 16 address lines during a memory-access cycle. Each of these address lines is connected to the address inputs of all the memory components attached to the address bus. Thus, the 6800 CPU is the transmitter communicating simultaneously with all the memory devices—the receivers.

It might be thought that a unidirectional line with one transmitter feeding many receivers need consist of nothing more than a copper wire or printed circuit track, from a CPU, clock, or control output to the inputs of the devices requiring the signal on the bus. Except in the simplest of microprocessor systems, it is just not possible to connect the outputs of the CPU directly to the inputs of all the other devices served by the bus.

While at the "system level" the behavior of all logic elements may be described by Boolean expressions, the actual system is constructed from real components, the physical behavior of which must be taken into account. In fact, the use of Boolean algebra and the binary system by computer designers is not due to some special advantage inherent in the binary system, but rather to the difficulty of manufacturing logic elements with multilevel outputs. If the current level of semiconductor technology permitted the production of logic devices with ten distinct output states, a noise immunity as high as TTL, a chip density as great as NMOS, and a cost comparable to today's microprocessors, then the design of digital computers would change overnight.

The two-state devices most commonly employed in microprocessor systems are fabricated in TTL (bipolar), NMOS, or CMOS technologies. Some of the basic

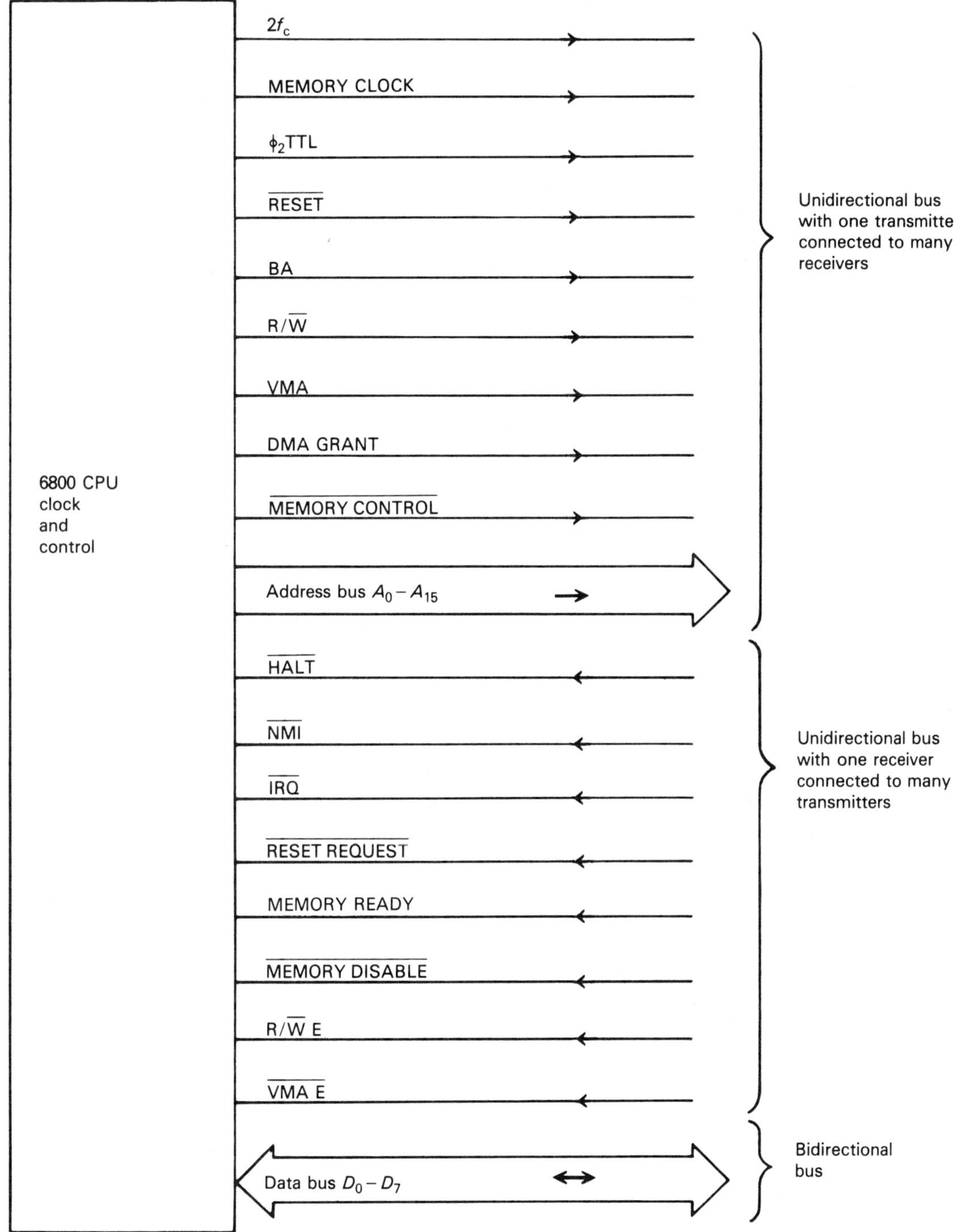

Figure 4.1 A microprocessor bus with information paths classified by data direction

properties of gates in each of these technologies are given in Table 4.2. It can readily be seen that each of these three technologies has characteristics differing greatly from the other two.

From an interfacing point of view the most important characteristics of digital devices are the voltage levels at their inputs and outputs and the currents which flow into and out of them. Logic elements are always described in terms of eight basic parameters: V_{OL}, V_{OH}, V_{IL}, V_{IH}, I_{IL}, I_{IH}, I_{OL}, I_{OH}. The definitions of these parameters are given in Table 4.1.

Table 4.1 The Principal Parameters of Logic Elements

1. V_{OL} is the maximum low-state output voltage of a logic element when it is driving a full load.
2. V_{OH} is the minimum high-state output voltage of a logic element when it is driving a full load.
3. V_{IL} is the maximum input voltage guaranteed to be accepted as a low-state input voltage.
4. V_{IH} is the minimum input voltage guaranteed to be accepted as a high-state input voltage.
5. I_{OL} is the maximum positive current which flows into a low-state output at not more than V_{OL}.
6. I_{OH} is the maximum negative current which flows out of a high-state output at not less than V_{OH}.
7. I_{IL} is the maximum negative current which flows out of an input held at V_{OL}.
8. I_{IH} is the maximum positive current which flows into an input held at V_{OH}.

From Table 4.2 it can be seen that the worst case low-level (logical zero) outputs, V_{OL}, of low power Schottky TTL, NMOS, and CMOS gates are 0.5 V,

Table 4.2 The Characteristics of Some Semiconductor Digital Logic Circuits

Characteristic	*Logic family*			
	Standard TTL	*Low-power Schottky TTL*	*NMOS*	*CMOS*
Propagation delay time (per gate) (ns)	10	9.5	25	35
V_{OL} (volts)	0.4	0.5	0.4	0.01
V_{OH} (volts)	2.4	2.7	2.4	4.99
V_{IL} (volts)	0.8	0.8	0.8	1.5
V_{IH} (volts)	2.0	2.0	2.0	3.5
I_{OL}	16 mA	8 mA	1.6 mA	0.4 mA
I_{OH}	−400 μA	−400 μA	−200 μA	−500 μA
I_{IL}	−1.6 mA	−0.4 mA	2.5 μA	10 pA
I_{IH}	40 μA	20 μA	2.5 μA	10 pA
Input capacitance (pF)		3.5	10−160	5

Note: The above values are typical and variations exist between gates of the same family. A negative sign indicates that the current flows out of a gate.

0.4 V, and 0.01 V, respectively. The maximum guaranteed low-level inputs, V_{IL}, to these gates are 0.8 V, 0.8 V and 1.5 V respectively. When the output of one gate is connected to the input of another, a low-level state is reliably detected only if the value of V_{OL} is less than, or equal to, the value of V_{IL}. From the above figures it is clear that the output of any of these three types of gate can be connected to the input of another gate, without breaking the requirement that $V_{OL} \leqslant V_{IL}$. Note that satisfying this requirement alone will not guarantee correct operation of the circuit. The difference between V_{IL} and V_{OL} is known as the low-state d.c. noise immunity of the gate.

Consider now the voltage levels at the inputs and outputs of these gates in a high-level (logical one) state. The worst-case logical one outputs, V_{OH}, of LS TTL, NMOS and CMOS gates are 2.7 V, 2.4 V, and 4.99 V, respectively. The corresponding values of V_{IH} (the lowest high-level signal guaranteed to be interpreted as a logical one) for these gates are 2.0 V, 2.0 V, and 3.5 V respectively. For reliable operation, the minimum value of V_{OH} for the driving gate must be greater than the minimum value of V_{IH} for the receiving gate. In this case the value of $V_{OH} - V_{IH}$ is known as the high-state d.c. noise immunity of the gate. Because the value of V_{OH} for an NMOS gate is 2.4 V, and the corresponding value of V_{IH} for a CMOS gate is 3.5 V, the output of an NMOS gate cannot be connected directly to the input of a CMOS gate, if reliable operation is to be guaranteed.

In addition to the need to match voltage levels at the inputs and outputs of gates, it is also necessary to consider the flow of current between gates. When a current flows into a gate, the gate is said to "sink" a current, and when the current flows out of the gate, it is said to "source" a current. For example, when the input of a low-power Schottky TTL gate is in a logical zero state ($V_{IL} \leqslant 0.8$ V), a current of 400 μA flows out of the input. The output circuit driving this gate must be able to sink the 400 μA, if the input voltage to the gate is to be held below 0.8 V. When the output of one gate is connected to the inputs of several other gates, the output circuit of the driving gate must be able to source or sink the current demanded by all the inputs.

In Fig. 4.2 an example of a unidirectional bus with one transmitter driving five receivers is given. The transmitter is an NMOS output stage (typical of CPU outputs), and the receivers are an NMOS gate, a TTL gate, a low-power Schottky TTL gate, a TTL gate with a PNP transistor input, and a CMOS gate. In each case the input circuit of a typical gate is presented, and it can be seen that each input circuit puts a very different load on the bus.

Figure 4.3 illustrates the current flow between the output of an NMOS gate and the input of a TTL gate for both the logical one and logical zero states. Whenever the NMOS gate is put into a low state it must be able to sink a current of up to 1.6 mA from the emitter of the transistor in the TTL gate. If the NMOS gate cannot sink this current, the voltage at the output of the NMOS gate may rise above the TTL gate's V_{IL}, and reliable operation may not occur. A similar situation exists in the logical one state, except that the NMOS output must provide a current of 40 μA to hold the TTL input in a high state.

According to the data sheet of the 6800, its TTL-compatible outputs are

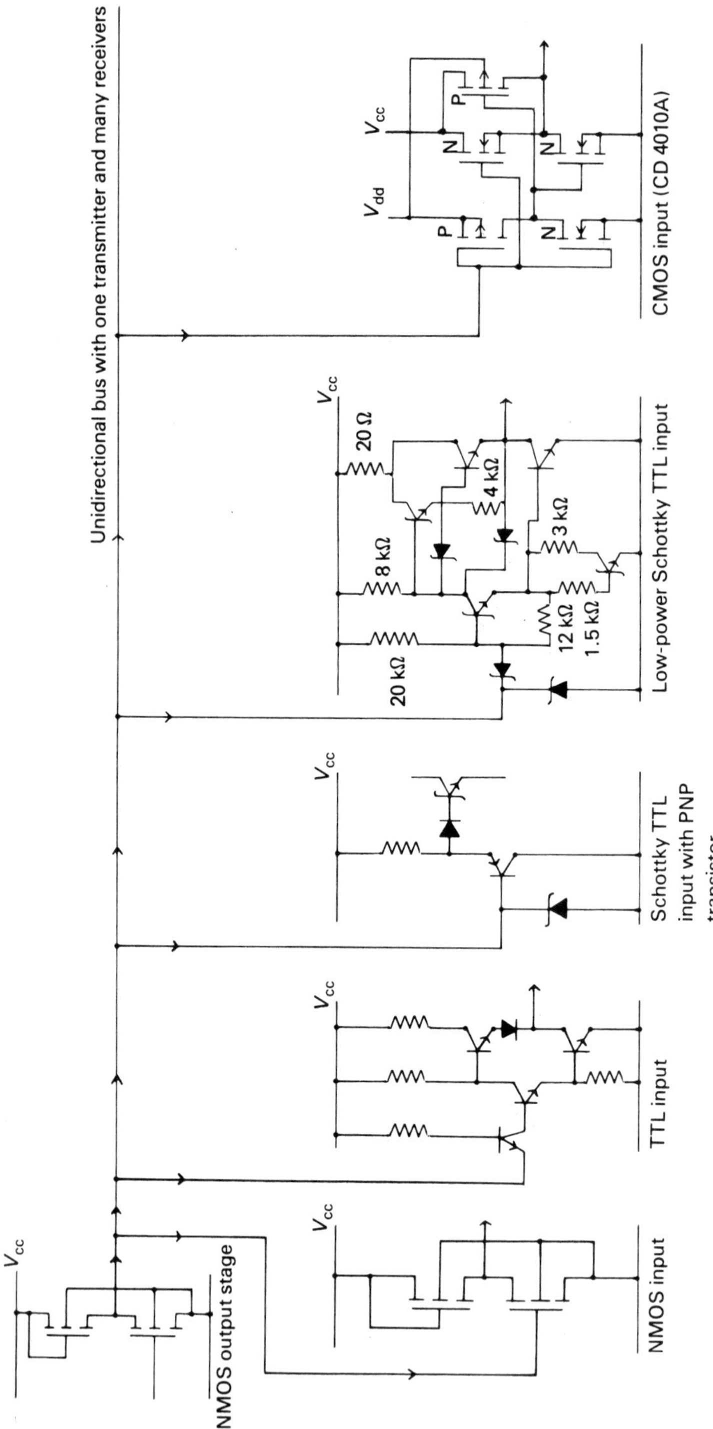

Figure 4.2 *The circuit diagrams of the input stages of some digital devices*

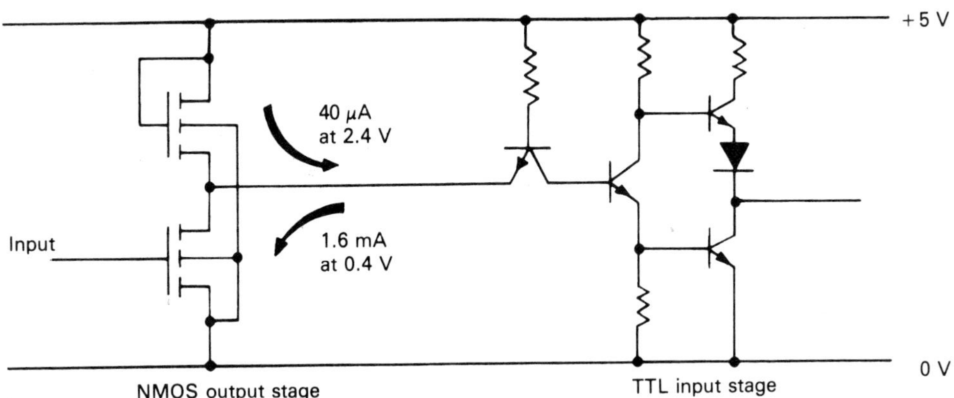

Figure 4.3 An NMOS stage driving a TTL stage

guaranteed to drive one TTL load. Although the voltage levels at the output of an NMOS gate are compatible with the voltage requirements of a TTL gate, the current-carrying capacity of an NMOS output circuit makes it unsuitable as a bus driver, where the bus is connected to several TTL input circuits.

In practice the output of an NMOS gate will probably drive more than one TTL input, because the parameters quoted for both technologies are worst-case values. While a home constructor or student may design circuits which work, but operate outside the manufacturer's published specifications, no reputable engineer would attempt such a thing. Anyone who designs a microprocessor system in an arbitary way, without studying the appropriate data sheets carefully, or by tweaking component values until the system works on the test bench, is inviting disaster if he later produces the design on a large scale. There are two popular alternatives to standard TTL gates—low-power Schottky TTL, and TTL gates with PNP input transistors. Low-power Schottky TTL gates have a maximum logical zero input current of -0.40 mA, which means that a TTL-compatible NMOS output can drive up to four LS–TTL gates. By putting PNP transistors in the input circuits of TTL gates it is possible to drive eight of these gates, each with an input current of -200 μA, from one NMOS output.

In most microprocessor systems, the devices connected to the system bus are memory chips and peripherals, both of which use NMOS technology. From Table 4.2 it can be seen that the input current flowing into the gates of NMOS FETs is of the order of 2.5 μA, a tiny fraction of the current flowing into TTL gates. For this reason it might easily be thought that many NMOS devices can be connected to a bus driven by the output stage of an NMOS gate. Under steady state conditions (no changes of logical state), the output of a single NMOS gate can drive many NMOS input circuits. Unfortunately another factor influencing circuit design is the capacitance associated with the gate of a MOSFET transistor. When the input to the gate of a MOSFET transistor changes state, a current flows into or out of the effective gate capacitance (see Fig. 4.4). Figure 4.5 shows the equivalent circuit of a MOSFET input stage when the input changes from a logical zero to a logical one, and presents a graph of the gate-source voltage as a function of time. Initially the voltage on the capacitor is approximately 0.2 V. When the active pull-up MOSFET in the driver is turned on, C begins to charge up exponentially towards V_{OH} through the effective resistance of the MOSFET load R. The input circuit of the NMOS gate responds to the change at its input only when the gate voltage reaches V_T, the switching threshold. The effect of the gate capacitance is to introduce a delay between the change of state at the gate input and the change of state at the output. As more NMOS gates are connected to the bus the total input capacitance increases, which in turn raises the time taken by the receivers to respond to changes at the transmitters. This delay eats into the access time of the memory components, and eventually the memories fail to respond to a read or write operation within the time available. The maximum load capacitance of any output of the 6800 is quoted by Motorola as 130 pF. This allows approximately eight NMOS inputs to be driven

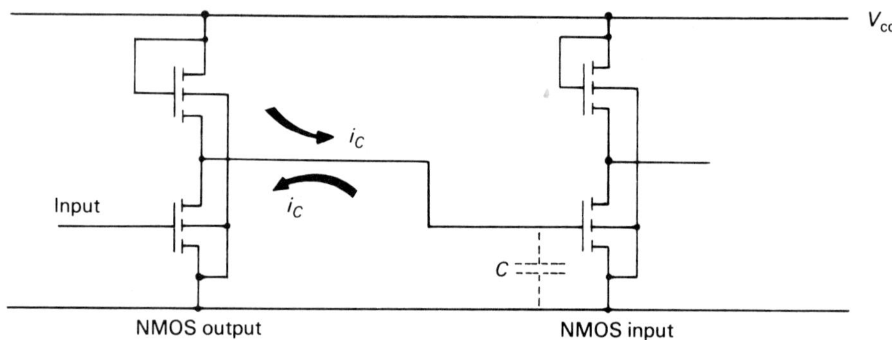

Figure 4.4 An NMOS stage driving an NMOS stage

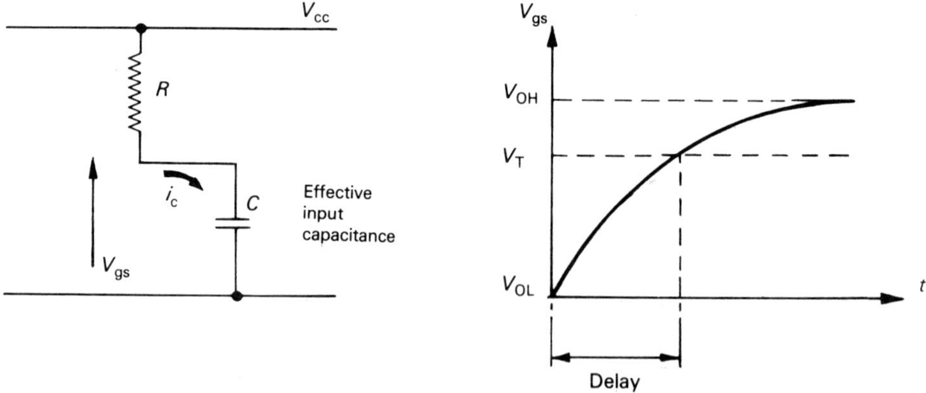

Figure 4.5 The gate-source voltage on an NMOS input stage during a low-to-high transition

directly by the 6800. Note that the effect of wiring capacitance should be added to the input capacitance. According to Motorola, address and data bus delays increase at a rate of approximately 0.5 ns/pF for purely capacitive loading.

To avoid loading the bus lines connected to the outputs of NMOS gates too heavily, a buffer (often called a bus driver) can be connected between the NMOS output and the bus. A buffer is a device which presents a very light load at its input, while providing an output drive capability far greater than the NMOS output stage.

Apart from economic considerations, a small penalty is paid for the use of bus drivers. Bus drivers have a transmission delay normally in the region of 6 to 20 ns. The simplest bus driver is a standard TTL buffer. In practice TTL gates are not used as bus drivers for three reasons:

(1) TTL gates source a relatively high input current in a logical zero state.
(2) TTL gates have a limited current drive capacity—a TTL output can sink only 16 mA in the logical zero state.
(3) The output of a TTL gate has a low-impedance path to ground in the logical zero state, and a low-impedance to V_{cc} in the logical one state because of its active pull-up transistor. This means that it is not possible for any other device to take control of a bus driven by a standard TTL gate.

The effect of connecting two TTL bus drivers to the same line is illustrated in Fig. 4.6. Suppose the outputs of two TTL gates, G_1 and G_2, were connected together. When the output of G_1 is forced into a logical zero state, transistor T_2 conducts and forms a low impedance path to ground. When the output of G_2 is forced into a logical one state, the output is actively pulled towards the V_{cc} rail by T_3 which is turned on. This active pull-up arrangement, known as a totem-pole output, provides a low-impedance path between the output and the V_{cc} rail which is important if highly capacitive loads are to be driven without seriously degrading the rise times of waveforms. Clearly, if the outputs of G_1 and G_2 are connected together, and are not in the same logic state, a low-impedance path exists between V_{cc} and

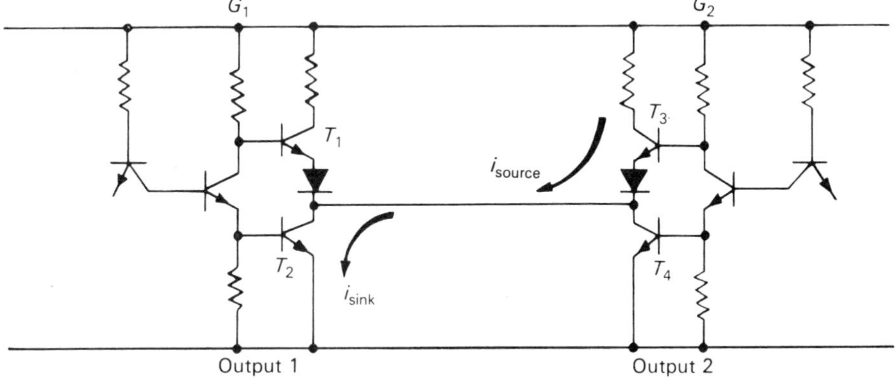

Figure 4.6 The effect of connecting the outputs of two gates together

ground. This causes the bus to assume an undefined logic state, and the power dissipated in the ICs due to the virtual short circuit between V_{cc} and ground may lead to their destruction.

Because of the three reasons above, standard TTL buffers are not normally used to drive buses.

4.1.2 Tri-state Buffers

A tri-state logic device is a circuit whose output can be in one of three states: a logical zero with a low-impedance path to ground; a logical one with a low-impedance path to the positive supply rail; and a high-impedance state in which the output is, effectively, floating. The circuit diagram of part of a tri-state buffer, the Texas Instrument 74LS366A, is given in Fig. 4.7. The actual buffer circuit itself is not radically different from other TTL circuits. In the 74LS366A there is a control circuit which has two inputs $\overline{E_1}$, $\overline{E_2}$, and if either of these control inputs is in a logical one state, transistor T_3 is turned off and T_5 turned on, causing point C to assume a low state. When C is low, diode D_1 is forward biased, cutting off transistors T_7 and T_9. Diode D_2 is also forward biased, cutting off T_6 and hence T_{10}. Under these conditions both of the output transistors, T_9 and T_{10}, are simultaneously turned off, and the output is effectively isolated from the rest of the circuit, apart from some output capacitance and a leakage current through T_9 and T_{10} of the order of 20 μA at V_0 = 2.4 V and −20 μA at V_0 = 0.4 V.

The advantage of using tri-state buffers as bus drivers is that several transmitters may be connected to one line, as long as no more than one buffer is enabled at any time. This facility allows address bus drivers to be turned off, freeing

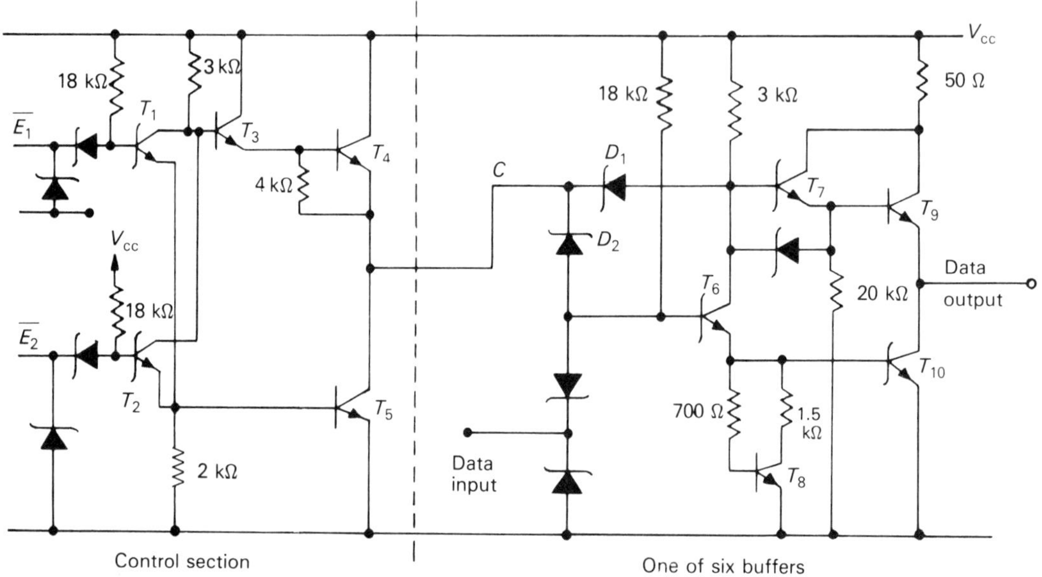

Figure 4.7 The circuit diagram of the TI 74LS366A hex inverting buffer

the address bus for DMA operations. Many tri-state buffers are built with PNP transistor inputs which source a current of only 200 μA in the logical zero state. Tri-state buffers are usually available in 16-pin DIL packages as hex buffers, or 20-pin DIL packages as octal buffers. The typical propagation delay of a tri-state buffer is 8 – 12 ns and some are capable of sinking 48 mA at V_{OL} = 0.5 V, and sourcing 5.2 mA at V_{OH} = 2.4 V. Typical parameters of some popular tri-state bus drivers are given in Table 4.3.

The SN74LS240 range of bus drivers made by Texas Instruments is unusual in that the input circuits have a built-in hysteresis effect. The result of this hysteresis is to make the switching threshold for a rising edge more positive than that for a falling edge. This property is beneficial because it reduces some of the effects of noise on the bus. Figure 4.8 illustrates the behavior of a gate with hysteresis and its effects on a noisy signal.

Table 4.3 The Parameters of Some Tri-state Drivers

Characteristic		*8T95 non-inverting hex buffer*	*DM81LS95 non-inverting hex buffer*	*74LS241 non-inverting octal buffer*
V_{IH} (min)	(volts)	2.0	2.0	2.0
V_{IL} (max)	(volts)	0.8	0.6	0.8
V_{OH} (min)	(volts)	2.4	2.7	2.4
V_{OL} (max)	(volts)	0.5	0.5	0.5
I_{IH} (max)	(μA)	40	20	20
I_{IL} (max)	(μA)	–400	–20	–200
I_{OH}	(mA)	–5.2	–2.6	–15
I_{OL}	(mA)	48	16	24
I_{OS} (max short-circuit current)	(mA)		–30	–225
t_{PLH} propagation delay high to low (ns)		6 (typ)	11 (typ) 16 (max)	12 (typ) 18 (max
t_{PHL} propagation delay low to high (ns)		5 (typ)	13 (typ) 16 (max)	12 (typ) 18 (max)
Tri-state enable/disable (ns)		12 (typ)	27 (max)	20 (typ) 30 (max)

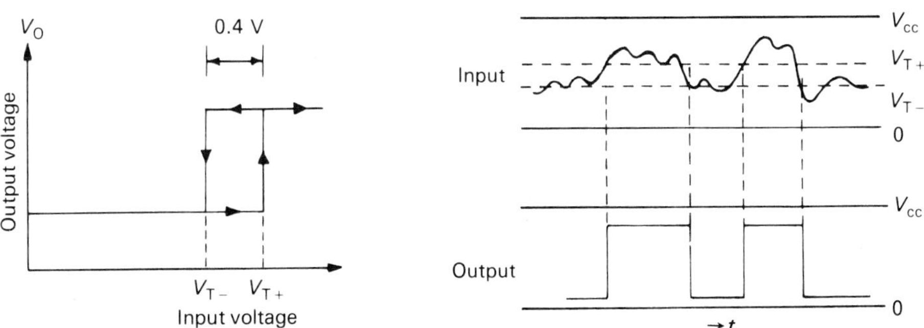

Figure 4.8 The input – output characteristics of a gate with hysteresis and its effect on a noisy digital waveform

4.1.3 Unidirectional Lines with Many Transmitters

An important class of information paths which make up the system bus consists of those having an arrangement in which many transmitters may speak to a single receiver. Some of the signals which fall into this group in a 6800 microprocessor system are

$\overline{\text{HALT}}$

$\overline{\text{DMA REQUEST}}$

$\overline{\text{RESET REQUEST}}$

$\overline{\text{IRQ}}$ ($\overline{\text{INTERRUPT REQUEST}}$)

$\overline{\text{NMI}}$

Figure 4.9 shows the arrangement of the $\overline{\text{IRQ}}$ line in a microprocessor system.

The design of a unidirectional bus with many transmitters connected to one receiver poses an important question. How is it possible for the output of more than one transmitter to be connected to a common line? As we have already seen, if the outputs of several TTL gates are connected together, and if two gates are forced into different output states simultaneously, a low impedance path exists between the V_{cc} supply rail and ground through the two gates. Such a situation leads not only to an undefined logic state on the bus but also to the possible destruction of the gates through which an (effectively) short-circuit current is flowing.

A possible solution to the problem of connecting together the outputs of more than one transmitter is to use transmitters with tri-state output circuits. While this may appear to be an ideal solution, a system whereby only one transmitter at a time is enabled has to be devised. This requires additional logic plus an extra bus line to tell other transmitters that the bus is currently in use.

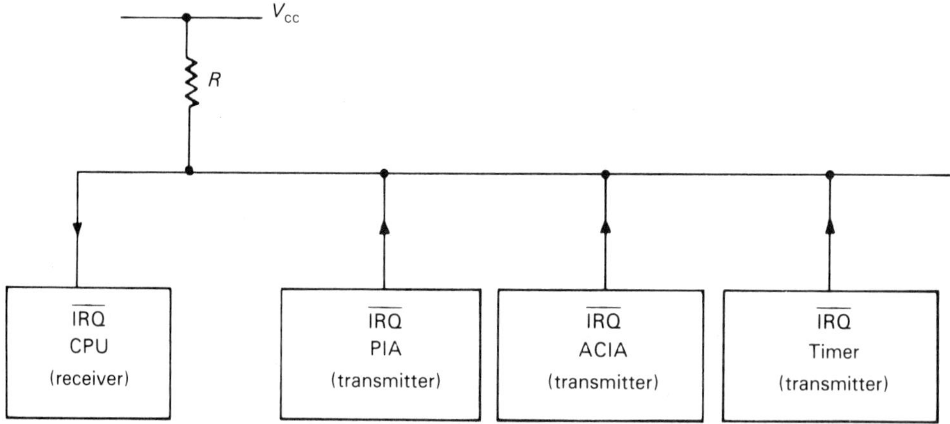

Figure 4.9 An example of an arrangement of a single receiver connected to a line driven by several transmitters

4.1.4 Open-collector Gates

The simplest technique of connecting the outputs of several gates to a common bus is to use gates with open-collector outputs. Such gates have an output circuit without a totem-pole output configuration and therefore no active pull-up. Consequently open-collector gates do not have a low-output impedance in both logic states. Figure 4.10 shows an arrangement where the outputs of two open-collector gates are connected to the same bus.

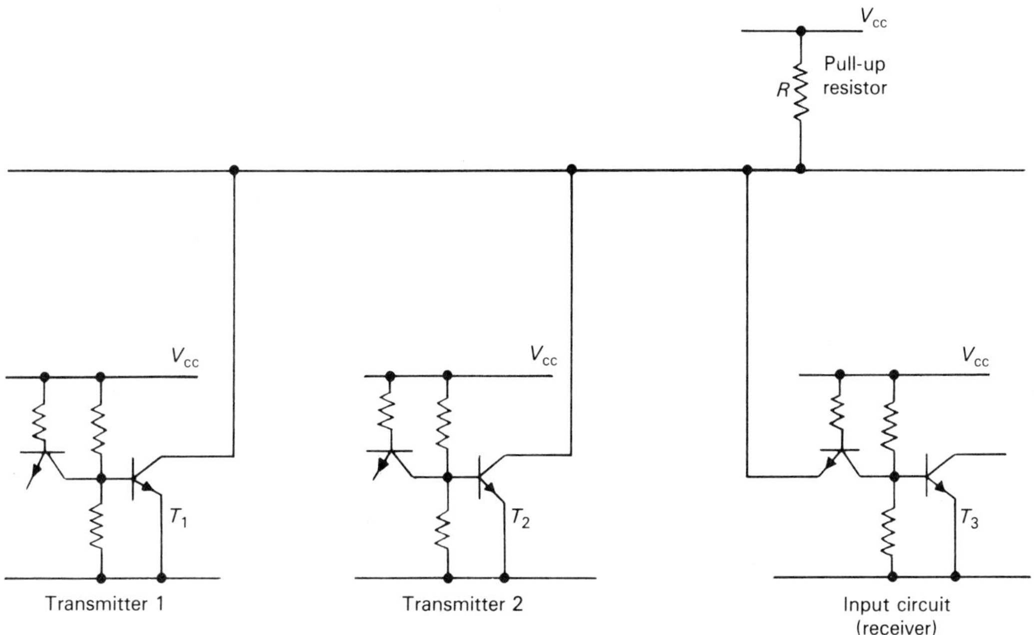

Figure 4.10 Two transmitters using open-collector gates connected to a bus

Imagine that, in Figure 4.10, the outputs of both transmitters are in a logical one state. In this case the output transistors, T_1 and T_2, of both gates are in the off state. Because the output circuits do not have active pull-up arrangements the bus is effectively disconnected from the two transmitters—apart from a small output capacitance and a leakage current. The external resistor R connected between the bus and the positive supply rail, V_{cc}, has the effect of pulling up the bus to a logical one state and providing the necessary input current to the receiver.

If either Transmitter 1 or Transmitter 2 changes state so that T1 or T2 is turned on, the bus is pulled down to the V_{cs} saturation voltage of the transistor in the on-state. Current can now flow out of the transistor in the receiver input circuit and into the output transistor in the on-state, causing the state of the bus to be recognized as a logical zero. If more than one transmitter is in the logical zero state, all that happens is that the current through R is divided between all the open-collector outputs, where the output transistor is in the on-state. Because the effect of the output of any transmitter going into the logical zero state is to pull the bus down to a logical zero state, this configuration is sometimes known as a wired OR circuit (when active-low logic levels are considered). The reason for having $\overline{\text{HALT}}$, $\overline{\text{RESET}}$, $\overline{\text{DMA REQUEST}}$ as active-low signals should now be clear.

In any arrangement of a bus driven by a number of open-collector outputs it is necessary to calculate a value for the pull-up resistor R. This value can be obtained by looking at the conditions which determine the upper and lower bounds for the pull-up resistor. The maximum value of R is the value which ensures that the bus output is greater than or equal to 2.4 V in the logical one state. In the logical one state, the current flowing through R is made up of two components: the leakage current in the output transistors feeding the bus, and the current which flows into the receiver input (see Fig. 4.11). Note that although we have considered the case of many transmitters connected to one receiver, there is no reason why more than one receiver cannot be connected to this bus. A typical value for the leakage current of open-collector outputs is 250 μA and the input current of a TTL gate in a logical one state is approximately 40 μA. Since the minimum voltage at the input to the receiver must be 2.4, the voltage across R is $V_{cc} - 2.4 = 2.6$. Hence

$$R_{max} = \frac{2.6}{m \times 0.00025 + 0.00004}$$

where m = number of transmitters. For $m = 10$, $R_{max} \simeq 1000\ \Omega$.

The minimum value of R is found by considering the logical zero condition. When the output transistor of an open-collector gate is turned on, current flows through the transistor via R. Clearly, the power dissipated in a transistor in the on-state should be limited to a safe value. The maximum value of the current which a gate may sink is I_{OL}—typically 16 mA for a TTL gate. The current into the collector of the output transistor is made up of two components, the current through R and the current from the input circuit of the receiver (I_{IL}). Thus in the case of one receiver the maximum current through R is (16 − 1.6) mA = 14.4 mA.

The minimum value of R is given by

$$R_{min} = \frac{V_{cc} - V_{OL}}{14.4\text{ mA}} = \frac{4.6\text{ V}}{14.4\text{ mA}} = 300\ \Omega$$

Note that the minimum value of the pull-up resistor is governed by the maximum current which can be sunk by the output transistor, and that this minimum value of R is significantly greater than the output impedance of a gate with an active pull-up circuit. Consequently the switching times of open-collector circuits can be significantly greater than those of devices with active pull-up circuits when driving highly capacitive loads.

The NMOS equivalent of the open-collector output is the open-drain output, where the drain of the output transistor is not pulled up by an active MOSFET load. In Motorola's literature a pull-up resistor of 3 kΩ is recommended for open-drain circuits.

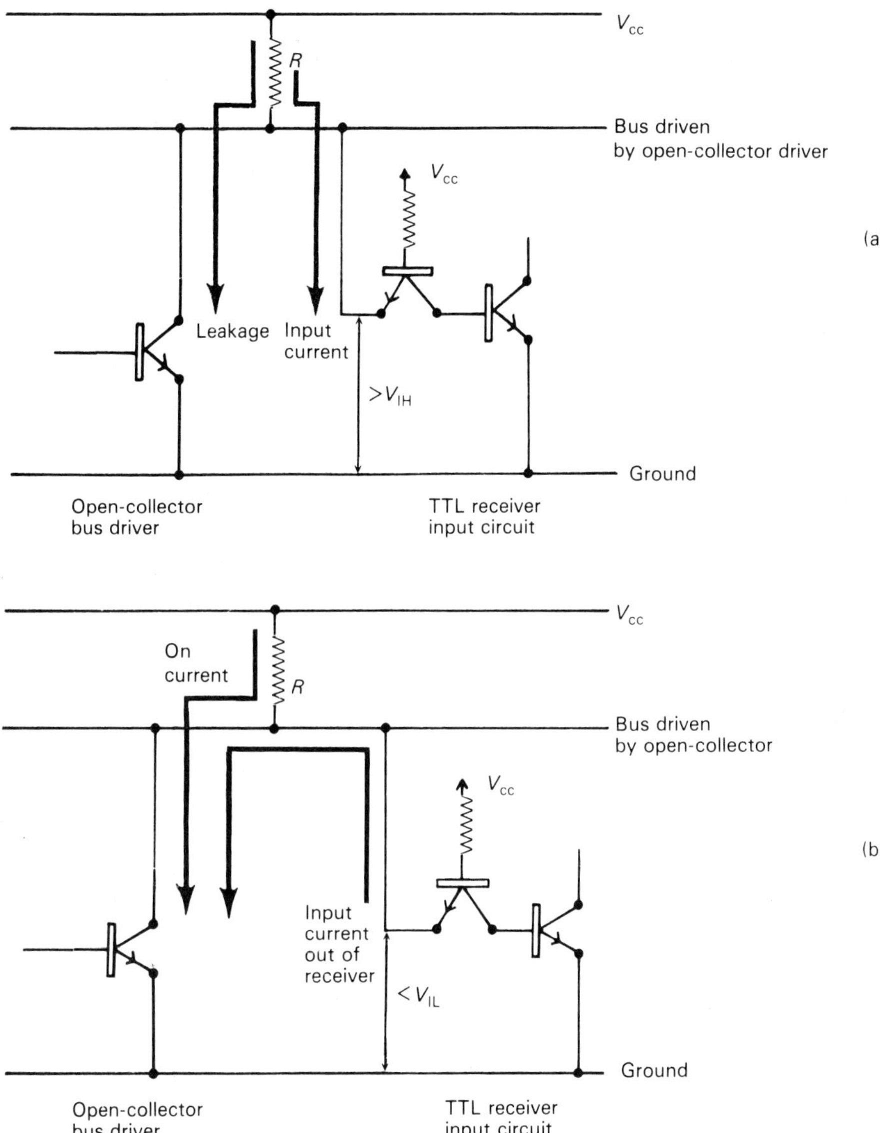

Figure 4.11 Current flow in open-collector bus drivers: (a) open-collector driver in a logical one state (b) open-collector driver in a logical zero state

4.1.5 Bidirectional Lines

During a CPU write cycle data is transferred from the CPU to the system memory, with the CPU acting as a transmitter and the memory components acting as receivers. During a CPU read cycle the position is reversed—the memory component currently addressed acts as a transmitter and the CPU acts as a receiver. Since data is never transferred in both directions simultaneously it is not necessary to have two separate data buses, one for data transfers to memory and one for data transfers from memory. In most microprocessor systems a bidirectional bus allows data to flow in both directions along a common highway.

As in the case of unidirectional lines with one transmitter and many receivers, it is necessary to use buffers to drive a bidirectional bus. However, the use of bidirectional buses immediately poses two questions: How is the direction of data transfer along the bus controlled, and how do we ensure that during a CPU read cycle one, and only one, device puts data on the bus at any instant?

The solution to the first question is found in the form of bidirectional bus drivers, or transceivers as they are often called. Bidirectional bus drivers are commonly available in the form of quad tri-state bus transceivers in a 16-pin DIL package, or as octal tri-state bus transceivers in a 20-pin DIL package. Figure 4.12 gives the pin-out, characteristics, and an example of the use of the 8T26 quad transceiver. The bus receiver is enabled by a logical zero ($\overline{\text{RECEIVER ENABLE}}$) and the bus driver by a logical one (DRIVER ENABLE).

By connecting the $\overline{\text{RECEIVER ENABLE}}$ input and the DRIVER ENABLE input of the 8T26 together, and calling the common line the transceiver control, a logical one on the transceiver control causes data to be transmitted to the bus and a logical zero causes data to be read from the bus.

During a CPU read cycle the CPU pulls its local transceiver control low, enabling its bus receiver (see Fig. 4.12). At the same time the transceiver control of

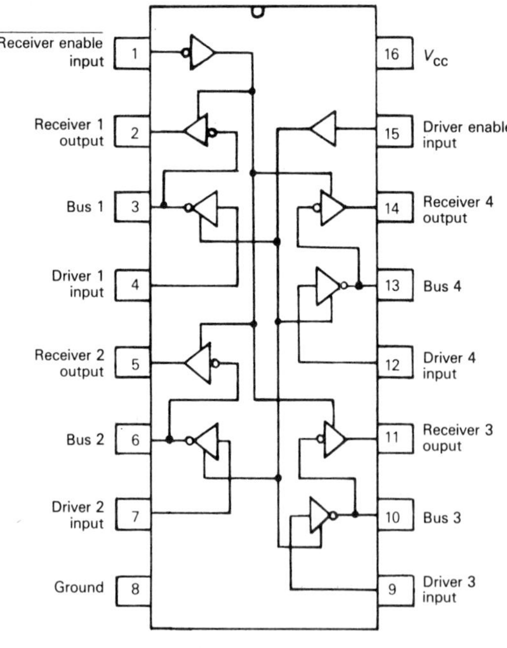

pin-out of the 8T26

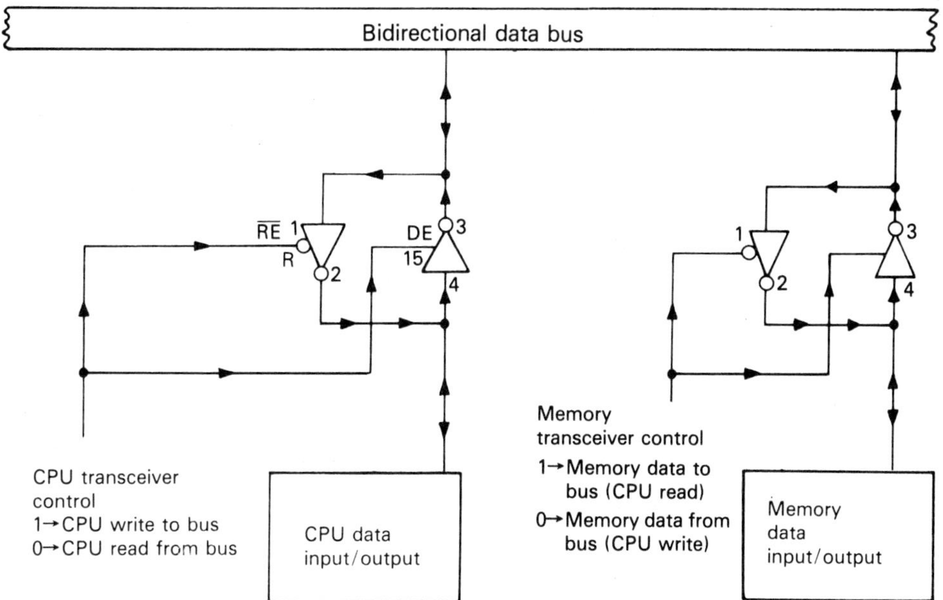

Figure 4.12 The 8T26 pin-out, characteristics, and use of a bidirectional bus driver

the memory interface must be pulled up into a logical one state to enable the bus driver to put data from the memory on to the data bus. The transceiver control signals at the CPU and the memory interface are normally derived from the CPU's READ/$\overline{\text{WRITE}}$ signal.

As stated above, an important problem associated with the use of bidirectional bus drivers is the danger of enabling more than one bus driver simultaneously during a CPU read cycle. The problem is illustrated in Fig. 4.13. During a CPU write cycle no difficulties exist—the CPU puts data onto the local data bus (i.e. local to the CPU and its associated components) and sets C_0 of Transceiver 0 high so that the data from the CPU is put on the system bus. During the write cycle, C_1 and C_2 of Transceivers 1 and 2 are brought low to enable the receivers and so transfer data to the memory inputs. In this situation the data is present simultaneously at the inputs of all memory (or peripheral) components. As only one memory component is enabled at a time no harm is done. Now consider what happens during a CPU read cycle. Suppose the CPU is reading a byte from a location within Memory Block 2. The control, C_2, of Transceiver 2 must be brought high to put the data on the data bus, and the control, C_0, of Transceiver 0 must be brought low to enable the CPU's data bus receiver. While this is happening, the control, C_1, of Transceiver 1 *must* be in a low (logical zero) state; otherwise the transmitter part of Transceiver 1 will be enabled, causing the outputs of two low-impedance drivers to be connected together simultaneously. The solution to this problem is to make the control inputs of the transceiver a function of the contents of the address bus. That is, any driver capable of putting data onto the data bus must be enabled only when the data at the input of the bus driver is *itself* valid.

Figure 4.13 also illustrates one of the most common errors made by the first-time designer of a microprocessor system. Many microprocessor systems have some memory directly connected to the CPU's own address and data bus rather than to the buffered system bus. This situation often arises in the case of the so-called single-board computer (SBC) where the small amount of memory on the board does not load the CPU bus sufficiently to require the use of buffers. It is sometimes argued that during a CPU read cycle to the local (unbuffered) memory, it does not matter if the receiver of bus Transceiver 0 is enabled (C_0 low) because there is no input to the receiver. This is a common fallacy. There is always an input to the receiver because the input line at the receiver must be at some potential between ground and V_{cc}. This input potential is either above or below the receiver's switching threshold and the receiver therefore has a low impedance output at either a logical one or a logical zero state. Whenever the CPU reads from its local memory, the system data bus receiver must be disabled (i.e. $C_0 = 1$).

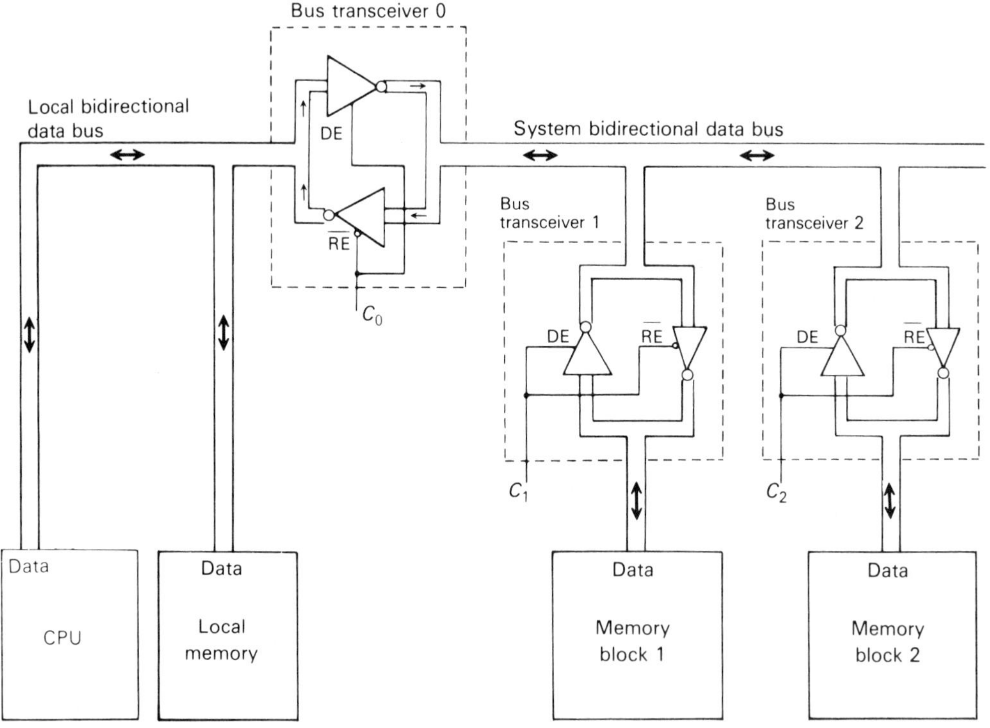

Figure 4.13 Interfacing the bidirectional data bus

4.2 THE TS1 BUS INTERFACE

In this section the interface between the CPU module of the TS1 and the system bus is described. The various signal paths of the TS1 bus may be arranged into three groups as illustrated by Table 4.4. These groups are formed on the basis of their interface requirements.

Table 4.4 The Lines of the TS1 Bus Grouped According to their Interface Requirements

Type of signal	*Name*	*Comments*
Group 1 Inputs to the CPU module with many transmitters driving one receiver on a unidirectional bus	$\overline{\text{HALT}}$ $\overline{\text{RESET REQUEST}}$ $\overline{\text{IRQ1}}$ to $\overline{\text{IRQ4}}$, $\overline{\text{IRQ}}$ $\overline{\text{NMI}}$ $\overline{\text{DMA REQUEST}}$ $\overline{\text{MEMORY DISABLE}}$ MEMORY READY (MR) $\text{R}/\overline{\text{W}}$ E $\overline{\text{VMA E}}$	All these lines are driven by open-collector or open-drain circuits. Each line has a pull-up resistor on the CPU module.
Group 2A Outputs from the CPU module with one transmitter driving many receivers on a unidirectional bus	MEMORY CLOCK $2f_c$ ϕ_2 TTL $\overline{\text{RESET}}$ $\overline{\text{MEMORY CONTROL}}$ DMA GRANT (DMAG) BA	All lines of Group 2A are driven by permanently enabled buffers.
Group 2B Outputs from the CPU module with one transmitter driving many receivers on a unidirectional bus	VMA $\text{R}/\overline{\text{W}}$ $A_0 - A_{15}$	All the lines of Group 2B are driven by tri-state buffers.
Group 3 A bidirectional data bus	$D_0 - D_7$	The data bus receivers at the CPU must be enabled only during a valid CPU read cycle when the CPU is accessing system (not local) memory. During a DMA operation the data transmitters must be disabled (floated).

Note: SDMS and SDSM (not shown in this table) are non-TTL-compatible lines carrying RS232-compatible data between master and slave processors. See Chapter 6 for an explanation of the RS232 standard.

The first group of lines includes all those which act as inputs to the CPU module. All these lines are driven by transmitters having open-collector or open-drain outputs. The only interface circuitry required by these lines is a pull-up resistor on each line at the CPU module.

In the second group of lines are all those having an arrangement of one transmitter driving many receivers. Each of these lines carries a signal which originates within the CPU module and is distributed to all the other modules in the system. This group can be divided into two subgroups. The first group includes those lines which do not require tri-state drivers, because each signal is generated by one, and only one, source. That is, the bus driver never relinquishes its control of the line in favor of some other driver. Examples of signals falling into this subgroup are the timing signals generated by the clock circuit. Even when the CPU is in the halt state, timing signals must be present on the system bus because they are needed by certain peripheral devices requiring a clock input to recognize and latch external events.

The second subgroup of lines having one transmitter driving many receivers is the group of lines which must use bus drivers with tri-state outputs. The most important member of this subgroup is the address bus. During a normal CPU memory-access cycle the address bus transmits a 16-bit address from the CPU to all the other modules connected to the TS1 bus. Whenever a DMA operation is requested by either the CPU entering the halt state, or by ϕ_1 being stretched and held in the logical one state, the CPU module must relinquish its control of the address bus, allowing some other module to take control. The VMA and $R/\overline{W}$ lines also fall into this subgroup because during a DMA operation both the VMA and $R/\overline{W}$ signals must be provided by a DMA controller.

The control of the VMA and $R/\overline{W}$ lines raises an important point. During the time that the address bus is floated, the VMA and $R/\overline{W}$ lines must never, themselves, assume a high-impedance state where their values are indeterminate, otherwise a spurious write operation may occur. The solution to this problem, adopted in the TS1 system, is to employ two lines $\overline{\text{VMA E}}$ and $R/\overline{W}$ E, which act as inputs to the CPU module. During a DMA operation the signal on the $\overline{\text{VMA E}}$ line is transferred to the VMA line and the signal on the $R/\overline{W}$ E line is transferred to the $R/\overline{W}$ line. In this way, the DMA controller puts its VMA and $R/\overline{W}$ signals on the $\overline{\text{VMA E}}$ and $R/\overline{W}$ E inputs to the CPU, which are acted upon only when either BA or DMA GRANT goes high indicating a DMA operation.

The third group of lines is the bidirectional highway which moves data between the CPU and memory components in both directions. This group requires the most complex control circuitry, because not only must the direction of the data transfer be controlled but two special cases must also be considered: DMA operations, and CPU read/write cycles to its local memory.

In order to understand the way in which the data bus transceivers are controlled, it is necessary to consider the seven possible states of the TS1 data bus. These states are defined in Table 4.5 (p. 78), together with the corresponding values of VMA, $R/\overline{W}$, BA and $\overline{\text{SELECT}}$ for each state. I have not included DMAG (DMA GRANT) in this table as its effect on the system bus transceivers is the same as BA. The $\overline{\text{SELECT}}$ signal is in a logical zero state if, and only if, the CPU is executing a valid read or write cycle to a memory location which is accessed from the system bus. That is, the memory location is not part of the memory which is local to the CPU module.

The block diagram of the interface with the system bus on the CPU module is given in Fig. 4.14, and the circuit diagram of this interface is given in Fig. 4.15.

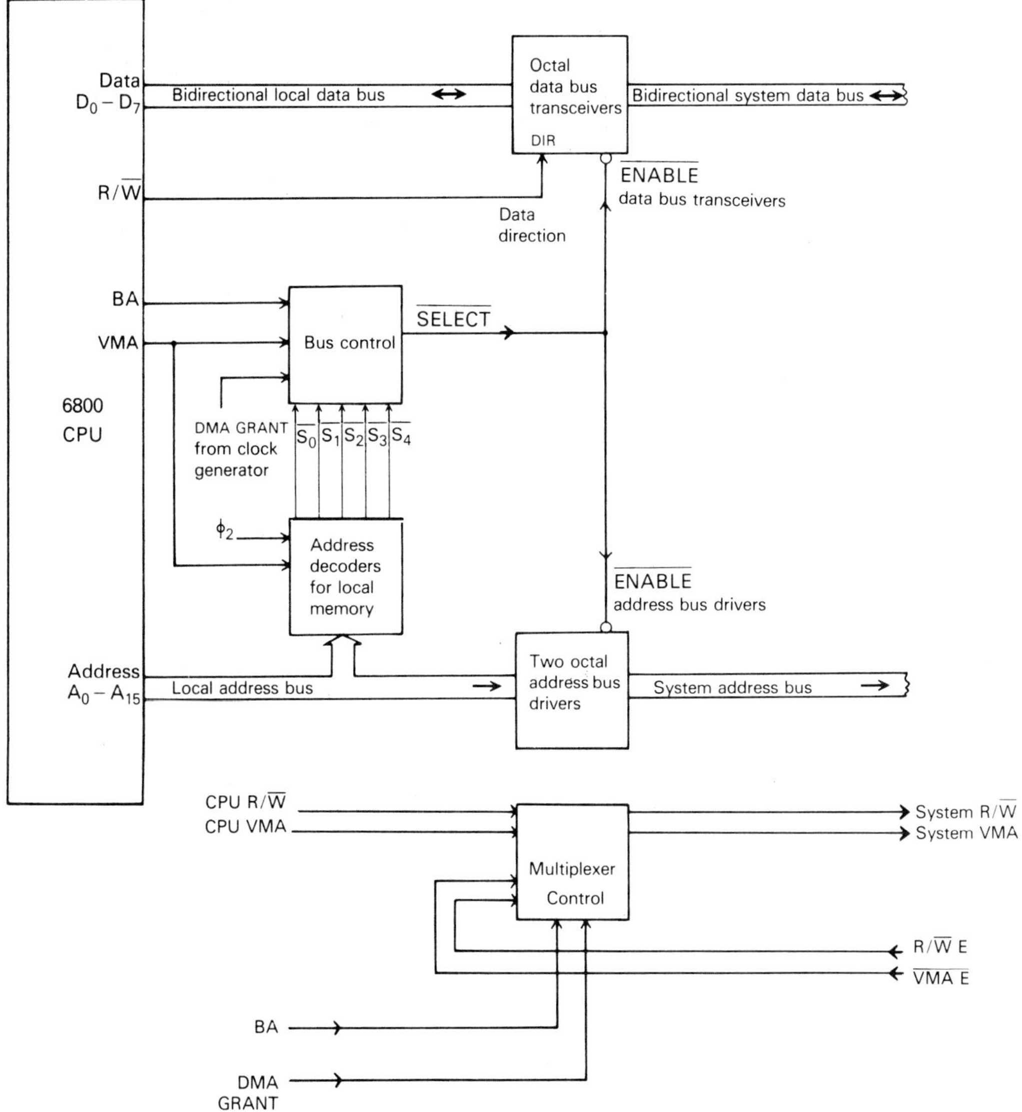

Figure 4.14 Block diagram of the TS1 interface

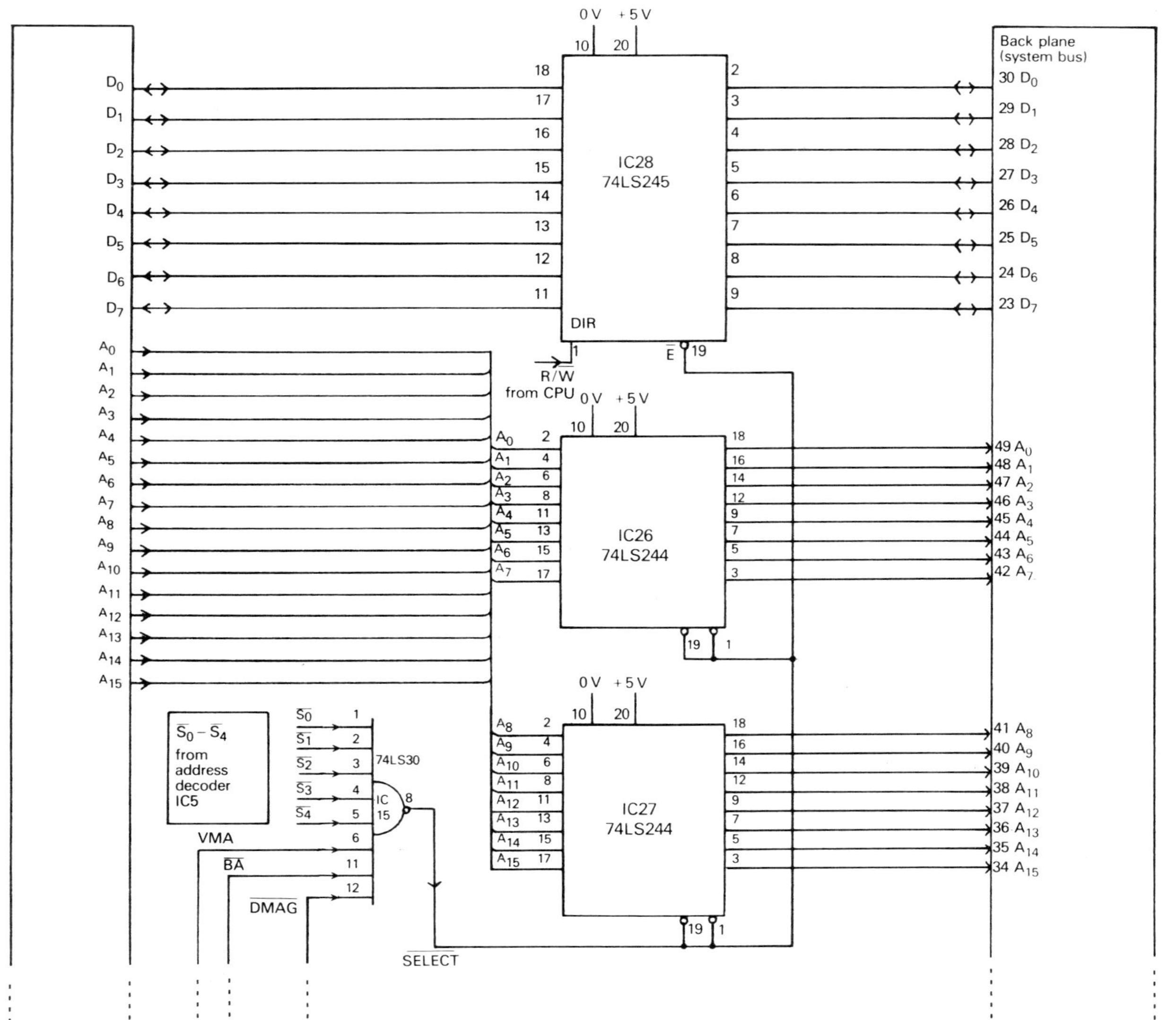
0 V +5 V
IC28
74LS245
DIR
$\overline{E}$
$R/\overline{W}$
from CPU
IC26
74LS244
IC27
74LS244
Back plane
(system bus)
30 D_0
29 D_1
28 D_2
27 D_3
26 D_4
25 D_5
24 D_6
23 D_7
49 A_0
48 A_1
47 A_2
46 A_3
45 A_4
44 A_5
43 A_6
42 A_7
41 A_8
40 A_9
39 A_{10}
38 A_{11}
37 A_{12}
36 A_{13}
35 A_{14}
34 A_{15}
D_0
D_1
D_2
D_3
D_4
D_5
D_6
D_7
A_0
A_1
A_2
A_3
A_4
A_5
A_6
A_7
A_8
A_9
A_{10}
A_{11}
A_{12}
A_{13}
A_{14}
A_{15}
$\overline{S_0}$ – $\overline{S_4}$
from
address
decoder
IC5
74LS30
IC 15
VMA
$\overline{BA}$
$\overline{DMAG}$
$\overline{SELECT}$

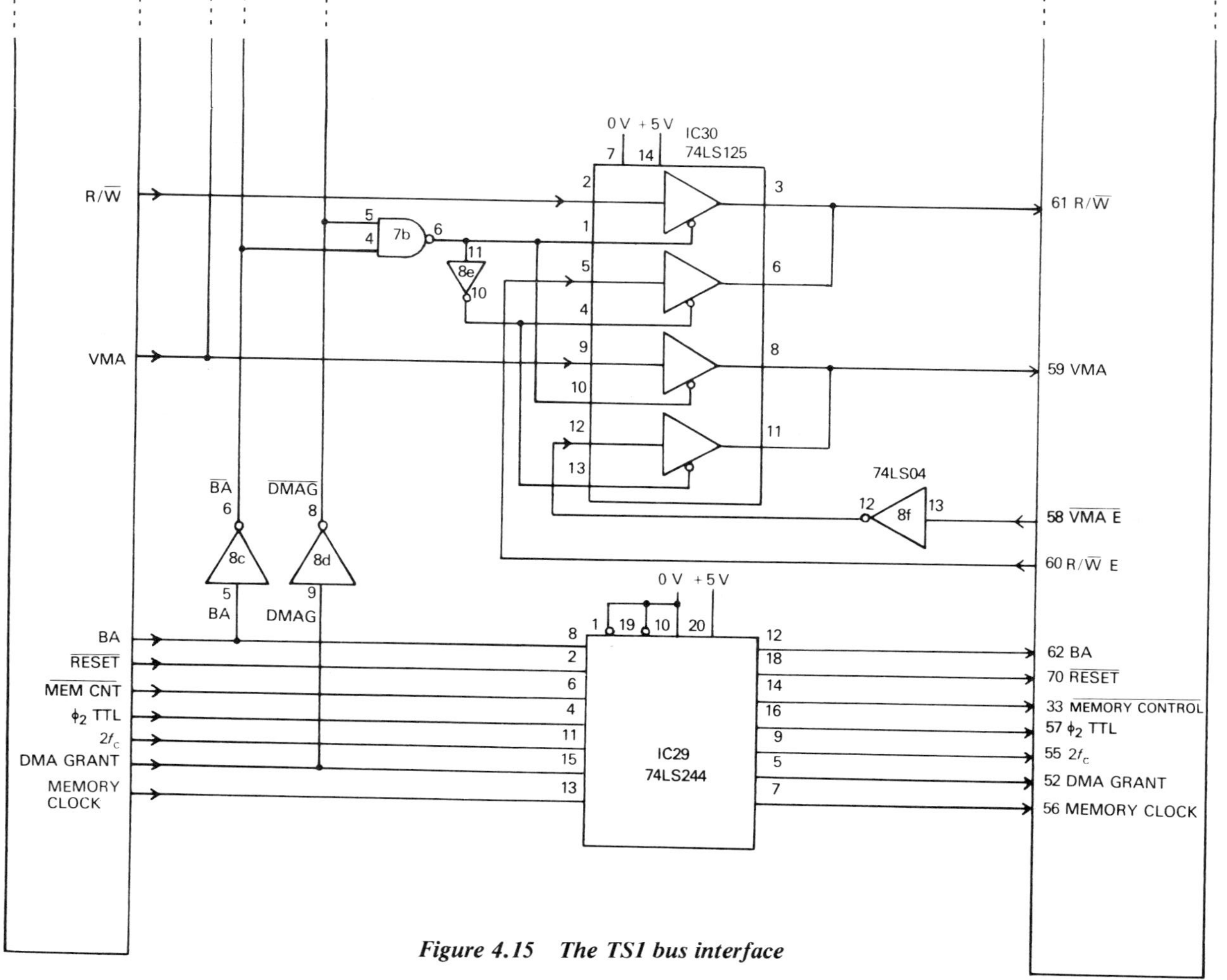

Figure 4.15 The TS1 bus interface

Table 4.5 The Seven Possible States of the TS1 Data Bus

State	Operation	System control signals				Data transceivers	
		VMA	*R/$\overline{W}$*	*BA*	*$\overline{SELECT}$*	*Driver*	*Receiver*
1	CPU read from local memory	1	1	0	1	off	off
2	CPU write to local memory	1	0	0	1	off	off
3	CPU read from system memory	1	1	0	0	off	enabled
4	CPU write to system memory	1	0	0	0	enabled	off
5	CPU internal operation	0	1	0	1	off	off
6	DMA operation by stretching ϕ_1	VMA E	R/$\overline{W}$ E	0	1	off	off
7	DMA operation by halting the CPU	VMA E	R/W E	1	1	off	off

A key feature of this circuit is the use of a single signal, $\overline{\text{SELECT}}$, to control both the data and address bus buffers. This has the effect of turning off (floating) the address bus drivers whenever either the data bus transmitters or receivers are in the off state. This action is not strictly necessary because the address bus driver need be floated only during a DMA operation. However, floating the address bus during a local memory access or a CPU internal operation is not harmful. Indeed, because both the address and data buses are floated whenever the CPU is not explicitly using the system memory, a second processor could be used in an arrangement which allows it to access the system memory while the first processor (in the CPU module) is busy accessing its local memory.

The $\overline{\text{SELECT}}$ signal is generated by NANDing the $\overline{S_0}$, $\overline{S_1}$, $\overline{S_2}$, $\overline{S_3}$, $\overline{S_4}$, $\overline{\text{BA}}$, VMA, and $\overline{\text{DMA GRANT}}$ signals. If all these signals are in a logical one state, $\overline{\text{SELECT}}$ is low, enabling the data bus transceivers and address bus drivers. When one of these signals goes low, $\overline{\text{SELECT}}$ rises to a logical one state and disables the data bus transceivers and the address bus drivers. The five signals $\overline{S_0}-\overline{S_4}$ are generated by the CPU address decoders (described in the next chapter), and indicate by going (active) low a CPU access to its local ROM, RAM, or peripherals.

The address bus buffers are two 74LS244 octal bus drivers. These bus drivers are arranged internally as two groups of four drivers, a separate, active-low $\overline{\text{ENABLE}}$ input being used to control each group of drivers. To operate the 74LS244 as an octal bus driver, the two $\overline{\text{ENABLE}}$ inputs must be connected together. Figure 4.16 shows the internal arrangement and the pin-out of the 74LS244.

The eight data bus transceivers needed to buffer the data bus are available in the form of a single chip, the 74LS245. This is a very easy chip to use because it has two control inputs, an $\overline{\text{ENABLE}}$ input, and a DIR input, which determines the direction of the data transfer. The $\overline{\text{ENABLE}}$ input of the 74LS245 is connected to the $\overline{\text{SELECT}}$ signal so that whenever $\overline{\text{SELECT}}$ is in the logical one state, both the data bus drivers and receivers are in the off state. The DIR input of the 74LS245 is

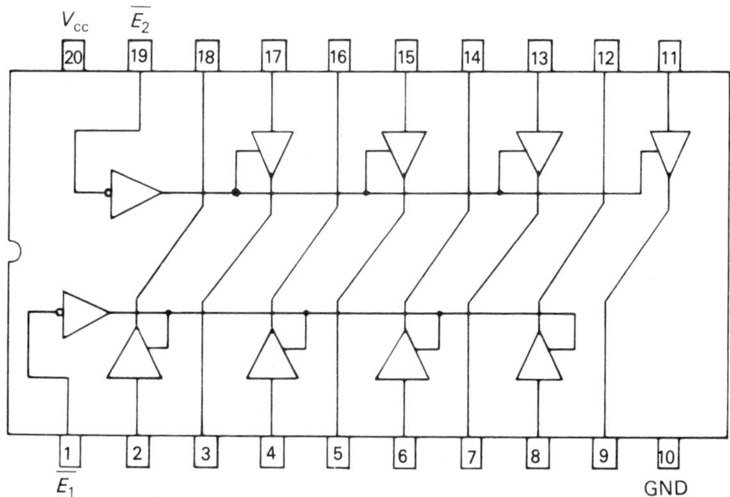

Figure 4.16 The internal arrangement and pin-out of the SN74LS244

simply connected to the CPUs R/$\overline{\mathrm{W}}$ line. Figure 4.17 shows the internal arrangement and the pin-out of the 74LS245.

The R/$\overline{\mathrm{W}}$ and VMA system bus lines require some explanation. During all normal (i.e. non-DMA) operations, the system bus R/$\overline{\mathrm{W}}$ and VMA lines contain the buffered values of the R/$\overline{\mathrm{W}}$ and VMA outputs from the CPU.

Whenever a DMA operation is signalled by either BA or DMA GRANT rising to a logical one state, the R/$\overline{\mathrm{W}}$ and VMA buffers are switched off. At the same time

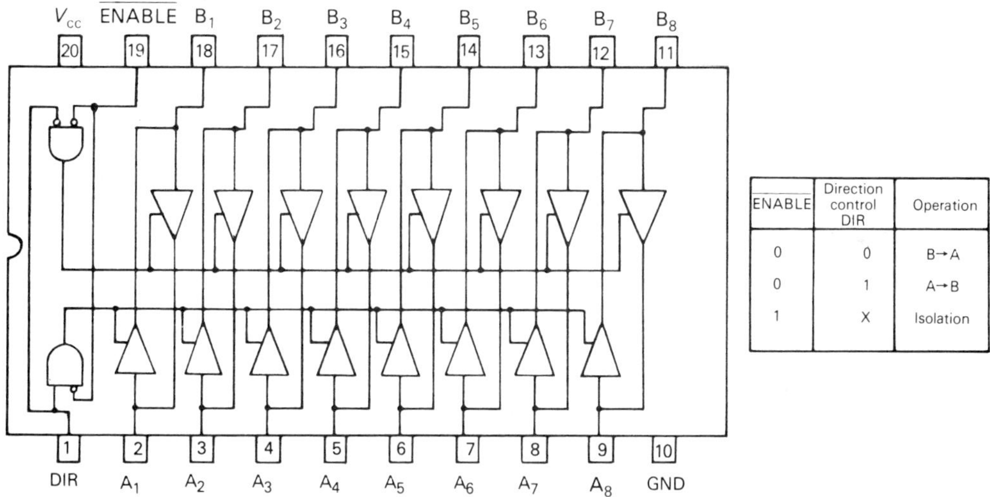

$\overline{\text{ENABLE}}$	Direction control DIR	Operation
0	0	B→A
0	1	A→B
1	X	Isolation

Figure 4.17 The internal arrangement and pin-out of the SN74LS245

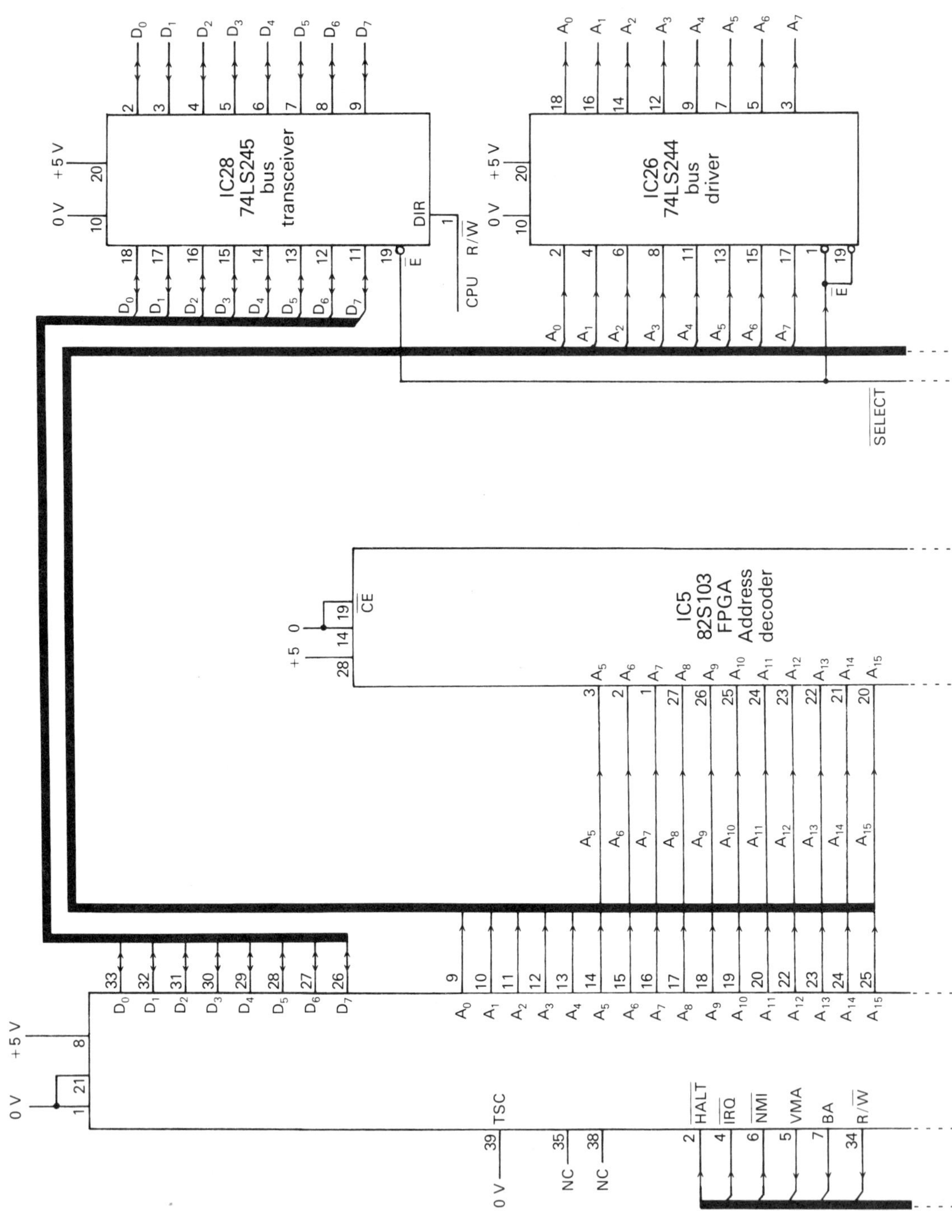
IC28
74LS245
bus
transceiver
IC26
74LS244
bus
driver
IC5
82S103
FPGA
Address
decoder
SELECT
CPU R/W
DIR
TSC
HALT
IRQ
NMI
VMA
BA
R/W
0 V
+5 V
NC

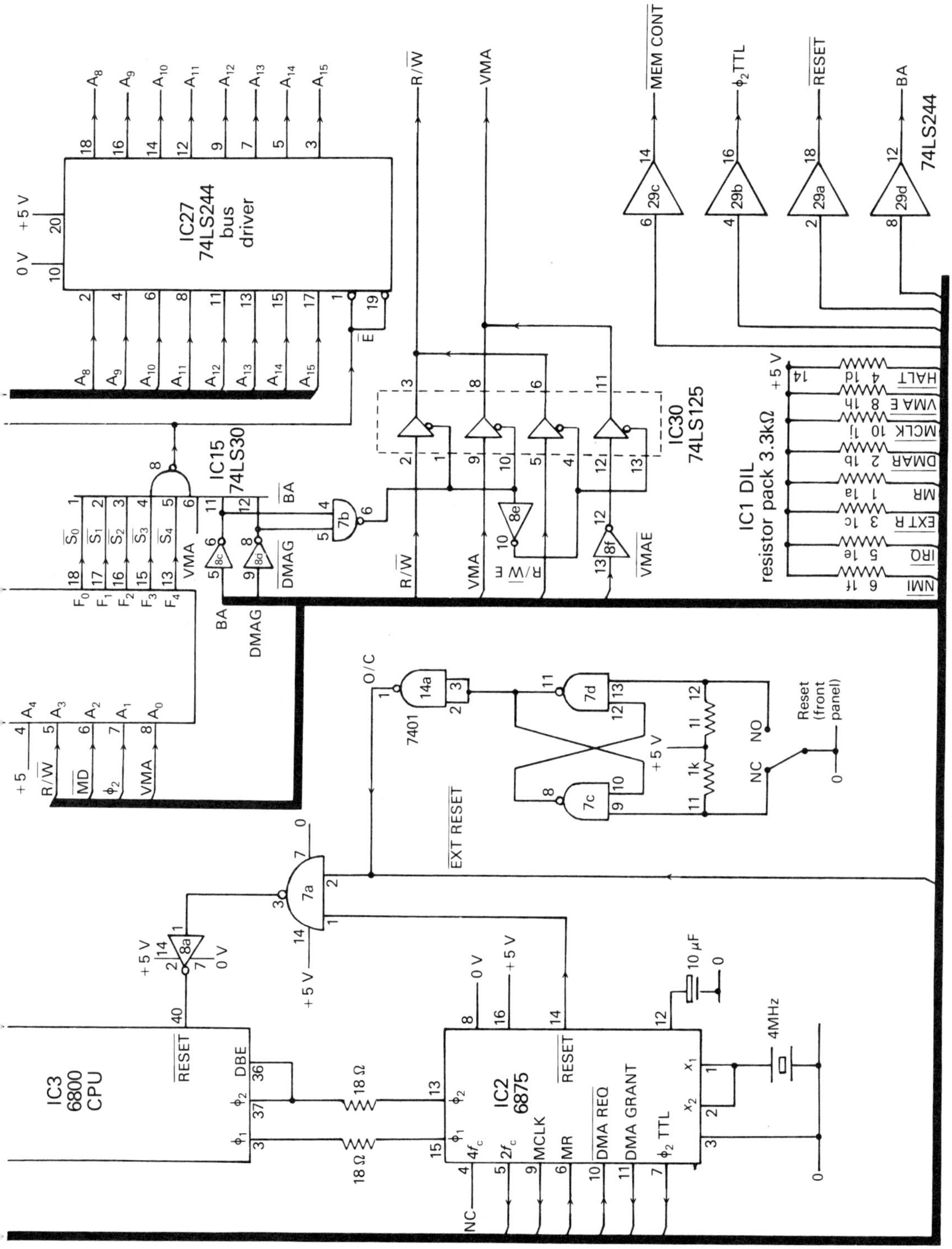

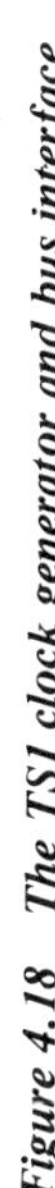

Figure 4.18 The TS1 clock generator and bus interface

two other tri-state buffers are enabled and put the current values of the R/$\overline{\text{W}}$ E and $\overline{\text{VMA E}}$ lines onto the R/$\overline{\text{W}}$ and VMA system bus respectively. Hence, during a DMA operation, the R/$\overline{\text{W}}$ E and $\overline{\text{VMA E}}$ input lines from the DMA controller are used to initiate read/write cycles. The R/$\overline{\text{W}}$ E line has a pull-up resistor which selects the read mode, unless an open-collector or an open-drain driver pulls the line down to force a write cycle. This pull-up resistor avoids the danger of a spurious write cycle. In a similar manner a pull-up resistor is used to hold $\overline{\text{VMA E}}$ high until the DMA controller pulls $\overline{\text{VMA E}}$ down (and therefore sets VMA high) in a DMA operation.

The combined clock generator and bus interface circuits of the CPU module are given in Fig. 4.18.

SUMMARY

In this section we have examined the characteristics of the data-carrying lines which make up the TS1 bus. Some move data from one source to many receivers, some move data from one of many possible sources to a single receiver, while others move data in different directions depending on whether the CPU is executing a read or a write cycle. Each of these three types of line has its own particular characteristics which must be taken into account when designing a bus interface.

Possibly the greatest asset to the designer of buses is the tri-state bus driver. The output of this device can be turned off in the sense that it is disconnected from the low-impedance bus drivers, allowing it to float with the bus. Consequently, many tri-state devices may be connected to a given line and as long as only one of them has its output enabled no conflict occurs between the various bus drivers. Such an arrangement permits many memory components to have their data lines wired in parallel, provided that only the chip currently being addressed is enabled.

This section concluded with the circuit diagram of the interface between TS1's CPU card and the system bus. Special attention has been paid to the need to turn off the data bus drivers whenever the CPU is accessing its own local memory, or when a DMA operation is taking place.

PROBLEMS

1 Some engineers are not entirely happy with the concept of the tri-state bus driver. They argue that a failure of the bus control logic can lead to one or more bus drivers trying to access the bus simultaneously. Such a difficulty does not exist with open collector bus drivers. Is their opinion valid, and are their fears justified? If they are, what can be done to alleviate this problem?

2 When the TS1's data and address buses are floated by BA or DMAG going high, the signals on the R/$\overline{\text{W}}$ and VMA lines are obtained from the R/$\overline{\text{W}}$ E and $\overline{\text{VMA E}}$ buses, respectively. Is this a good idea? Wouldn't it have been better to float R/$\overline{\text{W}}$ and VMA together with the data and address buses during a DMA operation?

3 Is it worthwhile deriving a scheme which does away with the need for an address bus? An address from the CPU is valid towards the end of a ϕ_1 high clock phase, but data transfer does not take place until late in a ϕ_2 high clock phase. Consequently, it should be possible to create a common address and data bus, with the address being multiplexed onto the bus at the start of a cycle, and the data later in the cycle. This arrangement could be extended further to use a single 8-bit bus, the address being transferred as two 8-bit bytes. Devise an arrangement to implement these schemes. To answer this question a knowledge of the 6800's timing requirements is needed (see Appendix A2).

5

The System Memory

The performance of a microprocessor system may be thought of as being influenced by four factors: the instruction set of the microprocessor, the speed of the microprocessor, the addressing techniques employed by the microprocessor, and the memory.

The instruction set determines the way in which a program is executed. A microprocessor with a primitive instruction set requires more instructions to carry out a given task than a microprocessor with a sophisticated instruction set. For example, multiplication can be performed by a single instruction (TMS9900, 6809), or by means of a series of instructions using a shifting and adding algorithm. Of course, what constitutes a good instruction set depends very much on the type of application for which the microprocessor is to be used. The microprocessor systems designer should beware of manufacturers who quote a large number of instructions for their microprocessor. It is not the total number of instructions that gives a microprocessor its power, but their usefulness.

The speed of a microprocessor determines the rate at which instructions are executed. There is little point in having a microprocessor with a very powerful instruction set if it takes longer to execute a given task than an alternative microprocessor which has a simpler instruction set, requiring more instructions per task, but which operates at a speed more than compensating for any deficiencies in its instruction set.

The addressing techniques used by a microprocessor determine the way in which it accesses data from the memory. Widely used addressing techniques are absolute addressing, indexed addressing, page-based addressing, indirect addressing, relative addressing, stack addressing and literal (or immediate) addressing. Often the power of a particular microprocessor lies in its range of addressing techniques rather than in its instruction set. For example, the Z80 is an upgraded version of the 8080, just as the 6809 is an upgraded version of the 6800. However, the Z80 has been upgraded by the addition of a very large number of new instructions but only a small improvement in the number of addressing techniques, while the 6809 has been upgraded by the addition of several new addressing modes and just a few new instructions. It is expected that the improvement in performance of the 6809 over the 6800 will be far greater than the improvement in performance of the Z80 over the 8080. Why? Because the addition of new instructions is meaningless unless they are frequently used, but the addition of new addressing modes means that the existing instructions can be used more efficiently.

The fourth factor which influences a microprocessor system is the memory which holds the program and all the data needed by it. All microprocessors contain a certain amount of on-chip memory. This internal memory (accumulators, index registers, stack pointers etc.) is used to speed up computation by means of special fast addressing techniques to operate on data within the CPU chip itself. Some microprocessors also have some general-purpose random access memory (which may be read/write or read only memory) on-chip. This memory does not usually speed up computation and is used in dedicated applications where a one or two chip system is required.

Memory is important in a microprocessor system because without sufficient memory to perform its allocated task, the microprocessor is useless. What actually constitutes sufficient memory is a very difficult question to answer. Even in a dedicated microprocessor application the memory requirements for a program written in a well-structured high-level language may be different from those for the same program written in assembly language and using every possible trick to cut down the number of bytes. Programs written in assembly language which employ all manner of clever devices to squeeze the last byte out of the program (including the dangerous practice of self-modifying code) are not only difficult to debug or modify, but are also potential time bombs waiting to explode at the worst possible moment.

In a general-purpose microprocessor system the memory requirements are often quite complex, involving a trade-off between speed, cost and complexity. Consider the case of a microprocessor system using a high-level language compiler with a mini-floppy bulk storage system. If a relatively small read/write random-access system memory is used, the overall cost is reduced, but the compiler may need many time-consuming passes to compile a program. If the system memory is very large, fewer passes are required to perform the compilation and the system is faster but more expensive.

5.1 MEMORIES—SOME DEFINITIONS

Before dealing with the types of memory component suitable for the TS1's memory system it is helpful to define a few terms.

Memory Cell

A memory cell is the smallest unit of information storage, and can hold a single logical zero or a logical one.

Access Time

The access time is one of the most important parameters of any memory component, and is the time taken to read data from a given memory location, measured from the start of a read cycle initiated by a change in the logical state of one or more of the memory component's input lines. The access time is made up of two parts: the time taken to locate the required memory cell (address decoding time); and the time taken for the data to become available from the memory cell. Because many semiconductor memories have identical read and write access times, the access time of a memory component is normally taken to mean the read or write access time. However, this is not always true in the case of dynamic memories.

Random Access

When a memory is configured so that the access time of any cell within it is constant, and is independent of the actual location of the cell, the memory is then said to be random-access memory (RAM). In practice this means that the CPU does not have to worry about the time taken to read a word from memory (or write a word to memory), because all read/write cycles have the same duration. The term RAM is usually employed to describe read/write memory, where data may be read from the memory or written into the memory. This usage is incorrect, because random access indicates only the property of constant access time, and has nothing to do with the memory's ability to modify its data. In order to be consistent with other literature, throughout this book "random-access memory" means "random-access read/write memory", unless otherwise stated.

Serial Access

In a serial-access memory the time taken to access data is dependent on the physical location of the data within the memory. The data moves past some read/write device so that in accessing any given memory cell, the waiting time depends on how long the memory cell takes to move to the read/write device. Examples of serial access memories are magnetic tapes, magnetic disks, shift registers and magnetic bubble memories.

Volatile Memory

Volatile memory loses its contents when the source of power is removed. This term applies to most semiconductor memory where the data are stored as a charge on a capacitor, or as the state of a transistor in a bistable circuit.

Read-only Memory (ROM)

A read-only memory is a memory whose contents cannot be altered under normal operating conditions. True read-only memories are by definition non-volatile, but pseudo read-only memories may be realized by using a read/write memory with its write function disabled. By popular usage "read-only memory" has come to mean read-only random-access memory. It is, of course, possible to have read-only serial-access memories.

Static Memory

Once data has been written into a static memory cell, it remains there until it is altered either by over-writing it with new data or by removing the power if the memory is volatile. Static semiconductor memory cells usually employ cross-coupled transistors to hold the data.

Dynamic Memory

In a dynamic memory the data is stored in the form of a charge on a capacitor. Because the capacitor is not perfect, the charge gradually leaks away, discharging the capacitor and losing the data. When dynamic memories are used, some additional circuitry is needed to periodically restore the charge on the capacitors in an operation known as memory refreshing.

Semi-static (edge-activated) Memory

A semi-static memory array uses fully static memory cells to store data, but has address decoding and control circuits which operate in a dynamic mode. That is, they are clocked by their control inputs or by transitions on the address bus. A semi-static memory consumes less power than a fully static memory of an equivalent size.

Programmable Read-Only Memory (PROM)

A programmable read-only memory is a type of ROM which can be programmed by the user (as opposed to the manufacturer) once and once only.

Erasable and Programmable Read-Only Memory (EPROM)

An erasable and programmable read-only memory is a read-only memory which can be programmed by the user, have its contents erased and then be reprogrammed. The erasure of data from an EPROM almost always necessitates its removal from its normal location in a circuit.

Electrically Alterable Read-Only Memory (EAROM)

The EAROM is a programmable read-only memory which can be programmed and erased electrically without removing it from its normal location. The EAROM may be thought of as a non-volatile RAM.

5.1.1 Static Random-access Memory

In cases where a microprocessor system is used as a general-purpose digital computer, the bulk of the system memory is likely to be either static or dynamic read/write random-access memory, because a wide variety of different programs are run on the computer. When a microprocessor is used in a dedicated application, e.g. a chemical process controller, the bulk of the memory is more likely to be read-only memory because the program does not have to be changed.

Static RAM is widely employed in microprocessor application largely because it is very easily implemented. Unlike dynamic memories static memories do not require any action to periodically refresh their contents. Figure 5.1 shows the circuit diagram of a typical NMOS static storage cell. The most significant feature of this cell is that six transistors are required to store each bit of data. Dynamic memory cells store their data as a charge on the inter-electrode capacitance of a single transistor, and therefore require fewer transistors per cell than static memories. Because there are more components per cell in a static memory, a dynamic memory of a given chip size can always store more data than a corresponding static memory

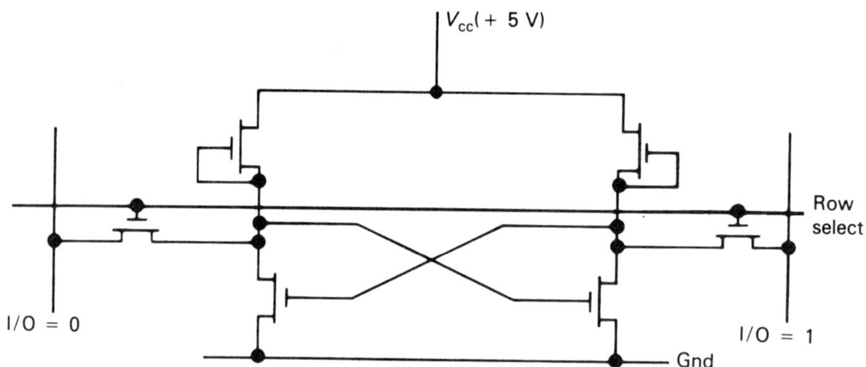

Figure 5.1 The storage cell of a static memory element

of the same chip size. Furthermore the average power per bit consumed by a dynamic memory is lower than that of an equivalent static memory.

From the above remarks it would appear that static memories are much inferior to dynamic memories. Although this is often true for large memory systems, the extra cost and complexity of dynamic memory-refresh circuits makes static memory look much more attractive in small systems.

Static RAM chips, built with NMOS technology, are available in several configurations. As semiconductor technology develops, new memory chips with greater capacities appear. This has the effect of reducing the price of the older chips of lower capacity. In Table 5.1 several static RAM chips are described in terms of the number of bits per chip, the arrangement of the data as words × bits per word, the number of pins, the access time, and the power dissipation.

In addition to the details given in Table 5.1 there is also a variation in the facilities offered by different memories. Some chips have a common data input/output arrangement while others have separate pins for data input and output. A few chips have a power down facility which allows the data to be retained if the power-supply voltage falls to not less than 2.4 V. Such an arrangement enables batteries to provide the relatively low power needed to retain the memory data during a temporary power failure. The TMS4046 and TMS4047 chips take power conservation during power down one step further. These chips have two power-supply pins, one for the address decoding, control, and buffer circuits, and one for the memory array itself. Under power down or stand-by conditions only the power to the memory array is required at $V_{cc} \geqslant 2.4$ V. This reduces the power dissipation from 250 mW when active to 12 mW when powered down.

The majority of memory chips have a single enable or chip-select input, which is used to switch on the three state data buffers in a read cycle, and to permit data to be stored in the chip in a write cycle. The MC6810 is a rather unusual memory component because it has six chip-select inputs, four of which are active low and two active high. This chip has been designed to be used in circumstances where the read/write memory requirements are low and memory decoding circuits can be omitted by using the high-order address lines (A_{15}, A_{14},...) to select the RAM. The subject of address decoding is dealt with in detail later in this chapter.

Table 5.1 The Characteristics of some Static RAM Chips

Static RAM Type	*Total bits*	*Arrangement*	*Power (mW) Typ*	*Max*	*Access time (ns)*	*Pins*
Motorola MCM6810A	1024	128 × 8		350	450	24
Intel 2102A	1024	1024 × 1	165	275	350	16
Intel 2101A	1024	256 × 4	175	275	350	22
Intel 2111A	1024	256 × 4		300	350	18
AMI S4025-4	1024	1024 × 1		265	45	16
EMM/SEMI 35391	2048	256 × 8		394	400	22
Intel 2114	4096	1024 × 4		710	450	18
Intel 2147	4096	4096 × 1	500		90	18
TI TMS4044-45	4096	4096 × 1	275	495	450	18
TI TMS40L45-45	4096	1024 × 4	250	370	450	18
Mostek MK4118-4	8192	1024 × 8		400	250	24
TI TMS4016-25	16384	2048 × 8	495		250	24

5.1.2 Dynamic Random-access Memory

The dynamic memory cell uses only a single transistor to store its data in the form of a charge on a capacitor. Figure 5.2 illustrates the basic simplicity of a dynamic memory cell. Because the charge on the capacitor gradually leaks away, any data stored in the memory cell is lost after several milliseconds. Most dynamic memory chips have a guaranteed data retention period of 2 ms. In order to avoid the loss of data the charge on the capacitor must be periodically restored by rewriting the data into the memory cell in an operation known as refreshing.

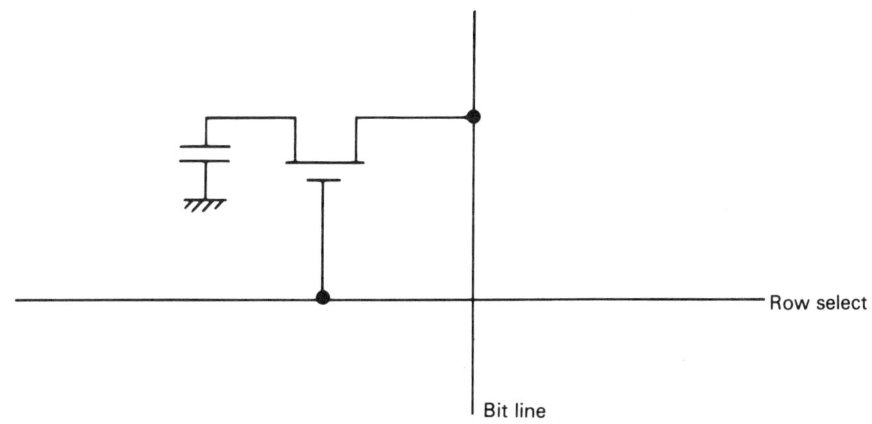

Figure 5.2 The storage cell of a dynamic memory element

Fortunately, the majority of dynamic RAMs have been constructed in such a way as to make the memory-refresh operation relatively easy. The dynamic memory chip is arranged as an array of rows and columns so that a typical 4K chip would have 64 rows and 64 columns. It is not necessary to refresh each memory cell individually, but instead, a whole row of memory cells are refreshed in a single operation called a refresh cycle. A typical memory-refresh cycle involves little more than a pseudo-read cycle. That is, a read operation is executed, while the chip is de-selected. To perform a refresh cycle, additional logic is usually necessary to multiplex the dynamic RAM's address lines between the CPU address bus and the refresh counter, which must cycle through the 64 row addresses. Further logic is required to synchronize the refresh operation with the CPU, either by slowing down or halting the CPU in a DMA type operation, or by executing a refresh cycle whenever the CPU is not using the system bus (i.e. the ϕ_1 high phase). Whenever the memory-refresh cycle does not involve the CPU, it is said to be transparent because the dynamic memory appears to the CPU as a block of static memory.

Just as there is a wide range of static memory chips the dynamic memory chip is also available in a variety of formats. Popular dynamic memory sizes are 4K $\times$ 1 and 16K $\times$ 1, and the 64K $\times$ 1 chip is now available. Because a considerable fraction of the cost of a memory component is in the packaging rather than the silicon chip itself, there has been a tendency to put 4K and 16K dynamic memory chips in 16-pin DIL packages. Such a small package cannot accommodate all the address lines necessary to access a given memory cell. To get round this difficulty, the address lines are multiplexed between the row and column addresses of any memory cell. Two new pins are required to implement the address multiplexing. These are the row-address strobe ($\overline{RAS}$) and the column-address strobe ($\overline{CAS}$), which are used to indicate that the address pins hold the address of a row and a column of a cell in the memory array respectively. The block diagram of a typical 4K dynamic RAM, the 2104A, is given in Fig. 5.3.

A particular problem associated with dynamic memories is that of power supplies. Not only do many dynamic RAMs require three separate power supplies of 12 V, 5 V and -5 V, but the current requirements are transitory. The average power consumed by a dynamic RAM is much lower than that of a corresponding static RAM. However, during a memory-access cycle (read/write/refresh), the current requirements of a dynamic RAM may increase by 60 mA in 5 – 10 ns. This current transient corresponds to a current demand increasing at the rate of more than 6×10^6 A/s! A well-designed dynamic memory system requires careful attention to the layout of the memory printed-circuit board, and the selection and positioning of decoupling capacitors.

Dynamic memory components are best suited to large memory systems where their cost, package count, average power consumption, and access time* make them much more cost effective than static memories. In small systems or systems constructed by the microprocessor enthusiast, the problems associated with the

* Static RAMs can be obtained with access times lower than dynamic RAMs, but commonly available dynamic RAMs are often faster than commonly available static RAMs.

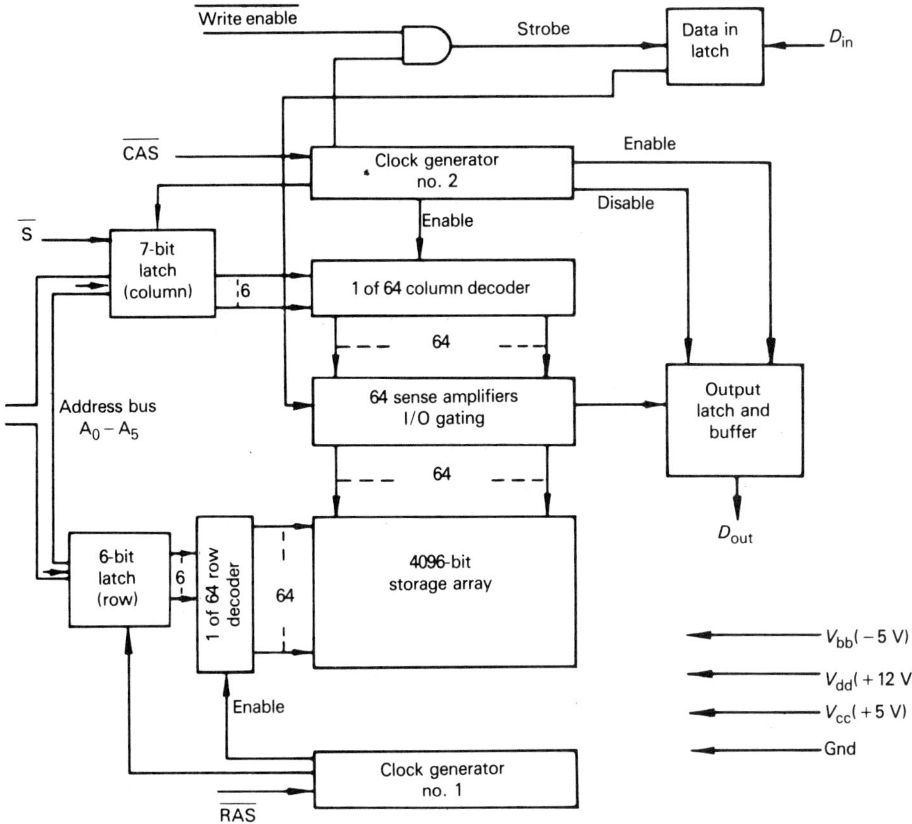

Figure 5.3 The internal arrangement of a 2104A 4096 × 1 bit dynamic RAM

refreshing of dynamic memories plus their power-supply requirements justify the use of static memories.

The designers of dynamic memories have realized that if they are to capture a share of the memory market for small microprocessor systems, they must overcome some of the limitations of dynamic memories. Mostek have been one of the first companies to produce a dynamic memory with the advantages of both conventional static and dynamic memories. The Mostek MK4816(P) series of dynamic memories is byte-organized as 2048 × 8 bits, unlike most dynamic memories, which are bit-organized as 4096 × 1 or 16 384 × 1 bits. The MK4816-3 has an access time of 200 ns, a cycle time of 360 ns and uses a single 5 V power supply. Its power requirement is only 150 mW, and it can be operated in a power-down mode where it needs only 25 mW to retain data. A special feature of the MK4816 is that it can be refreshed in the normal way (128 refresh cycles in 2 ms), or the system refresh logic can be eliminated by utilizing the MK4816's own internal refresh control logic.

5.1.3 Read-only Memory

Read-only memories are memories whose data can be accessed in a read operation, but cannot be altered in a normal write cycle. Although ROM is often regarded as a special type of RAM in which the data is frozen permanently in the memory cells, or cannot be altered without physically removing the ROM component from the memory system, an ordinary read/write RAM can be used as a ROM merely by disabling the write function, or by generating an interrupt whenever an attempt is made to write to a protected area of RAM.

ROM has several applications in a microprocessor system. Some of the most important applications are as follows:

(1) When a microprocessor is first supplied with power, it either executes a jump to a particular memory location, or loads its program counter with the contents of a particular memory location. For example the 6800, when reset, loads its program counter with the contents of locations FFFF and FFFE. Hence in a 6800 system some memory must exist at FFFE/F (or at least respond to these addresses). This memory usually holds the system's monitor or operating system, which must be retained after the power supply has been switched off. Clearly what is required is non-volatile memory, and ROM is used because it is, by its very nature, non-volatile.

(2) Programs which are not normally modified may be held in ROM to save the time lost in loading them from paper tape, cassette, or disk every time they are required. Such programs may be part of the operating system itself or interpreters for languages like BASIC. Compilers are not usually held in ROM because, unlike interpreters, they may be discarded after they have compiled a program.

(3) In order to speed up mathematical computations, ROMs are often used to hold the values of mathematical functions. For example a $1K \times 8$ ROM can hold 1024 values of sin (x), where x is in the range $0°$ to $90°$, giving a resolution of approximately $0.1°$. Interpolation can be employed to generate values of sin (x) for intermediate values of x. When used in this way the ROM becomes a function generator with the address lines as the input and the data lines as the output.

(4) A ROM is used in raster scan display systems to convert the binary character code, usually ASCII, into a pattern of dots which is displayed on a television screen.

(5) If a table of the addresses of a 2^n word by m-bit ROM is drawn with a table of the contents of the corresponding memory locations written alongside the addresses, it can be seen that the result is the truth table of a logic element with n inputs and m outputs. ROMs may therefore be used to replace TTL logic elements in applications where complex logic functions are required. High-speed bipolar ROMs are normally found in this application. We shall shortly see how ROMs may be used in address decoding networks.

Mask-programmable ROM

Mask-programmable ROM is programmed at the time of its manufacture by modifying one of the masks used in the photolithographic process by which LSI devices are made. Because of the great expense involved in making and testing a new LSI device, the mask-programmable ROM is cost-effective only when produced in large quantities. Mask-programmable ROMs are almost always byte orientated and are available in sizes of 1K – 8K bytes.

Most of the applications involving a mask-programmable ROM are in high-volume, dedicated systems where the high cost of developing and testing the ROM can be spread over many systems. In small microprocessor systems used either as development tools or as hobby computers, the mask-programmable ROM often appears in the form of a monitor, which is the microprocessor's "operating system", and is used to load other programs, modify them (if necessary), and then execute them. One of the most (in)famous monitors is Motorola's MIKBUG, which, although developed for the MEK 6800D1 development system, has become a standard for most 6800-based hobby computers.

The EPROM

A more useful type of ROM, from the small-scale user's point of view, is the erasable and programmable ROM (EPROM). This device may be programmed, erased, and then reprogrammed by the user. The operation of the EPROM is quite remarkable. Figure 5.4 illustrates the basic principle of the EPROM memory cell, which consists of a single field-effect transistor whose gate is totally isolated from the rest of the circuit by being embedded in an insulating layer of silicon dioxide. The gate is then said to be "floating". Above the floating gate is a second gate, the control gate, which is connected to the row decoder circuits in the memory array. The cell is programmed by grounding source and substrate and applying a high voltage to the control gate (25 V). The potential difference between the control gate and the substrate causes electrons to be injected through the silicon dioxide and become trapped on the floating gate. The device is remarkable because the charge will remain on the floating gate for many years because of the almost perfect

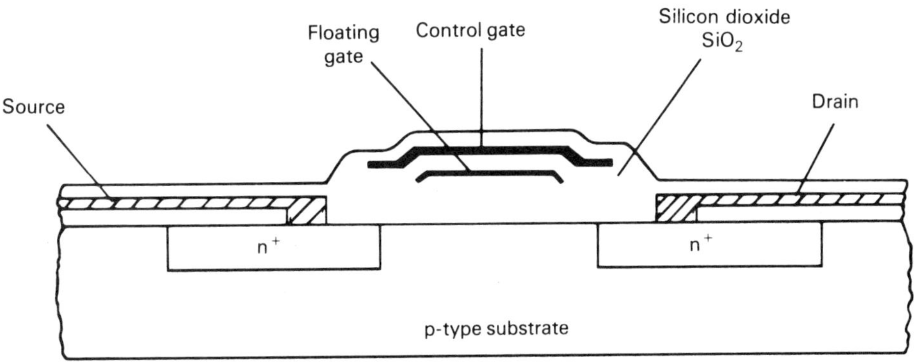

Figure 5.4 The structure of an EPROM memory cell

insulating properties of the silicon dioxide. The effect of the charge on the floating gate is to inhibit the flow of current between source and drain when the transistor is selected by the appropriate column address. Thus the trapped charge determines whether the transistor is in the on or off state when selected, and hence whether a 0 or 1 is stored in the cell.

The memory cell may be erased by illuminating it with ultraviolet light, at a wavelength of 2537 Å. The UV radiation imparts sufficient photon energy to the trapped electrons to enable them to escape through the silicon dioxide to the substrate. There are three consequences of this mode of erasure:

(1) In order to illuminate the cell with UV light, a quartz window must be put in the package, directly above this chip. This increases the cost of packaging.
(2) Because the whole chip is illuminated all cells are simultaneously erased. It is not possible to modify an EPROM selectively.
(3) Because UV light sources are expensive and bulky, it is necessary to remove the EPROM from its normal place in the microprocessor system and transport it to a UV light eraser. After erasing the EPROM it must be reprogrammed, an operation which is frequently carried out in a special programming machine. It is possible to program the EPROM *in situ*, but it is not usually worth the effort of providing a programmer in every microprocessor system.

The early EPROMs (e.g. the 1702A) were relatively small (256 bytes) and required several operating voltages. Currently available EPROMs can be obtained in 1K×8, 2K×8, 4K×8 and 8K×8 configurations, and operate with a single 5 V supply. The TS1 microprocessor system uses the low-cost 2516 EPROM which is organized as 2048 bytes. This allows the use of a relatively sophisticated monitor.

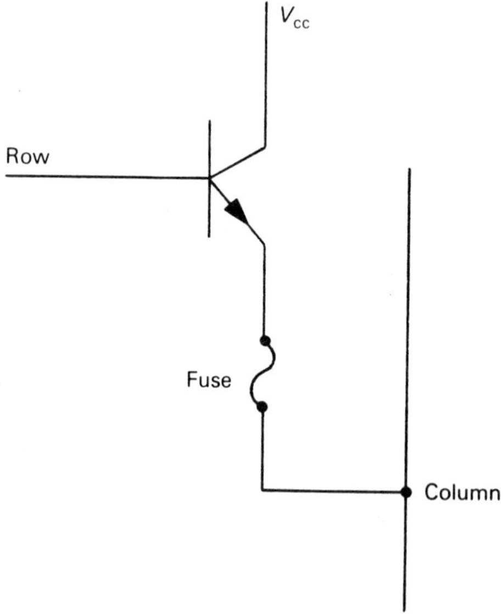

Figure 5.5 The memory cell found in a fusable-link PROM

The Field-programmable ROM (FPROM)

The field-programmable ROM is a bipolar device which may be programmed only once by the user. A typical FPROM (usually abbreviated to PROM) uses a single bipolar transistor memory cell. In the emitter of the transistor is a fuse consisting of a link made from one of four materials: nichrome, polycrystalline silicon, platinum silicide, or titanium tungsten. A cell of a fusible link FPROM is illustrated in Fig. 5.5.

During programing the fuses are blown (made open-circuit) by passing a large current pulse through the transistor by means of the row- and column-decoding circuitry. When a memory cell is selected in a read cycle, the row input to the transistor's base turns it on, and the column line is pulled towards V_{cc} if the fuse is intact, or left floating if the fuse has been blown.

Bipolar FPROMs are often characterized by relatively few bits per chip, and very fast access times (50 ns). The FPROM is often used in conjunction with bit-slice technologies where very high-speed processing is required. When FPROMs are found in microprocessor systems, they are frequently employed as address decoders, where a single 16-pin 32×8 FPROM can save several TTL packages.

5.2 THE TIMING DIAGRAM

A glance at the data sheet of any memory component always reveals one or more timing diagrams. A timing diagram shows the temporal relationship between the events which take place during a read or write cycle. Another way of looking at a timing diagram is to regard it as a cause-and-effect diagram, where, for example, the arrival of a new address is the cause and the output of new data is the effect. Figure 5.6 depicts the read-cycle timing diagram of a TMS40L45 1024-word by 4-bit static RAM. Anyone contemplating connecting a particular memory chip to a microprocessor system bus must first determine whether or not the timing requirements of the microprocessor and memory are compatible.

Consider the timing diagram in Fig. 5.6. All symbols and abbreviations are those used by Texas Instruments in their own literature. The values of the parameters defined in Fig. 5.6 are listed in Table 5.2 for the 450 ns version of the RAM. It is most unfortunate that semiconductor manufacturers use their own individual terminology in describing their products. It is often a tedious task to match up the timing diagram of manufacturer A's microprocessor with the timing diagram of manufacturer B's peripheral.

The specification of the TMS40L45 describes it as a fully static RAM requiring no clocks or timing strobe. This is an important feature because some memory components are either semi-static or else have clocked latches which make stringent demands on the timing arrangements.

In Fig. 5.6 the timing diagram of the address bus appears as two parallel lines which cross over at points A and B. The use of two parallel lines is a convention which means that the logic may be either high or low. In the case of the address bus, it is highly probable that some address lines are in the logical one state while others are in the logical zero state.

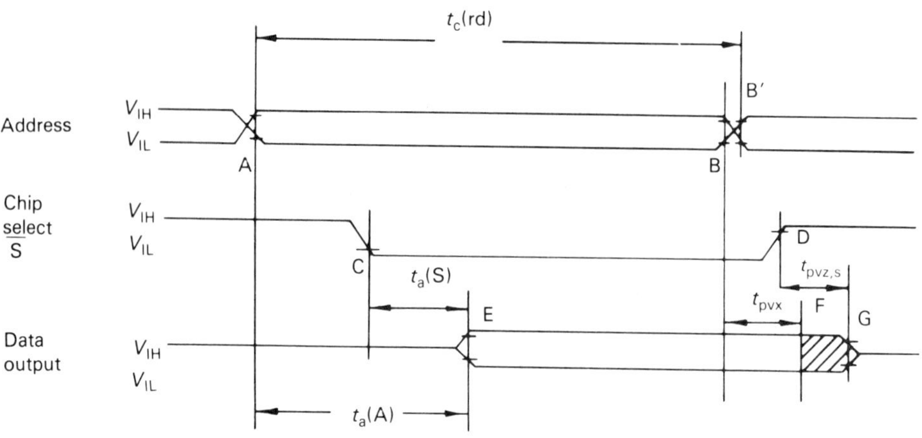

Figure 5.6 The read-cycle timing diagram of the TMS40L45 static RAM

It is not the actual state of the address bus that is of interest, but the time at which the contents of the address bus become stable for the duration of the current memory-access cycle. At point A in Fig. 5.6 the contents of the address bus have become stable, and this point is used as a reference for some of the timing measurements. Because logic transitions are never instantaneous, it is usual to represent a change of state by a sloping line, and to mark the point (or points) from which measurements are made. In most areas of digital electronics the reference points are taken as 10% and 90% of the upper logic level. Sometimes the reference levels are taken as V_{IL} and V_{IH} (0.8 V, 2.0 V) on inputs, and V_{OL} and V_{OH} (0.4 V, 2.4 V) on outputs.

Between points A and B the address bus contains the address of the location in the RAM which is to be read. During this time the address must not change. The difference between points B and B′ is that at B the contents of the address bus have started to change to the new values which will be used in the next cycle. It is not until point B′ that the new contents of the address bus become valid once more. The time between point A and B′ is the cycle time for a read operation, and is quoted as a minimum of 450 ns. That is, a microprocessor must not initiate a second read cycle until at least 450 ns after the start of the current read cycle. The TMS40L45 has an R/$\overline{W}$ input which does not appear in its read-cycle timing diagram. It must therefore be assumed that the R/$\overline{W}$ input to the RAM is the logical one state for the entire duration of the read cycle.

Consider now the data output of the TMS40L45. Up to point E, the contents of the data bus are represented as a single line midway between the two logic levels. This convention signifies that the data bus is floated, or in the high-impedance state. The internal data bus drivers of the TMS40L45 are in the high-impedance state until point E, which occurs t_a(S) seconds after point C, at which the chip-select input becomes active. The time between points A and E is t_a(A) seconds, and is the time taken from the point at which the contents of the address bus are first stable, to the

Table 5.2 The Timing Parameters of the TMS40L45-45

Symbol	*Parameter*	*Value (ns)* *min*	*max*
t_c(rd)	Read-cycle time	450	
t_a(S)	Access time from chip select		120
$t_{PVZ,S}$	Output disable time after chip select high		100
t_{PVX}	Output data valid after address change	10	
t_a(A)	Access time from address valid		450
t_c(wr)	Write-cycle time	450	
t_{su}(A)	Address set-up time	0	
t_w(W)	Write-pulse width	200	
t_h(A)	Address hold time	20	
t_{su}(S)	Chip-select set-up time	200	
t_{su}(D)	Data set-up time	200	
t_h(D)	Data hold time	0	

time at which the contents of the data bus first contain valid data. This time is quoted as having a maximum value of 450 ns. That is, the data should be valid no later than 450 ns after the start of a read cycle.

The chip-select input, $\overline{S}$, must take its active low transition at least t_a(S) seconds before the ouput data is required. The timing diagram says nothing about the relationship between point C and point A. This implies that $\overline{S}$ can assume its active low state at any time, as long as the t_a(S) requirement is satisfied. This is a consequence of the static nature of this RAM, and implies that data is continually being accessed from the RAM, and that all the chip-select input does (in a read cycle), is to enable the tri-state data output buffers. If $\overline{S}$ goes low early in the read cycle, data is put on the data bus no later than t_a(S) seconds after the active transition of $\overline{S}$. However, the data will not be valid until t_a(A) seconds after the address has become stable (point A).

At the end of the read cycle, point B, the contents of the address bus are in the process of changing to their new values. Because the memory does not respond instantly to changes on the address bus, the contents of the data bus are still valid until point F, which occurs not less than t_{PVX} seconds after point B. This is often called the guaranteed data-hold time of the memory. After point F, the data bus drivers are still in the low-impedance state, but the data is no longer valid. This situation is often indicated by shading the region between the two logic levels.

At point D the chip-select input makes its low-to-high transition, signalling that the chip's data bus drivers can once more be switched into the high-impedance state. It is not until point G, $t_{PVZ,S}$ seconds after point D, that the data bus returns to its high-impedance state, and the memory component is de-selected.

5.2.1 The Write Cycle

The write-cycle timing diagram for a TMS40L45 static RAM is given in Fig. 5.7. This timing diagram is a little more complex than the corresponding read-cycle

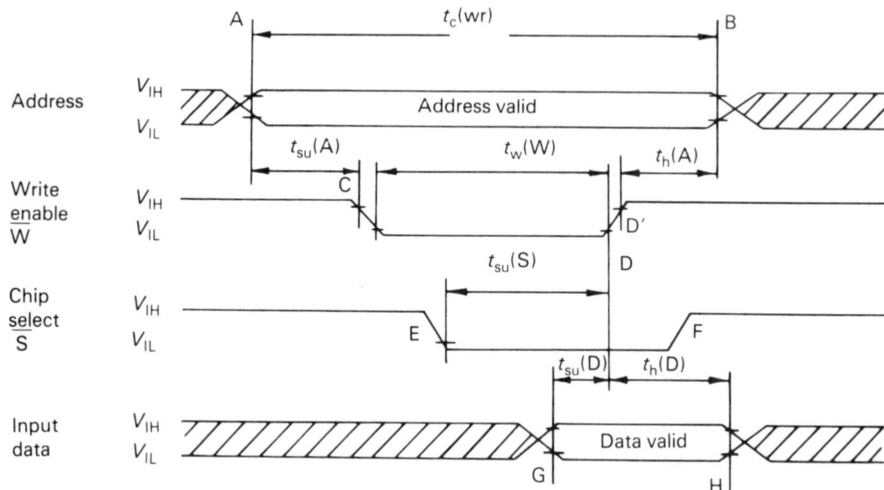

Figure 5.7 The write-cycle timing diagram of the TMS40L45 static RAM

timing diagram, because the action of the write enable ($\overline{W}$) input must also be considered.

No harm can be done to the stored data when $\overline{W} = 1$, as reading a memory cell does not affect its contents no matter how many times a read cycle takes place, but if $\overline{W}$ goes low when the contents of the address bus or data are not valid, there is a danger of writing erroneous data into the memory.

Between point A and B, in Fig 5.7, the contents of the address bus are stable. The duration of AB is called the write-cycle time, t_c(wr), and must not be less than 450 ns for a TMS40L45-45. The write-enable input to the RAM, $\overline{W}$, makes its high-to-low transition at point C. The time between the point at which the address bus is stable (A) and the point at which $\overline{W}$ goes low (C) is defined as t_{su}(A). The minimum value of t_{su}(A) is quoted as 0 ns. At first sight this may appear a little strange. What it really means is that $\overline{W}$ may make its high-to-low transition only after the contents of the address bus have become stable, and not before. In order to successfully execute a write cycle, $\overline{W}$ must remain low for a minimum of t_w(W) seconds, the write-pulse width, before rising to a logical one state at point D.

Point D is the time at which $\overline{W}$ has passed the 10% V_{OH} level and point D′ is the time at which W has reached the 90% V_{OH} level. It is important to note that point D′ must occur at least t_h(A) seconds before the contents of the address bus begin to change at point B. The time between D′ and B, t_h(A), is known as the address-hold time.

The active-low transition of the chip-select input, $\overline{S}$, must occur at least t_{su} (S) seconds before the rising edge of the $\overline{W}$ input at point D. The chip-select input may make its low-to-high transition any time after it has satisfied the condition that $t_{su}(S) \geqslant 200$ ns. However, should $\overline{S}$ remain low while $\overline{W}$ is high, a read cycle occurs, and the RAM's data bus drivers assume a low-impedance state.

The system data bus must contain the contents of the data to be written into the currently addressed memory cell from point G to point H. Between G and H the data bus must be stable. Point G must occur at least t_{su}(D) seconds before the low-to-high transition of $\overline{W}$ at D. This period is known as the data set-up time. After point D the data must be held stable for another t_h(D) seconds, the data-hold time.

5.2.2 The Microprocessor Timing Diagram

The designer of a microprocessor system is not simply interested in the timing diagrams of memory chips alone, but in the relationship between them and the timing diagrams of the microprocessor read/write cycles. Figures 5.8 and 5.9 give the timing diagrams of the 6800 read and write cycles respectively, and Table 5.3 defines the symbols used in these diagrams. Note that the style of these diagrams differs slightly from those of Texas Instrument's RAM. Moreover Motorola and TI each use their own symbols in their respective timing diagrams.

Table 5.3 The Timing Parameters of the MC6800 CPU

Symbol	*Parameter*	*Value (ns)* *min*	*max*
t_r	Clock-pulse rise time		100
t_{AD}	Address delay		270
t_{AH}	Address-hold time	30	
t_H	Data-hold time	10	
t_{acc}	Peripheral read access time		530
t_{DSR}	Data set-up time (read)	100	
t_{DDW}	Data delay time (write)		225

In Fig. 5.8 the read-cycle timing diagram of a 6800 CPU with a 1000 ns cycle time (f_{clock} = 1 MHz) is given. The CPU puts the values of R/$\overline{W}$, the current address, and VMA on to the system bus no later than t_{AD} seconds (270 ns) after the start of a clock cycle. The contents of all these lines remain constant* until at least t_{AH} seconds (30 ns) after the end of a clock cycle, signified by the rising edge of ϕ_1. At the start of a read cycle the data bus is in a high-impedance state, and remains in that state until the tri-state data bus drivers in the memory are turned on. The time at which this occurs is unimportant as long as valid data is on the data bus no later than t_{acc} seconds (the maximum value of the peripheral read access time) after the contents of the address bus have become stable. Of course, the data at the input terminals to the CPU is not valid until the memory component has responded by outputting valid data. The data must be valid no later than the maximum value of $t_{AD} + t_{acc}$ seconds after the start of a cycle (i.e. 270 + 530 = 800 ns). The data from the memory must be valid for a certain time before the end of a memory-access cycle. This time is t_{DSR} seconds, which is known as the data set-up time. At the end of a cycle the data must remain valid for a further period of not less than t_H seconds (the data-hold time) after the falling edge of ϕ_2.

* To be precise, t_{AH} is measured from the 0.4 V point on the rising edge of ϕ_1 to the 0.8 V or 2.0 V points on the address lines which represent the maximum value of V_{IL} and the minimum value of V_{IH} respectively.

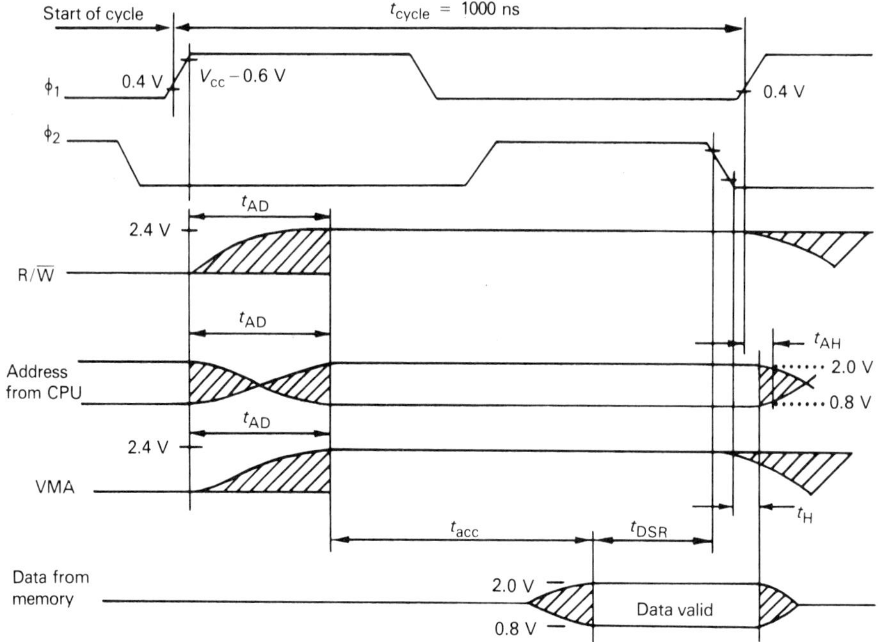

Figure 5.8 The read-cycle timing diagram of an MC6800 CPU

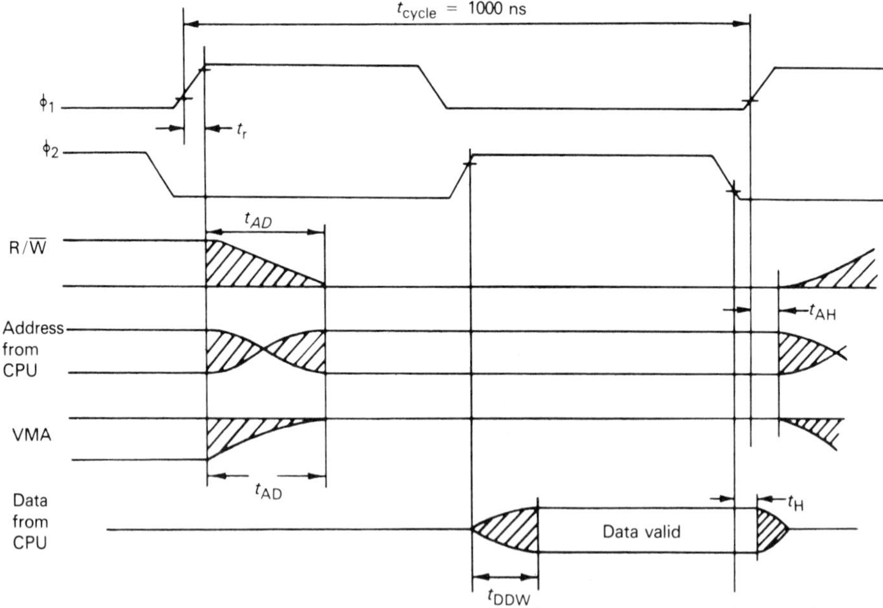

Figure 5.9 The write-cycle timing diagram of an MC6800 CPU

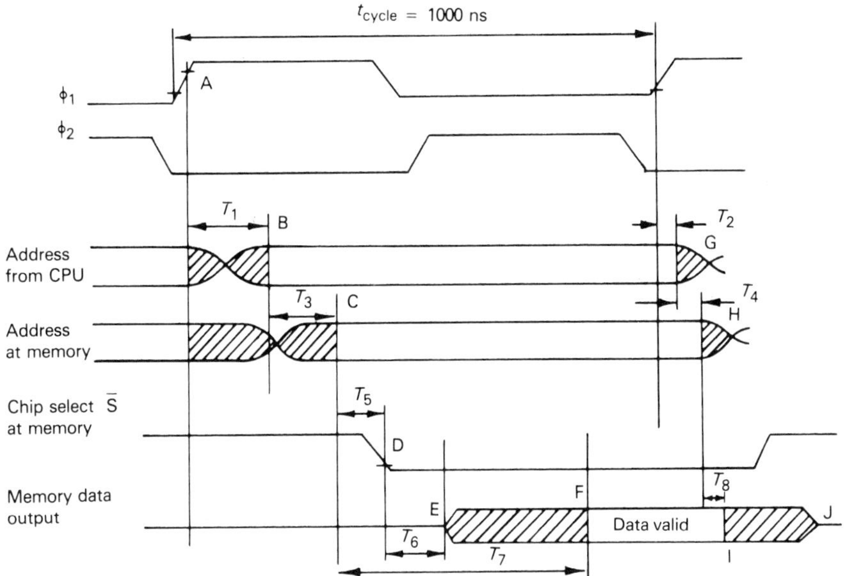

Figure 5.10 The read-cycle timing diagram of the MC6800 CPU related to the TMS40L45 static RAM

In a CPU write cycle, depicted in Fig. 5.9, the CPU supplies the values of R/$\overline{\text{W}}$, the memory address, and VMA just as it does in a read cycle. However, in this case the value of the data to be written into the currently addressed memory location must also be provided. The time at which valid data from the CPU appears on its data bus is dependent on the data bus drivers inside the CPU itself. These drivers are enabled by the DBE input to the CPU, which in normal operations is strapped to the CPU's ϕ_2 clock input. The contents of the data bus become valid no less than t_{DDW} seconds (the data delay time) after the rising edge of ϕ_2. (The data can be made valid earlier if DBE is forced into a logical one state no earlier than 150 ns after the start of a ϕ_1 active-high clock phase.) At the end of a write cycle, signified by the falling edge of ϕ_2, the CPU maintains the contents of the data bus for at least a further t_H seconds (the data-hold time).

Combining the CPU and RAM Timing Diagrams

In Fig. 5.10 the read-cycle timing diagrams of the 6800 CPU and of the TMS40L45-45 static RAM are combined. The job of the microprocessor systems designer is to determine whether or not this timing diagram violates any of the restrictions set out in the 6800 and TMS40L45-45 data sheets.

A CPU memory-access cycle begins at A, with the rising edge of the ϕ_1 clock pulse. It is not until B, after the delay of T_1 seconds, that the contents of the address bus first become valid. In Fig. 5.10 the values of VMA and R/$\overline{\text{W}}$ are not given, because it can be seen from Fig. 5.8 (the 6800 read-cycle timing diagram), that the timing arrangements of the address bus, VMA and R/$\overline{\text{W}}$ outputs of the 6800 are nominally identical. The address inputs to the RAM do not become valid until point C, T_3 seconds after point B. This additional delay is due to the address buffers. The address lines from the CPU are buffered onto the system bus at the CPU card and buffered from the system bus at the memory card. The worst-case delay of two 74LS244 buffers in series is 40 ns.

The chip-select input to the RAM, $\overline{\text{S}}$, makes its high-to-low transition at point D, T_5 seconds after point C. The chip-select delay, T_5, is due to the address-decoding circuit, which generates $\overline{\text{S}}$ from the high-order address lines ($A_{15} - A_{12}$ for a 4 K block of RAM). A typical value for T_5 is 40 ns, but the actual value depends on the type of address-decoding circuitry used. Fortunately, the value of T_5 is unimportant in most applications because it is very much shorter than the access time of the RAM. At point E, T_6 seconds after the chip has been selected, the effect of the active-low transition on the RAM's chip-select input is to turn on its tri-state data bus drivers. Although data has now been put onto the data bus, it is not yet valid. The contents of the data bus first become valid at point F, which occurs at $T_1 + T_3 + T_7$ seconds after the start of a clock cycle. Using the worst-case values for T_1, T_3, T_7, point F occurs no later than $270 + 40 + 450 = 760$ ns after the start of a read cycle.

The 6800 requires the contents of the data bus to be valid for at least 100 ns (t_{DSR}) before the end of the ϕ_2 active-high clock phase. At a clock cycle time of 1000 ns, the data (using the above figures) is valid approximately 240 ns before the rising edge of ϕ_2. The data set-up time requirement of the 6800 is therefore satisfied by a wide margin.

The only other critical timing requirement of a 6800 read cycle is that the data should remain valid for t_H seconds (the data-hold time), after the falling edge of ϕ_2. The value of t_H is given as not less than 10 ns. No problems are presented here for the following reasons:

(1) The address from the CPU is held for T_2 seconds ($T_2 = t_{AH}$) after the rising edge of ϕ_1. As the minimum value of T_2 is 30 ns, the data cannot begin to change until after the address has changed. That is, the data remains valid for at least 30 ns after the falling edge of ϕ_2. Note that the falling edge of ϕ_2 occurs before the rising edge of ϕ_1.

(2) Although the address at the CPU begins to change at point G, the address at the input to the RAM does not change until at least T_4 seconds later. T_4 is the minimum delay through the address buffers, and is not to be confused with T_3, which is the maximum delay through the address buffers. Whether we are interested in the maximum or the minimum propagation delay through a buffer (or any other digital circuit), depends on the effect of that delay on the system. For example, at the beginning of a cycle when the address first becomes valid we take the maximum value of the delay because this value gives us a worst case result. At the end of the cycle when we would like the address to linger (to satisfy the address hold times of memory components) we assume

that the delay through the buffer will be at its minimum. The designer of any system must assume that all components will collectively act against him by being at the end of their tolerance range that will cause the most trouble. The designer must therefore choose components which will still operate satisfactorily under these conditions.

(3) The RAM has a data hold time of T_8 ($T_8 = T_{pvx}$) seconds which is specified as not less than 10 ns.

Although the data remains valid until point I, which more than satisfies the CPU's data-hold time requirement, not until J is the data bus once more floated. In a well-designed system, no other device attempts to use the data bus until after point J, otherwise a clash between two bus drivers (in their low-impedance states) occurs. Fortunately, many 6800-based systems use the active-high phase of the ϕ_2 clock to control data bus drivers, which avoids any data-bus contention problems resulting from memory-access cycles extending into the first few nanoseconds of the following ϕ_1 clock phase.

In the above example delays due to data bus drivers have not been considered in order to keep the complexity of Fig. 5.10 to an acceptable level. In practice Schottky TTL bus drivers and receivers seldom cause problems in NMOS microprocessor systems because the propagation delays through these buffers are very much smaller than the clock-cycle times of the CPUs. Care must be taken, however, in systems where several buffers are connected in series, and these buffers are controlled by combinatorial logic elements which also introduce additional timing delays into the system. The cumulative effect of these delays becomes significant when the access time of the RAM is dangerously close to the time for which the CPU maintains a valid memory address on its address bus.

Many 6800-based microprocessor systems require RAMs with a considerably lower access time than the above example would suggest. Although the CPU puts out an address, VMA, and $R/\overline{W}$ signals during the ϕ_1 clock phase, the address-decoding arrangements are often designed to employ ϕ_2 as an enabling signal, reducing the time for which the address is valid (i.e. at the input to the RAM) by approximately 200 ns.

5.3 ADDRESS DECODING

The 6800, in common with many other microprocessors operating on data words of eight bits, has an address bus consisting of 16 lines, designated $A_0 - A_{15}$, where A_0 is the least significant bit. The microprocessor uses the address bus to indicate, to a peripheral or memory component, some unique address, and then, depending on the nature of the operation being performed, transmits data to the data bus or receives data from it. Each of the 16 address lines can assume a logical one or a logical zero state, which means that the address bus spans a total of $2^{16} = 65\ 536$ locations. In many text books 2^{16} is written as 64K, where $1K = 1024 = 2^{10}$. While this usage of "K" to represent 1024 is very convenient, it is a departure from the usage for SI units normally found in scientific texts, where "K" represents degrees Kelvin. In this book "K" always stands for 1024, as there is no ambiguity.

The choice of a 16-bit address bus for a microprocessor with an 8-bit data word is quite logical. Each address can readily be stored as two consecutive bytes in memory. Furthermore, a maximum of 64K uniquely addressable locations is sufficient for a wide spectrum of microprocessor applications, from instrumentation to word-processing machines. Unfortunately, when microprocessors are used in the role of general-purpose digital computers, the upper limit of 64K uniquely addressable locations becomes important if certain high-level languages are employed. Sometimes a compiler alone may contain more than 64K bytes of data. In such cases memory-management systems are required to overcome these limitations. These systems typically use overlay or virtual-memory techniques, which operate by storing only part of a program in RAM at any one time.

The remainder of the program is stored on a disk and is transferred into RAM when required. A microprocessor with a 24-line address bus can readily overcome many of the problems arising from a limited memory, by providing 2^{24} (16 777 216) uniquely addressable locations. However, a microprocessor with such a large number of address lines is not cost-effective in applications where very small memories are needed, because a larger and more expensive package is required to house the microprocessor (unless the address and data lines are multiplexed). Moreover, a microprocessor with a 24-line address bus would normally be expected to operate on data words of at least 16 bits to take full advantage of the available memory.

The 64K uniquely addressable locations which form the memory of a microprocessor with a 16-bit address bus are often imagined as being laid out, side by side, in a column of 64K locations, numbered sequentially from 00 . . . 0 to 11 . . . 1. This imaginary column is often referred to as an address space. Because various regions of this address space can be grouped together into blocks of consecutive locations, the resulting grouping is usually called a memory map. The blocks forming the memory map may refer to hardware devices (i.e. blocks of RAM, ROM), or they may refer to logical entities (i.e. programs, subroutines, editors, etc.). Figure 5.11 illustrates these concepts.

If the memory of a microprocessor system were constructed from memory components with 64K uniquely addressable locations, the problem of address decoding would not exist. Each of the microprocessor's address output lines, $A_0 - A_{15}$, would simply be connected to the corresponding address input lines of the memory component. However, in the majority of microprocessor systems, not only do the actual memory components have fewer than 64K uniquely addressable locations, but the type and size of the memory components is often mixed (e.g. $4K \times 1$ RAMs and $1K \times 8$ ROMs). The TS1 microprocessor system is constructed from memory components ranging from $4K \times 8$ bits to 2×8 bits. It is this wide range of memory components that frequently causes problems for the designer of microprocessor systems.

Consider the situation illustrated by Fig. 5.12, where two $1K \times 8$ memory components are connected to a system address bus, consisting of 16 lines. The ten system address lines $A_0 - A_9$ are connected to the address inputs of the two memory components, M1 and M2. Whenever a location (one of $2^{10} = 1024$) is addressed in

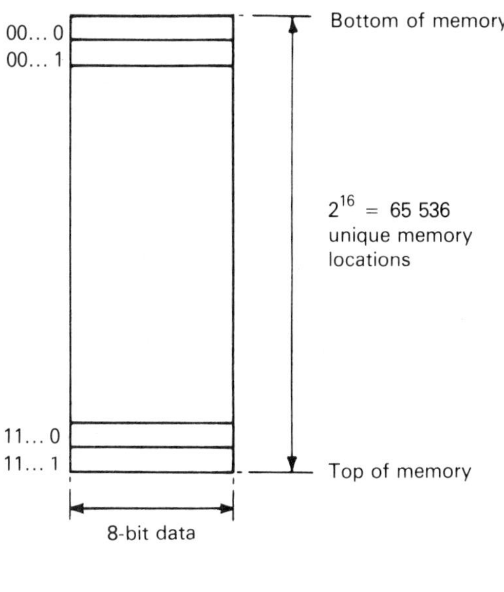

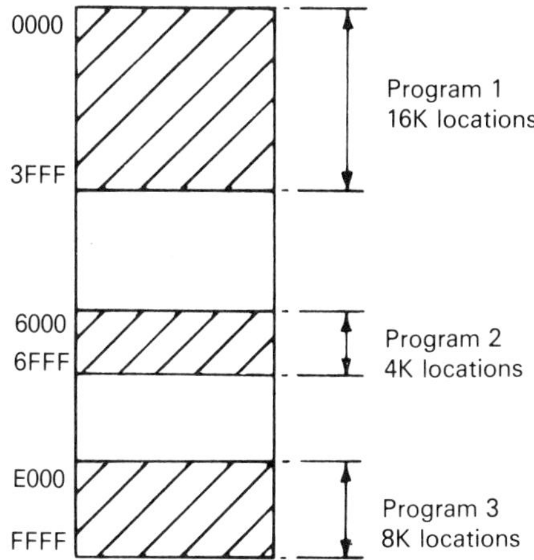

Figure 5.11 Address space (upper) and memory map (lower). The map is of a system whose memory space is divided into three unequal blocks

M1, the corresponding location is addressed in M2. The data outputs of M1 and M2 are connected to the system data bus. Because the data outputs of both M1 and M2 are connected together, it is necessary that the data bus drivers in the memory components are tri-state devices. That is, only one of the memory components at a time may put data onto the system data bus. This is done by including a chip-select input in each of the memory devices. All memory components have at least one chip-select input (which is normally active low), and some memory components have several. Whenever the chip-select input of M1 or M2 is inactive (i.e. in a logical 1

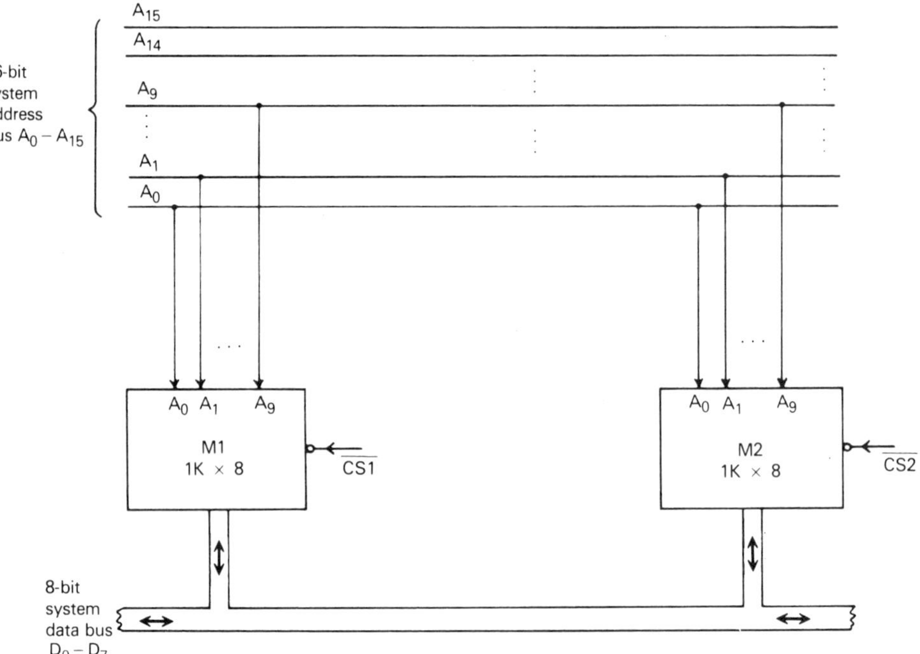

Figure 5.12 An ilustration of the necessity for address decoding

state) the appropriate data bus drivers are turned off, and no data is put on the data bus.

Let $\overline{CS1}$ be made a function of the address lines A_{10} to A_{15}, so that $\overline{CS1} = f_1(A_{15}, A_{14}, A_{13}, A_{12}, A_{11}, A_{10})$. Similarly, let $\overline{CS2}$ be a function of the same address lines, so that $\overline{CS2} = f_2(A_{15}, A_{14}, A_{13}, A_{12}, A_{11}, A_{10})$. Suppose we choose f_1 and f_2 subject to the constraint that there are no values of $A_{15}, A_{14}, \ldots, A_{10}$ which cause $\overline{CS1}$ and $\overline{CS2}$ to be low simultaneously. Under these circumstances, the conflict between M1 and M2 is resolved, and the memory map of the system now contains two disjoint 1K blocks of memory. There are several different strategies for decoding $A_{10} - A_{15}$ (i.e. choosing f_1 and f_2). These strategies may be divided into three groups: partial address decoding, full address decoding, and block address decoding.

5.3.1 Partial Address Decoding

Partial address decoding is the simplest, and consequently the most inexpensive form of address decoding to implement. Figure 5.13 demonstrates how two 1K blocks of memory can be connected to a system address bus in such a way that both blocks of memory are never accessed simultaneously. The conflict between M1 and M2 is resolved by connecting $\overline{CS1}$ directly to A_{15} of the system address bus, and by connecting $\overline{CS2}$ to A_{15} via an invertor. In this way M1 is selected whenever $A_{15} = 0$, and M2 is selected whenever $A_{15} = 1$. Although we have succeeded in distinguishing

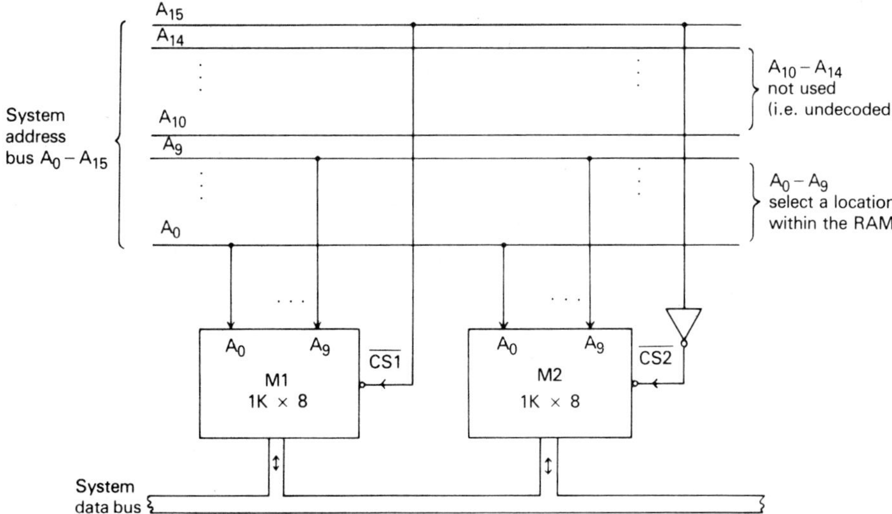

Figure 5.13 A simple example of partial address decoding

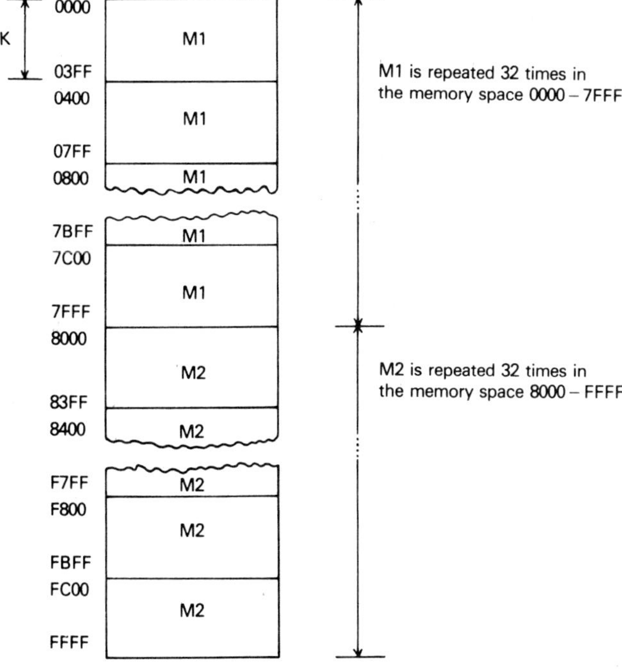

Figure 5.14 The memory map corresponding to Figure 5.13

between M1 and M2 for the cost of a single invertor, a heavy price has been paid. Because $A_{15} = 0$ selects M1, and $A_{15} = 1$ selects M2, it follows that either M1 or M2 will always be selected. Thus, although the system address bus can specify 64K unique addresses, only 2K different locations can be accessed. In this case, the address lines $A_{10} - A_{14}$ take no part in the address-decoding process, and consequently have no effect on the selection of a location within either M1 or M2. Figure 5.14 gives the memory map of the above system, from which it can be seen that M1 is repeated 32 times in the lower half of the memory space, and M2 is repeated 32 times in the upper half of the memory space.

Partial address decoding is widely used in small, dedicated systems where low cost is of paramount importance. The penalty paid when a partial address-decoding scheme is employed is that it prevents full use of the microprocessor's 64K address space and frequently makes it difficult to expand the memory system at a later date.

A more realistic example of partial address decoding is provided by Motorola's MEK 6800D1 evaluation kit.* A simplified version of the partial address decoding employed in this kit is given in Fig. 5.15. All the addressable devices in this kit have more than one chip select (sometimes called chip enable), which makes them well-suited to partial address-decoding schemes. The MC6810 128-byte RAM has four active-low chip selects, and two active-high chip selects, while the memory-mapped peripherals (PIA and ACIA) have one active-low chip select and two active-high chip selects. The mask-programmed ROM, MIKBUG, which contains the system's monitor (operating system), has four active-high chip selects, of which three are used for address-decoding purposes.

Although this ROM contains 1024 addressable locations, for historical reasons only 512 bytes are used, and the A_9 input of ROM is permanently connected to ground. Table 5.4 shows how the chip-select inputs of the memory and peripheral components decode the higher-order address lines so that the microprocessor can access a location within any given memory component, without enabling any of the other memory components.

Consider the selection of RAM 6 which is located at A000 – A07F. RAM 6 is enabled by $A_{15}.\overline{A_{14}}.A_{13}.\overline{A_{12}}$. Because RAM 1 – RAM 5 are enabled by $\overline{A_{15}}$, no conflict occurs between them and RAM 6. Similarly, the PIAs and ACIA are enabled by $\overline{A_{13}}$, avoiding a conflict with RAM 6 (enabled by A_{13}). Finally, RAM 6 is distinguished from the ROM by A_{14} with $\overline{A_{14}}$ enabling RAM 6 and A_{14} enabling the ROM. Although RAM 6 can be accessed without enabling any of the other memory components, RAM 6 itself occupies 4K of memory space because address lines $A_7 - A_{11}$ are not used to select it, and consequently the 128 bytes of RAM 6 are repeated 32 times in this 4K memory space.

By inspecting Table 5.4 it can readily be seen that each device may be addressed without accessing any other device, but it is also possible to select simultaneously two or more of the peripherals (PIA/ACIA). The peripherals are selected by

* The MEK 6800D1 evaluation kit is now obsolete but it does provide a valuable example of how not to design a microprocessor system. In all fairness to Motorola, the MEK 6800D1 was designed for its cost effectiveness rather than its versatility.

$A_{15}.\overline{A_{13}}.A_i$, where $i=2$, 3, or 4. If $A_{15}=1$, $A_{13}=0$, $A_2=1$, then PIA 1 is selected, and if $A_{15}=1$, $A_{13}=0$, $A_3=1$, then PIA 2 is selected. However, if $A_{15}=1$, $A_{13}=0$, $A_2=1$ and $A_3=1$, then both PIA 1 and PIA 2 are simultaneously selected; a condition which must not be allowed to occur.

Table 5.4 The Address Table Corresponding to Fig. 5.15

Device	*Address*	A_{15}	A_{14}	A_{13}	A_{12}	A_{11}	A_{10}	A_9	A_8	A_7	A_6	A_5	A_4	A_3	A_2	A_1	A_0
RAM 1	0000 – 007F	0						0	0	0	×	×	×	×	×	×	×
RAM 2	0080 – 00FF	0						0	0	1	×	×	×	×	×	×	×
RAM 3	0100 – 017F	0						0	1	0	×	×	×	×	×	×	×
RAM 4	0180 – 01FF	0						0	1	1	×	×	×	×	×	×	×
RAM 5	0200 – 027F	0						1	0	0	×	×	×	×	×	×	×
PIA 1	8004 – 8007	1		0											1	×	×
PIA 2	8008 – 800B	1		0										1		×	×
ACIA	8010 – 8011	1		0									1				×
RAM 6	A000 – A07F	1	0	1	0						×	×	×	×	×	×	×
ROM	E000 – E1FF	1	1	1				†	×	×	×	×	×	×	×	×	×

× represents 1 or 0 and is used to select a location within the device

A blank entry in an address column implies that the address is not used in the selection of the device. The address is then said to be a "don't care" condition.

† The A_9 input of the 1K ROM is permanently connected to a logical zero converting the ROM into a 512-byte ROM.

The MEK 6800D1 kit was designed to teach engineers about the behavior of microprocessors at the hardware and machine-code levels. To operate the kit all that is required is a VDT or Teletype, and a power supply. The monitor program (called MIKBUG by Motorola) which is resident in the ROM, enables the user to enter his own programs from the keyboard, modify them and then run them.

By using partial address decoding Motorola kept the cost of this kit to a minimum. As we have seen, the kit has a RAM at A000 which is where the stack is located, an input/output port at 8004, and a ROM at E000. These addresses have been chosen to simplify the design of the kit.

The MEK 6800D1 has had a remarkable effect on the amateur and even the small-scale professional market. Much 6800 software has been developed on, or for, this kit. This software also locates a stack in the RAM at A000, and frequently uses the input/output subroutines within MIKBUG. Consequently, several 6800 microprocessor systems produced by other manufacturers also locate their stack in the RAM at A000, input/output at 8004 and a MIKBUG ROM (or a modification of this ROM) at E000. Note that although the 6800 loads the contents of memory locations FFFE and FFFF into the program counter after the $\overline{\text{RESET}}$ input goes high, in practice the contents of E1FE and E1FF are loaded into the program counter, because in the MEK 6800D1 kit, address lines A_{10} – A_{12} are not used to select the ROM.

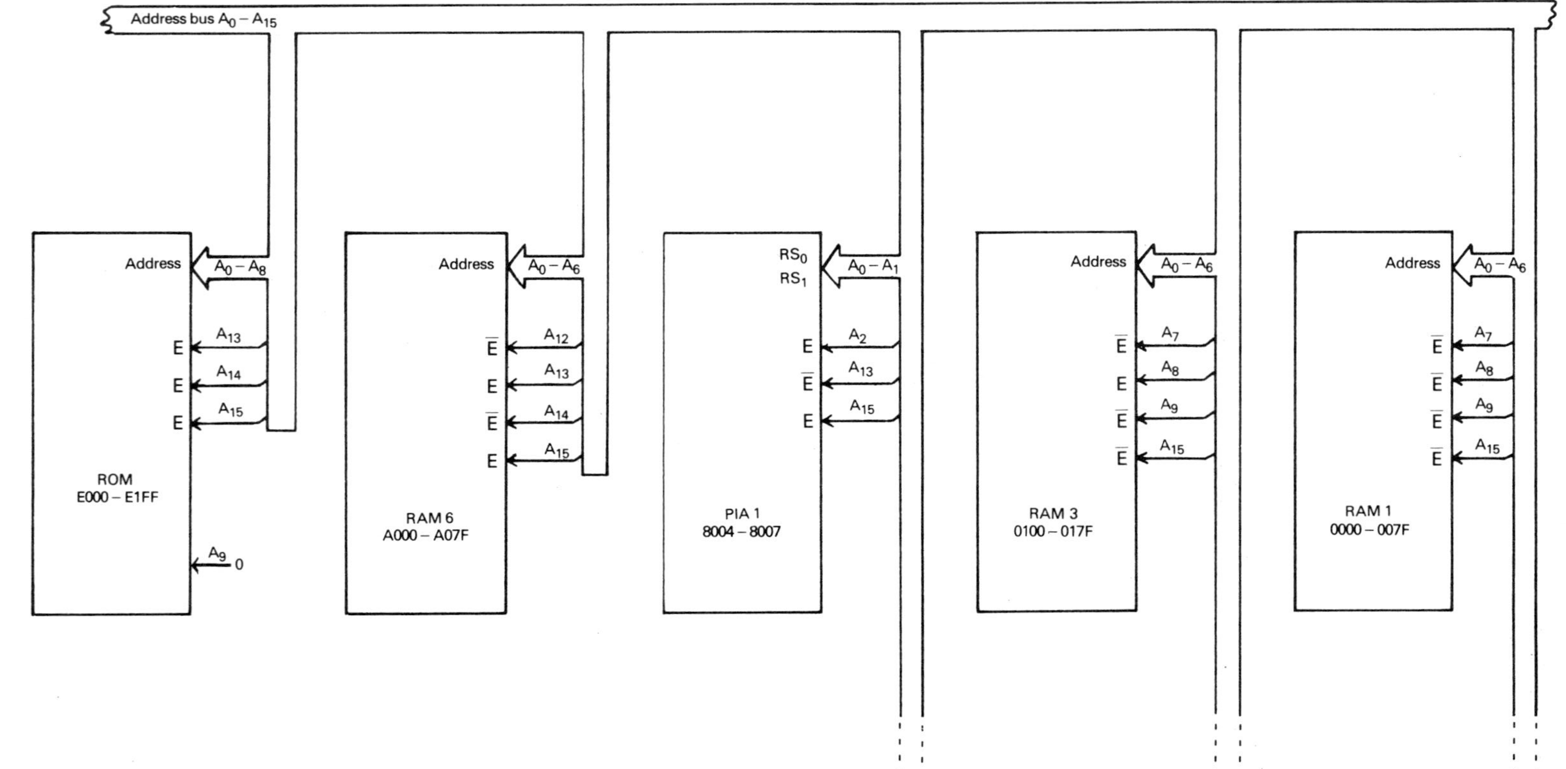

Address bus $A_0 - A_{15}$
Address
$A_0 - A_8$
A_{13}
A_{14}
A_{15}
ROM
E000 – E1FF
A_9 0
Address
$A_0 - A_6$
A_{12}
A_{13}
A_{14}
A_{15}
RAM 6
A000 – A07F
RS_0
RS_1
$A_0 - A_1$
A_2
A_{13}
A_{15}
PIA 1
8004 – 8007
Address
$A_0 - A_6$
A_7
A_8
A_9
A_{15}
RAM 3
0100 – 017F
Address
$A_0 - A_6$
A_7
A_8
A_9
A_{15}
RAM 1
0000 – 007F

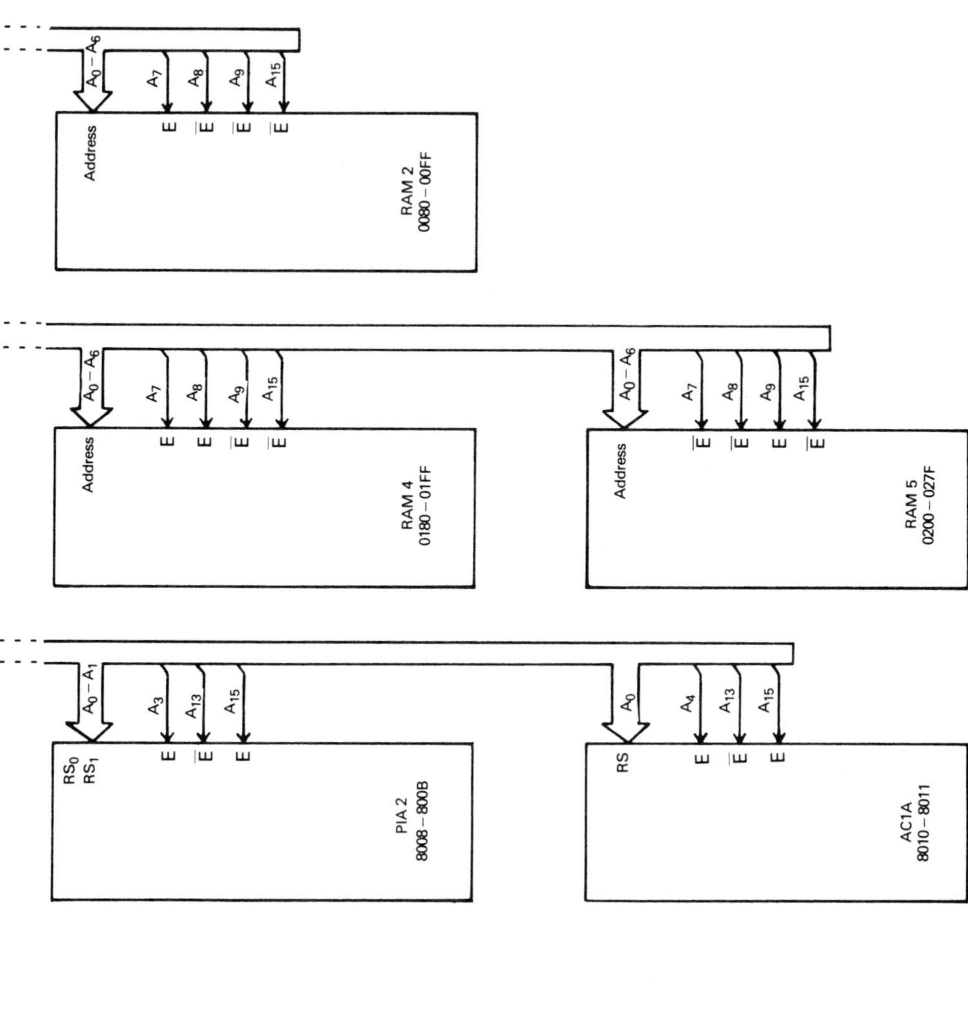

Figure 5.15 A simplified diagram of the partial address decoding scheme used in the Motorola MEK 6800D1 evaluation kit

5.3.2 Full Address Decoding

A microprocessor system is said to have full address decoding when each addressable location within a memory component responds to a single address on the system's address bus. That is, all the microprocessor's address lines, $A_0 - A_{15}$, are used to access each physical memory location, either by specifying a given device or by specifying an address within it.

In the MEK 6800D1 evaluation kit partial address decoding avoids the expense of address decoding networks (see Fig. 5.15 and Table 5.4). If all the memory devices in this kit are to be fully decoded, then the blank entries in the address columns in Table 5.4 (don't care conditions) must be removed by making the selection of the memory device a function of these hitherto undecoded address lines. For example, it can be seen from Table 5.4 that address lines A_{14} and $A_{12} - A_3$ take no part in the selection of PIA 1. If PIA 1 is to be fully address decoded, then it should be provided with a further 11 active-low chip-select inputs—an unrealistic solution, or additional random logic must be employed to decode these 11 address lines.

It will be demonstrated in the next section that full address decoding is difficult to implement by means of random logic, due to the large number of variables involved in the decoding process. However, two relatively new logic devices, the programmable logic array (PLA), and the programmable gate array (PGA), are particularly suited to full address decoding schemes. Note that if full address decoding were to be applied to the MEK 6800D1 kit, then a supplementary ROM would have to be located at FFFE/F to hold the system's restart vector, because the MIKBUG ROM at E000 – E1FF would no longer respond to addresses FFFE and FFFF.

The advantage of full address decoding is that it allows the whole 64K memory address space to be utilized, an important factor in large systems. Unfortunately, unless full address decoding is implemented by means of a PLA or PGA, a rather large amount of logic may be required.

5.3.3 Block Address Decoding

Block address decoding is a compromise between partial address decoding and full address decoding. It avoids the inefficient memory usage of partial address decoding, by dividing the memory space into a number of blocks. These blocks are sometimes referred to as pages.

In a typical application of block address decoding, a microprocessor's 64K memory space is divided into 16 blocks of 4K. This action often requires nothing more than a relatively inexpensive component to decode the four high-order address lines, $A_{12} - A_{15}$, into 16 lines. Each of these 16 lines is associated with one of the binary states of the four address lines. The 16 outputs of this address decoder can then be used as the chip-select inputs of memory components. The advantage of block address decoding is that no memory component can occupy a memory space larger than a single block. In practice, real microprocessor systems often employ a combination of partial address decoding, full address decoding, and block address decoding. For example, a system may have block address decoding with 4K blocks, in which case 4K× 1 RAMs or 4K× 8 ROMs will be fully address decoded. If several PIAs share the same 4K block of memory by using the PIAs' chip-select inputs, we have an example of partial address decoding within a block of memory.

5.4 ADDRESS-DECODING TECHNIQUES

There are several different ways in which the three address-decoding strategies defined in the last section may be implemented. In general, address-decoding techniques may be divided into four groups: address decoding using random logic, address decoding using *m*-line to *n*-line decoders, address decoding using PROMs and address decoding using programmable logic arrays.

5.4.1 Address Decoding Using Random Logic

Random logic is the term which describes a system constructed from small-scale TTL logic, with AND, OR, NAND, NOR gates and invertors. When address decoding with random logic is implemented, the chip-select input of a memory component is derived from the appropriate address lines by means of a number of TTL gates. For example, if a PIA located at 8004 is to be fully decoded, the circuit in Fig. 5.16 is suitable. The PIA has two register select lines, leaving 14 address lines to be decoded. The address of the PIA, $8004_{16} = 10000000000001XX_2$, may be decoded with a 2-input NAND gate, 13 invertors, and a 13-input NAND gate, as in Fig. 5.16.

Full address decoding using random logic is costly in terms of the large number of integrated circuits required, especially in cases where several different memory devices are to be selected. Because a circuit implemented by means of random logic is tailor-made for a specific application, it lacks the flexibility inherent in some of the other forms of address-decoding circuit.

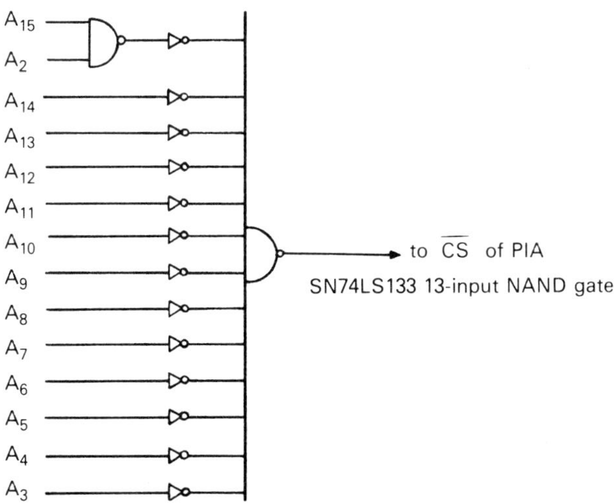

Figure 5.16 Example of address decoding using random logic

5.4.2 Address Decoding Using *m*-line to *n*-line Decoders

The problems of address decoding can often by greatly diminished by means of data decoders which decode an m-bit binary input into one of n outputs, where $n=2^m$. The three most popular decoders are the 74LS154 4-line to 16-line decoder, the 74LS138 3-line to 8-line decoder, and the 74LS139 dual 2-line to 4-line decoders. Figures 5.17 – 5.19 give the pin-outs and truth tables for the 74LS154, 74LS138 and 74LS139 respectively. All three decoders have active-low outputs, which makes them particularly suitable for address-decoding applications, because the majority of memory components have active-low chip-select inputs.

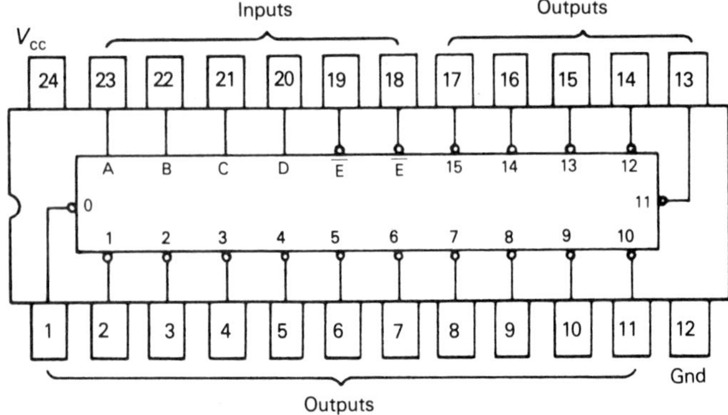

74LS154 truth table

Inputs						Outputs															
$\overline{E1}$	$\overline{E2}$	D	C	B	A	0	1	2	3	4	5	6	7	8	9	10	11	12	13	14	15
0	0	0	0	0	0	0	1	1	1	1	1	1	1	1	1	1	1	1	1	1	1
0	0	0	0	0	1	1	0	1	1	1	1	1	1	1	1	1	1	1	1	1	1
0	0	0	0	1	0	1	1	0	1	1	1	1	1	1	1	1	1	1	1	1	1
0	0	0	0	1	1	1	1	1	0	1	1	1	1	1	1	1	1	1	1	1	1
0	0	0	1	0	0	1	1	1	1	0	1	1	1	1	1	1	1	1	1	1	1
0	0	0	1	0	1	1	1	1	1	1	0	1	1	1	1	1	1	1	1	1	1
0	0	0	1	1	0	1	1	1	1	1	1	0	1	1	1	1	1	1	1	1	1
0	0	0	1	1	1	1	1	1	1	1	1	1	0	1	1	1	1	1	1	1	1
0	0	1	0	0	0	1	1	1	1	1	1	1	1	0	1	1	1	1	1	1	1
0	0	1	0	0	1	1	1	1	1	1	1	1	1	1	0	1	1	1	1	1	1
0	0	1	0	1	0	1	1	1	1	1	1	1	1	1	1	0	1	1	1	1	1
0	0	1	0	1	1	1	1	1	1	1	1	1	1	1	1	1	0	1	1	1	1
0	0	1	1	0	0	1	1	1	1	1	1	1	1	1	1	1	1	0	1	1	1
0	0	1	1	0	1	1	1	1	1	1	1	1	1	1	1	1	1	1	0	1	1
0	0	1	1	1	0	1	1	1	1	1	1	1	1	1	1	1	1	1	1	0	1
0	0	1	1	1	1	1	1	1	1	1	1	1	1	1	1	1	1	1	1	1	0
0	1	x	x	x	x	1	1	1	1	1	1	1	1	1	1	1	1	1	1	1	1
1	0	x	x	x	x	1	1	1	1	1	1	1	1	1	1	1	1	1	1	1	1
1	1	x	x	x	x	1	1	1	1	1	1	1	1	1	1	1	1	1	1	1	1

Figure 5.17 The 74LS154

The 74LS154, in addition to its four inputs A, B, C and D, has two active-low $\overline{\text{ENABLE}}$ inputs. Unless both of these $\overline{\text{ENABLE}}$ inputs are in the zero logic state, the binary code at the input of the 74LS154 is ignored, and all outputs remain in the logical one state. This important facility may be employed in one of three ways. Firstly, the $\overline{\text{ENABLE}}$ input may be used to strobe the outputs, allowing them to be synchronized with an external event.

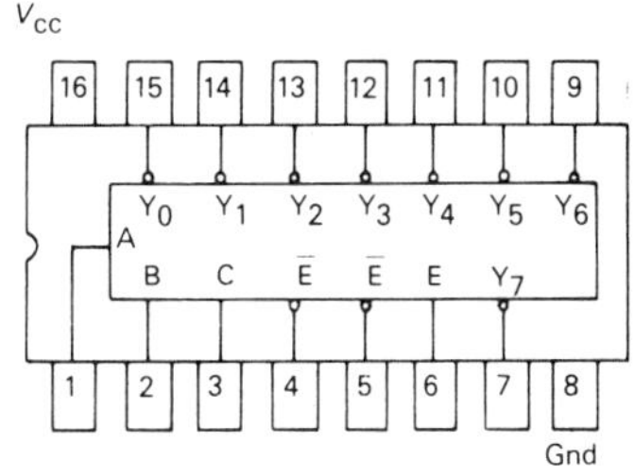

74LS138 truth table

Inputs						Outputs							
$\overline{E1}$	$\overline{E2}$	E3	C	D	A	Y0	Y1	Y2	Y3	Y4	Y5	Y6	Y7
1	1	0	x	x	x	1	1	1	1	1	1	1	1
1	1	1	x	x	x	1	1	1	1	1	1	1	1
1	0	0	x	x	x	1	1	1	1	1	1	1	1
1	0	1	x	x	x	1	1	1	1	1	1	1	1
0	1	0	x	x	x	1	1	1	1	1	1	1	1
0	1	1	x	x	x	1	1	1	1	1	1	1	1
0	0	0	x	x	x	1	1	1	1	1	1	1	1
0	0	1	0	0	0	0	1	1	1	1	1	1	1
0	0	1	0	0	1	1	0	1	1	1	1	1	1
0	0	1	0	1	0	1	1	0	1	1	1	1	1
0	0	1	0	1	1	1	1	1	0	1	1	1	1
0	0	1	1	0	0	1	1	1	1	0	1	1	1
0	0	1	1	0	1	1	1	1	1	1	0	1	1
0	0	1	1	1	0	1	1	1	1	1	1	0	1
0	0	1	1	1	1	1	1	1	1	1	1	1	0

Figure 5.18 The 74LS138

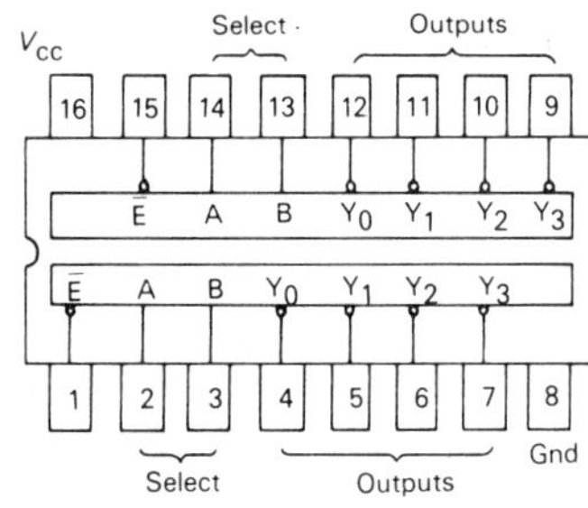

74LS139 truth table

Inputs			Outputs			
$\overline{E}$	B	A	Y0	Y1	Y2	Y3
1	x	x	1	1	1	1
0	0	0	0	1	1	1
0	0	1	1	0	1	1
0	1	0	1	1	0	1
0	1	1	1	1	1	0

Figure 5.19 The 74LS139

For example, in a 6800 system one of the $\overline{\text{ENABLE}}$ inputs may be connected to the CPU's VMA output (via an invertor because VMA is active -high), so that none of the 74LS154's outputs may go low and select a memory component until there is a valid address on the system bus. Secondly, one of the $\overline{\text{ENABLE}}$ inputs can be connected directly to an address line in order to select a block of memory. For example, if $\overline{\text{E1}}$ of the 74LS154 is connected to A_{15}, the 16 outputs divide the lower 32K of memory space (0000 – 7FFF) into 16 blocks of 2K. Thirdly, the $\overline{\text{ENABLE}}$ inputs make it easy to connect two or more decoders in series. For example, if the first 74LS154 is used to decode address lines A_{15}, A_{14}, A_{13} and A_{12}, the 64K memory space is divided into 16 blocks of 4K. If one of the outputs of the first 74LS154 is connected to the $\overline{\text{ENABLE}}$ input of a second 74LS154, and the second decoder is used to decode A_{11}, A_{10}, A_9 and A_8, then the outputs of the second 74LS154 divide the selected 4K block into 16 segments, each of 256 bytes.

Consider the effect of a single 74LS154, plus a little random logic, on the example in Fig. 5.15 (Evaluation Kit MEK 6800D1). In this kit no address decoding is used other than partial address decoding employing the chip-select inputs of the memory components. Figure 5.20 gives the basic circuit diagram of the MEK 6800D1 arrangement, but with the addition of a 74LS154 4-line to 16-line decoder to achieve block address decoding. The address table corresponding to Fig. 5.20 is given in Table 5.5. It can be seen from this table that all the RAMs and the ROM are fully address decoded, because the chip-select inputs of these memory components decode the address lines not decoded by the 74LS154. The PIAs and the ACIA now occupy a block of 4K, and it is no longer possible to select two or more peripherals simultaneously.

A simpler circuit than that in Fig. 5.20 can be constructed by omitting some of the random logic, except for the invertor interfacing the active-low output of the decoder to the active-high enable input of the ROM. In order to achieve full address decoding for the RAMs and the ROM, invertors are sometimes necessary when the sense of the chip-select input of a memory component differs from the sense of the address line enabling the memory components. The three NOR gates remove the possibility of selecting two or more peripherals simultaneously. Each of the NOR gates has its output connected to the active-high chip-select input of a peripheral component. The output of the NOR gate is high only when both inputs are in the low state.

By applying a relatively small amount of additional logic to the circuit in Fig. 5.15, we have now constructed a system which can readily be expanded. It should be noted that the system in Fig. 5.20 will not function correctly unless a ROM is added at FFFE/F to respond to the system's restart vector. The ROM at E000 – E1FF is now fully decoded and will not therefore respond to the reset or interrupt vectors.

Table 5.5 The Address Table Corresponding to Fig. 5.20

Device	*Address*	A_{15}	A_{14}	A_{13}	A_{12}	A_{11}	A_{10}	A_9	A_8	A_7	A_6	A_5	A_4	A_3	A_2	A_1	A_0
RAM 1	0000 – 007F	0	0	0	0	0	0	0	0	0	×	×	×	×	×	×	×
RAM 2	0080 – 00FF	0	0	0	0	0	0	0	0	1	×	×	×	×	×	×	×
RAM 3	0100 – 017F	0	0	0	0	0	0	0	1	0	×	×	×	×	×	×	×
RAM 4	0180 – 01FF	0	0	0	0	0	0	0	1	1	×	×	×	×	×	×	×
RAM 5	0200 – 027F	0	0	0	0	0	0	1	0	0	×	×	×	×	×	×	×
PIA 1	8004 – 8007	1	0	0	0								0	0	1	×	×
PIA 2	8008 – 800B	1	0	0	0								0	1	0	×	×
ACIA	8010 – 8011	1	0	0	0								1	0	0		×
RAM 6	A000 – A07F	1	0	1	0	0	0	0	0	0	×	×	×	×	×	×	×
ROM	E000 – E1FF	1	1	1	0	0	0	*	×	×	×	×	×	×	×	×	×

decoded by the 74LS154

* A_9 of the ROM is permanently grounded

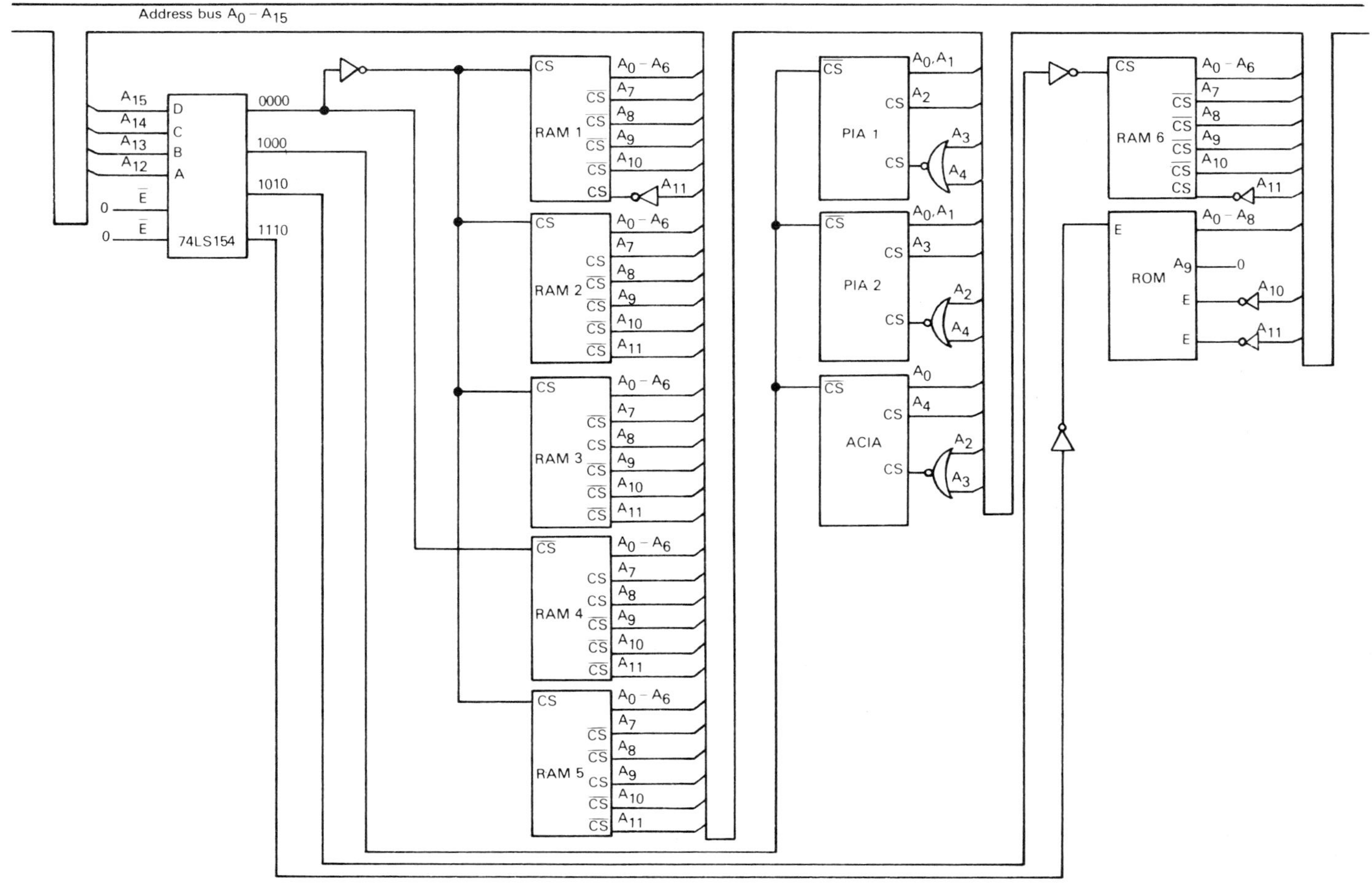

Figure 5.20 Application of the 74LS154 decoder to the MEK 6800D1 evaluation kit

The 74LS138 3-line to 8-line decoder is almost certainly the most popular address-decoding device found in microprocessor systems. It has a smaller package than the 74LS154—16 pins as opposed to 24. Because the 74LS138 has three enable inputs, two active-low and one active-high, it is particularly useful when decoders are to be connected in series, or when the enable inputs are to be connected to address lines in order to reduce the size of the block of memory being decoded. Figures 5.21(a) – (e) show some of the many ways in which the 74LS138 may be used. Note that VMA acts as an enable input to the decoders, synchronizing the decoder outputs with valid memory-access cycles.

Consider now an example of address decoding using the 74LS138 3-line to 8-line decoder. A microprocessor system is to be designed with, initially, 8K bytes of static RAM in the range 0000 – 1FFF, and with provision for the addition of further 4K blocks of RAM up to a maximum of 32K bytes. The read/write memory is the 4K× 1 static RAM with 12 address lines, and a single, active-low chip-select input. The microprocessor is to have a 2K EPROM monitor in the range F800 – FFFF. Provision must be made for at least eight memory-mapped peripherals in the 512 byte range E000 – E1FF.

Table 5.6 gives the address table of the above system, and demonstrates how three 74LS138s divide the memory space into blocks of suitable size for the RAM, ROM and peripherals. Figure 5.22 gives a simplified circuit diagram of the address decoding circuitry, and Fig. 5.23 illustrates the memory map of this system. It is easy to see the advantages of this form of address decoding (i.e. block decoding). Firstly, RAM, ROM or peripheral devices can be added without further alterations to the address-decoding circuitry, simply by employing the unused outputs of the three decoders. Secondly, the system is flexible. By modifying the connections between the decoder circuits and the memory components they select, the effective address of those memory components may be altered.

Table 5.6 Address Table of a Microprocessor System

Device	*Address*	A_{15}	A_{14}	A_{13}	A_{12}	A_{11}	A_{10}	A_9	A_8	A_7	A_6	A_5	A_4	A_3	A_2	A_1	A_0
RAM 1	0000 – 0FFF	0	0	0	0	×	×	×	×	×	×	×	×	×	×	×	×
RAM 2	1000 – 1FFF	0	0	0	1	×	×	×	×	×	×	×	×	×	×	×	×
⋮																	
RAM 8	7000 – 7FFF	0	1	1	1	×	×	×	×	×	×	×	×	×	×	×	×
		decoded by IC1															
P1	E000 – E03F	1	1	1	0	0	0	0	0	0	0						
P2	E040 – E07F	1	1	1	0	0	0	0	0	0	1						
⋮																	
P8	E1C0 – E1FF	1	1	1	0	0	0	0	1	1	1						
							decoded by IC3										
ROM	F800 – FFFF	1	1	1	1	1	×	×	×	×	×	×	×	×	×	×	×
		decoded by IC2															

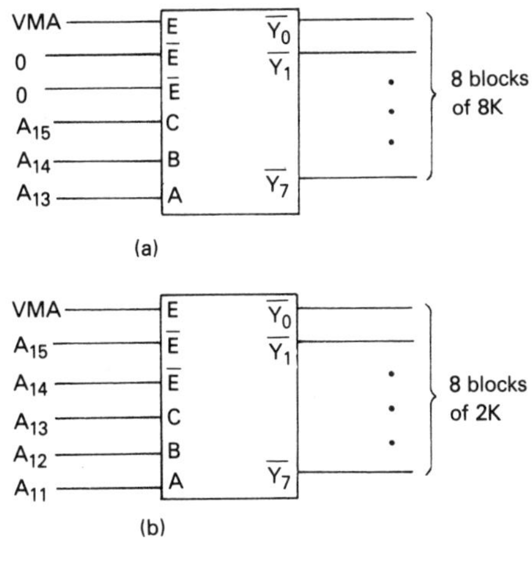

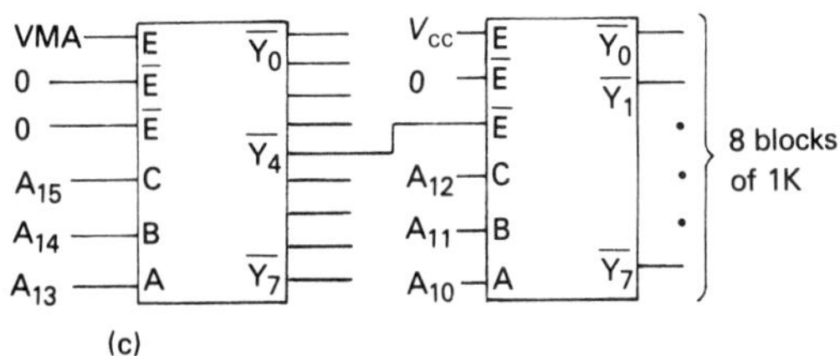

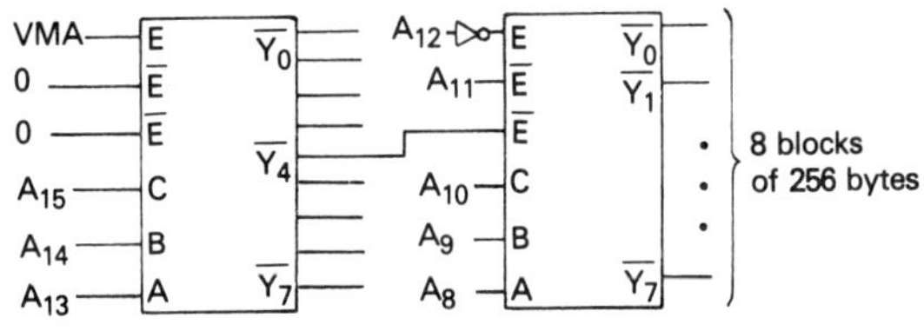

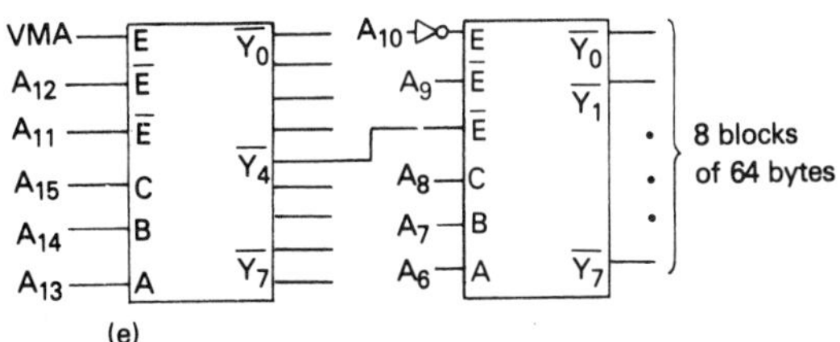

Figure 5.21 Some applications of the 74LS138: **(a)** *one used to divide 64K into 8 blocks of 8K* **(b)** *one used to divide the lower 16K of memory space into 8 blocks of 2K* **(c)** *two used to divide the 8K block 8000-9FFF into 8 blocks of 1K* **(d)** *two used to divide the 8K block 8000-9FFF into 8 blocks of 256 bytes in range 8000-87FF* **(e)** *two used to divide the 2K block 8000-87FF into 8 blocks of 64 bytes in range 8000-81FF*

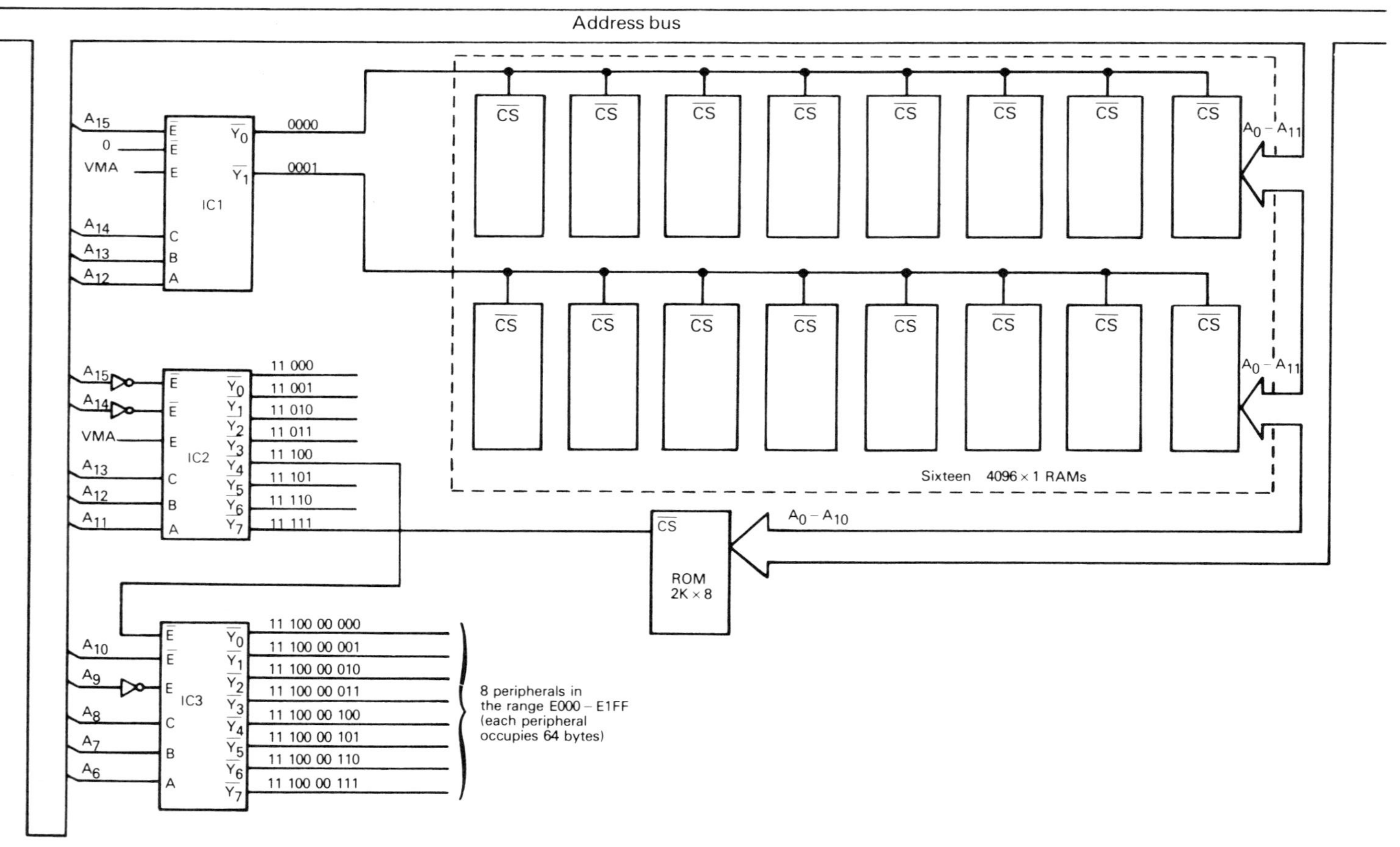

Figure 5.22 Address decoding arrangement of microprocessor system defined in Table 5.6

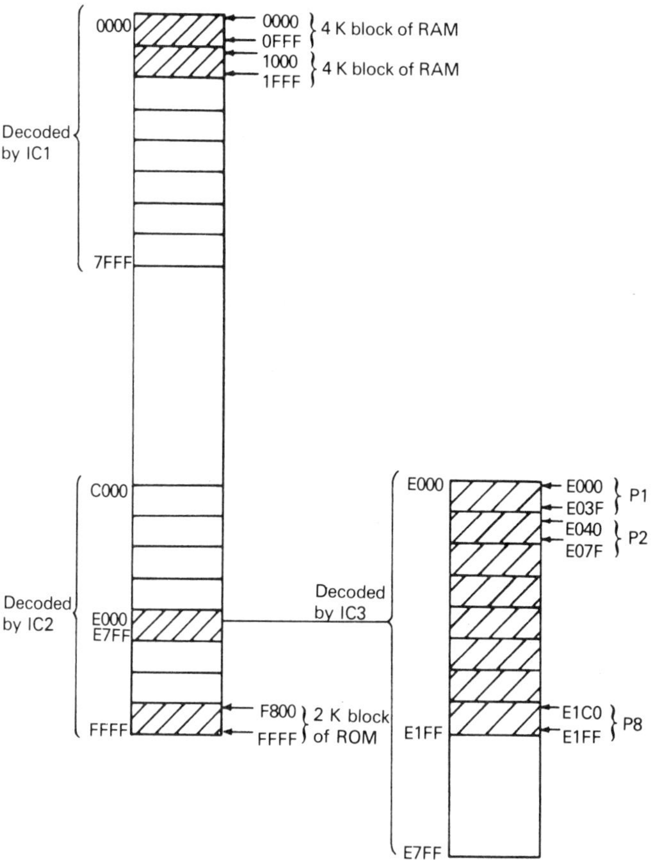

Figure 5.23 The memory map of the arrangement shown in Figure 5.22 and Table 5.6

The 74LS139 dual 2-line to 4-line decoder is not normally found alone in address-decoding arrangements. Instead, it is often combined with the 74LS138. The 74LS138 divides part (or all) of the memory space into eight blocks, and the 74LS139 then divides one (or two) of these blocks into 4 segments. Figure 5.24 shows how a 74LS139 is connected to a 74LS138 in such a way as to decode eight 1K blocks of memory between 4000 and 5FFF.

The 74LS139 can also act as a random logic element, with three inputs X, Y, Z and four outputs P, Q, R, S. Figure 5.25 defines the relationship between the inputs and outputs of the 74LS139. A possible application of the 74LS139 as a logic element is illustrated in Fig. 5.26. The inputs are VMA, $R/\overline{W}$ and $\overline{\phi_2}$, and the outputs are an active-low read strobe and an active-low write strobe. Such an arrangement is useful when a non-6800 series peripheral is to be connected to a 6800-based system.

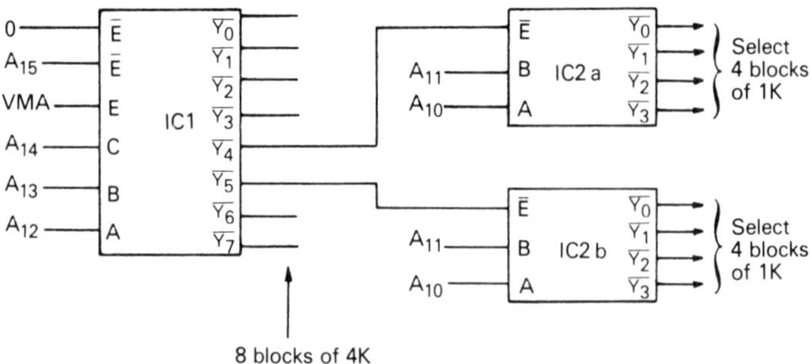

Figure 5.24 Example of the use of the 74LS139 (IC1 = 74LS138, IC2 = 74LS139)

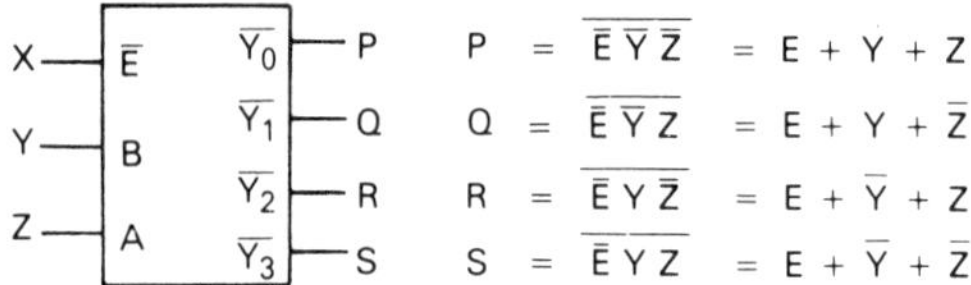

Figure 5.25 The 74LS139 as a logic element

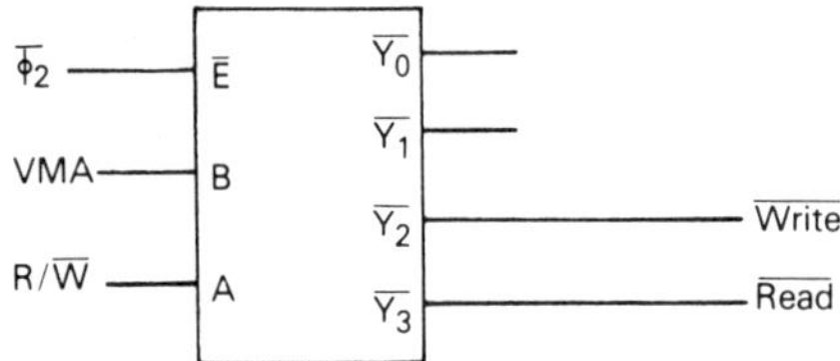

Figure 5.26 Example of the use of the 74LS139 as a logic element

5.4.3 Address Decoding with the PROM

Address decoding is the art of extracting the chip-select signal of a memory component from a number of address lines. The techniques of address decoding described earlier in this section employ either random logic, or m-line to n-line decoders (which are themselves collections of random logic elements in a single package) to decode address lines. An alternative approach is to use a field-programmable read-only memory to generate the signals needed to select the memory components. The PROM is, in fact, serving as a function generator, its address lines forming the inputs, and its data lines the outputs.

A PROM has n address inputs which select one of 2^n unique memory locations. Each of these locations, when accessed, puts a word on to the PROM's m data lines. Whereas random logic generates chip-select signals directly, the PROM looks up their values in a table. The bipolar PROM is a popular form of address decoder, particularly in professional, or OEM, microprocessor systems. The access time of a

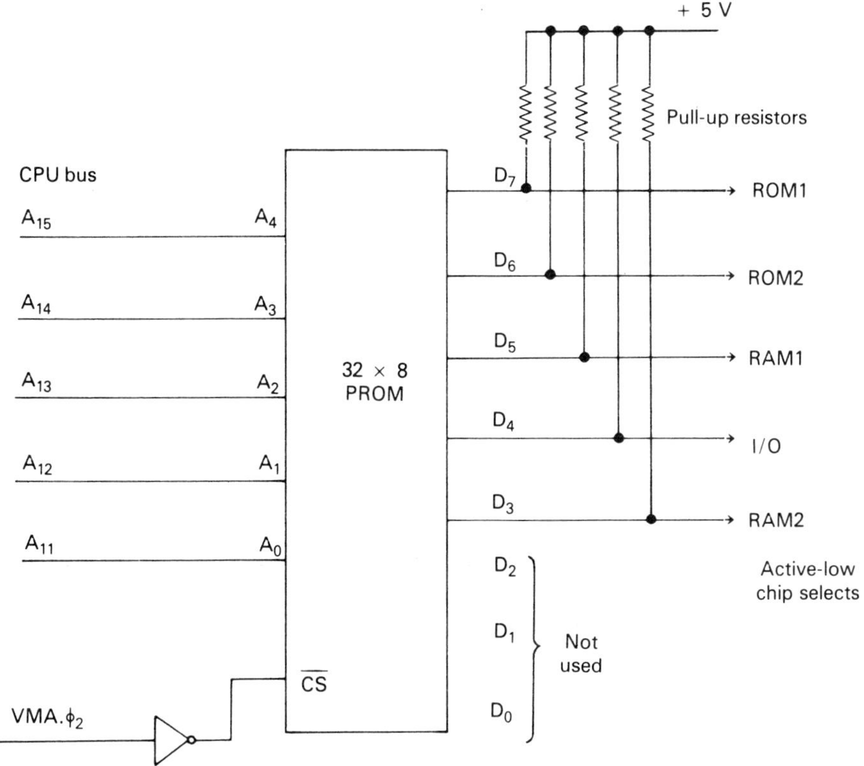

Figure 5.27 The 32×8 PROM as an address decoder

PROM is in the region of 50 ns, which is comparable with the delay incurred by two low-power Schottky TTL *m*-line to *n*-line decoders connected in series. Furthermore, it is sometimes possible to perform all the address decoding required by a small microprocessor system, with a single PROM. This saves valuable space on the microprocessor board, and makes the debugging or modification of the system easier.

Field-programmable bipolar ROMs are available in a wide range of formats, from 32×8 (256 bits) to 2048×8 (16 384 bits). Many PROMs are available in two versions, one with open-collector data outputs, and one with tri-state data-output drivers controlled by a chip-select input.

Consider the example of a PROM address decoder illustrated by Fig. 5.27 and Table 5.7. A microprocessor system is to have 16K bytes of RAM at 0000 – 3FFF, 2K bytes of memory-mapped I/O at 8000 – 87FF, 2K bytes of RAM at A000 – A7FF, 4K bytes of ROM at E000 – EFFF, and 4K bytes of ROM at F000 – FFFF. As the smallest block of memory to be selected is 2K bytes (i.e. 2^{11}), any address-decoding arrangement must involve the five address lines $A_{11} – A_{15}$. There are five blocks of memory to be decoded, so the PROM must have at least five data outputs. In Fig. 5.27, a 32×8 PROM decodes the five highest-order address

Table 5.7 The PROM as an Address Decoder

	System address lines												
	A_{15}	A_{14}	A_{13}	A_{12}	A_{11}								
	PROM address inputs					*PROM data outputs*							
Address range	A_4	A_3	A_2	A_1	A_0	D_7	D_6	D_5	D_4	D_3	D_2	D_1	D_0
0000 – 07FF	0	0	0	0	0	1	1	1	1	0			
0800 – 0FFF	0	0	0	0	1	1	1	1	1	0			
1000 – 17FF	0	0	0	1	0	1	1	1	1	0			
1800 – 1FFF	0	0	0	1	1	1	1	1	1	0			
2000 – 27FF	0	0	1	0	0	1	1	1	1	0			
2800 – 2FFF	0	0	1	0	1	1	1	1	1	0			
3000 – 37FF	0	0	1	1	0	1	1	1	1	0			
3800 – 3FFF	0	0	1	1	1	1	1	1	1	0			
4000 – 47FF	0	1	0	0	0	1	1	1	1	1			
4800 – 4FFF	0	1	0	0	1	1	1	1	1	1			
5000 – 57FF	0	1	0	1	0	1	1	1	1	1			
5800 – 5FFF	0	1	0	1	1	1	1	1	1	1			
6000 – 67FF	0	1	1	0	0	1	1	1	1	1			
6800 – 6FFF	0	1	1	0	1	1	1	1	1	1			
7000 – 77FF	0	1	1	1	0	1	1	1	1	1			
7800 – 7FFF	0	1	1	1	1	1	1	1	1	1			
8000 – 87FF	1	0	0	0	0	1	1	1	0	1			
8800 – 8FFF	1	0	0	0	1	1	1	1	1	1			
9000 – 97FF	1	0	0	1	0	1	1	1	1	1			
9800 – 9FFF	1	0	0	1	1	1	1	1	1	1			
A000 – A7FF	1	0	1	0	0	1	1	0	1	1			
A800 – AFFF	1	0	1	0	1	1	1	1	1	1			
B000 – B7FF	1	0	1	1	0	1	1	1	1	1			
B800 – BFFF	1	0	1	1	1	1	1	1	1	1			
C000 – C7FF	1	1	0	0	0	1	1	1	1	1			
C800 – CFFF	1	1	0	0	1	1	1	1	1	1			
D000 – D7FF	1	1	0	1	0	1	1	1	1	1			
D800 – DFFF	1	1	0	1	1	1	1	1	1	1			
E000 – E7FF	1	1	1	0	0	1	0	1	1	1			
E800 – EFFF	1	1	1	0	1	1	0	1	1	1			
F000 – F7FF	1	1	1	1	0	0	1	1	1	1			
F800 – FFFF	1	1	1	1	1	0	1	1	1	1			
						a	b	c	d	e	unused in this application and hence left unprogrammed		

a : 4K ROM1 F000 – FFFF
b : 4K ROM2 E000 – EFFF
c : 2K RAM1 A000 – A7FF
d : 2K I/O 8000 – 87FF
e : 16K RAM2 0000 – 3FFF

lines. Although the PROM has eight data outputs, only five of them are needed in this application, leaving the remaining three unconnected. These three outputs may be used to expand the system at a later date. In this example the PROM is enabled by connecting its active-low chip-select input to ϕ_2.VMA via an invertor. In this way, the PROM responds to an input only during the ϕ_2 clock phase of a cycle in which there is a valid address on the system bus. Unfortunately, whenever $\overline{CS}$ is high, the data output lines of the PROM are left floating. This situation occurs whether the PROM has tri-state or open-collector outputs. If the outputs of the PROM are allowed to float, there is a danger that a memory component may be enabled spuriously and data corrupted. To avoid this condition, pull-up resistors must be connected to the outputs of the PROM, to force them into a logical one state whenever the PROM is de-selected. Two alternative approaches to this problem are:

(1) To permanently enable the PROM. The enable signal ϕ_2.VMA may be combined with one of the address lines. For example A_{15} may be combined with ϕ_2.VMA to give $A_{15}.\phi_2$.VMA. Note that this action restricts valid addresses to those for which A_{15} is high.
(2) As in case 1, the PROM is permanently enabled, but ϕ_2.VMA is connected to one of the PROM's address inputs. This has the effect of doubling the size of the smallest block of memory which can be accessed by the PROM.

In the circuit in Fig. 5.27 an 8-bit word is put on to the outputs of the PROM whenever ϕ_2.VMA is high, otherwise the outputs are pulled up into the logical one state. Table 5.7 gives the relationship between $A_{11}-A_{15}$ of the system address bus (connected to A_0-A_4 of the PROM), and the outputs of the PROM D_0-D_7. In order to understand the action of the PROM, consider the behavior of D_7. There are 32 entries in the D_7 column, of which 30 are high and two are low. The two low entries occur at $A_{15}\,A_{14}\,A_{13}\,A_{12}\,\overline{A_{11}}$ and $A_{15}\,A_{14}\,A_{13}\,A_{12}\,A_{11}$, and select the 4K block of ROM at F000 – FFFF. Note that A_{11} does not affect the selection of this ROM, and is therefore a don't care condition.

Now consider the behavior of the PROM's D_5 output. In Table 5.7 the column corresponding to D_5 has a single, logical zero entry at $A_{15}\,\overline{A_{14}}\,A_{13}\,\overline{A_{12}}\,\overline{A_{11}}$. In this case all five address lines take part in the selection of the 2K block of RAM at A000 – A7FF. One important distinction between the PROM and the *m*-line to *n*-line decoder should now be clear. The *m*-line to *n*-line decoder decodes *n* equal-sized blocks of memory while the PROM may decode blocks of memory of varying size. The selection of the 16K block of RAM at 0000 – 3FFF is performed by D_3. In the column corresponding to D_3 there are eight logical zero entries. By inspecting Table 5.7 it can readily be seen that these zeros span all the 8 possible combinations of A_{11}, A_{12}, A_{13} for which $A_{14}=0$ and $A_{15}=0$. Therefore, the 16K block of RAM is selected whenever $A_{15}=0$ and $A_{14}=0$, irrespective of the values of $A_{11}-A_{13}$.

As we have just observed, the PROM can select blocks of memory of differing size. A PROM with *n* address inputs (i.e. 2^n words) can fully decode a block of memory with a minimum size of $2^{16}/2^n=2^{16-n}$ bytes, in a microprocessor system with a 16-bit address bus. Larger blocks of memory can be decoded by increasing the number of active entries (in our case, zeros) in the data column of the PROM's address/data table. The size of the block of memory decoded by a data output is equal to the minimum block size multiplied by the number of active entries in the appropriate data column. For example, in Table 5.7 $n=5$ gives a minimum block size of $2^{16-5}=2^{11}=2$K bytes. In the column corresponding to D_3 there are 8 active entries, indicating a total block size of $8\times 2\text{K}=16$K bytes.

Although the PROM address decoder is frequently found in commercial applications, it is not as popular with those who wish to build just one or two systems. The small-scale user may find the effort involved in programming a PROM unworthy of the savings gained. These savings are usually equivalent to one or two 16-pin DIL packages. A serious disadvantage of the PROM becomes apparent only when more than five or six address lines are to be decoded. As the number of entries in the PROM's look-up table doubles for each additional address input, a very large PROM becomes necessary, where 8 or more lines must be decoded. For example, if a minimum block size of 64 bytes were required, the PROM would need 10 address inputs, corresponding to 1024 words. Such a large PROM is tedious to program, unless the programming is done automatically.

5.4.4 Address Decoding Using the Field-programmable Logic Array

The field-programmable logic array (FPLA) is possibly the most versatile logic element available (microprocessors excluded), yet many engineers are unaware of its existence. Three barriers stand between the FPLA and the popularity it deserves: firstly it is a relatively expensive device (although it is often cheaper than the random logic it replaces), secondly, it has to be programmed by fusing links, and thirdly, its operation can at first sight appear to be rather complex.

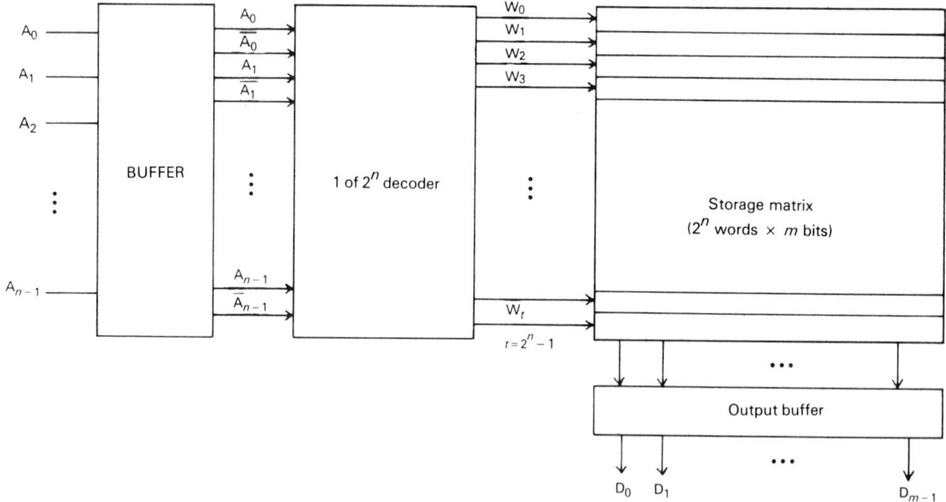

Figure 5.28 The internal arrangement of a PROM

In order to understand the nature of the FPLA it is instructive to look at the PROM and explain the action of the FPLA in terms of a modified PROM. Figure 5.28 gives a conceptual illustration of the PROM. A PROM contains an address decoder with which it decodes the n address inputs into a one of 2^n lines output. These 2^n outputs access an array of 2^n locations, each containing an m-bit data word which forms the output of the PROM. Thus, a PROM with n address inputs is capable of storing 2^n m-bit words. Sometimes we are not interested in every one of the 2^n words held in the PROM. For example, imagine a microprocessor system which has memory devices at the following locations:

(1) 0000 – 3FFF (16K bytes)
(2) 8000 – 801F (32 bytes)
(3) A000 – A07F (128 bytes)
(4) FE00 – FFFF (512 bytes)

If we were to implement full address decoding with a PROM, it would have to decode a minimum block size of 32 bytes. This would require a PROM of $2^{16-5} = 2^{11} = 2048$ addressable locations. As there are four blocks of memory to be decoded, the PROM must have a capacity of at least $2048 \times 4 = 8192$ bits.

Intuitively the above result appears wasteful. After all, we have only four devices to decode. The greatest number of address lines needed to select a device is 11, and the smallest number is 2. What we need is a decoder able to select one device using A_{15} and A_{14} alone, and yet to select another device using $A_{15} - A_5$. Furthermore, this decoder should not waste storage space on address combinations, for which no device is selected. The FPLA is a component which fulfils the above requirements.

The simplest way of looking at an FPLA is to regard it as a special type of ROM. Indeed, the FPLA is often described in the same terms used to specify a PROM, e.g. 48 words $\times$ 8 bits. Figure 5.29 illustrates, in a simplified form, the internal arrangement of the FPLA. The essential difference between the PROM and the FPLA is that the former uses a one of 2^n-line decoder to select a word in the storage matrix, while the latter has a programmable address matrix. In Fig. 5.29 the programmable address matrix has p outputs which select one of p words in the storage matrix. These p outputs are generated from the address inputs (and their complements) by fusing links in the address matrix. By fusing the appropriate links each of the outputs of the address matrix can be made a function of A_i or $\overline{A_i}$, or if both links corresponding to A_i and $\overline{A_i}$ are blown, A_i can be made a don't care condition. As these p outputs are obtained by AND-ing address inputs, they are called product terms.

FPLAs are, typically, arranged in a 48×8 format. The Signetics 82S100 has 16 input variables and a 28-pin package, and the Intersil IM5200 has 14 input variables and a 24-pin package. Figure 5.30 shows the internal arrangement of the 82S100. In this diagram it can be seen that the storage array, which holds 48 words, is logically equivalent to eight 48-input OR gates, and the eight outputs are known as sum terms. Note also that the eight outputs can be made active-high or active-low by

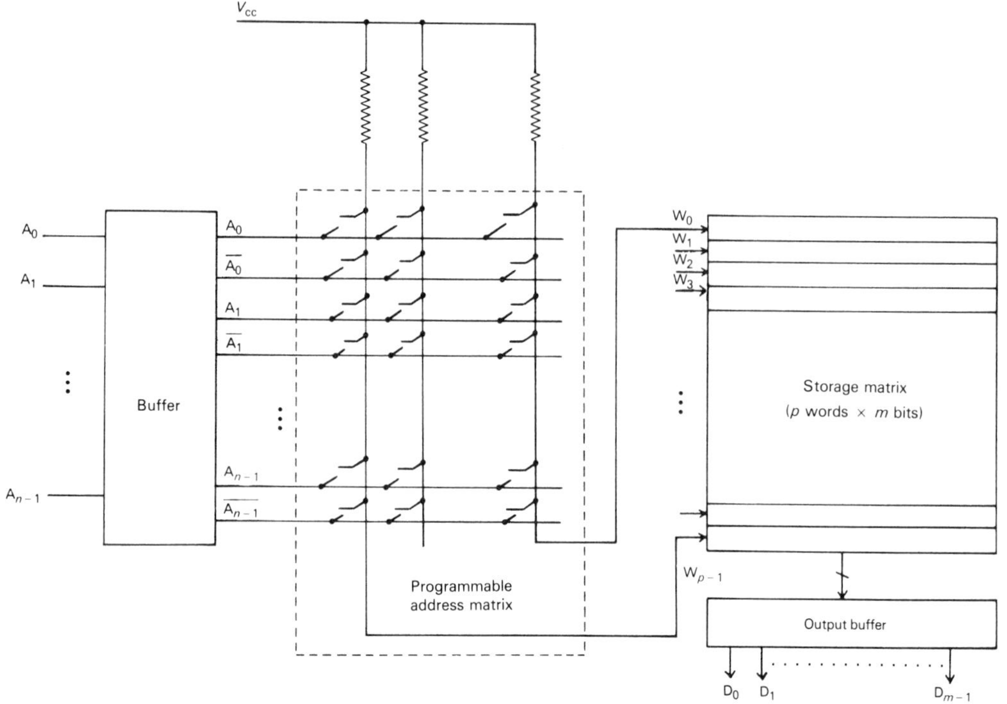

Figure 5.29 The internal arrangement of an FPLA

means of exclusive-or gates which can be programmed as either buffers or invertors.

When the FPLA is programmed as an address decoder, only eight of the 48 product terms are needed. In the example given above the four product terms are

$$\begin{aligned}
&(1) \quad P_0 = \overline{A}_{15}\,\overline{A}_{14} \\
&(2) \quad P_1 = A_{15}\,\overline{A}_{14}\,\overline{A}_{13}\,\overline{A}_{12}\,\overline{A}_{11}\,\overline{A}_{10}\,\overline{A}_{9}\,\overline{A}_{8}\,\overline{A}_{7}\,\overline{A}_{6}\,\overline{A}_{5} \\
&(3) \quad P_2 = A_{15}\,\overline{A}_{14}\,A_{13}\,\overline{A}_{12}\,\overline{A}_{11}\,\overline{A}_{10}\,\overline{A}_{9}\,\overline{A}_{8}\,\overline{A}_{7} \\
&(4) \quad P_3 = A_{15}\,A_{14}\,A_{13}\,A_{12}\,A_{11}\,A_{10}\,A_{9}
\end{aligned}$$

The sum terms can be programmed so that

$$D_0 = \overline{P_0}, \quad D_1 = \overline{P_1}, \quad D_2 = \overline{P_2}, \quad D_3 = \overline{P_3}.$$

In this case full address decoding has been achieved with a single component, even though the four memory devices occupy widely differing sections of the microprocessor's memory map.

The FPLA can be viewed in many different lights. We have just described it as a powerful address decoder, capable of decoding memory blocks of 32K bytes to one single byte without requiring an excessive amount of internal storage. Another approach is to regard the FPLA as a very powerful function generator.

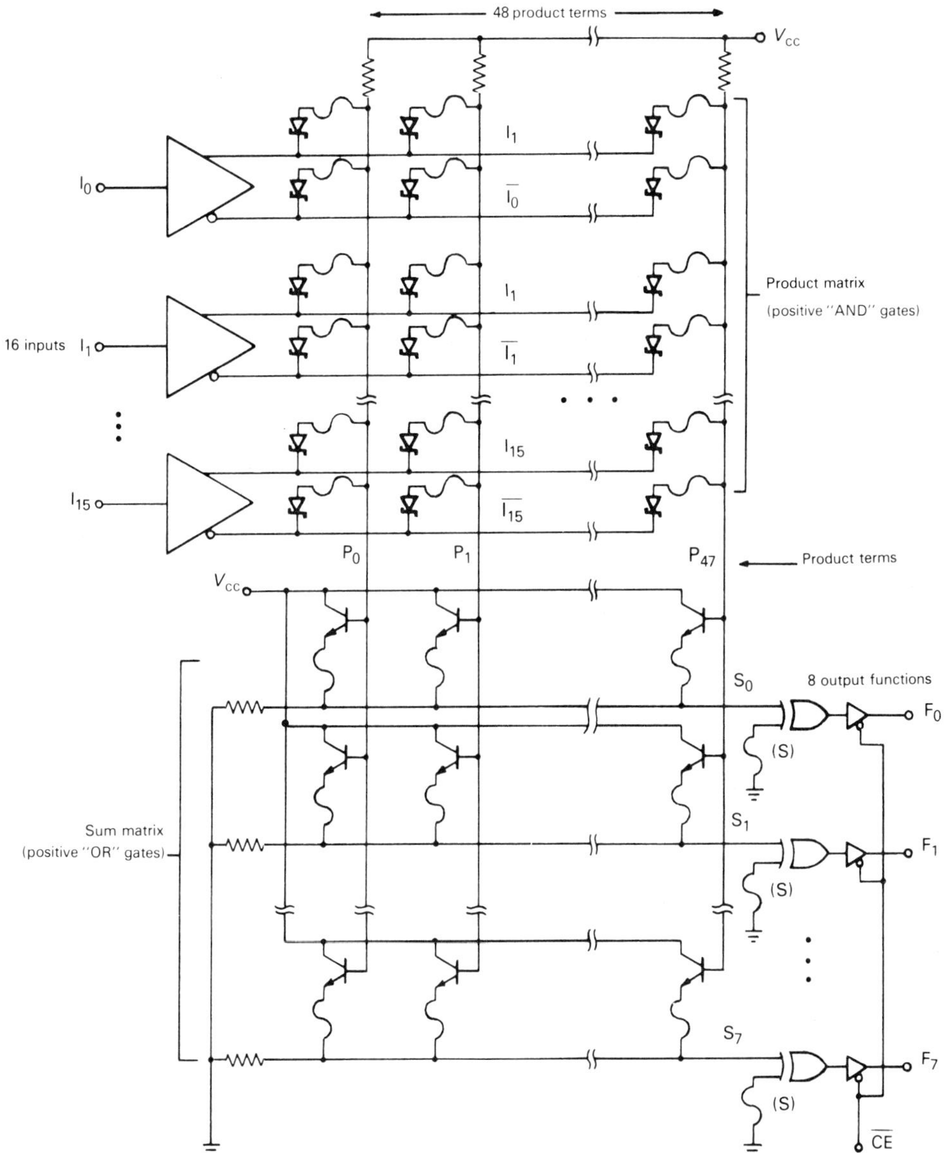

Figure 5.30 The internal arrangement of the Signetics 82S100

The FPLA can, in one package, synthesize eight logical functions, expressed in sum of products form, where each product term has up to 16 variables, and each sum term is composed of up to 48 product terms. Yet another way of looking at the FPLA is to regard it as an associative memory. A PROM responds to each address at its input terminals, but the FPLA responds only to a subset of the possible addresses at its input. That is, the FPLA associates an output with some, but not all, of the inputs.

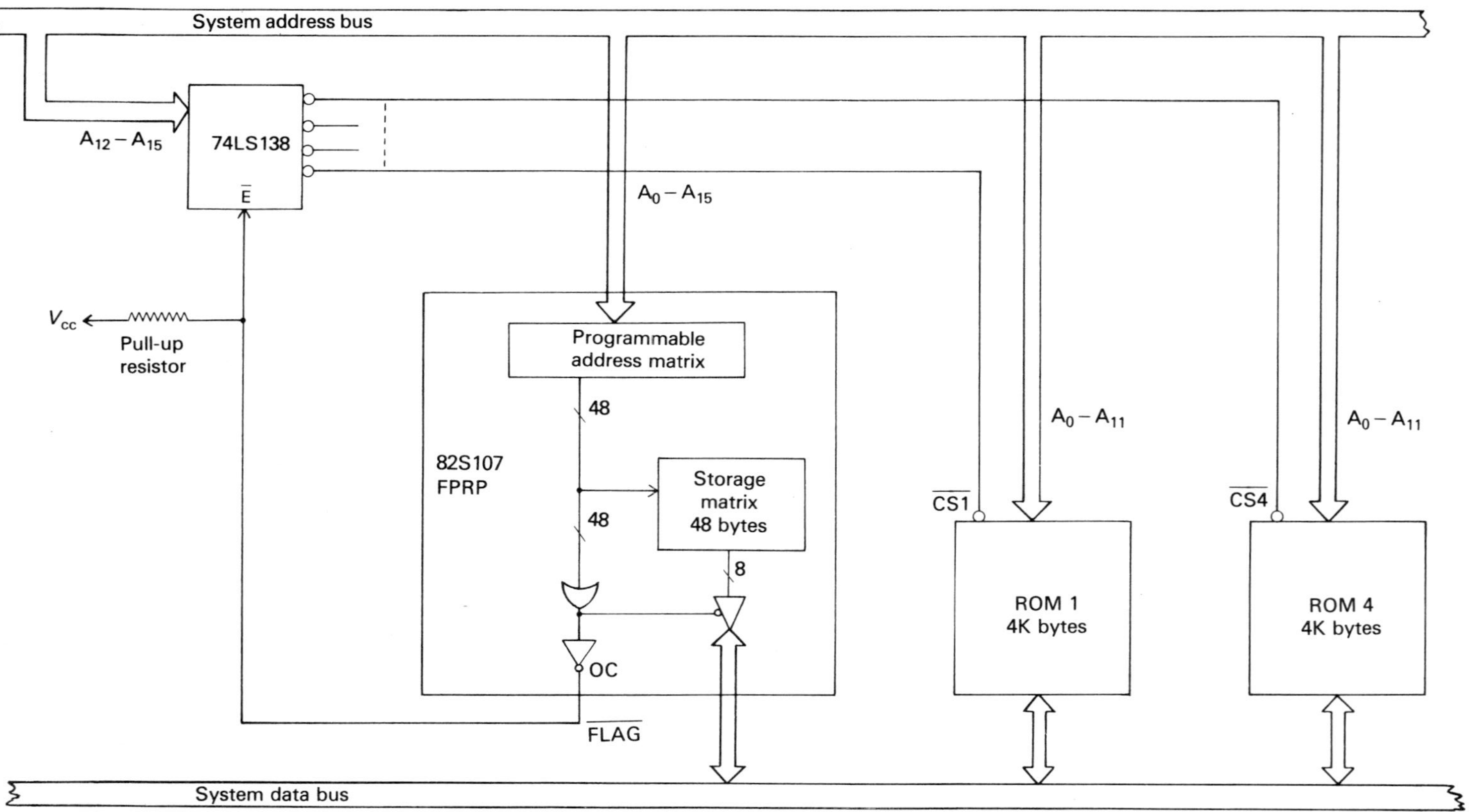

Figure 5.31 The use of the field-programmable ROM patch

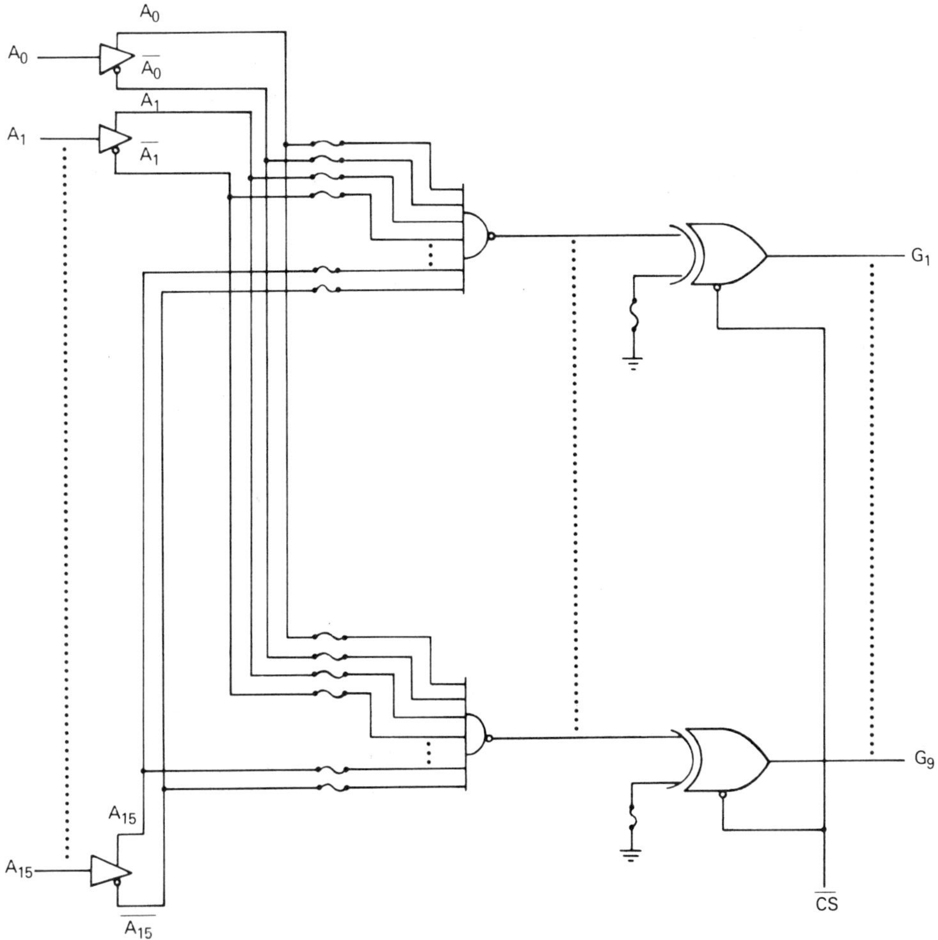

Figure 5.32 The internal arrangement of the 82S103 field-programmable gate array

An interesting variant of the FPLA is the Signetics 82S107 field-programmable ROM patch (FPRP). This device is organized as 48 words of 8 bits, addressed by a 16-bit input. Each of these words can be assigned a unique address within the 64K address space spanned by the 16 inputs. Whenever one of these 48 words is addressed, an active-low flag output is asserted. The $\overline{\text{FLAG}}$ output is open-collector so that several $\overline{\text{FLAG}}$ outputs may be connected together if expansion beyond 48 words is required. The purpose of this device is to alter the effective contents of a ROM without modifying the ROM itself. Figure 5.31 shows how this is done. In normal operation the ROM(s) put data on to the data bus whenever they are enabled by the address decoder. However, when one of the 48 addresses within the FPRP's address matrix appears on the address bus, the FPRP forces its $\overline{\text{FLAG}}$ output low, disabling the address decoder and hence the ROM which would otherwise have put its data on the data bus. Instead, the FPRP puts the modified data on to the data bus. Although the FPRP is an expensive way of modifying a small ROM, it can be very cost-effective in a system with very large ROMs, or with several ROMs which need fewer than 48 bytes to be altered.

When an FPLA is employed as an address decoder, it is often the programmable address matrix that is being exploited, and not the 48×8 storage array. For this reason Signetics have introduced the Field Programmable Gate Array (FPGA), which has the decoding power of the FPLA, without its cost and complexity. The FPGA is nothing more than nine 16-input AND/NAND gates in a single 28-pin package. The 16 inputs may be programmed to be true, false, or don't care, permitting the FPGA to select up to nine blocks of memory, each with a size of one to 32K bytes. Figure 5.32 illustrates the internal arrangement of the 82S103 FPGA.

Address Decoding in the TS1

The full details of the address-decoding techniques applied to TS1's CPU module are given in Section 5.6. However, it is worthwhile to indicate here which of the various approaches to address decoding described in this section have been chosen. There are nine blocks of memory to be decoded with sizes from 8 to 4K bytes. Because of this wide range of block sizes an 82S103 FPGA has been selected to perform the primary address decoding. A single 74LS138 3-line to 8-line decoder serves as a secondary decoder for the five on-board memory-mapped peripherals. In this way a rather complex address-decoding scheme is implemented by two integrated circuits.

5.5 MEMORY-MAPPED INPUT–OUTPUT

A microprocessor system which transfers data between the CPU's accumulator and input or output devices by means of its normal memory reference instructions is said to employ memory-mapped input/output. That is, the input or output ports are located within the system's memory map.

Memory-mapped input/output is a concept which often causes the engineer who is just beginning to get involved with microprocessors a certain amount of misunderstanding. This confusion is compounded by those who associate memory-mapped input/output with a particular microprocessor, as if this form of input/output were a property of the microprocessor itself. Any digital system with an addressable memory is also capable of memory-mapped I/O. In particular, the 6800 is often associated with memory-mapped I/O, while the TMS9900 or the 8080 are not, even though memory-mapped I/O may be applied to all three microprocessors with equal ease.

The 6800 is forced to implement memory-mapped I/O simply because it has no other means of inputting or outputting data. This does not mean that the 6800's designers forgot to implement other forms of I/O, but that memory-mapped I/O appeared to be the best compromise. Some microprocessors provide a direct serial

I/O port in the microprocessor itself by allowing the programmer to set the state of an output pin or to read the state of an input pin. A popular microprocessor which has on-chip serial input/output ports is the SC/MP. This approach to I/O is most cost-effective when the microprocessor is part of a control system. Typical examples include the control of a motor or relays, or the sensing of the status of switches or pushbuttons.

Another way of moving data between the "outside world" and the CPU involves data transfers on the microprocessor's data bus. As all but the simplest of microprocessor systems require several I/O ports, it is often possible to specify a particular I/O port by means of the microprocessor's address bus. For example, the 8080 can address up to 256 I/O ports by using the lower-order eight bits of the address bus, $A_0 - A_7$, to select a given port. Of course, the microprocessor must also indicate to the peripherals that an I/O operation is taking place. This may be done with additional pins on the CPU indicating a peripheral read or write operation. The 8080 avoids the need for additional pins by multiplexing status information on to the data bus. This status information includes the type of operation currently being executed. A separate controller chip, the 8228, latches the status information and generates the necessary input/output strobes. In order to perform this type of I/O, known as programmed I/O, instructions must be provided to read data from a peripheral and to write data to a peripheral.

The above technique of programmed I/O differs from memory-mapped I/O in two ways. Firstly, additional instructions must be included for I/O operations and, secondly, additional status information must be extracted from the CPU to indicate the presence of an I/O operation. The designers of the 6800 CPU have chosen to employ memory-mapped I/O as the only way of transferring data between peripherals and the CPU for the following reasons:

(1) Memory-mapped I/O needs no new instructions because it uses existing memory-access operations.
(2) As a memory-mapped I/O operation is indistinguishable from a normal memory-access operation, no additional I/O status pins are required. Also, by not multiplexing status information and data on the data bus, the 6800 does not require an additional controller chip.

The decision of the 6800's designers not to implement programmed I/O is not unreasonable. However, it must be realized that memory-mapped I/O is simply an absence of other types of I/O, forcing the designer to employ a part of the system's random-access memory space as I/O ports. In fact, memory-mapped I/O may be implemented in any microprocessor system to replace or augment its own I/O techniques.

One of the simplest types of memory-mapped I/O port is illustrated in Fig. 5.33. During a CPU read cycle, data from the input port is put onto the system's data bus by means of tri-state buffers, and during a CPU write cycle, data is latched into eight D flip-flops from the data bus. This I/O port uses two control signals to effect its operation: a read strobe and a write strobe. These control strobes are derived

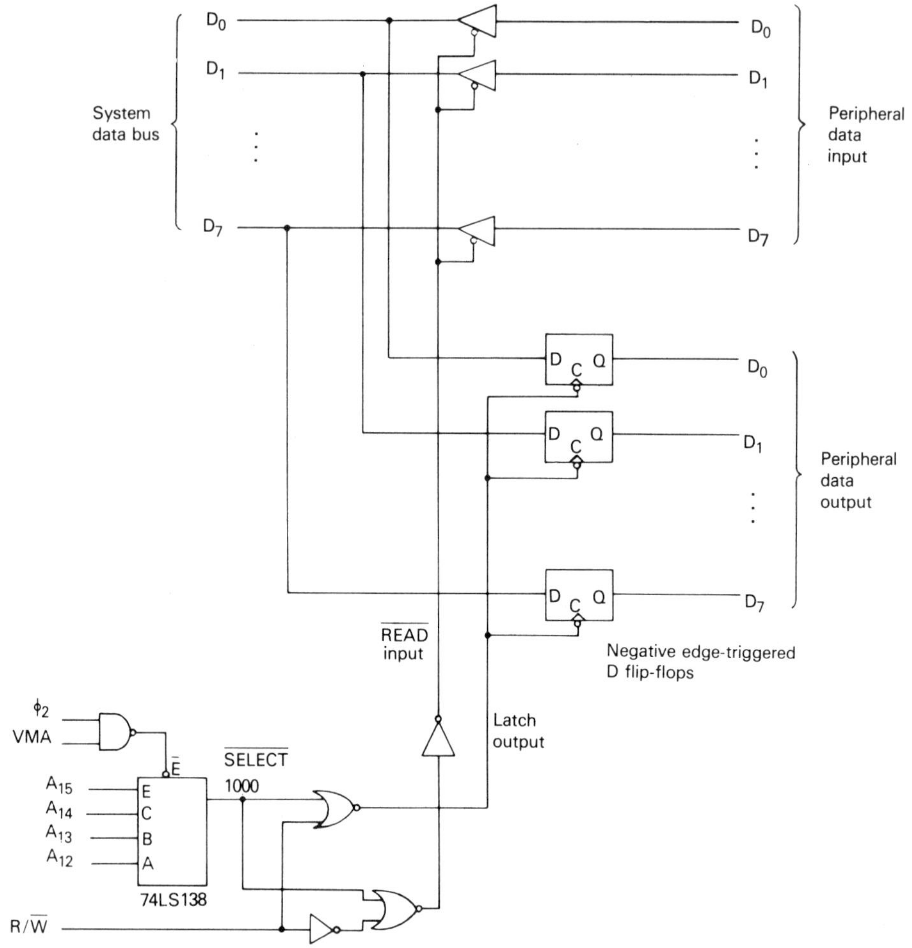

Figure 5.33 A simple memory-mapped input/output port

from a combination of the higher-order address lines, VMA, ϕ_2 and R/$\overline{\text{W}}$. The address lines $A_{15} - A_{12}$ are connected to a 74LS138 3-line to 8-line decoder so that the $\overline{\text{SELECT}}$ output goes active low whenever the CPU puts the address 8XXX on to the address bus. The 74LS138 is enabled by ϕ_2 and VMA which ensures that data transfers take place only in the ϕ_2 active-high portion of a valid memory-access cycle. Additional TTL logic generates the read and write strobes from the $\overline{\text{SELECT}}$ signal and the CPU's R/$\overline{\text{W}}$ signal. Data may now be read from the input port by means of the memory reference instruction LDA A \$8000, and data may be written to the output port by means of the instruction STA A \$8000.

Because of the relatively low cost of mass-produced LSI circuits, semiconductor manufacturers have made a wide range of input/output ports, some of which are specifically designed for programmed I/O modes, while others are specifically designed for memory-mapped I/O modes. With a little care, it is often possible to use manufacturer's programmed I/O port in a memory-mapped application. This is normally done by deriving the required read and write strobes from existing memory-access control signals (i.e. VMA, ϕ_2, $R/\overline{W}$). Whenever such an exercise is carried out it is of great importance to check that the data and address set-up and hold times of the peripheral are compatible with the CPU. As the cost of an LSI circuit is largely independent of its complexity, many of the memory-mapped I/O peripherals have very sophisticated features. In particular these chips are designed to be programmable, enabling the user to operate the peripheral in a wide variety of modes. A good example is the 6845 CRT controller which performs most of the operations of a raster scan display. This chip has 18 on-chip registers, making it possible to display data in a wide variety of formats.

Unfortunately the use of memory-mapped input/output has four disadvantages:

(1) By locating peripherals in the system's memory space, the total amount of RAM available for programs and data is reduced. Of course, one or two I/O ports does not seem much in a total memory space of 64K bytes, but when block address decoding is employed, a single peripheral may occupy 4K bytes of the memory space.

(2) The memory-mapped I/O ports must be located *somewhere* in memory. The location of the I/O port may conflict with programming requirements. For example, many 6800 systems locate their I/O ports in the 4K block 8000 – 8FFF. This restricts the maximum contiguous program to 32K bytes. Such a restriction seemed unimportant when the systems first appeared and 32K bytes of memory were very expensive. However, with the rapid drop in the cost of memory components, the location of an I/O port at 8000 appears less satisfactory.

(3) It is often assumed that because memory-mapped I/O ports occupy a portion of the system's memory space, any memory reference instruction can be used with one of them. This is not true. In order to reduce the number of address lines connected to these peripheral chips (and save the cost of a pin), the $R/\overline{W}$ input is often used as a pseudo address line, so that some of the registers are read-only, while others are write-only. For example, two registers may share the same address. One register holds the peripheral's status and can only be read by the CPU, and the other register defines some property of the peripheral and can only be written to by the CPU. If, however, it were decided to increment the contents of the control register by means of the INC instruction, a failure would occur. The INC operation would read the contents of the *status* register, increment this value and store the result in the *control* register. The only way that the contents of the control register can be incremented is to store a copy of their value in RAM, read this value, increment it and store the result in the control register of the periphal.

(4) One of the least considered aspects of memory-mapped I/O is the effect of a system failure on the behavior of the I/O port. A system failure (program

crash) is unlikely to affect an I/O port using programmed I/O because the chance of issuing an erroneous command to a correctly addressed peripheral is relatively small. However, when a memory-mapped peripheral occupies part of the system's memory space (especially if block address decoding is employed) the chance of a system crash affecting the I/O port is much greater. The state of the port may be altered by a wide range of memory-reference instructions. While this may not always be an important problem, consider the effect on a peripheral connected to a floppy-disk controller. If the program fails and an erroneous memory reference operation is made to the peripheral, a potentially disastrous command may be issued to the disk controller (e.g. format the disk!).

There are several ways of diminishing this problem. Clearly by employing full address decoding to select the peripheral, the chance of a random memory reference operation accessing the peripheral is less than in the case where the peripheral occupies a 4K (or more) block of memory. A more ingenious technique would involve two memory-mapped peripherals in the following arrangement. The first peripheral, when a given data word is written to it, fires a monostable which has a relatively short period—say several microseconds. The output of the monostable is used to enable the second peripheral. Clearly, if the programmer does not correctly access the first peripheral, the second peripheral is disabled, effectively removing the danger of any system crash issuing an unwanted I/O operation. Even if the first peripheral is accidentally accessed and the monostable fired, the second peripheral must then be accessed before the monostable times out. This solution must be carefully examined in any given implementation as, for example, problems may arise if an interrupt occurs after the monostable has been fired but before the second peripheral has been accessed.

5.6 MEMORY COMPONENTS ON THE CPU MODULE

The CPU module lies at the heart of the TS1 microprocessor system and contains the microprocessor, clock and control circuitry, data and address bus buffers, together with a small quantity of memory and a few memory-mapped peripherals. It is not strictly necessary to include memory on the CPU module but, as with almost all microprocessor systems, a little memory is added to the CPU module. There are two reasons for adopting this approach. Firstly there is often room on the CPU module for some memory. It would be foolish to leave valuable space empty simply because the control and buffer circuits did not fill up all the available space. Secondly, sufficient memory is normally included on the CPU module to enable it to be tested independently of the rest of the system. That is, a primary design objective of the TS1's CPU module is the ability to operate in a stand-alone mode as a single-board computer.

Two types of memory are required by any microprocessor system—random-access read/write memory (RAM) and random-access read-only memory (ROM).

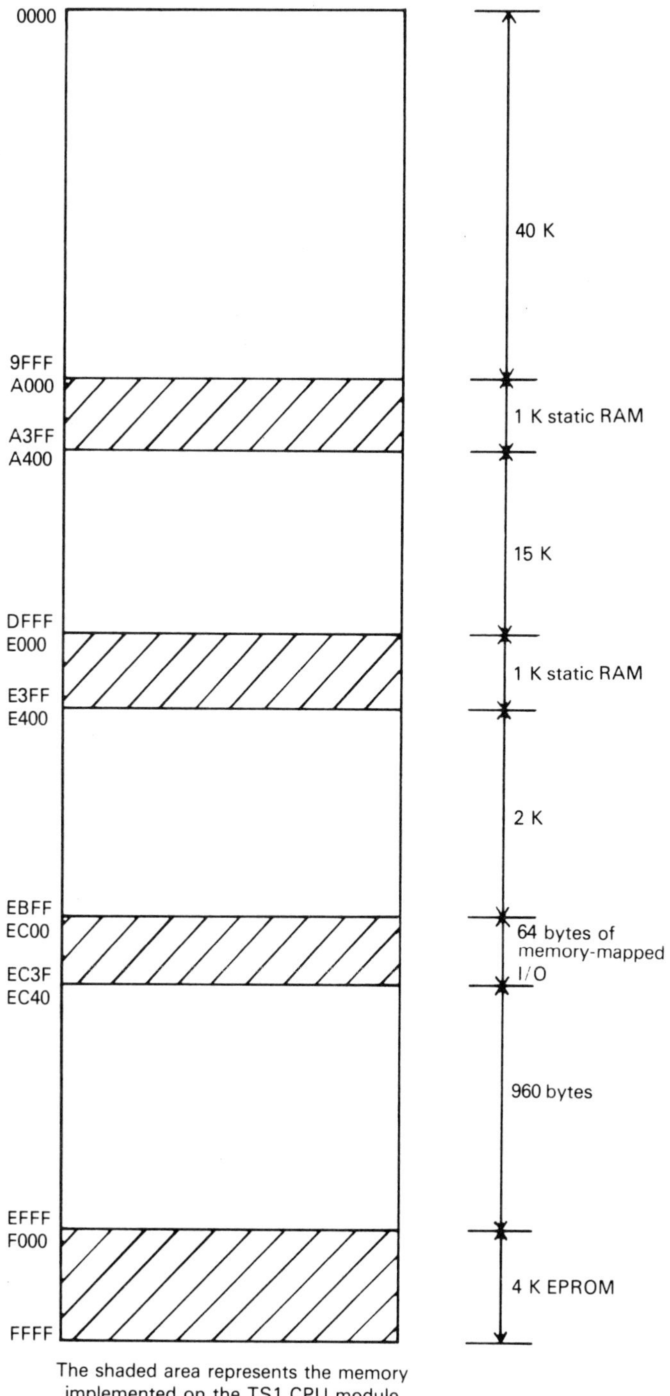

The shaded area represents the memory implemented on the TS1 CPU module

Figure 5.34 The memory map of the TS1's CPU module

The ROM is needed to hold the microprocessor's monitor program. A monitor may be no more than a minimal bootstrap loader capable of reading a program from a paper tape and then transferring control to the newly loaded program. Most monitors have a wider range of facilities than the minimal loader. These facilities may vary from the ability to display and modify a given memory location, to a fully fledged disk-operating system. The RAM on the CPU module fulfils two roles. It provides working space for any data required by the monitor, and it holds the system stack (at least until the stack is moved elsewhere under software control). It is normal programming practice to define the location of the stack immediately after a reset. Until the stack has been defined subroutines and interrupts cannot be handled.

Having decided that it is a good idea to put some memory on the CPU module, it is necessary to choose the type of memory, and its location within the CPU's address space. The memory map of the TS1's CPU module is given in Fig. 5.34. The allocation of the memory space may appear arbitrary, but the location of ROM, RAM, and memory-mapped peripherals has been chosen subject to the following guide lines.

The ROM

The 6800 is reset by loading the contents of memory locations FFFE/F into the program counter. Consequently it is necessary to locate some ROM at FFF8 – FFFF to hold the reset, NMI, IRQ and SWI interrupt vectors. Of course, it is not necessary to physically locate this ROM at FFF8 – FFFF but to ensure that the ROM which holds the vectors responds to addressing within the range FFF8 – FFFF. It is a common practice to locate the monitor ROM, in 6800-based microprocessor systems, at the top end of memory in the region of the interrupt vectors. In this way a single ROM serves the dual purpose of a monitor and of a table containing the addresses of interrupt-handling routines. Alternatively, a small fusible link PROM of 32 words × 8 bits may be located at FFE0 – FFFF. This arrangement permits the modification of the reset and interrupt vectors without reprogramming an EPROM, or scrapping an existing mask-programmed ROM.

Currently available EPROMs have formats of 256 × 8, 512 × 8, 1024 × 8, 2048 × 8, 4096 × 8 and 8192 × 8. The two smaller EPROMs have disappeared from new designs because of their low bit density per chip, relatively high access times and multiple power-supply requirements. The TS1 is designed to accommodate a monitor in the 4096 × 8 EPROM because such a large EPROM provides enough room for a fairly advanced monitor. Many microprocessor monitors are 1024 bytes long. A 4K EPROM is, in fact, large enough to house some of the simpler versions of BASIC; especially those performing all numerical operations in 2s complement, 16-bit integer arithmetic. The TS1's monitor does not fill the entire 4K EPROM. Any room in the EPROM not taken up by the monitor is left for frequently used subroutines which may be called from any program. The location of the TS1's monitor EPROM is in the 4K memory space F000 – FFFF. In the current version of the TS1 a TMS2516 2K × 8 EPROM holds the monitor. This EPROM has been selected because it is cheaper than the TMS2532. Figure 5.35 illustrates the difference between the 2532 and 2516 EPROMs in the read mode.

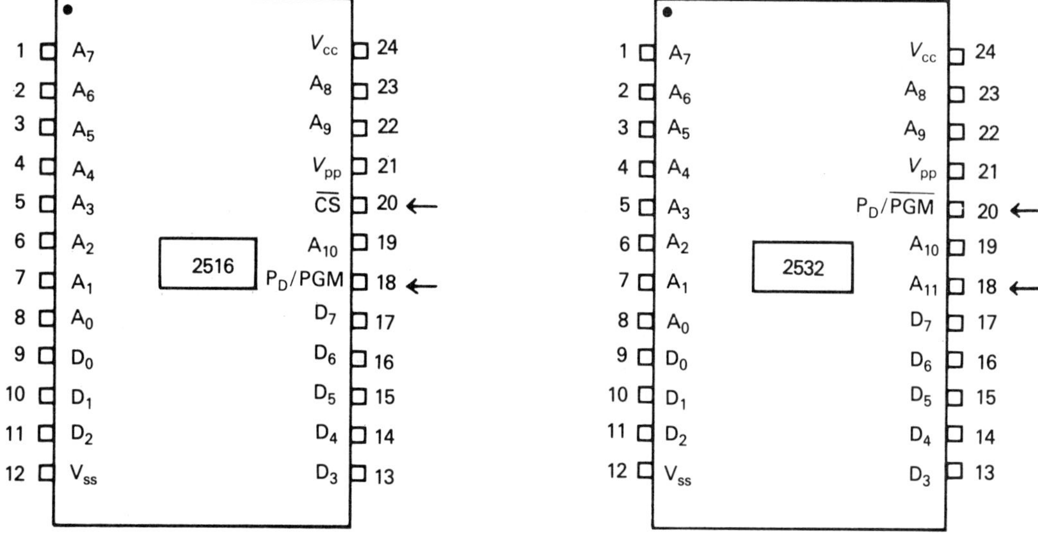

Note: The pins not common to both the 2516 and the 2532 are arrowed.

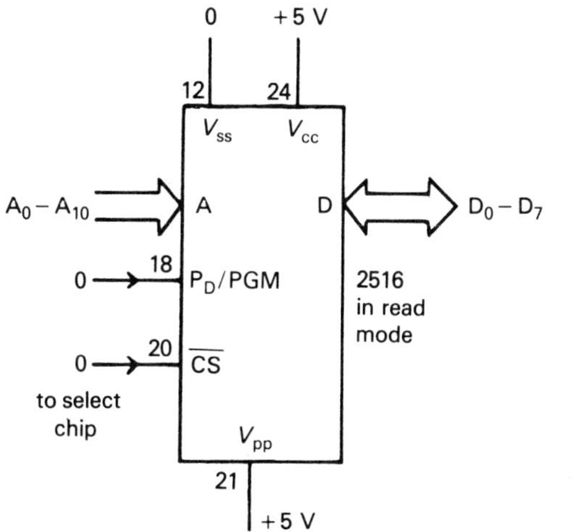

Note: Power dissipation may be cut by 80% by applying a logical 1 to the P_D/PGM pin while the chip is de-selected.

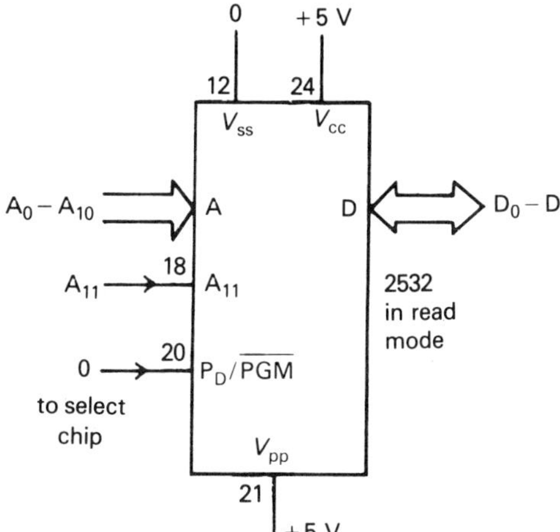

Note: The $P_D/\overline{PGM}$ pin acts both as a chip select and power down pin. When the chip is not selected (P_D/PGM high) the power dissipation is automatically reduced by 80%.

Figure 5.35 The difference between 2516 and 2532 EPROMs

The Memory-Mapped Input/Output

It is necessary to select not only the location of memory-mapped I/O devices but also their types. A wide range of memory-mapped peripheral devices is available in the 6800 series. Only three types of peripheral are located on the TS1's CPU module. Any additional I/O facilities not provided by the CPU module may readily be included in a separate module or in other modules where space permits. The five memory-mapped peripherals located on the CPU module are:

ACIA 1 An asynchronous serial data link through which the CPU communicates with the system's console (i.e. VDT or teletype).

ACIA 2 An asynchronous serial data link through which the CPU communicates with a second CPU. The two microprocessors together form a dual processor system.

PIA 1 A dual 8-bit port which interfaces to a two-channel digital-to-analog convertor.

PIA 2 A dual 8-bit port which interfaces to a multi-channel analog-to-digital convertor.

PTM A programmable timer module which is able to generate square waves or single pulses under software control. The PTM can also measure the frequency or period of a waveform present at its input.

Having decided what type of memory-mapped I/O devices are to be put on the CPU module it is necessary to locate them somewhere within the microprocessor's 64K memory space (less the 4K monitor space at F000 – FFFF). In general it would be unwise to locate the memory-mapped I/O devices at the bottom end of memory because the 256 bytes in the range 0000 – 00FF are associated with the 6800's direct-memory addressing mode where a single byte specifies an address rather than the two bytes needed to specify an absolute address. In order to have the largest possible block of contiguous memory available to user programs it is a good idea to locate the memory-mapped I/O as close to the system monitor as possible.

The MEK 6800D1 evaluation kit, followed by many other 6800-based systems, has its memory-mapped I/O ports located at 8000, limiting the greatest block of contiguous RAM to 32K. While 32K may once have seemed adequate for almost all microprocessor applications, there are many applications where 48K or more bytes of RAM are necessary. If software designed for MEK 6800D1 systems (and their adaptations) is to be run on the TS1, the user will not normally experience difficulties resulting from the absence of a memory-mapped I/O peripheral at 8004. This is because much of the software written for these systems does not communicate directly with the I/O port at 8004 but instead calls I/O subroutines within MIKBUG. Hence, to input a character from the system console the software uses the operation "JSR E1AC", where E1AC is the location of MIKBUG's "input a character" routine.

Complications arise when the software directly accesses the I/O peripheral at 8004. For example, a particular BASIC interpreter which performed all input/output operations by means of subroutine calls to MIKBUG, failed to operate when the subroutine addresses were modified to suit a new monitor which did not locate an I/O device at 8004. After carefully examining the interpreter's source code (a laborious process), it was found that the status of the input port at 8004 was periodically checked to see if the break-in key had been pressed. Once this problem had been rectified the interpreter operated successfully.

The memory-mapped I/O peripherals on the TS1's CPU module are located in part of the 1K memory space immediately adjacent to the monitor ROM at EC00. This leaves a total of 59K of memory space from 0000 to EBFF for RAM, ROM or further memory-mapped peripherals. In the present design each of the five peripherals is allocated 8 bytes of memory space, which is the number of bytes required by a PTM. As the 5 peripherals are selected by a 3-line to 8-line decoder, the total memory space actually occupied by the peripherals is $8 \times 8 = 64$ bytes (EC00 – EC3F). Full address decoding is employed on the CPU module, permitting other modules to locate their memory-mapped peripherals in the region EC40 – EFFF, and hence to avoid any reduction in the memory space available for RAM or ROM.

The Random-access Memory

The RAM located on the CPU module has the dual function of defining the system stack after a reset, and holding the monitor's temporary variables. The total RAM requirements are relatively small. Many 6800-based systems employ a single 6810 128-byte RAM for this purpose. As most of these systems locate their stack at A042 in an MC6810 from A000 to A07F, the TS1 also provides RAM in this range to ensure compatibility with existing software. However, the TS1 uses two $1K \times 4$-bit RAM components to establish 1K bytes of memory from A000 to A3FF. The region A000 – A07F is not employed by the TS1 monitor in order to avoid any potential conflict with 6800 software designed to use the MIKBUG scratchpad area at A000 – A07F.

A second 1K block of RAM is located at E000 – E3FF. In an earlier version of the TS1, the region E000 – E3FF was dedicated to memory-mapped I/O devices. This approach led to considerable difficulties when attempts were made to run software designed for MIKBUG-based systems. While it is relatively easy to edit out references to MIKBUG's input/output subroutines on programs whose source is paper tape or cassette, and then to replace the MIKBUG addresses with the corresponding addresses in the system's own monitor, the addition of a disk drive and controller causes considerable difficulty. Once the disk operating the system has been loaded, the existing monitor can be used to modify it so that it interfaces with the system's own I/O subroutines. Unfortunately the operating system cannot be loaded, in the first place, without MIKBUG's I/O routines. The solution adopted is to locate RAM in the range normally occupied by MIKBUG (E000 – E1FF, which is 512 bytes). Whenever a program designed to operate in a MIKBUG environment is to be run, a modified copy of MIKBUG is loaded into the region E000 – E1FF. The

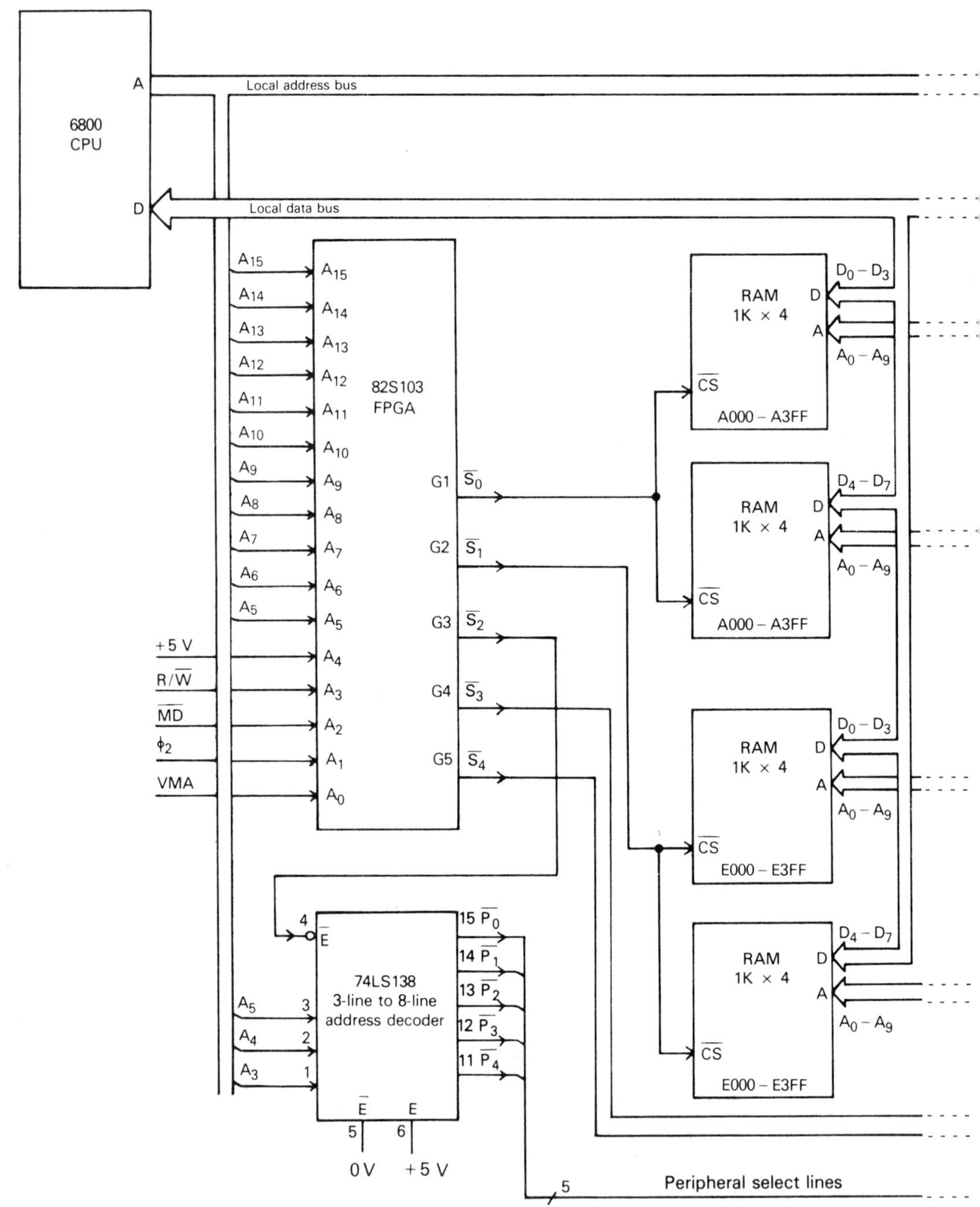

Figure 5.36 Memory components on TS1's CPU module

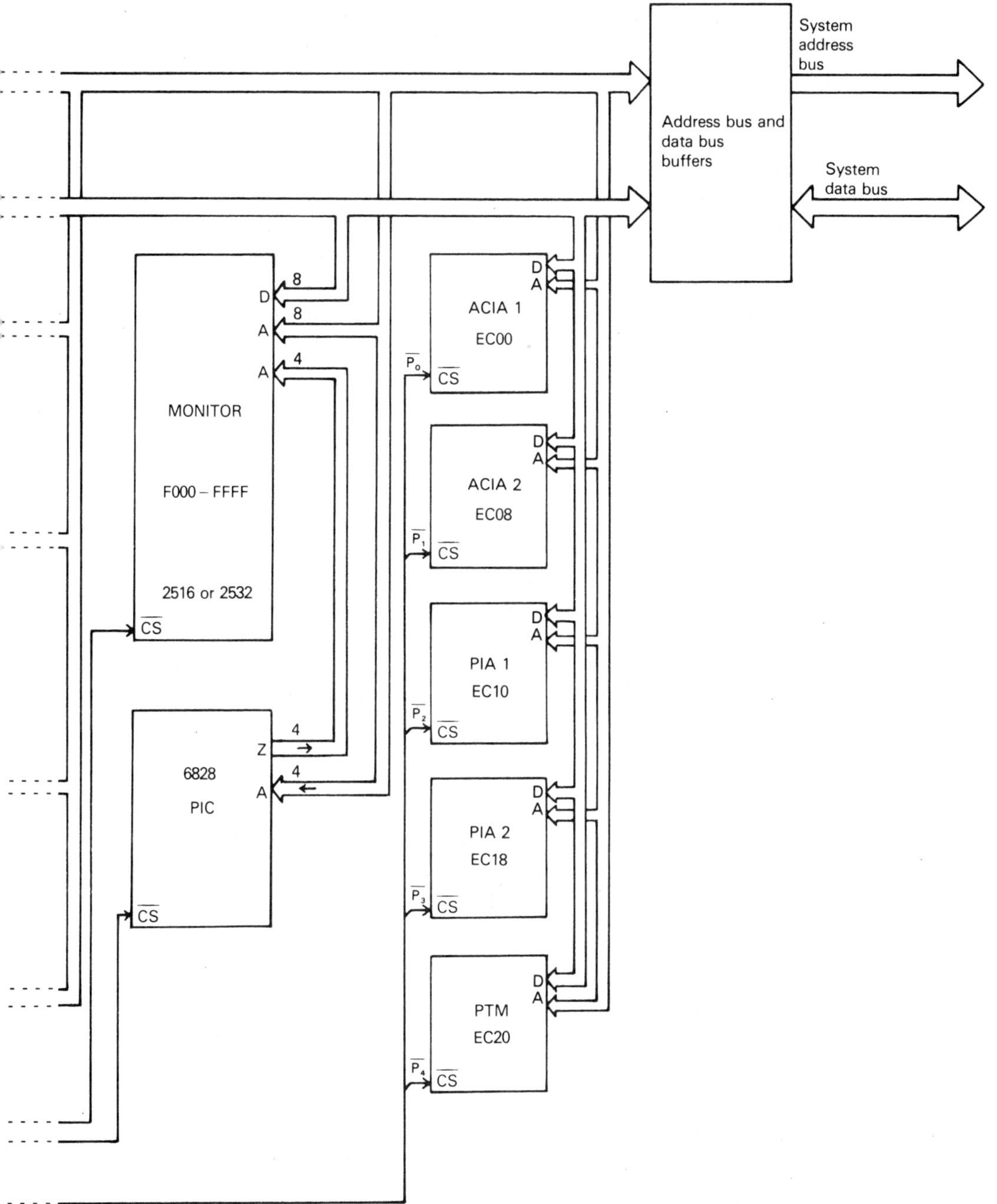
System
address
bus
Address bus and
data bus
buffers
System
data bus
8
D
8
A
4
A
MONITOR
F000 – FFFF
2516 or 2532
CS
6828
PIC
Z
4
A
4
CS
ACIA 1
EC00
D
A
P0
CS
ACIA 2
EC08
D
A
P1
CS
PIA 1
EC10
D
A
P2
CS
PIA 2
EC18
D
A
P3
CS
PTM
EC20
D
A
P4
CS

modified version of MIKBUG may be a full copy of MIKBUG with modified I/O subroutines, or links to the system's monitor at the points where MIKBUG performs character input/output, prints a character string, or returns to the monitor control level.

The address-decoding scheme of the TS1's CPU module is presented in Table 5.8, and Fig. 5.36 gives a block diagram. In order to avoid wasting valuable memory space, full address decoding has been chosen to implement the address decoding scheme. A variety of logic devices may be selected to effect the address decoding. However, the wide disparity in the number of address lines to be decoded between the peripherals (13 lines) and the ROM (4 lines) suggests the FPGA. The five peripherals are arranged at 8-byte intervals so that a 3-line to 8-line decoder may be used to select one of eight (possible) peripherals in a 64-byte block. Counting the peripherals as a single block, five blocks of memory need decoding. An FPGA capable of decoding up to 9 blocks of memory is used, and hence facilities are available for either expanding the on-board memory, or for modifying the existing addressing arrangements. Table 5.9 gives the programming requirements of the 82S103 FPGA.

The address inputs of 82S103 may be programmed to be active-high (H), active-low (L), or don't care (—). Note that the inputs to the FPGA are designated $A_0 - A_{15}$, although they are not synonymous with the CPU's address lines. The largest block of memory to be decoded is the monitor ROM at F000 – FFFF and the smallest block is the priority interrupt controller (PIC) at FFF8. Section 6.1.4 deals with the operation of the PIC, a device which is able to trap a "read IRQ vector" operation to FFF8/9 and to substitute a new vector whose value depends on one of eight interrupt request inputs.

Table 5.8 The Address-decoding Arrangements of the TS1's CPU Module

Device	*Start address*	*End address*	*Number of bytes*	A_{15}	A_{14}	A_{13}	A_{12}	A_{11}	A_{10}	A_9	A_8	A_7	A_6	A_5	A_4	A_3	A_2	A_1	A_0
RAM	A000	A3FF	1024	1	0	1	0	0	0	×	×	×	×	×	×	×	×	×	×
RAM	E000	E3FF	1024	1	1	1	0	0	0	×	×	×	×	×	×	×	×	×	×
Peripheral 1	EC00	EC07	8	1	1	1	0	1	1	0	0	0	0	0	0	0	×	×	×
Peripheral 2	EC08	EC0F	8	1	1	1	0	1	1	0	0	0	0	0	0	1	×	×	×
Peripheral 3	EC10	EC17	8	1	1	1	0	1	1	0	0	0	0	0	1	0	×	×	×
Peripheral 4	EC18	EC1F	8	1	1	1	0	1	1	0	0	0	0	0	1	1	×	×	×
Peripheral 5	EC20	EC27	8	1	1	1	0	1	1	0	0	0	0	1	0	0	×	×	×
Peripheral 6	EC28	EC2F	8	1	1	1	0	1	1	0	0	0	0	1	0	1	×	×	×
Peripheral 7	EC30	EC37	8	1	1	1	0	1	1	0	0	0	0	1	1	0	×	×	×
Peripheral 8	EC38	EC3F	8	1	1	1	0	1	1	0	0	0	0	1	1	1	×	×	×
ROM	F000	FFFF	4096	1	1	1	1	×	×	×	×	×	×	×	×	×	×	×	×
PIC* read	FFF8	FFF9	2	1	1	1	1	1	1	1	1	1	1	1	1	1	0	0	×
PIC write	FFE0	FFFF	32	1	1	1	1	1	1	1	1	1	1	1	×	×	×	×	×

*PIC = Priority interrupt controller—details of this device will be given in a later section.

Table 5.9 Programming Table for the 82S103 FPGA

	FPGA INPUTS																*Output*	
Gate	A_{15}	A_{14}	A_{13}	A_{12}	A_{11}	A_{10}	A_9	A_8	A_7	A_6	A_5	A_4	A_3	A_2	A_1	A_0	*O*	*Device*
1	H	L	H	L	L	L	-	-	-	-	-	H	-	-	H	H	L	RAM
2	H	H	H	L	L	L	-	-	-	-	-	H	-	-	H	H	L	RAM
3	H	H	H	L	H	H	L	L	L	L	-	H	-	-	-	H	L	Peripherals
4	H	H	H	H	-	-	-	-	-	-	-	H	H	H	H	H	L	ROM
5	H	H	H	H	H	H	H	H	H	H	H	H	-	H	-	H	L	PIC
6																		Not used
7																		Not used
9																		Not used
	A_{15}	A_{14}	A_{13}	A_{12}	A_{11}	A_{10}	A_9	A_8	A_7	A_6	A_5	1	$R/\overline{W}$	$\overline{MD}$	ϕ_2	VMA		
	Connections to the FPGA's inputs																	

Note: $\overline{MD}$ = $\overline{\text{MEMORY DISABLE}}$ and when active low disables the system ROM and PIC.

Address lines $A_5 - A_{15}$ of the address bus from the CPU are connected to inputs $A_5 - A_{15}$ respectively of the FPGA and these are programmed according to the address map of Table 5.8. The remaining five inputs of the FPGA are not "wasted" but are allowed to act as auxiliary chip-select inputs in the following way:

A_0 (pin 8) This is made active-high and is connected to the CPU's VMA output so that a memory device on the CPU module may be activated only when there is a valid address on the address bus.

A_1 (pin 7) This is made active-high and is connected to the ϕ_2 TTL clock output. Consequently devices may be activated only when ϕ_2 is high. Two exceptions to this rule are the peripherals and the PIC. The peripherals must be selected 160 ns before ϕ_2 goes high and the PIC should be selected early as explained in Section 6.1.

A_2 (pin 6) This is made active-high for the selection of the monitor ROM and the PIC. Otherwise it is a don't care condition. By connecting this pin to the $\overline{\text{MEMORY DISABLE}}$ line from the bus, the monitor ROM can be "turned off" by activating the $\overline{\text{MEMORY DISABLE}}$ line.

A_3 (pin 5) This line is a don't care condition for all outputs except the monitor ROM, in which case it is programmed to be active-high. By connecting this pin to the CPU's $R/\overline{W}$ output, the monitor can be accessed only by a read operation to it. This action is necessary because it is possible to write to the PIC whose address space overlaps that of the ROM. Without making the selection of the ROM a function of the $R/\overline{W}$ line a write to the PIC would cause the CPU and the ROM to try to control the data bus simultaneously. Section 6.1.4 makes it clear why it is necessary to write to the PIC.

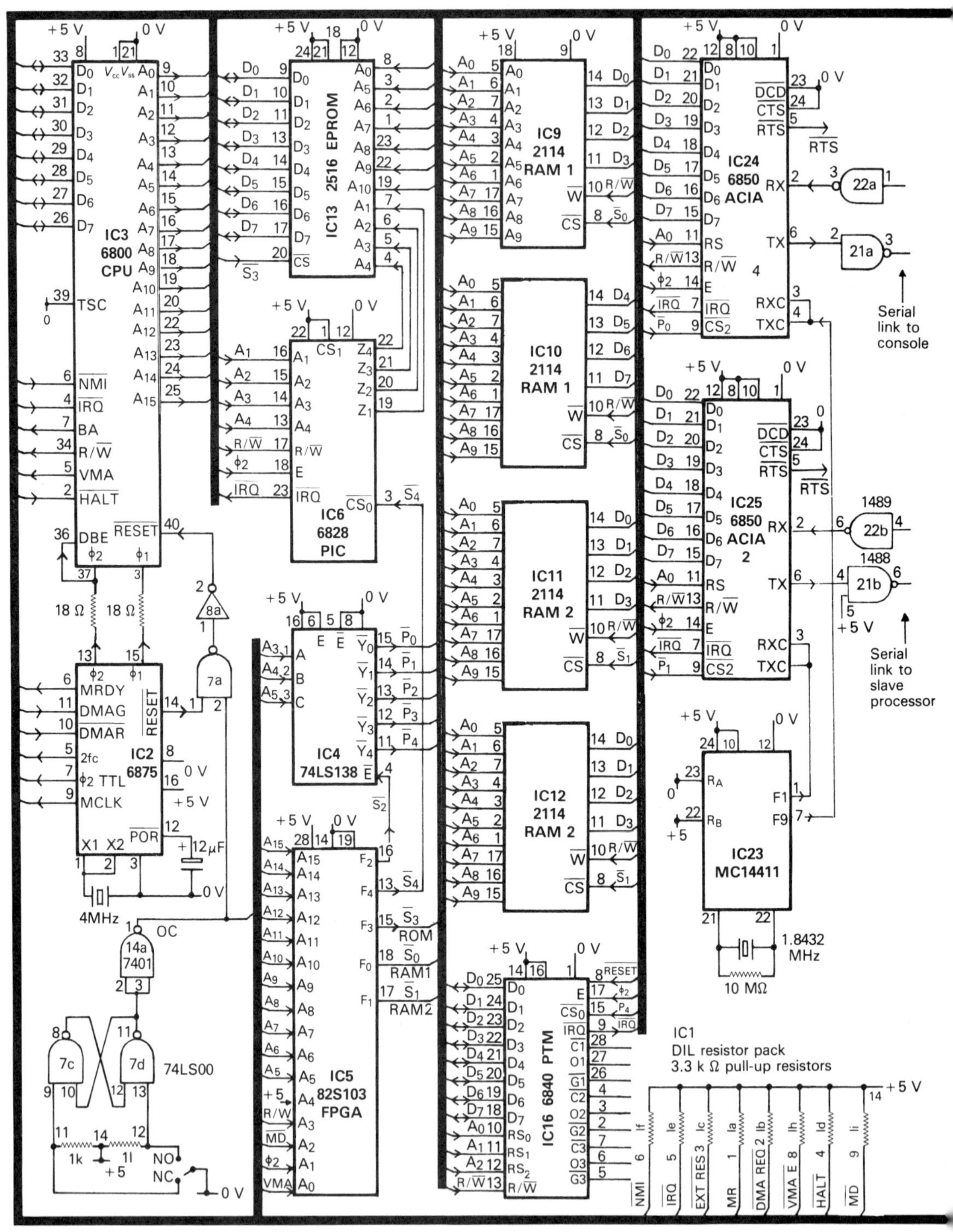
IC3
6800
CPU
TSC
NMI
IRQ
BA
R/W
VMA
HALT
DBE
RESET
18 Ω
18 Ω
IC2
6875
MRDY
DMAG
DMAR
2fc
φ2 TTL
MCLK
POR
X1 X2
12μF
4MHz
0 V
OC
14a
7401
7a
8a
7c
7d
74LS00
1k
1l
+5
NO
NC
IC13 2516 EPROM
CS
IC6
6828
PIC
CS1
CS0
IC4
74LS138
IC5
82S103
FPGA
ROM
RAM1
RAM2
IC9
2114
RAM 1
IC10
2114
RAM 1
IC11
2114
RAM 2
IC12
2114
RAM 2
IC16 6840 PTM
IC24
6850
ACIA
DCD
CTS
RTS
RX
TX
RXC
TXC
22a
21a
Serial
link to
console
IC25
6850
ACIA
2
1489
22b
1488
21b
Serial
link to
slave
processor
IC23
MC14411
1.8432
MHz
10 MΩ
IC1
DIL resistor pack
3.3 k Ω pull-up resistors
NMI
IRQ
EXT RES 3
MR
DMA REQ 2
VMA E 8
HALT
MD
+5 V

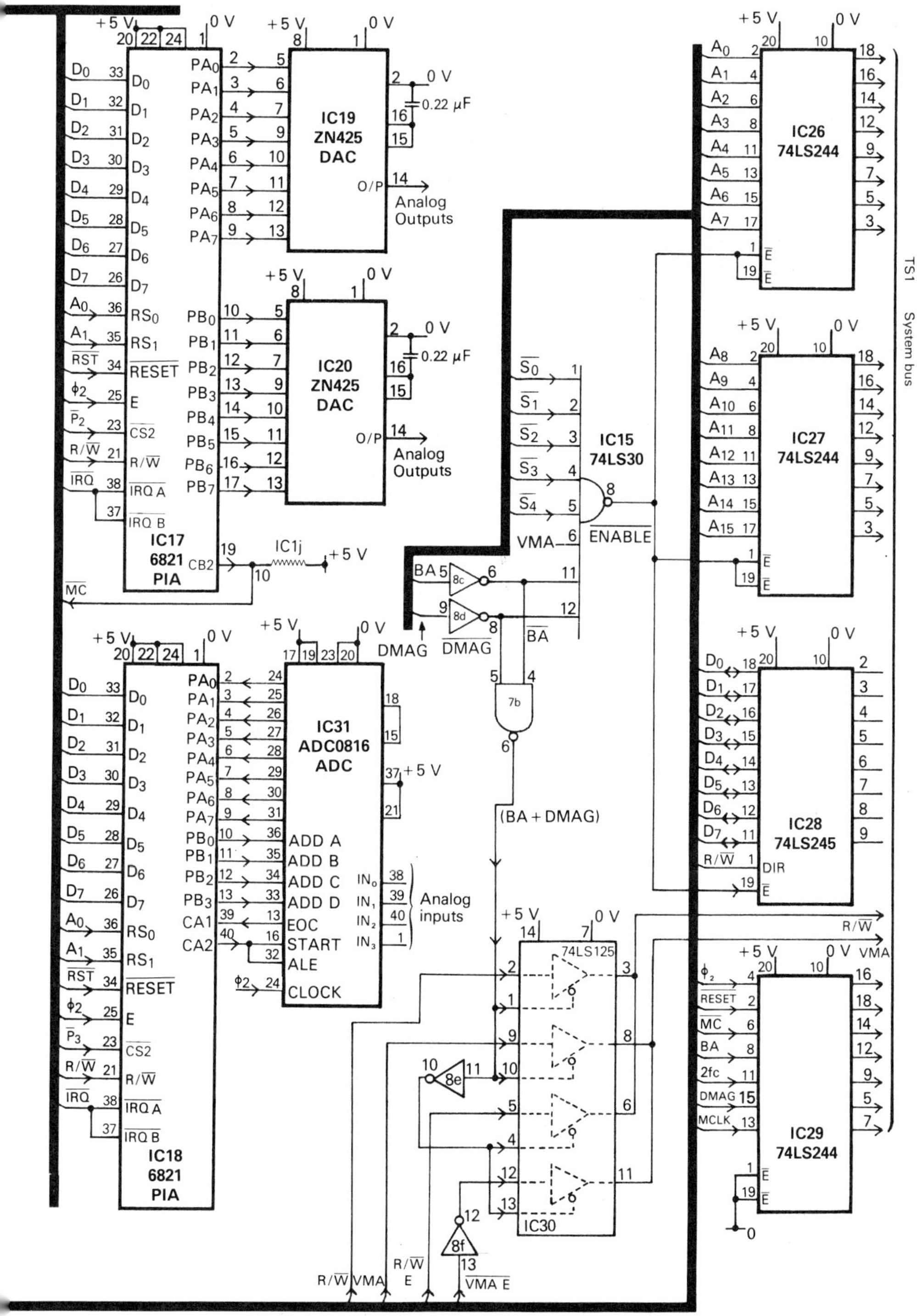

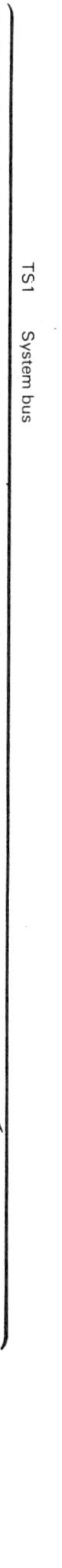

Fig. 5.37 The circuit diagram of the TS1's CPU module

A_4 (pin 6) This pin is active-high for the selection of all devices and is permanently connected to V_{cc} (logical 1). Pin 6 has been programmed active-high simply in case an additional enable input is needed at a later date.

The FPGA is programmed in the same way as a PROM by blowing its fusible links in a special purpose programmer. The FPGA used in the TS1 was kindly supplied and programmed according to Table 5.9 by Mullard Ltd.

The circuit diagram of the address-decoding arrangement of TS1's CPU module is given in Fig. 5.37.

5.7 A MEMORY MODULE FOR THE TS1

The TS1 microprocessor system is capable of expanding its memory to the full 64K bytes which may be directly addressed by the CPU. As 7K bytes of memory are located on the CPU module itself (4K ROM, 2K RAM, and 1K I/O), a total of 57K bytes of memory space are available to the user. In fact, only 64 bytes of the 1K bytes reserved for memory-mapped I/O are actually decoded by the CPU module. This leaves $1024 - 64 = 960$ bytes in the region EC40 – EFFF available for I/O port expansion from the system bus.

The TS1 is intended as a general-purpose microprocessor system and therefore needs sufficient RAM to tackle a wide range of problems. A rough guide to memory requirements may be obtained by looking at the size of some typical programs: BASIC interpreter 4K – 12K, editor, assembler, text processor 4K – 8K. If the microprocessor is to execute programs written in BASIC, additional room is required for the source program—say 20 – 60 bytes per line of source code. For this reason 16K bytes may be regarded as the minimum RAM requirement, and 24K or 32K bytes as a target to aim for.

Having decided that the total memory requirement falls in the range 16 – 32K, the next step is to select a suitable memory component from which to construct the memory module. Although static RAM is more expensive than dynamic RAM, especially for large memories where the cost of refresh circuitry is more than offset by the relatively low cost of dynamic RAM, the TS1's memory module is built from static memory components, avoiding the power-supply problems associated with dynamic RAM.

Several types of static RAM component are at the disposal of the designer. The format of some of these chips are 256×4, 1024×1, 1024×4, 4096×1, 1024×8 and 2048×8. In general the larger the RAM (i.e. number of bits per chip), the lower the average power consumption, the higher the speed, and the greater the ease with which the RAM module may be constructed. A 32K-byte memory module requires the following number of chips:

256 off $1K \times 1$ chip or 256×4 chip
64 off $4K \times 1$ chip or $1K \times 4$ chip
32 off $1K \times 8$ chip
16 off $2K \times 8$ chip

Unfortunately, the cost per bit of a static RAM rises with the density of bits per chip. This increase in cost is not only due to technological factors but to supply and demand. The TS1's memory module is built from 4K static RAM chips as these appear to be the most cost-effective solution at the time of writing. The 4K chip is available in two formats—4096 × 1 and 1024 × 4 bits. The latter format is best suited to small byte-wide memories such as the two 1K × 8 blocks on the CPU module. When a large amount of memory is required the 4K × 1 chip is the more suitable alternative for two reasons. Firstly, as this chip has 12 address lines, $A_0 - A_{11}$, only 4 of the CPU's address lines, $A_{12} - A_{15}$, remain to be decoded. Secondly, this chip has only one data line per 4K bytes of memory, and hence does not put a heavy load on the data bus. A 24K block of memory has only 6 data lines connected together. If 1K × 4 memory chips were used to form the memory, there would be 24 loads on the data bus.

Figure 5.38 shows the basic arrangement of a memory module constructed from 4K × 1 static RAM chips. The memory components are arranged in columns of 8, each column forming a block of memory with 4096 words of 8 bits. The address lines of all the memory components are connected together so that A_i of one chip is connected to A_i of each of the other chips. Two octal tri-state bus drivers buffer the address from the system bus onto the memory module's internal address bus. Note that only 12 of the 16 buffers are used by address lines $A_0 - A_{11}$. This leaves three of the unused buffers for ϕ_2, VMA and $R/\overline{W}$. The address buffers are permanently enabled because there is never a need to float the memory module's internal address bus. Each of the 4K × 1 memory components has separate pins for data input and data output, unlike the 1K × 4 memory components where a single pin serves as both a data in and data out terminal. In this design the data in and data out pins are simply strapped together.

Data transfers between the system bus and the memory module's internal data bus are buffered by a single octal transceiver.

The data-bus transceiver, 74LS245, has two control inputs: an active-low enable input and a direction of data transfer input. The direction of data transfer input is connected to the system's $R/\overline{W}$ line and is therefore determined by the CPU. During a CPU read cycle it is necessary to ensure that no two (or more) data-bus drivers are enabled simultaneously. This is done by making the enable input of the data bus transceiver a function of the contents of the address bus, so that only the module currently addressed has its data-bus transceiver enabled.

The address decoding on the TS1's RAM module is made flexible so that the address space may be expanded from 4K to 32K in blocks of 4K. A 3-line to 8-line decoder (74LS138) divides the 32K bytes of RAM for which $A_{15} = 0$, into eight blocks of 4K. The actual 4K block of memory selected is a function of A_{12}, A_{13} and A_{14}. The decoder is enabled by ϕ_2.VMA so that data transfers take place only during the ϕ_2 clock phase of a valid memory access cycle. It can be seen from Fig. 5.38 that the active-low outputs of the decoder are connected to the chip-select inputs of the 4K blocks of RAM. The same outputs are also connected to the inputs of a NAND gate. As long as no block of RAM is enabled (i.e. it is not addressed), all the outputs of the decoder are in a logical 1 state and, consequently, the output of the NAND

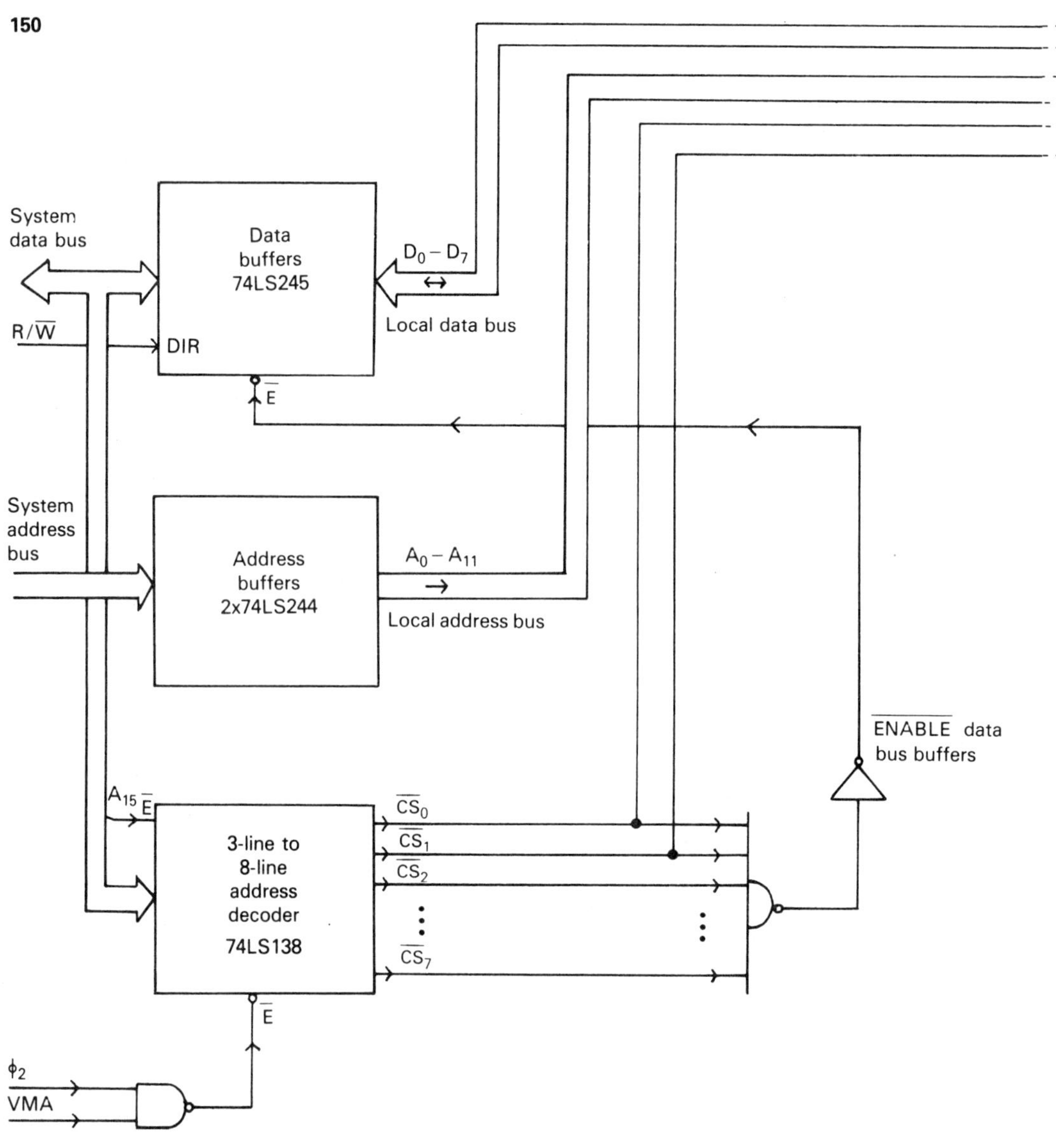

Note: Only seven of the eight bits of RAM are shown here for convenience.

Figure 5.38 The basic address-decoding arrangements of the TS1 memory module

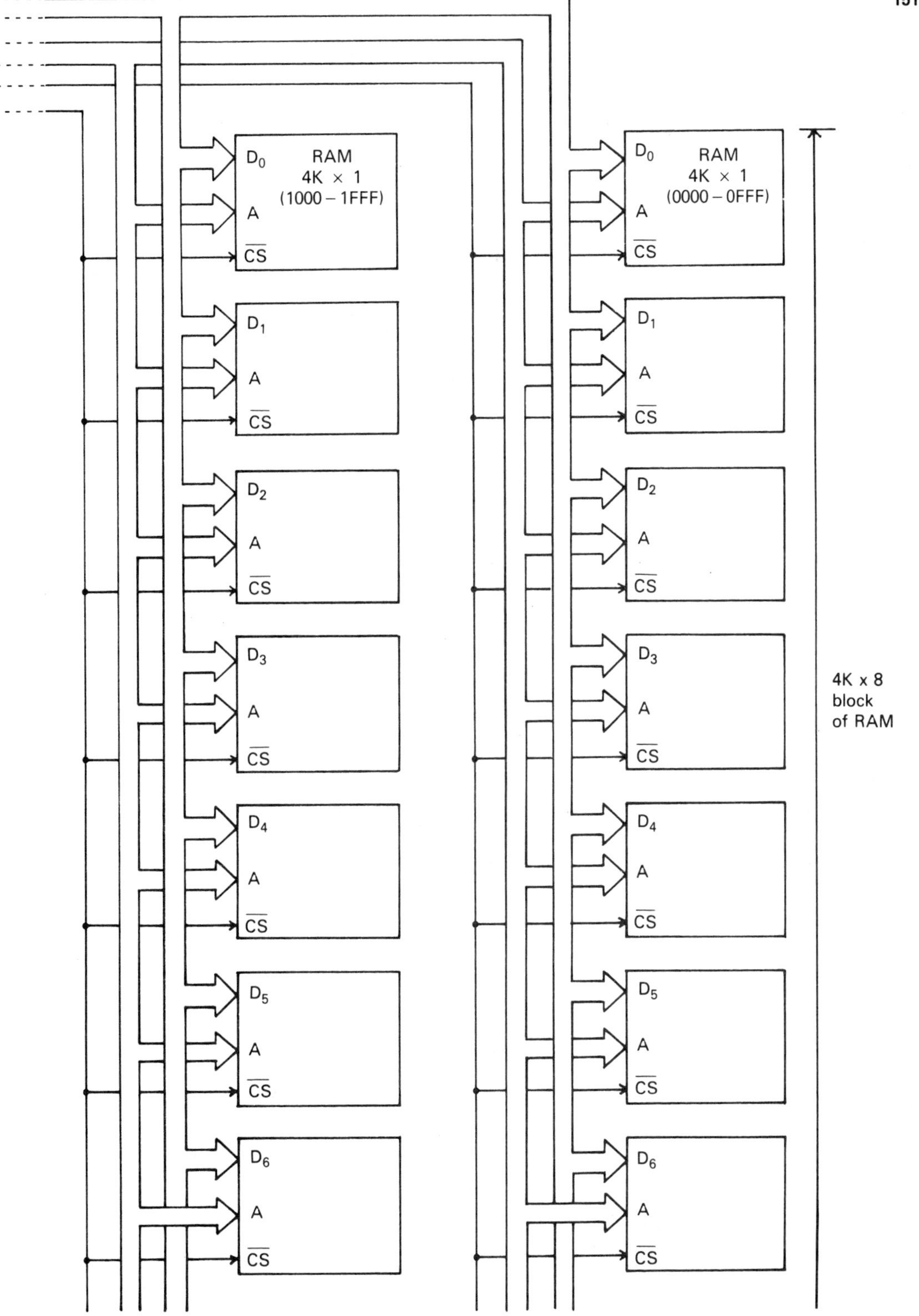
D0
RAM
4K × 1
(1000 – 1FFF)
A
CS
D1
A
CS
D2
A
CS
D3
A
CS
D4
A
CS
D5
A
CS
D6
A
CS
D0
RAM
4K × 1
(0000 – 0FFF)
A
CS
D1
A
CS
D2
A
CS
D3
A
CS
D4
A
CS
D5
A
CS
D6
A
CS
4K x 8
block
of RAM

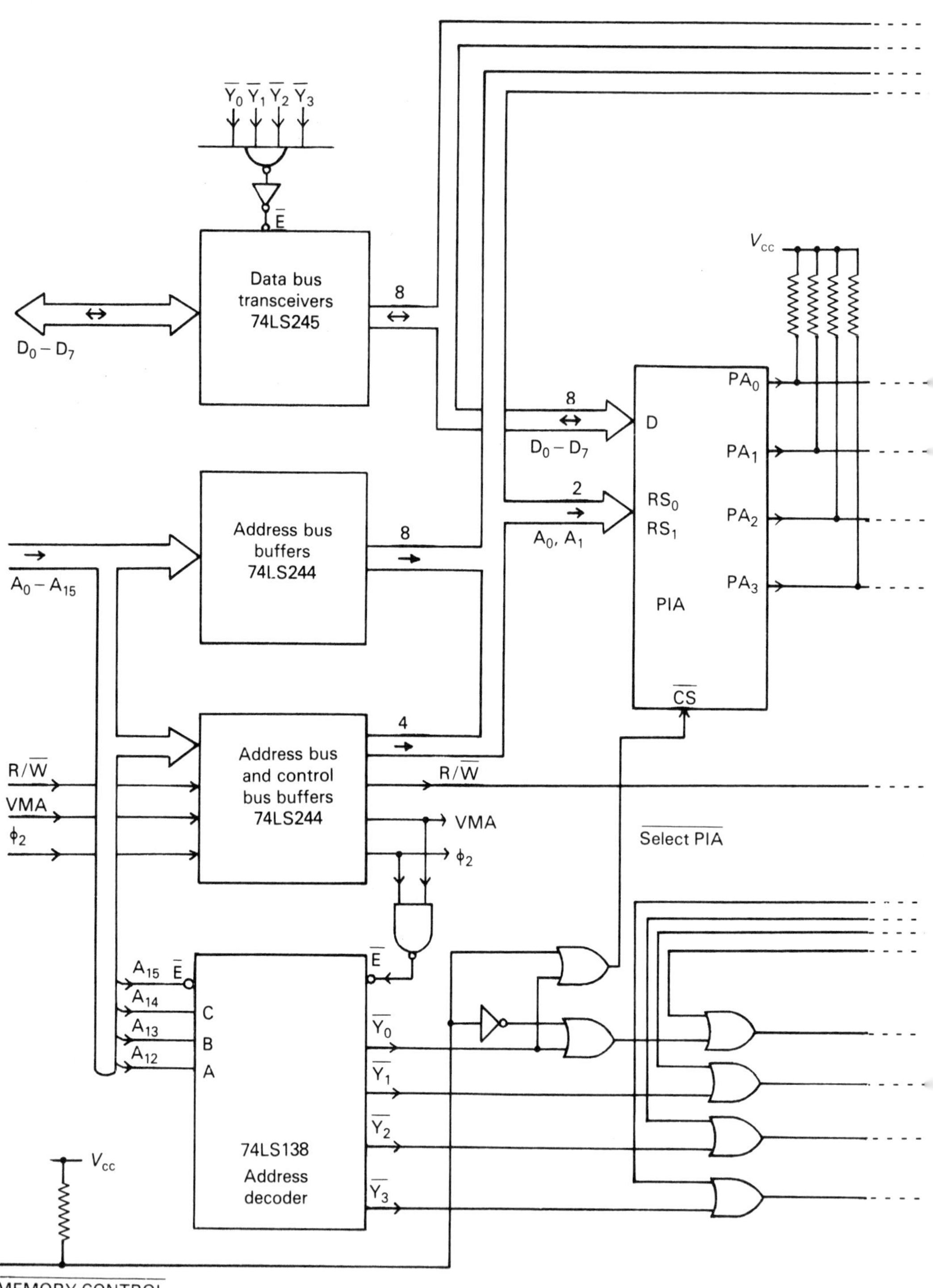

$\overline{Y_0}$ $\overline{Y_1}$ $\overline{Y_2}$ $\overline{Y_3}$
$\overline{E}$
Data bus transceivers 74LS245
8
$D_0 - D_7$
V_{cc}
8
D
$D_0 - D_7$
PA_0
PA_1
2
RS_0
RS_1
PA_2
A_0, A_1
Address bus buffers 74LS244
8
$A_0 - A_{15}$
PA_3
PIA
$\overline{CS}$
4
Address bus and control bus buffers 74LS244
$R/\overline{W}$
VMA
ϕ_2
$R/\overline{W}$
VMA
ϕ_2
$\overline{\text{Select PIA}}$
A_{15} $\overline{E}$
A_{14}
A_{13}
A_{12}
C
B
A
$\overline{E}$
$\overline{Y_0}$
$\overline{Y_1}$
$\overline{Y_2}$
$\overline{Y_3}$
74LS138 Address decoder
V_{cc}
$\overline{\text{MEMORY CONTROL}}$

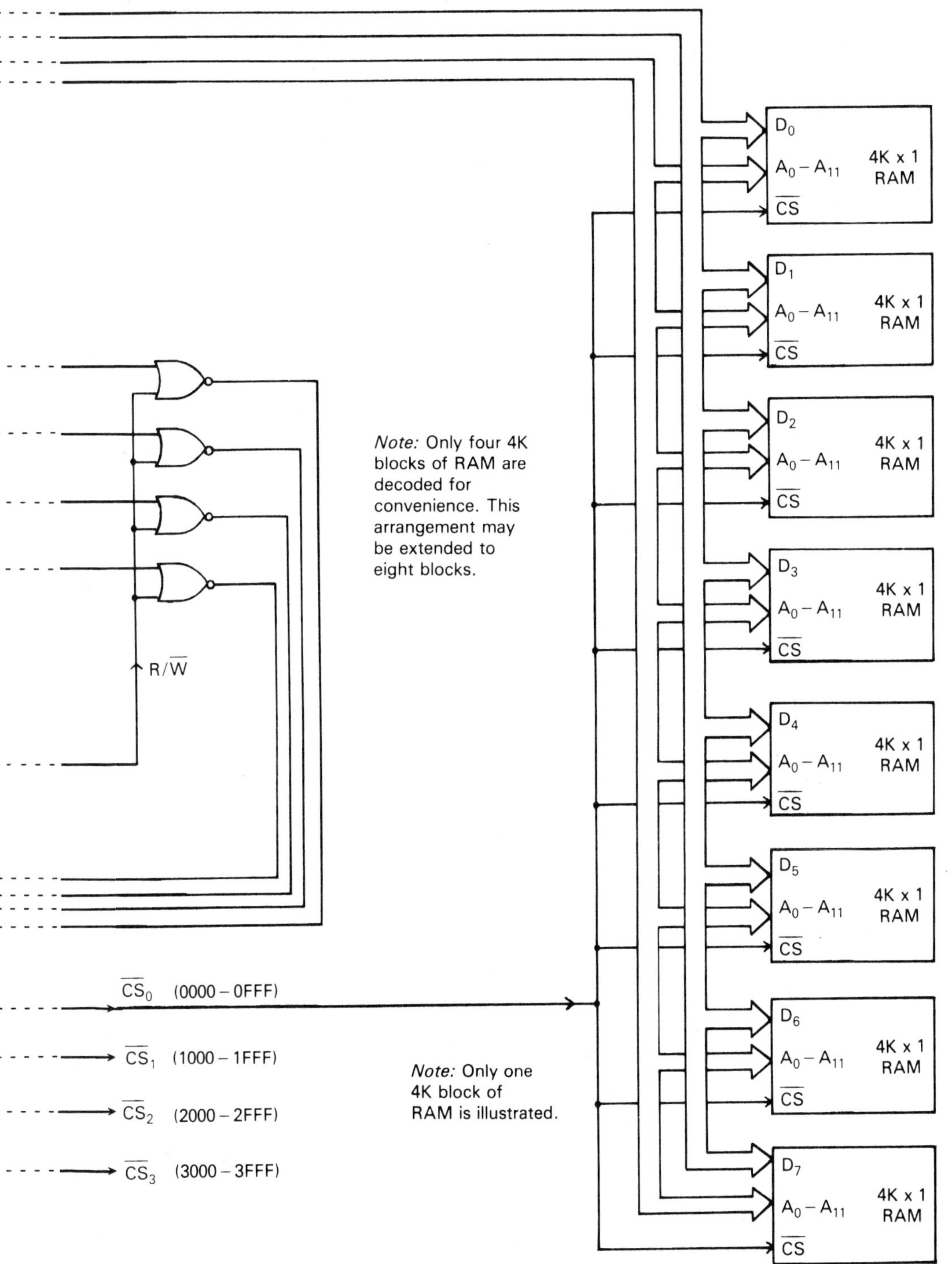

Figure 5.39 The basic arrangement of the TS1 memory module

gate is in a logical 0 state. This output is inverted and is connected to the $\overline{\text{ENABLE}}$ input of the data-bus transceiver. Clearly, as long as no block of RAM is selected, the $\overline{\text{ENABLE}}$ input of the data-bus transceiver is high and the data-bus buffers are turned off.

As soon as one of the blocks of RAM is selected, the output of the NAND gate goes high, and the $\overline{\text{ENABLE}}$ input to the data-bus transceiver goes low, permitting the transfer of data in a direction determined by the state of the CPU's R/$\overline{\text{W}}$ line. By using an 8-input NAND gate it is possible to expand the memory from one block of 4K to 8 blocks of 4K, a total of 32K bytes. Unused inputs to the NAND gate should be tied to a logical 1 (i.e. +5 V, preferably through a 1 kΩ resistor.

Write Protecting Read/Write Memory

One of TS1's system control lines, $\overline{\text{MEMORY CONTROL}}$, originates from a PIA in the CPU module. After the initial application of power, or following a system reset, the $\overline{\text{MEMORY CONTROL}}$ line is pulled up to a logical 1 by means of a pull-up resistor. This line may be pulled down into its active-low state by defining the appropriate PIA control line as an output and then clearing it. The control of a PIA is dealt with in Section 6.2.1—here it is sufficient to note that the PIA's output may be set or cleared under software control.

The $\overline{\text{MEMORY CONTROL}}$ line has been provided in the TS1 for largely illustrative purposes. As implemented in the TS1, this line serves to "qualify" the meaning of an address on the system address bus. As long as $\overline{\text{MEMORY CONTROL}}$ is high, all addresses on the address bus have their normal (or usual) meaning. When $\overline{\text{MEMORY CONTROL}}$ is pulled down, an alternative meaning may be given to the contents of the address bus. This facility can be used to expand the memory space into two blocks of 64K, with the $\overline{\text{MEMORY CONTROL}}$ line acting as "A_{16}". Note that this technique does not permit a jump from one block of 64K to another block of 64K because to change the state of $\overline{\text{MEMORY CONTROL}}$ involves an access to the PIA. Clearly, a jump cannot be made from one block to another by executing a jump instruction and by modifying the PIA's $\overline{\text{MEMORY CONTROL}}$ output before the jump has been completed.

In TS1's memory module the $\overline{\text{MEMORY CONTROL}}$ line has the effect of dividing the lowest-order 4K block of RAM (0000 – 0FFF) into two regions (see Fig. 5.39). Whenever $\overline{\text{MEMORY CONTROL}}$ is high the normal 4K block of RAM is selected. However, when $\overline{\text{MEMORY CONTROL}}$ is low a memory-mapped peripheral, a PIA on the memory module, is selected whenever a location within the lowest 4K of memory is addressed. The PIA, which is described in more detail in a later section, controls the way in which the 4K blocks of RAM are accessed. Figure 5.40 shows how the PIA can add a write-protect facility to any of the 4K blocks of RAM. A read/write memory is said to have write protection when data in the memory can be read but not modified. In Fig. 5.40 the active-low chip-select input of a block of memory is derived from three signals—$\overline{\text{SELECT}}$ from the memory decoder, R/$\overline{\text{W}}$ from the system bus, and $\overline{\text{WRITE PROTECT}}$ from the PIA. As long as the input to the OR gate marked X is a logical zero, the output of the OR gate is identical to the $\overline{\text{SELECT}}$ input. That is, the RAM is selected whenever a location within it is addressed. Now, when X = 1 the output of the OR gate is high and the RAM cannot be selected. The value of X is determined by R/$\overline{\text{W}}$ and $\overline{\text{WRITE PROTECT}}$. X is high if, and only if, R/$\overline{\text{W}}$ = 0 and $\overline{\text{WRITE PROTECT}}$ = 0. Thus, if a write cycle is attempted to a block of memory with write-protection, X is forced high, causing the RAM to be de-selected. Table 5.10 gives the truth table for Fig. 5.40 and illustrates how write-protect is effected.

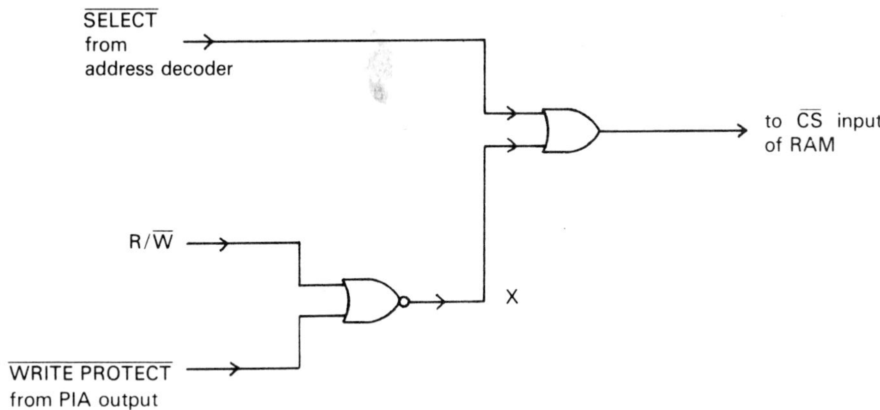

Figure 5.40 The write-protect logic circuit

Table 5.10 The Truth Table of the Write-project Circuit

$\overline{\textit{WRITE PROTECT}}$	$R/\overline{W}$	$\overline{\textit{SELECT}}$	$\overline{\textit{CS}}$	
1	1	1	1	
1	1	0	0	
1	0	1	1	
1	0	0	0	
0	1	1	1	
0	1	0	0	
0	0	1	1	
0	0	0	1	← the write-protect action forces $\overline{\text{CS}}$ high

In order to give write protection to a block of memory, the following sequence of actions must be carried out. Firstly, the $\overline{\text{MEMORY CONTROL}}$ line from the CPU module is set to a logical zero under software control. Secondly, the PIA on the memory module is accessed and zeros written into the outputs required to add memory protection to one or more blocks of RAM. Thirdly, $\overline{\text{MEMORY CONTROL}}$ is once more set to a logical one to allow the lowest 4K block of RAM to be accessed.

In principle the $\overline{\text{MEMORY CONTROL}}$ line may be used to add further peripheral devices to the memory module. The advantage of increasing the number of I/O ports in this way is that the number of ports may be expanded without eating into the microprocessor's precious memory space. This arrangement suffers from the disadvantage that before one of these ports can be accessed $\overline{\text{MEMORY CONTROL}}$ must be cleared, and after a port has been accessed $\overline{\text{MEMORY CONTROL}}$ must be returned to its logical one state. A further problem posed by the action of the $\overline{\text{MEMORY CONTROL}}$ line is that, if the stack were located in the lowest 4K block of memory and $\overline{\text{MEMORY CONTROL}}$ had been set to zero, then an interrupt would attempt to store the contents of the working registers in non-existent memory locations. Similarly, care must be taken when accessing the lowest 4K block of RAM from a subroutine (or interrupt-handling routine) as the state of $\overline{\text{MEMORY CONTROL}}$ may not be known in the subroutine.

An extension of the write-protect facility is the indication that a memory-write violation has occurred. Such an indication may be provided in the form of a warning light or by the generation of an interrupt request. A write-violation occurs whenever $R/\overline{W}=0$, $\overline{\text{WRITE PROTECT}}=0$, $\overline{\text{SELECT}}=0$. On detecting this condition $\overline{\text{IRQ}}$ (or $\overline{\text{NMI}}$) can be forced low to generate an interrupt directly, or one of the PIA's control lines can be used to latch an interrupt into the PIA (see Section 6.2), or to light an LED. Figure 5.41 illustrates how a write-protect violation may be detected and latched. An RS flip-flop is formed by two cross-coupled NAND gates. Whenever an illegal write operation is made to a block of write-protected memory the Q output of the flip-flop is set. The $\overline{Q}$ output of the flip-flop can be used to light an LED which will remain on until the flip-flop is reset under software control from a PIA, or by a system reset. This arrangement may be made to cause an interrupt, if desired, by connecting the Q output of the flip-flop to one of the PIA's control lines. Figure 5.42 gives the full circuit diagram of TS1's RAM module.

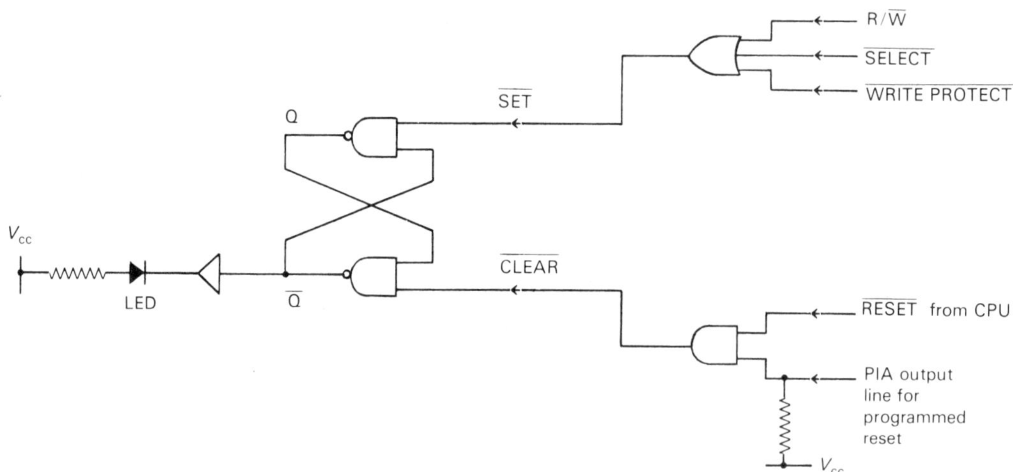

Figure 5.41 A write-protect violation detector

Using the Memory-protect Facility

In order to activate the memory-protect facility of TS1's RAM module it is necessary to force the system $\overline{\text{MEMORY CONTROL}}$ line low to select the PIA on the RAM module. Data may then be written into the PIA's side-A output register: a zero to write-protect a 4K block of RAM, and a one to remove such protection. After this has been done the $\overline{\text{MEMORY CONTROL}}$ line is then raised to its inactive-high state to permit normal system operation.

The program to carry out memory protection is given in Listing 5.1. Understanding this program requires a knowledge of the operation of the PIA which is dealt with in Section 6.2, and the reader may wish to skip this part until Section 6.2 has been read. Two fragments of a longer program, "PROT" and "UNPROT" cause a 4K block of RAM at 0000 – 0FFF to be write-protected and unprotected, respectively. These fragments call three subroutines which in this example are located at E000. The first subroutine "MCCLR" puts the $\overline{\text{MEMORY CONTROL}}$ line in a logical zero state by writing 110 into bits 5, 4, 3 of the B-side control register of PIA1 on the CPU module. Similarly "MCSET" resets the $\overline{\text{MEMORY CONTROL}}$ line. The subroutine "WPROT" writes the contents of accumulator A into the PIA's side A data register on the RAM module; this subroutine also sets up the PIA and defines side A as an output port.

The most important aspect of these programs is that the "PROT" and "UNPROT" parts must not lie within the region 0000 – 0FFF, or any other part of memory affected by the state of the $\overline{\text{MEMORY CONTROL}}$ line, as once "MCCLR" is invoked this region is populated by the RAM module's PIA and not its RAM.

SUMMARY

After a brief introduction to some of the concepts of memory components this chapter has examined some of the properties of the memory timing diagram and shown how they must be interpreted in the light of the CPU's own read/write timing requirements.

The bulk of this chapter has been dedicated to the concept of memory decoding, the mapping of the address space of a memory component onto the CPU's memory space. The art of address decoding involves juggling with the cost, speed, flexibility and amount of board space taken by the various address-decoding networks available to the designer. The properties of four types of address decoder have been examined: *m*-line to *n*-line decoder, PROM, FPLA and FPGA.

Memory-mapped peripherals have been introduced and the way in which the peripherals on the CPU module have been assigned to the system memory map has been discussed.

This section includes the circuit diagram of TS1's CPU module and its address-decoding arrangements. Following this is TS1's memory module, which is capable of providing up to 24K bytes of read/write memory. A special feature of this module is the ability to write-protect any 4K block of memory so that its data cannot be corrupted by an unintentional write access.

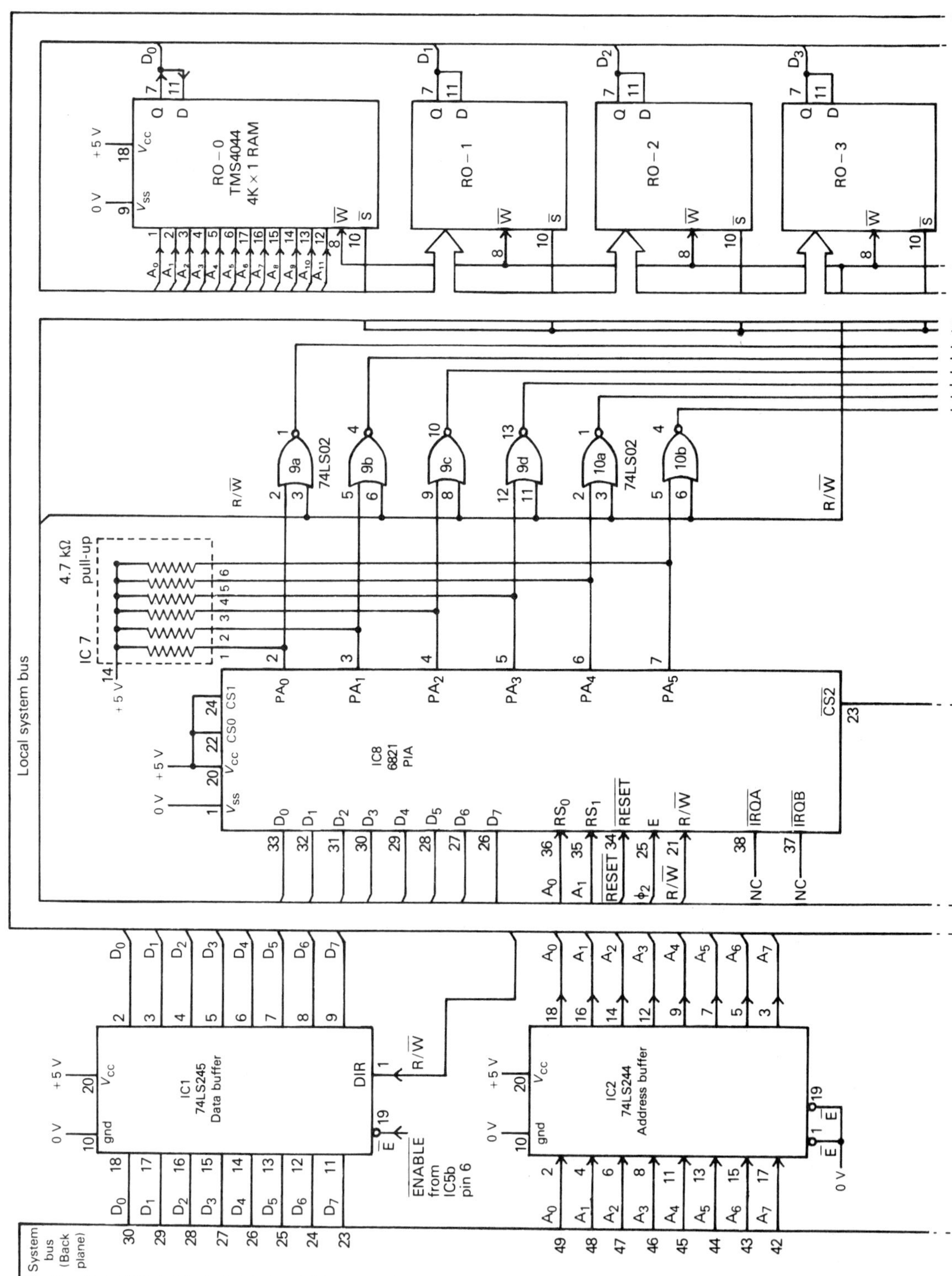
RO – 0
TMS4044
4K × 1 RAM
RO – 1
RO – 2
RO – 3
74LS02
4.7 kΩ pull-up
IC 7
Local system bus
IC8
6821
PIA
IC1
74LS245
Data buffer
IC2
74LS244
Address buffer
ENABLE from IC5b pin 6
System bus (Back plane)

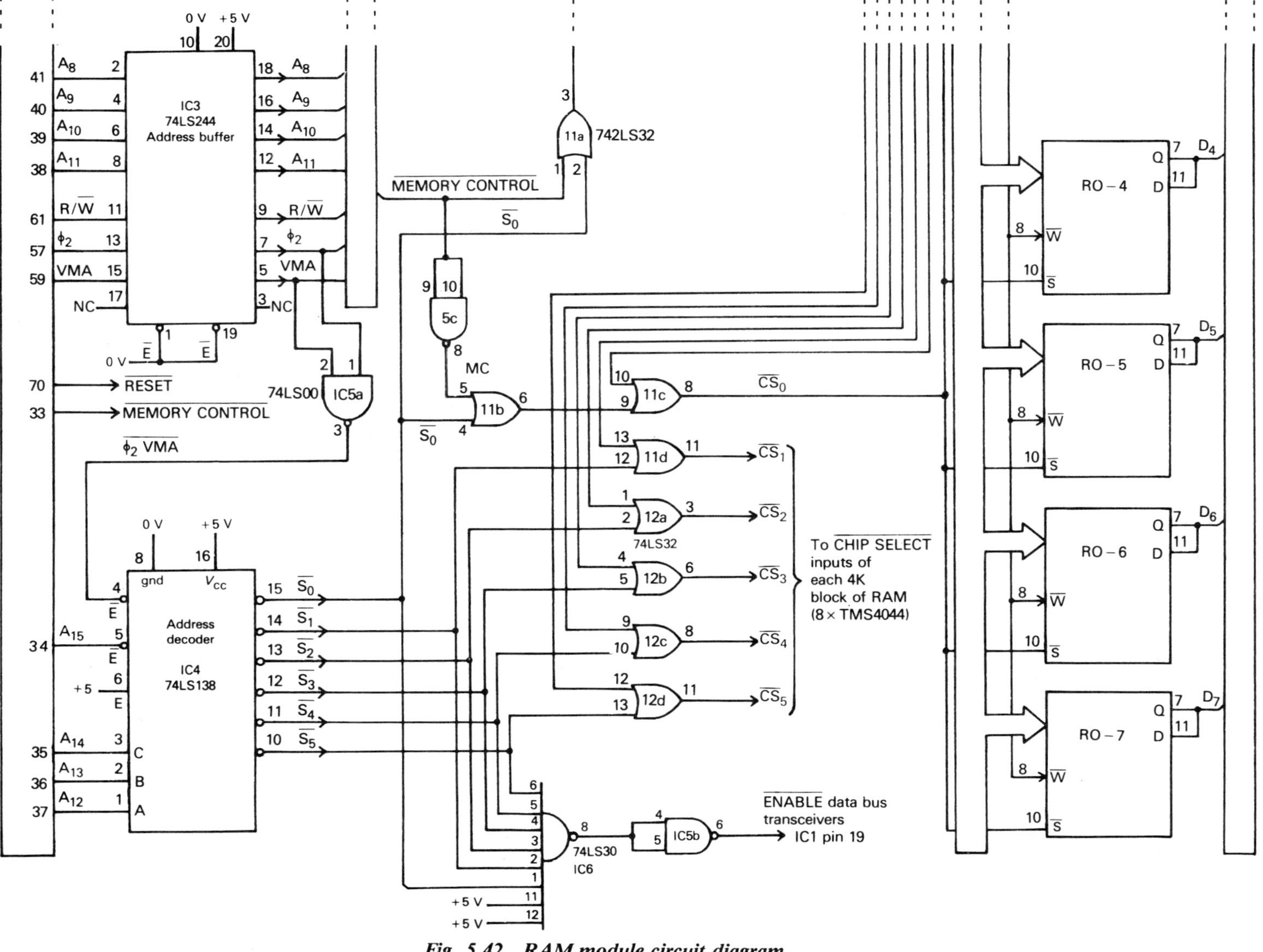

Fig. 5.42 RAM module circuit diagram

Listing 5.1 The implementation of the write-protect facility

```
         .
         .
         .
         .
         .
         .
PROT     JSR      MCCLR        clear memory control to access PIA on RAM module
         LDA  A #$FE           clear LS bit to write protect RAM 0000-0FFF
         JSR      WPROT        write to PIA on RAM module
         JSR      MCSET        restore memory control
         .
         .
         .
         .
UNPROT   JSR      MCCLR        clear memory control
         LDA  A #$FF           set all bits to remove memory protection
         JSR      WPROT        write to PIA
         JSR      MCSET        restore memory control
         .
         .
         .
         .
         .
         .
         .
         ORG      $E000
MPIAC    EQU      $EC13        PIA on CPU module (side B control)
RPIAD    EQU      $0000        PIA on RAM module (side A data)
RPIAC    EQU      $0001        PIA on RAM module (side A control)
*
MCCLR    LDA  A MPIAC          get PIA status/control word
         ORA  A #%00110000     set bits 4 and 5
         AND  A #%11110111     clear bit 3
         STA  A MPIAC          write to control register to clear memory control
         RTS                   return
MCSET    LDA  A MPIAC          get PIA status/control word
         ORA  A #%00111000     set bits 3, 4 and 5
         STA  A MPIAC          write to control register to set memory control
         RTS                   return
WPROT    PSH  A                save accumulator A
         CLR      RPIAC        select DDR by clearing control register bit 2
         LDA  A #$FF           select side A as output
         STA  A RPIAD          write ones into DDR
         LDA  A #$04           set bit 2 to select data register
         STA  A RPIAC
         PUL  A                restore accumulator A
         STA  A RPIAD          write it into data register
         RTS
```

PROBLEMS

1. Is the choice of an FPGA as the address decoder on the CPU module a good idea?

2. If the FPGA were not available, how else could the address decoding on the CPU module be implemented?

3. Design address-decoding networks to satisfy the following memory maps:

	(a)		(b)
RAM1	0000 – 0FFF	RAM	0000 – 03FF
RAM2	1000 – 1FFF	I/O 1	E800– E803
I/O 1	C000– C001	I/O 2	E804– E807
I/O 2	C002– C003	ROM	F800– FFFF
ROM	F000– FFFF		

   Compare and contrast the various ways of implementing the address-decoding networks in the above two examples. How would the decision to employ partial address decoding affect the design of the decoders?

4. A write-only port is located at 8000, and is written to from an instruction (STA A 8000) at FE00. Design an address-decoding network for this port so that it will respond to a write made from FE00 but not to a write made from any other location.

5. Memory-mapped I/O wastes memory space. Devise an arrangement whereby one I/O port is used to define several others. That is, by writing a number into a port at location X, the port at location Y can be defined as an ACIA, PIA etc.

6. If 64K-bit memory components were used to implement the memory space of a 6800 system, how would the designer deal with the requirements of memory-mapped I/O?

7. In some microprocessor systems, a nine-bit wide memory is used. The ninth bit is a parity bit defined by

$$d_8 = d_0 \oplus d_1 \oplus \cdots \oplus d_7.$$

   Bit d_8 is generated during a CPU-write cycle and stored in the memory. When the CPU reads from the memory a new value of d_8 is calculated and compared with the stored value. If they are different an error is assumed to have occurred and an interrupt generated. Design the logic circuitry needed to implement this arrangement.

8. Suppose a certain non-6800-system compatible I/O device were to be used in a 6800 system. This device has the following property. At the end of a CPU-write cycle, the data at its input must be held for at least 150 ns after the $\overline{CS}$, R/$\overline{W}$ and address buses have changed. How would this device be interfaced to a 6800 bus?

6

Input/Output: A Closer Look

In Chapter 5 we described how the 6800 has to effect all data transfers between the microprocessor system and the outside world by means of memory-mapped I/O ports.* While a simple latch may serve as an adequate output port for an LED display, or a tri-state buffer may be perfect for sensing the position of a switch, the general-purpose microprocessor system needs a more sophisticted form of I/O to deal with the wide range of devices to which it may be connected.

In order to free the CPU from the mundane tasks associated with input or output operations, the microprocessor manufacturers have provided the engineer with a broad spectrum of interface devices. These I/O devices often have circuit complexities which rival those of the CPU itself. If the cost of LSI interface chips is to be kept down, they must be manufactured in large quantities and hence any given chip must be versatile enough for a wide range of applications. This versatility is made possible by making a multi-function I/O device and then allowing the particular function required to be selectable under software control. For example, a typical parallel port has eight lines which can be defined as inputs or outputs (or any combination of either) simply by loading the appropriate control code into one of the peripheral's registers.

The currently available input/output peripherals may be loosely grouped into three types:

(1) *Serial ports* This group includes those peripherals which communicate with each other, or with other external devices, by means of a single data link (or two links if bidirectional data tranfers are required). Such devices are commonly employed to interface the CPU with a VDT or a Teletype, or with another microprocessor system which is situated remotely. Serial ports are able to take a byte of data (or part of a byte) and transmit it serially, bit by bit.

* An exception to this rule is input/output by means of DMA, where data is transferred between the system memory and peripherals without the intervention of the CPU.

Conversely, the serial port can receive a stream of serial bits and assemble them into a byte, which can then be moved to the microprocessor's accumulator. Because there are several possible ways of formatting data, the serial interface can be set, under software control, to operate in the required mode.

(2) *Parallel ports* A parallel port operates, simultaneously, on all the eight bits of a data word, unlike a serial port. The parallel port may have, typically, 16 or 24 I/O lines, which can be defined under software control as input or output lines. Additional control lines are always provided to indicate to external devices that data is available from the port, or to indicate to the CPU that data is available at the port.

(3) *Special-function ports* Once the microprocessor manufacturers had produced serial and parallel I/O ports, which were essential if the microprocessors were to be efficiently interfaced with VDTs and tape or disk storage devices, they began to create a range of peripherals to perform specific functions. One of the first such devices was the programmable timer which, by means of internal counters, is able to count events, measure intervals, and generate either single pulses or continuous squarewaves. Special-purpose memory-mapped peripherals have been developed to replace large amounts of MSI TTL circuitry in the following applications.

DMA controller The DMA controller contains all the logic necessry to transfer a given number of words between a peripheral (e.g. disk) and RAM. Such an operation involves generating the addresses of the memory locations into (or from) which data is moved, together with the control signals necessary to execute a write (or a read) cycle.

CRT controller The CRT controller replaces much of the logic found in a VDT. With a little additional hardware the CRT controller permits a block of data, stored in RAM, to be displayed on a standard television screen. Some CRT controllers allow the format (i.e. number of rows and columns of data) of the display to be defined by software.

Keyboard interface The keyboard controller scans a matrix of keys to produce a code, depending on the position of the key in the matrix, and a strobe to indicate that a key has been pressed. The keyboard may be designed to generate ASCII-encoded data (the normal representation of alphanumeric characters) or data representing the functions of a cash register.

Floppy-disk controller This is a very sophisticated device, approaching the microprocessor chip in its complexity. A floppy-disk controller handles the sequence of operations needed to move data between the CPU and the floppy-disk interface. The floppy-disk controller is also able to format (i.e. initialize) a floppy disk to the IBM 3470 standard.

IEEE interface controller The IEEE 488-1975 is a standard digital interface designed to transmit digital data between instruments and system components. This interface transmits or receives data, a byte at a time, and employs 16 lines, eight of which carry the data and eight of which handle the bus management. The IEEE bus is normally found in the world of automatic test equipment where programmable signal sources (power supplies and frequency generators) and programmable measuring equipment (voltmeters and frequency meters) can be controlled from it. A computer may be coupled to the bus so that it can set up the conditions under which a measurement is made, take the measurement, and perform any necessary computations on the result. The IEEE interface controller performs all the functions necessary to move data between the IEEE bus and the CPU.

In a later section three of the 6800 series peripherals are described: the 6821 parallel port, the 6850 serial port, and the 6840 programmable timer module. Before describing these devices in detail it is necessary to discuss two topics closely associated with I/O techniques: interrupts and handshakes. An interrupt is a request for attention by a peripheral. The CPU responds to this request by suspending its current activity and dealing with the cause of the interrupt. After the interrupt has been processed the CPU continues from where it left off. The power of an interrupt lies in its ability to reduce the amount of time the CPU spends in I/O activities. When a computer's I/O is said to be interrupt driven it means that the computer does not go looking for input (or checking to see that an output device is ready for more data), but that the computer can continue executing programs until an I/O device signals its request for attention by generating an interrupt. A more detailed account of interrupts is given in Section 6.1.

Handshaking is a transaction which takes place between a CPU and a peripheral, and involves the acknowledgement of a receipt of data. Conceptually, handshaking may be thought of as a form of recorded delivery. Normally the postman puts a letter through a letter box. He does not know whether the letter was actually received. In a recorded delivery the recipient signs for the letter (a handshake) which proves that the letter has been received.

In an earlier section a simple memory-mapped I/O port without provision for handshaking was described. This form of I/O is termed single ended because there is no feedback from the device receiving (or generating) the data. Consequently, the CPU is forced to operate in a conservative mode, sending (or receiving) data at a rate low enough to guarantee that the data is always ready either from the peripheral or for use by the peripheral. An illustration of the mechanism of handshaking is given in Fig. 6.1. Data is to be transmitted from a memory-mapped output device to a peripheral (e.g. a tape punch). Between points A and B, in Fig. 6.1, the data from the output device is stable. At point C the output device issues a data-available strobe which indicates the presence of valid data (cf. VMA in a 6800 system). The data-available strobe returns to zero at D before the data begins to change. When the peripheral has received the data, it sends an acknowledgement which occurs at point E. The duration CE represents the waiting time. What happens next depends on the way the handshaking is implemented. The active transition of the

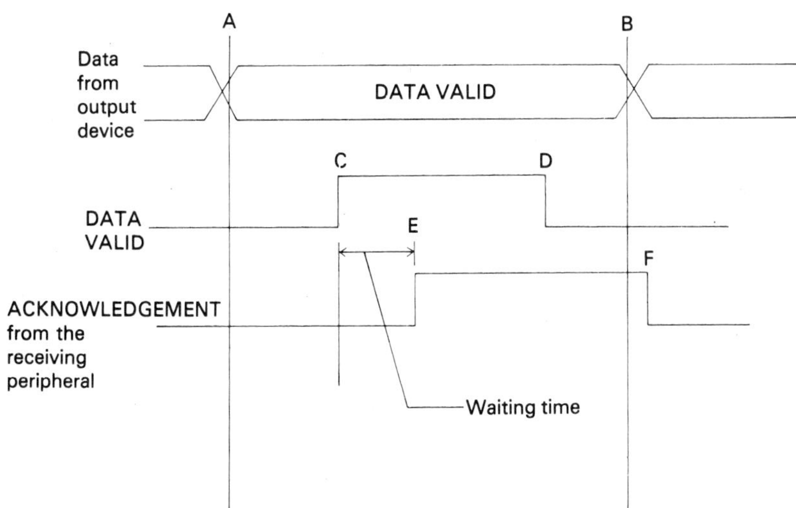

Fig. 6.1 The timing diagram of a handshaking operation

acknowledge line may be used to remove the data-available signal and therefore permit the execution of the next operation (asynchronous operation), or the CPU may continue normally after point B where AB is a fixed length of time (synchronous operation). The difference between these options depends on the purpose of the handshaking mechanism. In the former case the handshake is employed to let the CPU continue to the next operation as soon as the data has been received, while in the latter case the handshaking simply serves as a confirmation that the data has been received.

Data transfers involving a handshake can incur a penalty. If any part of the handshake sequence fails, the CPU may be "locked up". For example, if an acknowledgement is not received from a peripheral, because someone forgot to switch on a remote paper-tape punch, the CPU may be frozen into a permanent waiting state. As the paper-tape punch is often not vital to the running of the CPU (the system can happily continue with its other operations after printing "please switch on the paper-tape punch" on the system console), the handshake mechanism has proved a threat to the integrity of the system. To remove this danger many systems using a handshake also have a "time-out" mechanism which abandons the data transfer if an acknowledgement is not received within a reasonable period of time.

6.1 INTERRUPTS

A microprocessor executes instructions sequentially unless a JUMP or BRANCH operation causes the contents of the program counter to be modified. This arrangement can, under certain circumstances, be very inefficient. Suppose the microprocessor is reading data from a keyboard at an average rate of, say, two characters per second. In a 6800 system the CPU reads the status of a memory-mapped peripheral to determine whether a key has been pressed. If no key has been pressed a branch is made to the instruction which reads the status of the peripheral, and the cycle is continued until a key is pressed. Once a key has been pressed, the CPU reads the data and continues with the program. A read operation followed by a conditional branch takes the 6800 8 μs at a 1 MHz clock rate. If a key is pressed on average every 0.5 s, the CPU executes the "test status" loop 62 500 times per keystroke. This represents a considerable waste of valuable processing time. The last statement is meaningful only if the CPU has something else to do instead of periodically sampling the status of the keyboard. If the microprocessor is executing a single program, e.g. a calculation in BASIC, the loss of time is unimportant. But if the microprocessor is executing more than one program on a multiprogramming basis, the loss of CPU time is of vital importance.

An alternative arrangement to continually sampling the status of the keyboard is to let the keyboard indicate to the CPU that data is available after a key has been pressed. This arrangement has a clearly asynchronous nature because the CPU cannot know that a key is about to be pressed. Consequently a mechanism must be instituted which forces the CPU to stop its current sequence of operations and pay attention to the needs of the keyboard. The interrupt is such a mechanism.

An interrupt is an asynchronous signal, normally generated by a peripheral, which forces the CPU to suspend its normal sequence of operations and then to execute a program called an interrupt-service routine. When a microprocessor has been interrupted, it finishes its current machine instruction and then stores a copy of the address of its next instruction in a safe place. In this way the CPU knows where to return to after the interrupt-service routine has been executed.

The 6800 deals with interrupts in a more sophisticated manner than some other microprocessors. Following an interrupt the 6800 pushes all its working registers onto its stack, somewhere within its read/write memory space. After the interrupt has been dealt with, all the working registers can be restored to their original values by executing the RTI instruction (return from interrupt) and the CPU continues as if nothing had happened. This arrangement has two advantages. Firstly, it makes life easy for the programmer as he does not need to know where the working registers are stored, and does not have to bother about storing a subset of the working registers currently in use. Secondly, by using a stack mechanism to store the working registers, interrupts themselves may be interrupted. The principal disadvantage of this scheme is that all working registers are saved on the stack, irrespective of whether they are currently in use or not. This action wastes times in situations where only the A accumulator and the condition-code register are going to be used in the interrupt-handling routine.

Four types of interrupt are supported by the 6800. A non-maskable interrupt (NMI), a maskable interrupt (IRQ), a pseudo-interrupt (RESET), and a software interrupt (SWI). The software interrupt has all the characteristics of a hardware interrupt (NMI or IRQ), with the exception that it is initiated by a programmed instruction. The software interrupt is used as a very powerful programming aid, particularly for debugging purposes when a software interrupt forces all working registers onto the stack where they can be examined and displayed. The reset operation of the 6800 may best be thought of as a pseudo-interrupt because it has some, but not all, of the characteristics of an IRQ or an NMI. A reset is initiated by bringing the $\overline{\text{RESET}}$ input of the 6800 low for a minimum of eight clock cycles. When the 6800 detects a reset it loads the contents of memory locations FFFE and FFFF into the program counter. However, the working registers are not stored on the stack after a reset (because the stack is not defined prior to an initial reset following the power-up sequence), and there is no concept of return from reset. The reset does force the CPU to execute an initialization program in the same way that IRQs or NMIs force the CPU to execute an interrupt-handling routine.

After the CPU has recognized an interrupt and saved the working registers it must service the interrupt by executing an interrupt-handling routine. This requires the address of the interrupt-handling routine. The 6800 gets the address by loading the program counter with the contents of memory locations FFFC and FFFD following an NMI, and the contents of memory locations FFF8 and FFF9 following an IRQ. This is a form of indirect addressing because the effective address of the interrupt-handling routine must be obtained indirectly via another memory location. Such an arrangement is better than directly specifying the address of the interrupt-handling routine because it allows the programmer to locate his interrupt-handling routines anywhere within the 64K memory space. A disadvantage of this arrangement is that the 6800 cannot distinguish between an interrupt initiated by a particular device in an environment where many different devices are capable of initiating an interrupt. An alternative arrangement (lacking in the 6800) is to let the interrupting device supply the address of its own interrupt-handling routine via the data bus.

In any reasonably complex microprocessor system it is probable that several interface devices, each capable of initiating an interrupt, will be in use. These devices communicate with the CPU by means of the 6800's active-low $\overline{\text{IRQ}}$ input—the $\overline{\text{NMI}}$ input is normally reserved for special purposes and will be dealt with later. The $\overline{\text{IRQ}}$ input is level sensitive and requests the 6800 to begin an interrupt sequence whenever $\overline{\text{IRQ}} = 0$ (the $\overline{\text{NMI}}$ input is edge sensitive, which means that a non-maskable interrupt request is not generated by $\overline{\text{NMI}} = 0$ but by a 1 to 0 transition at the $\overline{\text{NMI}}$ input). In a typical 6800 system all the memory-mapped peripherals involved in the interrupt-request scheme have their open-drain $\overline{\text{IRQ}}$ outputs connected to the CPU's $\overline{\text{IRQ}}$ input. A pull-up resistor, typically 3.3 kΩ, is required at the CPU. In this way the 6800 can recognize an interrupt request but *not* the device which generated the interrupt.

After the 6800 has responded to an interrupt request, saved its registers on the stack, and executed a jump to the memory location whose address is stored at FFF8/9, it must determine what action is to be taken by locating the peripheral responsible for the interrupt request. Because all peripherals look the same to the 6800, the CPU must determine the cause of the interrupt by *asking* each peripheral in turn if it initiated the interrupt. This process is known as polling. All the memory-mapped peripheral devices designed to be compatible with the 6800 system have internal status registers containing one or more interrupt flags. Whenever a peripheral pulls $\overline{\text{IRQ}}$ low to initiate an interrupt, the appropriate interrupt flag is set within the peripheral. After the 6800 has recognized the interrupt all the interrupt-handling routine has to do is to examine all the status registers until the active interrupt flag has been located. Once this has been done and the CPU knows which peripheral requires attention, a jump can be executed to the interrupt-handling routine dealing specifically with the operation of the peripheral.

The polling procedure has the advantage of inherent simplicity. One basic interrupt-handling routine deals with all the peripherals and then directs the CPU to the appropriate routine once the cause of the interrupt has been found. Polling is simple because the hardware necessary to implement it is minimal and it is, therefore, cheap. The disadvantage of polling is that it becomes inefficient (i.e. wastes CPU time) when a large number of peripherals are to be polled. Suppose a 6800 system has 20 memory-mapped peripherals each capable of causing an interrupt. A polling routine might have a loop which takes 23 μs to check a single peripheral. To test each peripheral a total of 460 μs ≈ ½ms is taken. Clearly, if the last device to be tested initiates a large number of interrupts, at best the efficiency of the system is degraded and at worst the system simply collapses because successive interrupts cannot be handled in the time available. A partial solution to this problem is to poll the devices requiring rapid servicing first and relegate those devices which generate fewer interrupts or interrupts with larger intervals between them to the end of the polling list.

6.1.1 Interrupt Prioritizing

In an environment where more than one source of an interrupt is possible, but not all interrupts assume an equal importance, mechanisms are usually implemented to deal with interrupts which are either more important or whose servicing is more urgent than others. Such an arrangement is known as interrupt prioritizing. Two cases of multiple interrupt need to be considered. Firstly, it is possible for two interrupts to occur effectively simultaneously. That is, because the microprocessor tests its interrupt flag at the beginning of each instruction-fetch operation, two or more interrupts occurring during the previous operation are recognized simultaneously irrespective of the actual order of the interrupts. Secondly, an interrupt request may occur and later a second interrupt request may be generated while the first interrupt is being processed.

The prioritization of interrupts may be implemented in hardware, or software, or in a combination of both. The problem of effectively simultaneous interrupts may be dealt with by software polling as described above. By examining the interrupt flag of the most important peripheral first, prioritization is automatically implemented. Alternatively, the interrupt-request prioritization may be implemented in hardware by a priority encoder which has n input lines, one from each of the peripherals, and an interrupt-request strobe which is connected to the CPU's $\overline{\text{IRQ}}$ input. A second output of the priority encoder is connected to a latch, which may be read by the CPU. Whenever a peripheral generates an interrupt the priority encoder generates a strobe to the CPU and sets the latch with the number of the interrupt (i.e. 1 to n). The priority encoder is arranged to supply the number of the interrupt with the highest priority if more than one interrupt request input goes low. There are, in fact, many possible arrangements of a priority encoder.

The problem of interrupts being themselves interrupted becomes acute when some peripherals demand immediate attention. For example, if an interrupt is generated by a disk system transferring data to the CPU at a rate of one byte per 32 μs, then the interrupt must be serviced before the next byte is read from the disk, otherwise the current byte will be lost. Obviously it is reasonable to allow an interrupt initiated by a disk system to interrupt one initiated by a keyboard, but not vice versa. The priority encoder is designed to generate an interrupt request to the CPU only if a new interrupt has a greater priority than the current interrupt, and hence caters for nested interrupts.

The 6800 has an interrupt-mask bit in the condition-code register which, when set, inhibits the recognition of interrupt requests. After the 6800 has recognized an interrupt, it sets the interrupt-mask bit, disabling further interrupts. It is, of course, now up to the programmer whether further interrupts are permitted before the end of the current interrupt, when the old value of condition-code register is restored with its interrupt-request mask bit cleared. (If the pre-interrupt interrupt mask bit was not clear the interrupt would never have been serviced in the first place.) The programmer can therefore use the interrupt mask bit to stop further interrupts during any critical operation, and to permit nested interrupts during non-critical periods.

6.1.2 The Non-maskable Interrupt

The non-maskable interrupt, as its name suggests, cannot be masked at the CPU and hence a high-to-low transition on the $\overline{\text{NMI}}$ input always initiates the non-maskable interrupt sequence. Consequently the NMI is reserved for events which must be dealt with at the time they occur. Such events are a power-down condition or a real-time clock. It is possible to detect a failure of the mains power several milliseconds before the voltage at the terminals of the CPU falls below the point at which operation ceases or becomes unreliable. On detecting a power failure an NMI can be generated which saves the machine status and initiates an orderly shut down—this is especially important when disk systems are in use. The NMI can also be used to switch in alternative sources of power until the mains is restored.

A real-time clock keeps track of the actual time of day and may be implemented by updating a counter each time an NMI occurs. In this way the CPU always has access to a time-of-day clock. Furthermore, this clock is important in a multiprogramming environment when several programs are held simultaneously in memory and control is passed sequentially between the programs. Normally, each user program is assigned a number of ticks of the clock depending on its priority. After each program has used its allocation of ticks, control is passed to the next program. If, for any reason, the NMI was masked, the loss of a real-time clock interrupt would result in a discrepancy (possibly cumulative) between the microprocessor's internal record of the time and the actual time of day.

6.1.3 Vectored Interrupts

Some microprocessor systems employ an arrangement whereby the interrupting peripheral itself supplies the CPU with the information necessary to locate the interrupt-handling routine, without the need for polling. The actual mechanism by which the interrupting device communicates the address of its interrupt-handling routine varies from microprocessor to microprocessor. In some cases the contents of the address bus may be modified to provide an interrupt vector, while in other cases the interrupting device may use the data bus to issue a pseudo-operation, e.g. a reset or a jump to subroutine. The 6800 is sometimes (incorrectly) described as having a vectored-interrupt facility, because the response to an interrupt is to load the contents of memory locations FFF8/9 into the program counter. However, as the region FFF8 – FFFF is invariably ROM (because the reset vector must be retained while the power is switched off) the interrupt-request vector cannot be modified by the peripheral which caused the interrupt.

6.1.4 The 6828 Priority-interrupt Controller

Because the 6800 has only one interrupt request input a software polling arrangement must be implemented if two or more peripherals, capable of generating an interrupt, are to form part of the system. In order to avoid this time-consuming polling procedure, Motorola have introduced a hardware device giving the 6800 a vectored-interrupt facility. The 6828 priority interrupt controller (PIC) has eight active-low interrupt request inputs and produces an interrupt-request strobe together with a four-bit vector in response to a logical zero at one of its inputs. As we shall see, the operation of the PIC is entirely transparent to the 6800. The interrupt request inputs of the 6828 are prioritized by pin number (i.e. the priority of an input cannot be modified under software control).

Figure 6.2 illustrates how the 6828 PIC is used in a 6800 system. The 6828 is a rather unusual device, having some of the characteristics of a memory-mapped peripheral plus the features of an "engineering fix". The way in which the 6828 provides the 6800 with a vectored-interrupt facility is simple. In an unmodified 6800 system the program counter is loaded with the contents of memory locations FFF8 and FFF9 (the fixed interrupt vector) following an interrupt request. This operation cannot be modified because it is a function of the internal structure of the 6800. However, the 6828 solves the problem of the fixed interrupt vector by detecting an interrupt and then modifying the contents of the address bus to create an effective address, whose value is a function of the state of the 6828's inputs.

The 6828 has four address inputs which are connected to $A_1 - A_4$ of the system bus. The least significant address bit A_0 is not used, because all interrupt vectors consist of two bytes, one fetched from an even address ($A_0 = 0$) and one fetched from an odd address ($A_0 = 1$). The four address outputs of the 6828, labelled $Z_1 - Z_4$, are connected to the $A_1 - A_4$ address inputs of the ROM containing the reset and interrupt vectors. As long as the 6828 is unselected the values of $Z_1 - Z_4$ are identical to those of $A_1 - A_4$. That is, the low-order address bits are transmitted without modification. When the 6828 is selected by $\overline{CS0} = 0$ and $CS1 = 1$ and by $\overline{A_1}\,\overline{A_2}A_3A_4R/\overline{W} = 1$, the values of $Z_1 - Z_4$ are determined by which of its interrupt-request inputs are active. The above logical conditions correspond to a read access to memory locations FFF8 or FFF9, which is, of course, what happens after an interrupt. Thus, although the 6800 thinks it is fetching a constant address pointing to a single interrupt-handling routine, it is in fact fetching one of nine vectors corresponding to nine interrupt-handling routines.

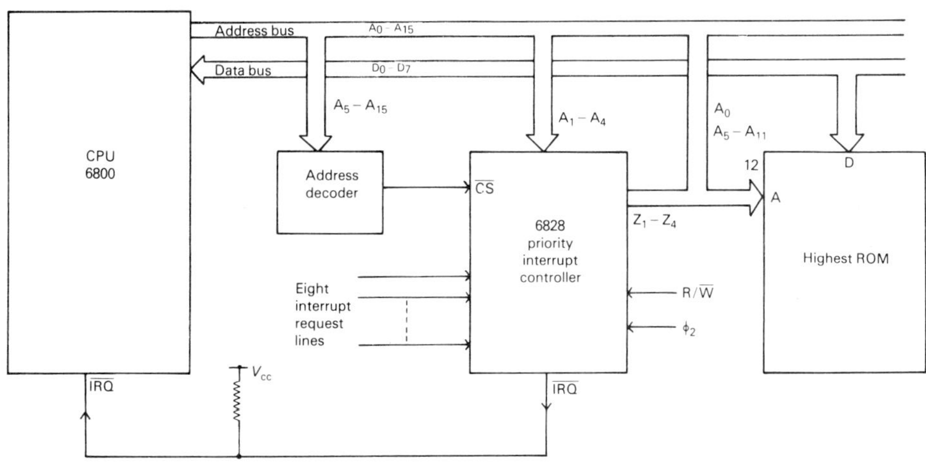

Fig. 6.2 The application of the 6828 PIC in a 6800 system

Table 6.1 gives the relationship between the address outputs of the 6828 and the interrupt request inputs. A useful facility of the 6828 is that it does not entirely usurp the normal interrupt action of the 6800. The $\overline{IRQ}$ output of the 6828 has an open collector output so that other peripherals may have their interrupt request output connected *directly* to the CPU's $\overline{IRQ}$ input. When one of these peripherals issues an interrupt request, the 6828 is bypassed and an interrupt vector is fetched from FFF8/9 as in an unmodified system. In this way existing polled interrupts can still be used with the 6828, or expansion beyond 8 interrupting devices by means of polling may be implemented.

Table 6.1 The Effect of the 6828 PIC on the Vector Fetched after an Interrupt Request

Interrupt-request input	*Address output when selected* Z_4	Z_3	Z_2	Z_1	*Equivalent hexadecimal address*	*ROM contains the address vector of*
$\overline{IN7}$ (highest)	1	0	1	1	FFF6/7	Priority 7 routine
$\overline{IN6}$	1	0	1	0	FFF4/5	6
$\overline{IN5}$	1	0	0	1	FFF2/3	5
$\overline{IN4}$	1	0	0	0	FFF0/1	4
$\overline{IN3}$	0	1	1	1	FFEE/F	3
$\overline{IN2}$	0	1	1	0	FFEC/D	2
$\overline{IN1}$	0	1	0	1	FFEA/B	1
$\overline{IN0}$ (lowest)	0	1	0	0	FFE8/9	0
NONE	1	1	0	0	FFF8/9	Default routine

Figure 6.3 gives a block diagram of the internal arrangement of a 6828 PIC. The heart of the 6828 is a 4-bit multiplexer which switches the four output address lines between the input address lines and an address chosen from a look-up table.

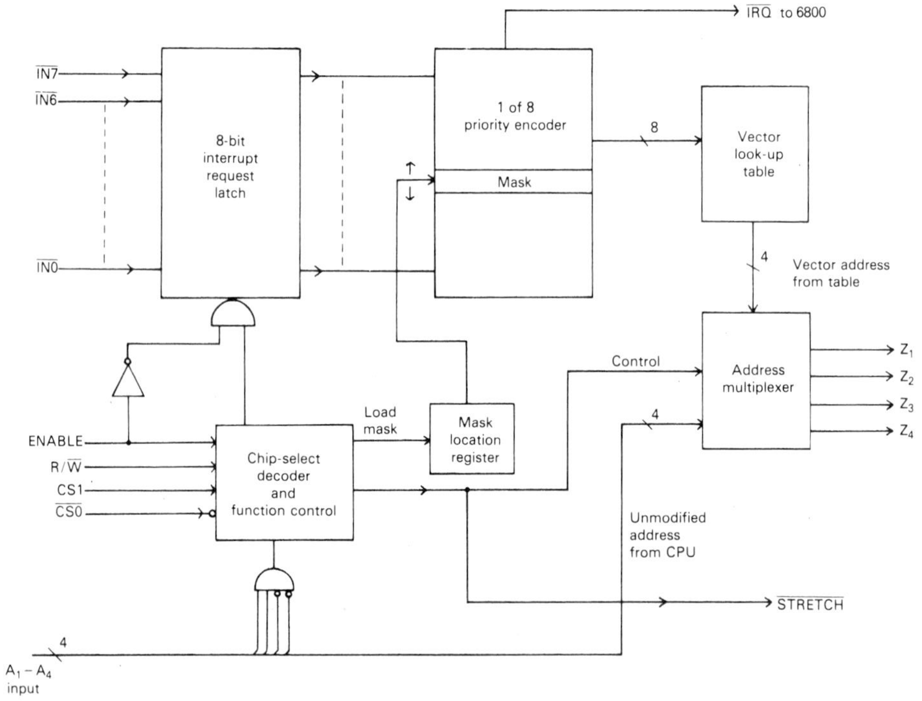

Fig. 6.3 The internal arrangement of the 6828 PIC

The particular address chosen from the table is determined by the peripheral which pulls down one of the 6828's interrupt-request inputs. The interrupt-request inputs are routed through a priority encoder ensuring that the address selected from the look-up table corresponds to the interrupt input with the highest priority. Priority is assigned sequentially, with $\overline{IN7}$ having the highest priority and $\overline{IN0}$ the lowest. If, for example, an interrupt occurs on $\overline{IN4}$, it can be interrupted by $\overline{IN5}$ or higher but not by $\overline{IN3}$ or lower.

A primitive form of masking can be applied to the 6828 interrupt inputs. By loading a number into a mask register all interrupts with a value (i.e. $\overline{IN}_x$, where x is the value) below that of the mask register are inhibited. Note that even if an interrupt-request input is masked, any interrupt-request input is latched into the input register and is dealt with when the mask is cleared. This arrangement allows interrupts to be pending. If the 6828 were a conventional memory-mapped peripheral, the interrupt mask would be set by writing to the device directly. Motorola have decided to save the eight data pins in the following rather unusual way. The CPU only reads from the interrupt-request addresses. Clearly a write operation to the ROM at these locations has no meaning. In order to load the 6828's mask register, a dummy write cycle is executed in the address range FFE0 – FFFF. Bits $A_1 - A_4$ on the *address bus* are then written into the mask register of the PIC. This action is contrary to normal microprocessor operation. Table 6.2 gives the relationship between $A_1 - A_4$ and the PIC's mask register.

Table 6.2 Programming the PIC Mask Register

Write address	*Address bus $A_1 - A_4$* A_4	A_3	A_2	A_1	*All interrupts less than this level are disabled*
FFE0 or FFE1	0	0	0	0	All interrupts enabled
FFE2 or FFE3	0	0	0	1	IN1
FFE4 or FFE5	0	0	1	0	IN2
FFE6 or FFE7	0	0	1	1	IN3
FFE8 or FFE9	0	1	0	0	IN4
FFEA or FFEB	0	1	0	1	IN5
FFEC or FFED	0	1	1	0	IN6
FFEE or FFEF	0	1	1	1	IN7
FFF0 to FFFF	1	×	×	×	All interrupts disabled

Example Executing the code "STA A FFE8" causes interrupt levels IN0 – IN3 to be disabled and interrupt levels IN4 – IN7 to be enabled. Note that the contents of accumulator A play no part in this operation; it is merely the act of writing to FFE8 that loads the mask register of the PIC.

Adding a 6828 to an existing system can create timing problems. In a system without a 6828 the ROM containing the IRQ vector outputs data t_{acc} seconds after the appearance of a valid address at its inputs. When a 6828 is included in the system, an additional delay is incurred at the address inputs of the monitor ROM. This delay results from the time taken by the 6828 to detect the address FFF8/9, access its look-up table and then provide an output. This delay is typically 125 ns.

On occasions when this delay is unacceptable, the $\overline{\text{STRETCH}}$ output of the 6828 may be used to hold the CPU's ϕ_2 clock phase in the high state. Figure 6.4 gives the timing diagram of the 6828.

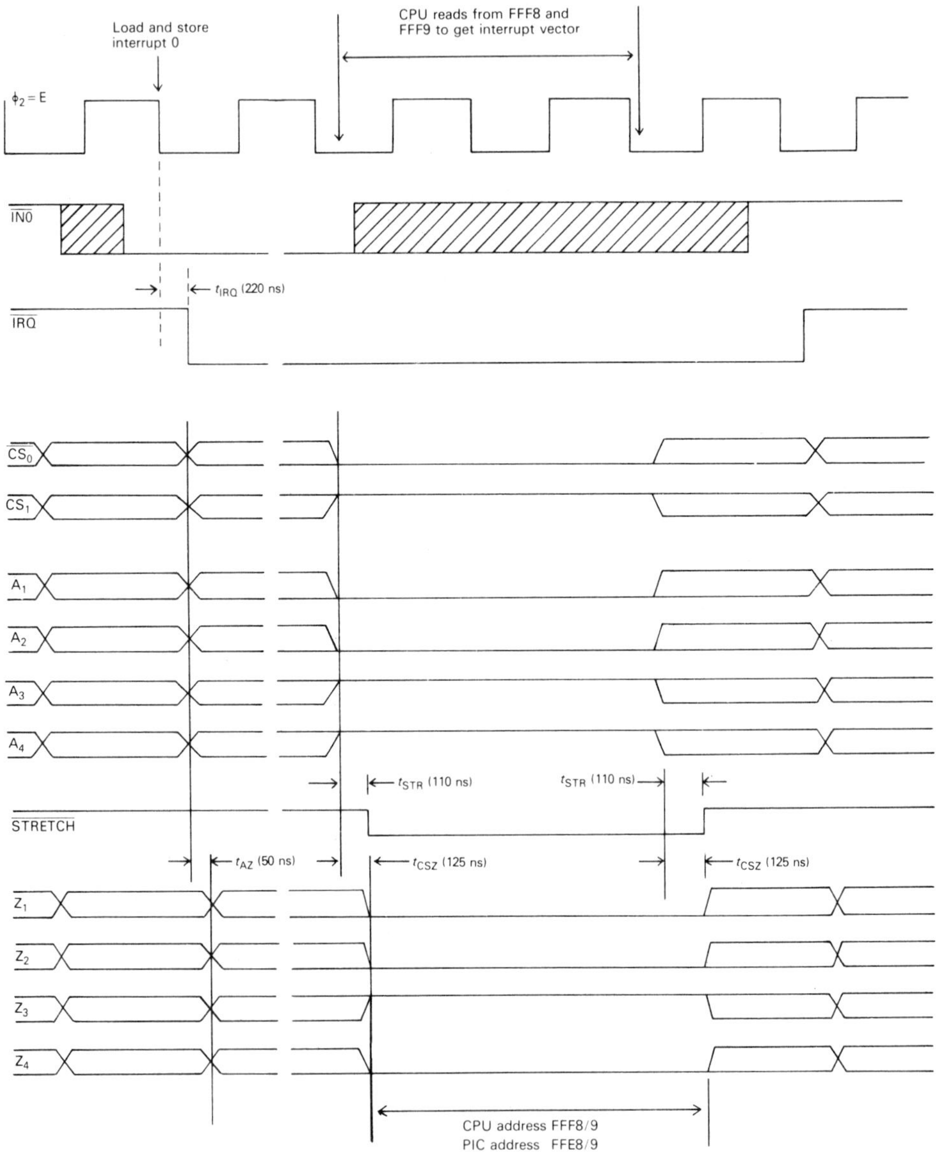

Fig. 6.4 The timing diagram of the 6828 PIC

The PIC on the CPU Module

The circuit diagram of the section of TS1's CPU module concerned with the handling of interrupts is given in Fig. 6.5. Whenever the CPU puts out a valid address in the range F000 – FFFF during the ϕ_2-high phase of a read cycle

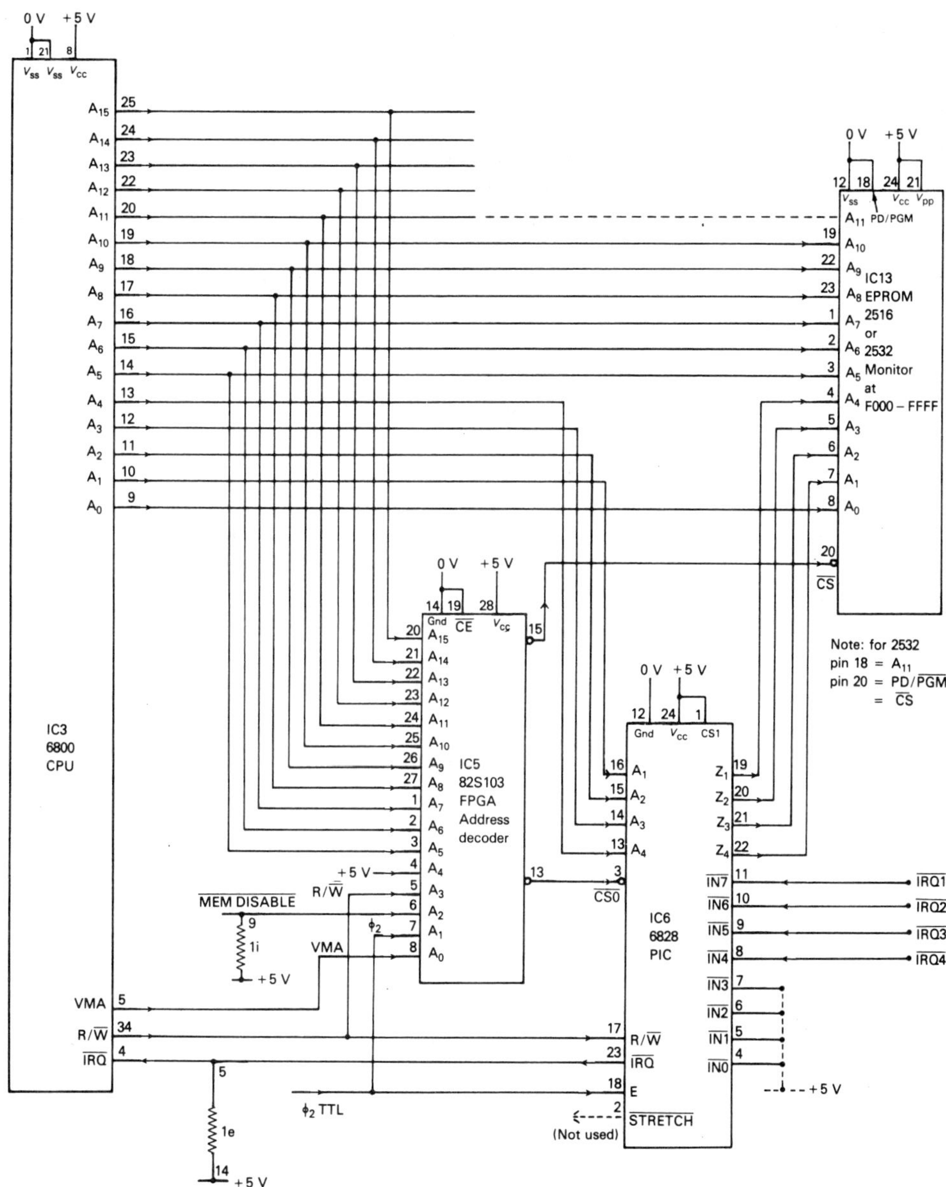

Fig. 6.5 The PIC on the CPU module

(see Table 5.9), the monitor ROM is enabled. The monitor has its address lines A_0 and A_5-A_{10} (plus A_{11} for a 2532) connected directly to the CPU. Address lines A_1-A_4 are routed to the monitor via the priority interrupt controller, IC6. The PIC is enabled whenever A_5-A_{15} and VMA are all high. In normal operation A_1-A_4 from the CPU are passed unmodified by the PIC to the monitor. When the CPU responds to an interrupt request by reading from FFF8 or FFF9, the PIC is enabled, detects a valid interrupt address and modifies A_1-A_4 to the monitor according to whichever of its eight interrupt-request inputs has been activated. The address-decoding arrangements for the PIC (Table 5.9) do not include ϕ_2. Whenever the PIC modifies the values of address lines A_1-A_4 following a selection by $\overline{CS0}.CS1.R/\overline{W}.\overline{A_1}.\overline{A_2}.A_3.A_4$, the address outputs to the monitor do not become valid until approximately 125 ns after the PIC's selection. Consequently if ϕ_2 took place in the enabling of the PIC (via $\overline{CS0}$ from the FPGA), the 125 ns delay in the PIC would have to be added to the ROM's access time. By not enabling the PIC with ϕ_2, the modified values of A_1-A_4 are present at the input to monitor ROM before the start of the ϕ_2 active-high cycle in which the read access is to take place.

Only four of the PIC's interrupt-request inputs have been connected to the back plane. These are the interrupts with the highest priorities $\overline{IN7}-\overline{IN4}$ and have been designated $\overline{IRQ1}-\overline{IRQ4}$ respectively. The unused interrupt-request inputs have been strapped to V_{cc} to avoid their spurious activation. Note that the PIC has internal 6 kΩ pull-up resistors at its interrupt-request inputs and therefore no additional pull-up resistors have been connected to $\overline{IRQ1}-\overline{IRQ4}$.

Using the PIC

Including a PIC in a 6800 system expands the number of interrupt-request vectors from one to nine, removing the need for software polling and adding a modicum of hardware prioritization. Instead of having a single interrupt-request handling routine at FFF8/9 it is now possible to have the address of nine such routines from FFE8/9 to FFF8/9. In this way the $\overline{IRQ}$ outputs of eight peripheral devices may be connected to the requisite inputs of the PIC—Section 6.2 deals with the interrupt mechanisms of three peripherals.

Two things should be made clear about the PIC. Firstly it is not wholeheartedly supported by Motorola. Because of the delay it introduces into the address paths of A_1-A_4 it is not well-suited to systems operating at 2 MHz with the MC68B00. Secondly, there are those who regard complex structures of prioritized interrupts as a positively bad thing. While a single real-time clock may not prove too much of a burden, a mixed bag of interrupts including keyboards, printers, timers, floppy-disk interfaces etc. may be a nightmare. Clearly with many possible sources of interrupt the system tends to become "asynchronous" and the programmer loses control of his own computer! Alternatives to complex interrupt-handling arrangements are software polling (power to the programmer), and autonomous subsystems. In the latter case a floppy-disk controller could be built round its own dedicated CPU, freeing the host CPU from the task of reading data from or writing data to the disk a sector at a time. Consequently, writing a block of data to the disk would require at most one interrupt request at the end of the operation, rather than numerous interrupts (one after each individual transfer) in the case of a disk controller without its own CPU.

6.2 SOME MEMORY-MAPPED PERIPHERALS

The range of microprocessor peripherals has expanded from the basic serial and parallel interfaces required in the vast majority of systems to quite esoteric devices found only in specialized applications. Table 6.3 gives details of some of the currently available interface chips, specifically designed for the 6800 CPU.

Table 6.3 The 6800 Series Interface Devices

Type	*Name*	*Description*
6820	PIA	Peripheral interface adapter—dual 8-bit parallel I/O port with handshake facilities.
6821	PIA	An improved version of the 6820.
6840	PTM	Programmable timer module—generates single or continuous pulses under software control.
6844	DMAC	Direct memory access controller—moves data between an external device and the system's RAM.
6850	ACIA	Asynchronous serial adapter—converts data from parallel to serial format and vice versa. Used to move data between the CPU and VDTs etc.
6852	SSDA	Synchronous serial data adapter—very similar to the 6850 except that the data is transmitted synchronously.
6845	CRTC	CRT controller—generates all the control and timing signals necessary to display the contents of a block of RAM on a raster scan display.
68488	GPIA	General-purpose interface adapter. Interfaces a 6800 system to the 16-line IEEE-488 bus.
6854	ADLC	Advanced data-link controller—a sophisticated synchronous serial data-link controller capable of very high data-transmission rates.
6843	FLDC	Floppy-disk controller—this device controls movement of data between a 6800 system and a floppy-disk unit.

In this section the 6821, 6850 and 6840 are described in some detail as these are the peripheral interface devices most likely to be found in the majority of microprocessor systems. The other devices in the above table are dedicated to specific functions and often can be used only with the addition of some further logic elements.

6.2.1 The 6821 PIA

The 6821 peripheral interface adapter contains the logic necessary to move data between the CPU's accumulators and one of two 8-bit ports. The eight lines which make up a port may be programmed individually to act as inputs or outputs, so that a port may, for example, be configured as 4 inputs and 4 outputs. Figure 6.6 gives a block diagram of the 6821. From this diagram it can be seen that the I/O ports, referred to as the "A side" and the "B side", appear symmetrical. In general this is true, but small differences in the behavior of these ports will be described when necessary. Each port has two control lines associated with it which can transform the port from a simple I/O latch into a device capable of performing a handshake or initiating interrupts, as required.

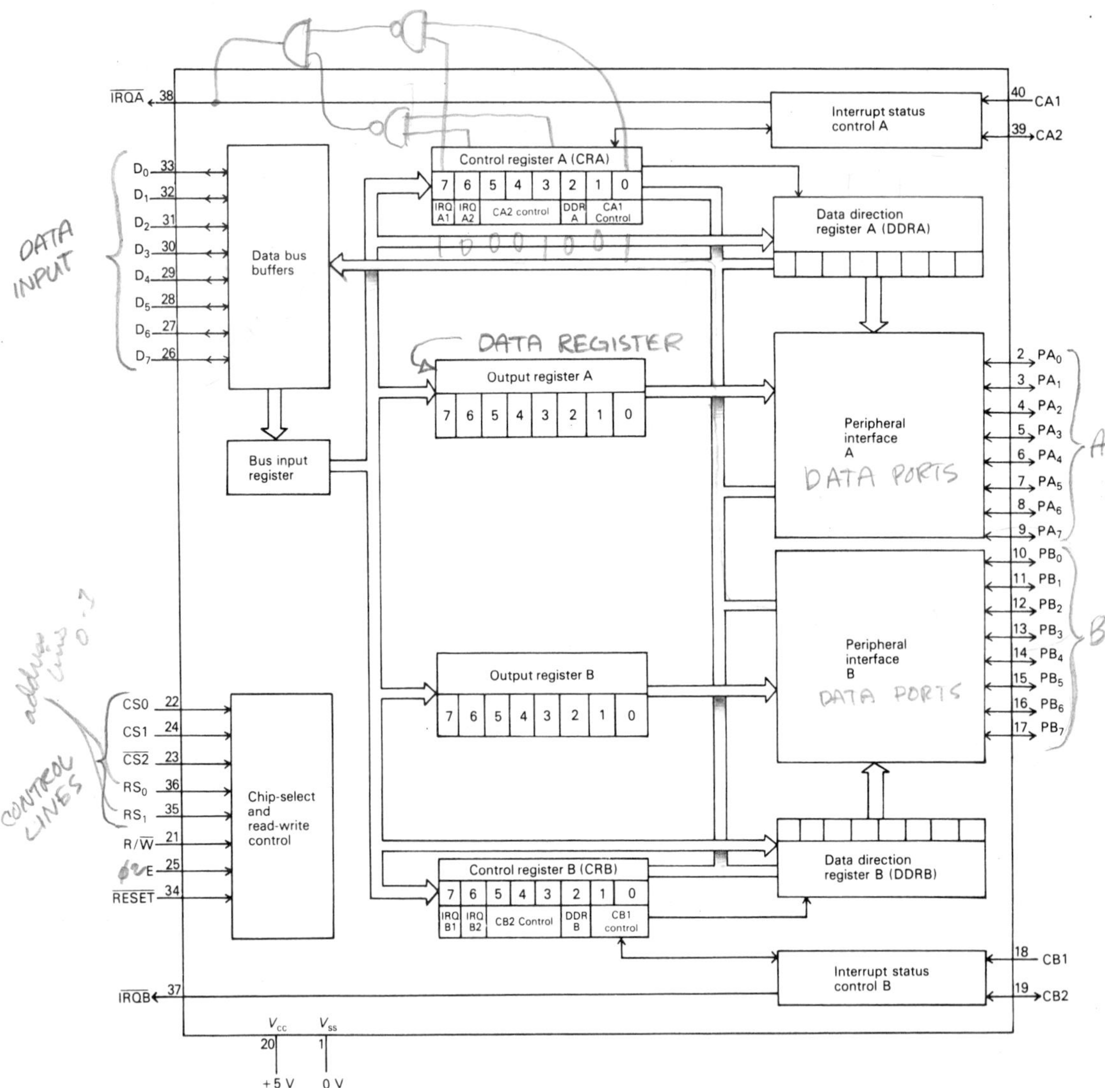

Fig. 6.6 The internal arrangement of the 6821 PIA

The interface between the PIA and the CPU is quite conventional. Fifteen of the PIA's "CPU-side" lines make the PIA look, to the CPU, like a block of RAM. These lines are the eight bidirectional data-bus lines, an $R/\overline{W}$ line, three chip selects (CS0, CS1, $\overline{CS2}$), an enable input (E), and two register select lines. The enable input is perhaps misnamed, as it is not simply an enable input but a timing input which is normally derived from the system's ϕ_2 clock. Timing on all other signals is referenced to the leading or trailing edge of the pulse at the E input. The two register-select lines (RS_0 and RS_1) are used by the CPU to discriminate between the PIA's internal registers and are normally connected to A_0 and A_1 of the CPU's address bus, respectively.

In addition to the interface to the CPU required for memory-mapped I/O, the PIA has a $\overline{RESET}$ input and two interrupt-request outputs ($\overline{IRQA}$ and $\overline{IRQB}$). The $\overline{RESET}$ input is connected to the CPU's $\overline{RESET}$ input so that the PIA is reset whenever the CPU is reset. On reset all the contents of the PIA's internal registers are set to logical zeros. This puts the PIA in a "safe" state with all its interface lines configured as inputs, and its interrupt-generating facility disabled. The two interrupt-request outputs are almost always strapped together and connected to the CPU's $\overline{IRQ}$ input. The $\overline{IRQA}$ output corresponds to interrupts generated by the PIA's A-side port and the $\overline{IRQB}$ output is similarly related to the B-side port. The PIA is the only one of the 6800-series peripherals with two distinct interrupt-request outputs.

In order to understand how the PIA operates and hence how it may be used, it is necessary to understand the function of its six internal registers. There are two peripheral data registers, two data-direction registers (DDR A, DDR B), and two control registers (CRA and CRB). The PIA is activated whenever CS0 and CS1 = 1, and $\overline{CS2} = 0$. A location within the PIA is selected by RS_0 and RS_1. However, as RS_0 and RS_1 can distinguish between no more than four of the six internal registers, some fix must be provided to obtain the necessary discrimination. Such a fix is carried out by making bit 2 of the control registers (written CRA_2 or CRB_2) act as a pointer to either the data register or the data-direction register. Table 6.4 shows how this is effected.

Table 6.4 The Register Selection Scheme of the PIA

RS_1	RS_0	CRA_2	CRB_2	*Location selected*
0	0	1	×	peripheral data register A
0	0	0	×	data direction register A
0	1	×	×	control register A
1	0	×	1	peripheral data register B
1	0	×	0	data direction register B
1	1	×	×	control register B

× = don't care

From Table 6.4 it can be seen that RS_1 determines which of the two sides of the PIA is selected, while RS_0 determines whether the control register or one of the pair of registers, formed by the peripheral data register and the data direction register, is selected. Thus the control registers can always be unconditionally accessed when $RS_0 = 1$, but to select a peripheral data register or a data-direction register, bit 2 of the appropriate control register must be set or cleared, respectively.

The peripheral data registers form the interface between the PIA and the outside world. When one of the PIA's 16 I/O lines is acting as an input, data is moved from the relevant pin through the peripheral data register onto the CPU's data bus during a read cycle. Conversely, when acting as an output the CPU latches a 1 or 0 into the appropriate bit of the peripheral data register which affects the state of the corresponding output pin of the PIA.

The data-direction registers determine the direction of data transfer on the PIA's 16 I/O pins. If a logical zero is written into bit *i* of DDR A, then bit *i* of the A-side peripheral data register is configured as an input. Conversely, writing a one into bit *i* of DDR A configures bit *i* of the A-side peripheral data register as an output. In this way the I/O lines of the PIA's A-side or B-side ports may be defined as inputs or outputs by writing an appropriate code into DDR A or DDR B, respectively. Consequently, the PIA's I/O lines can be defined dynamically and, if necessary, altered during the course of a program. The following example demonstrates how side A may be configured as an input, and side B as an output. The PIA is assumed to be located at "PIA", where PIA is the base address.

Step 1	Set bit 2 of CRA to zero to select DDR A	LDA	A	#00
		STA	A	PIA+1
Step 2	Write zeros into DDR A to set up side A as an input	STA	A	PIA
Step 3	Set bit 2 of CRB to zero to select DDR B	STA	A	PIA+3
Step 4	Write ones into DDR B to set up side B as an	LDA	A	#$FF
	output	STA	A	PIA+2
Step 5	Set bit 2 of CRA to 1 to enable data to be read	LDA	A	#$04
	from peripheral data register A	STA	A	PIA+1
Step 6	Set bit 2 of CRB to 1 to enable data to be written into peripheral data register B	STA	A	PIA+3

Once the above procedure has been carried out, data can be read from side A by reading from address "PIA" (LDA A PIA), and data may be written into side B by writing to address "PIA+2" (STA A PIA+2).

Besides determining the access to a data-direction register or a peripheral data register, the two control registers are responsible for the control of the two lines associated with each port of the PIA. Side A has CA1 (an input only line) and CA2 (an input or output line). Similarly CB1 and CB2 are associated with side B. In general the operation of CA1, CA2 and CB1, CB2 are similar—but important differences do exist. A description of control register A and CA1 and CA2 is given, and any difference in the behavior of the corresponding B-side lines will be dealt with as necessary.

Control register A has its eight bits divided into fields in the following way.

bit	7	6	5	4	3	2	1	0
function	IRQA1	IRQA2	CA2 control			DDR A	CA1 control	

CA1 control (CRA bits 0 and 1) The four possible combinations of these two bits may be used to detect transitions on the CA1 control input and generate an interrupt if required. Whenever an interrupt is caused by CA1, the interrupt flag, IRQA1, is set and $\overline{\text{IRQA}}$ goes low. After the CPU has read the contents of peripheral data register A IRQA1 (or IRQA2) is automatically reset. The relationship between the CA1 control input, CRA_0, CRA_1 and the interrupt flag (IRQA1) can be seen from Table 6.5.

Table 6.5 CA1 Control

CRA_1	CRA_0	*Transition of input line CA1*	*IRQA1 interrupt flag status*	*Status of PIA $\overline{IRQA}$ output*
0	0	negative edge	set on ↓ edge	masked (remains high)
0	1	negative edge	set on ↓ edge	enabled (goes low)
1	0	positive edge	set on ↑ edge	masked (remains high)
1	1	positive edge	set on ↑ edge	enabled (goes low)

From Table 6.5 it can be seen that the status of CRA_1 determines the sense of the transition on CA1 which causes bit 7 of CRA to be set. However, if CRA_0 is clear no interrupt request is generated to the CPU. Thus CA1 can be used as an auxiliary input if bit CRA_0 is clear, or as an interrupt request input if bit CRA_0 is set.

Data-direction access control (CRA bit 2) When $\text{RS}_0 = 0$, the data-direction access control bit determines whether data-direction register A or peripheral data register A is selected. When the PIA is reset, $\text{CRA} = 0$ so that the data-direction register is always available after a reset.

CA2 control (CRA bits 3, 4 and 5) The CA2 control input may be programmed to generate an interrupt request (in a similar way to CA1), or it may be programmed to act as an output. Bit 5 of the control register determines the function of CA2. If bit $5 = 0$, CA2 behaves as an interrupt request input (Table 6.6) and if bit $5 = 1$, CA2 behaves as an output (Table 6.7). From Table 6.6 it can be seen that the behavior of CA2, when acting as an interrupt-request input, is entirely analogous to that of CA1.

When CA2 is programmed as an output with $\text{CRA}_5 = 1$ it behaves in the manner defined in Table 6.7. It is in this mode that sides A and B of the PIA differ—a separate table (Table 6.8) gives the behavior of CB2 as a function of CRB_4 and CRB_3 when $\text{CRB}_5 = 1$. As the significance of the entries in Table 6.7 is not immediately apparent, further explanation is given case by case.

Table 6.6 CA2 Configured as an Input with $CRA_5 = 0$

CRA_5	CRA_4	CRA_3	Transition of input line CA2	IRQA2 interrupt flag status	Status of PIA $\overline{IRQA}$ output
0	0	0	negative edge	set on ↓edge	masked (remains high)
0	0	1	negative edge	set on ↓edge	enabled (goes low)
0	1	0	positive edge	set on ↑edge	masked (remains high)
0	1	1	positive edge	set on ↑edge	enabled (goes low)

Table 6.7 CA2 as an Output when $CRA_5 = 1$

Case	CRA_5	CRA_4	CRA_3	Output CA2 Cleared	Output CA2 Set
1	1	0	0	Low on the falling edge of E after CPU read side A data operation.	High when interrupt flag bit CRA_7 is set by an active transition of CA1 input.
2	1	0	1	Low on the falling edge of E after CPU read side A data operation.	High on the negative edge of the first E pulse occurring during a deselect state of the PIA.
3	1	1	0	Low when CRA_3 goes low as a result of a CPU write to CRA.	Always low as long as CRA_3 is low. Will go high on a CPU write to CRA which changes CRA_3 to a 1.
4	1	1	1	Always high as long as CRA_3 is high. Will be cleared on a CPU write to CRA that clears CRA_3.	High when CRA_3 goes high as a result of a CPU write to CRA.

Case 1 $CRA_5 = 1$, $CRA_4 = 0$, $CRA_3 = 0$. This is known as the handshake mode and is used when a peripheral is transmitting data to the CPU. A timing diagram of the action of the handshake mode of CA2 is given in Fig. 6.7, together with an explanation of the steps involved. In this mode CA2 goes high whenever a peripheral has data ready for reading, and remains high until the CPU has read the data from the PIA's data register.

Enable (ϕ_2)

CA1 interrupt request input

A

CA2 output

B

C

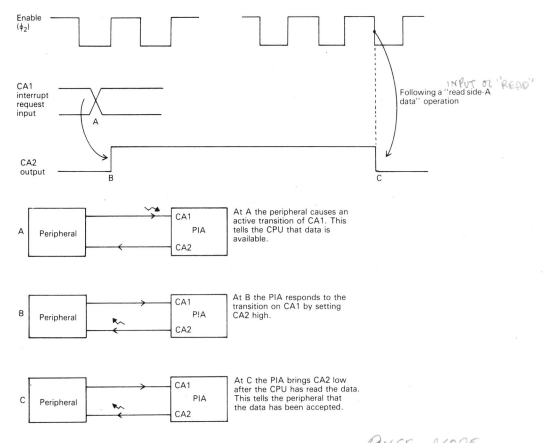

Following a "read side-A data" operation

A Peripheral CA1 PIA CA2

At A the peripheral causes an active transition of CA1. This tells the CPU that data is available.

B Peripheral CA1 PIA CA2

At B the PIA responds to the transition on CA1 by setting CA2 high.

C Peripheral CA1 PIA CA2

At C the PIA brings CA2 low after the CPU has read the data. This tells the peripheral that the data has been accepted.

Fig. 6.7 The handshake mode of CA2

Case 2 $CRA_5 = 1$, $CRA_4 = 0$, $CRA_3 = 1$. This mode is sometimes called the pulsed mode, input-programmed handshaking mode, or autohandshaking mode. Case 2 is illustrated in Fig. 6.8. Essentially, CA2 automatically produces a single pulse at a logical 0 level after the peripheral data register of side A has been read by the CPU.

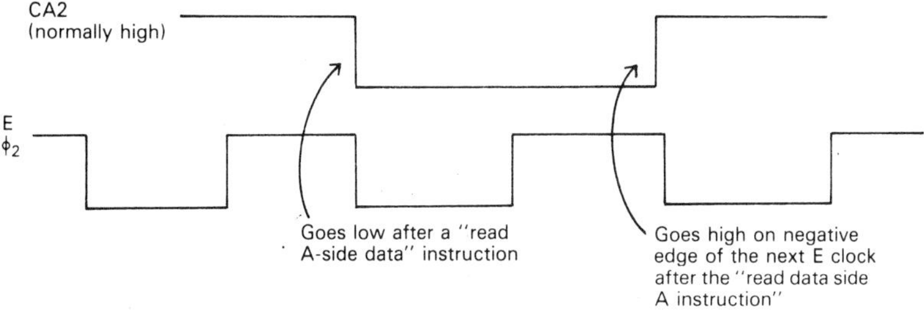

Fig. 6.8 The autohandshake mode of CA2

Case 3 $CRA_5 = 1$, $CRA_4 = 1$, $CRA_3 = 0$. In this mode CA2 is set to a logical zero and remains in that state until CRA_3 is set.

Case 4 $CRA_5 = 1$, $CRA_4 = 1$, $CRA_3 = 1$. Now CA2 is set to a logical one and remains in that state until CRA_3 is cleared. Cases 3 and 4 demonstrate the use of CA2 as an additional output, set or cleared under program control.

Differences between Side A and Side B Ports

The significant difference between Side A and B occurs in the behavior of CA2 and CB2 when programmed in the handshake or autohandshake modes. Side A performs handshaking operations when data is read from the PIA by the CPU. Side B performs handshaking operations when data is written into the PIA from the CPU. This difference becomes apparent when the cases of CB2 programmed as an output are considered (i.e. $CRB_5 = 1$).

Case 1 $CRB_5 = 1$, $CRB_4 = 0$, $CRB_3 = 0$. In this handshaking mode CB2 goes high whenever a peripheral is ready to receive data, and remains high until the CPU has written data into the PIA's side B data register. Fig. 6.9 gives the timing diagram of this mode of operation.

Case 2 $CRB_5 = 1$, $CRB_4 = 0$, $CRB_3 = 1$. In this mode the PIA tells the peripheral that data is available by putting a pulse on the CB2 line after data has been written into the PIA's side B data register. This mode is illustrated in Fig. 6.10.

Cases 3 and 4 These cases are entirely analogous to those of the A side.

Table 6.8 CB2 as an Output when $CRB_5 = 1$

Case	*CRB_5*	*CRB_4*	*CRB_3*	*Output CB2* *Cleared*	*Set*
1	1	0	0	Low on the rising edge of the first E pulse following a CPU write side B data operation.	High when the interrupt-flag bit CRB_7 is set by an active transition of the CB1 input.
2	1	0	1	Low on the rising edge of the first E pulse following a CPU write side B data operation.	High on the positive transition of the next E pulse following a deselect of the PIA.
3	1	1	0	Low when CRB_3 goes low as a result of a CPU write to CRB.	Always low as long as CRB_3 is low. Will go high on a CPU write to CRB which changes CRB_3 to a 1.
4	1	1	1	Always high as long as CRB_3 is high. Will be cleared on a CPU write to CRB that clears CRB_3.	High when CRB_3 goes high as a result of a CPU write to CRB.

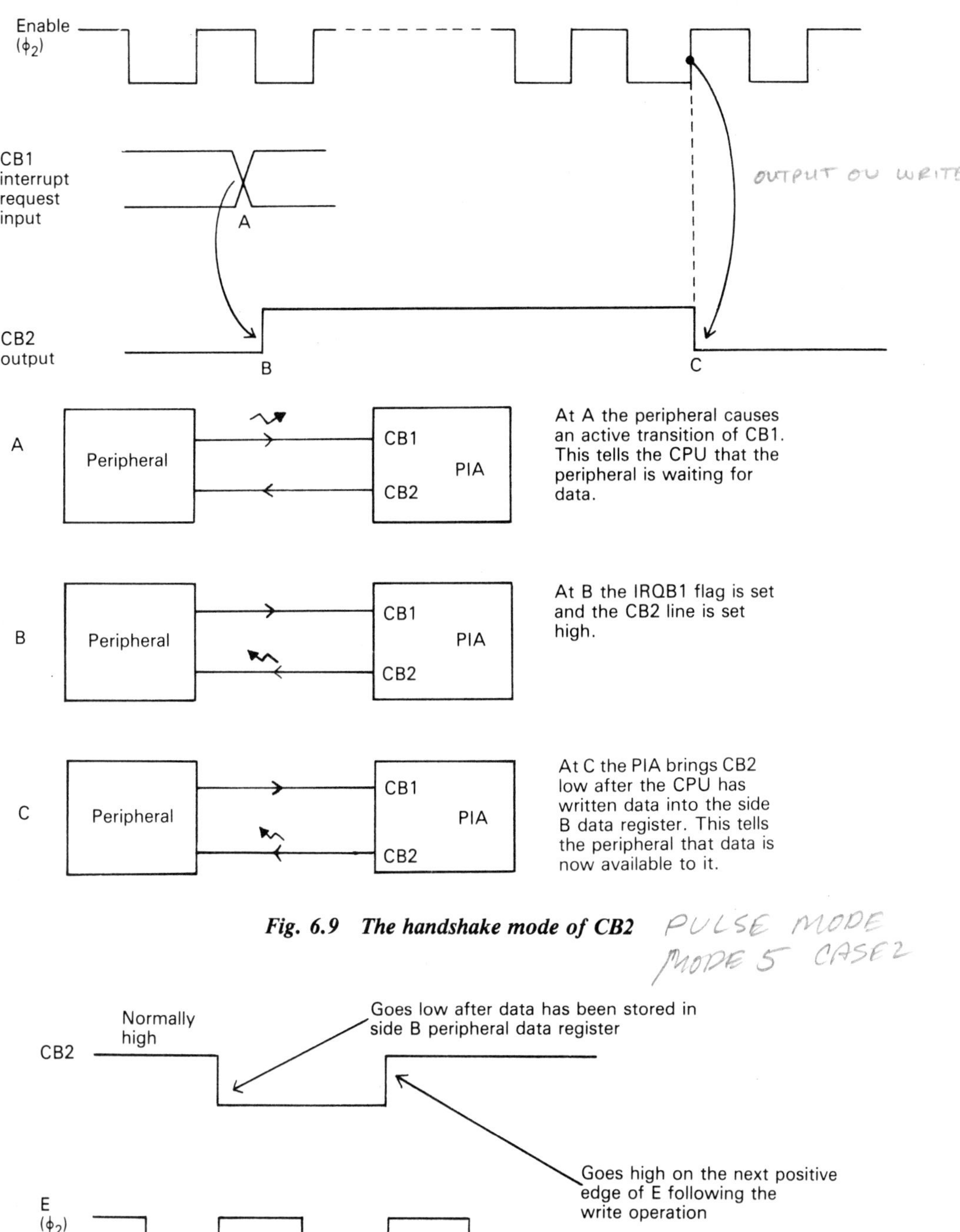
Enable
(ϕ_2)
CB1
interrupt
request
input
A
CB2
output
B
C
A
Peripheral
CB1
PIA
CB2
At A the peripheral causes an active transition of CB1. This tells the CPU that the peripheral is waiting for data.
B
Peripheral
CB1
PIA
CB2
At B the IRQB1 flag is set and the CB2 line is set high.
C
Peripheral
CB1
PIA
CB2
At C the PIA brings CB2 low after the CPU has written data into the side B data register. This tells the peripheral that data is now available to it.
Normally
high
CB2
Goes low after data has been stored in side B peripheral data register
Goes high on the next positive edge of E following the write operation
E
(ϕ_2)

Fig. 6.9 The handshake mode of CB2

Fig. 6.10 The autohandshake mode of CB2

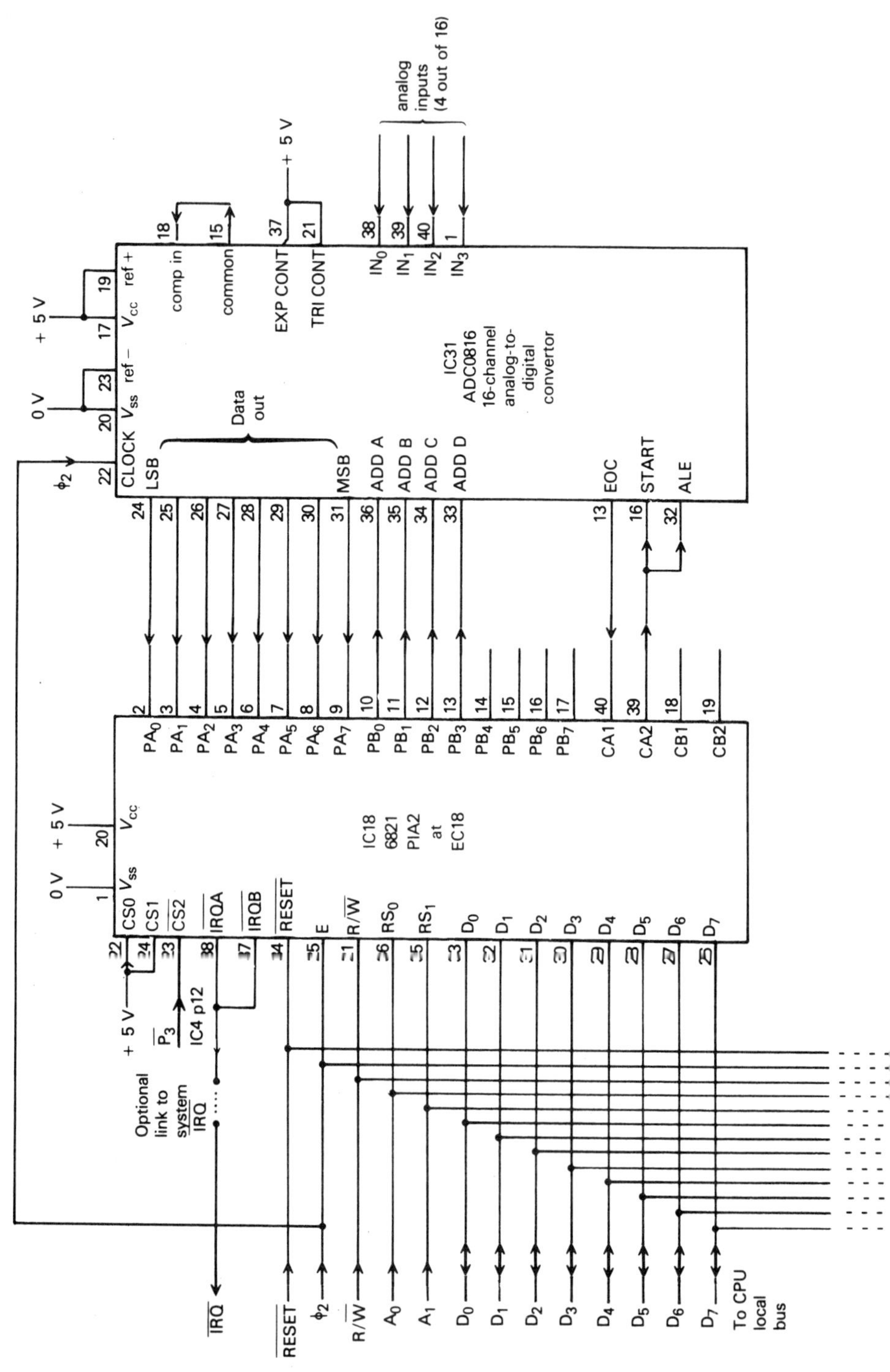
IC31
ADC0816
16-channel
analog-to-
digital
convertor
IC18
6821
PIA2
at
EC18
analog
inputs
(4 out of 16)
Data
out
Optional
link to
system
IRQ
To CPU
local
bus

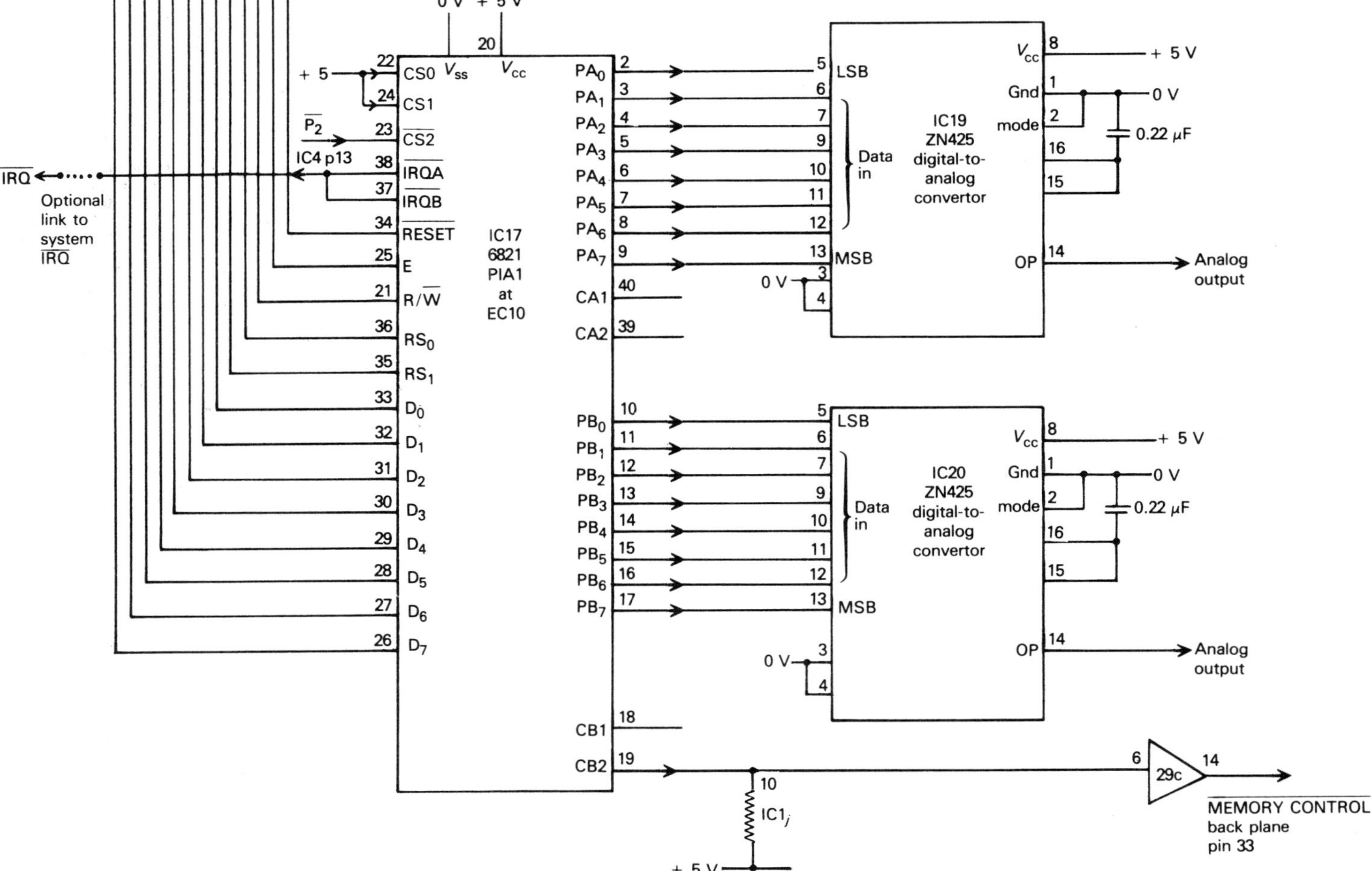

Fig. 6.11 The PIA on the CPU module

The PIA on the CPU Module

The circuit diagram of the arrangement of the two 6821 PIAs on TS1's CPU module is given in Fig. 6.11. Both these parallel I/O ports have been dedicated to controlling analog-to-digital and digital-to-analog convertors whose operation is covered in Section 6.8. It should be noted that the entire capacity of the PIAs is not taken up by these convertors: CA1, CA2 and CB1 of PIA1 are free, as are $PB_4 - PB_7$ and CB1, and CB2 of PIA2.

The interrupt request outputs of both PIAs are shown as being connected to the CPU's $\overline{IRQ}$ input by dotted lines. There is little point in wiring these PIAs up to the system $\overline{IRQ}$ line if they are not being operated in an interrupt-driven mode. Apart from reducing the loading on the $\overline{IRQ}$ line (leakage current into the open-drain output stage), the possibility of spurious interrupts from these PIAs is removed.

The CB2 control output of PIA2 is buffered by IC29c (74LS244) onto the system bus where it acts as the $\overline{\text{MEMORY CONTROL}}$ signal. This line can be set by loading CRB_5, CRB_4, CRB_3 with 111 (respectively), and cleared by loading 110 (respectively). Following a system reset CB2 is configured as an input and resistor $IC1_j$ pulls this line up into a logical one state.

An Example of the Use of the PIA

It is difficult to select the definitive application of the PIA because of its sheer versatility. A simple but effective demonstration of the PIA's capacity is given in Listing 6.1. The console input device is programmed to act as the keyboard of an electric organ with the CPU generating the timing and duration of the notes, and the PIA functioning as the output port. In order to produce the actual sounds it is necessary to connect the analog output of IC19 (pin 14) to the input of any audio amplifier (for example Fig. 6.71). If the PIA at EC10 (i.e. IC17) is not connected to a digital-to-analog convertor, any one of the PIA's side A output pins, $PA_0 - PA_7$, may be connected to the amplifier.

The program is entered at 0100_{16} and begins with a set-up procedure to configure side A of the PIA at EC10 as an output port. The main segment of the program consists of two parts, one which gets the note from the keyboard (keys 0 to ;), and another which generates "DUR" half cycles of the selected waveform.

An ASCII-encoded character is obtained from the keyboard by means of subroutine INPUT which is part of the TS1BUG monitor at FEB0. By subtracting 30_{16} from the character code the symbols for "0" to ";" are converted to the numbers 0 to 11. A check is carried out to ensure that the key pressed is within the range "0" to ";". The numeric value of the note is placed in memory location POINT + 1 and the contents of POINT, POINT + 1 moved to the X register. By loading accumulator B using the index register the actual value of the note in terms of the delay between successive half-cycles is obtained from the table.

Listing 6.1 The PIA as the output port of an electric organ

```
        NAM ORGAN
PIAD    EQU  $EC10                          PIA side A DDR/data register
PIAC    EQU  PIAD+1                         PIA side A control register
INPUT   EQU  $FEB0                          address of "input a char"
                                            subroutine
DUR     EQU  $0020                          duration of a note
        ORG  $0000
POINT   FDB  $0000                          pointer to note-table
TABLE   FCC  $FF, $F1, $E3, $D6, $CA, $BF   note-table
        FCC  $B4, $AA, $A1, $98, $8F, $87
        ORG  $0100                          program origin
        CLR  A
        STA  A  PIAC                        clear control—select DDR
        LDA  A  #$SFF
        STA  A  PIAD                        configure side A as O/P
        LDA  A  #$04                        set bit 2
        STA  A  PIAC                        select data register
*
START   JSR  INPUT                          get note character
        SUB  A  #$30                        ASCII to numeric conversion
        BMI  START                          minus—try again
        CMP  A  #$0B
        BHI  START                          positive—try again
        STA  A  POINT+1                     put note in LSB of pointer
        LDX  POINT                          put pointer in X reg
        LDA  B  2,X                         get note from table
        LDX  #DUR.                          load note duration
REPEAT  TBA                                 save note in A reg
        BSR  PLAY                           wait one half-cycle time
        DEX                                 decrement duration counter
        BNE  REPEAT                         continue to end of duration
        BRA  START                          get next note
*
PLAY    DEC  A                              decrement note value
        NOP                                 six microseconds timing delay
        NOP
        NOP
        BNE  PLAY                           cycle down until zero
        COM  PIAD                           invert all PIA outputs
        RTS
        END
```

The subroutine "PLAY" counts down from the value of the note (in accumulator A) to zero and then complements the contents of the PIA's side A data register. This has the effect of producing a square wave at each of the PIA's side A outputs.

This is a simple demonstration program with numbers 0–9, and ":" and ";" forming an octave. The relationship between the keys and the relative frequencies of the notes is given below.

Key	Note	Relative frequency	Relative note duration (hex)	Key	Note	Relative frequency	Relative note duration (hex)
0	C	1.00000	FF	6	F#	1.41421	B4
1	C#	1.05946	F1	7	G	1.49831	AA
2	D	1.12246	E3	8	G#	1.58740	A1
3	D#	1.18921	D6	9	A	1.68179	98
4	E	1.25992	CA	:	A#	1.78179	8F
5	F	1.33484	BF	;	B	1.88775	87

It should be appreciated that the notes of lower frequency have a longer duration than notes of a higher frequency because the duration of a note is defined as a fixed number of half cycles.

6.2.2 THE 6850 ACIA

The 6850 ACIA is nothing more than parallel to serial convertor and a serial to parallel convertor in a single 24 pin package. Although data may be moved between peripherals and the CPU by means of multi-way buses (e.g. the 16 line IEEE-488 bus) the cost of such a bus becomes prohibitive when data is to be moved over long distances. The simplest form of data link is a single wire carrying pulses distributed in time, rather than in space. Serial data links are commonly used to link the CPU with keyboards, teletypes, VDTs and modems. The ACIA is dealt with here because it is one of the three most popular 6800-series peripheral devices. The reader should, however, read this section in conjunction with Section 6.3 which deals with the serial data link in greater detail. The ACIA is called "asynchronous" because the clock at the receiver does not have to be synchronized with the clock at the transmitter and hence the data itself. The word clock refers here to the rate at which data is transmitted and not to the CPU clock. In an asynchronous system the receiver does not generate its local clock from the received data itself but uses a start bit (appended to each character transmitted in serial form) to trigger a local clock. Before going into detail about the ACIA it is necessary to understand the nature of an asynchronous data link.

Figure 6.12 gives a possible format for a single character of seven bits. It will be seen later that the 6850 is able to transmit or receive data in a variety of formats. During a period in which no data is being transmitted from an ACIA, the serial output of the ACIA is at a logical 1, which is called the "mark" condition. When a word is to be transmitted, the output of the ACIA is brought low (a mark-to-space transition) for a period of one bit time. The bit time is the reciprocal of the rate at which successive serial bits are transmitted. This initial bit is called the start bit and tells the receiver that a stream of bits, representing a character, are about to be

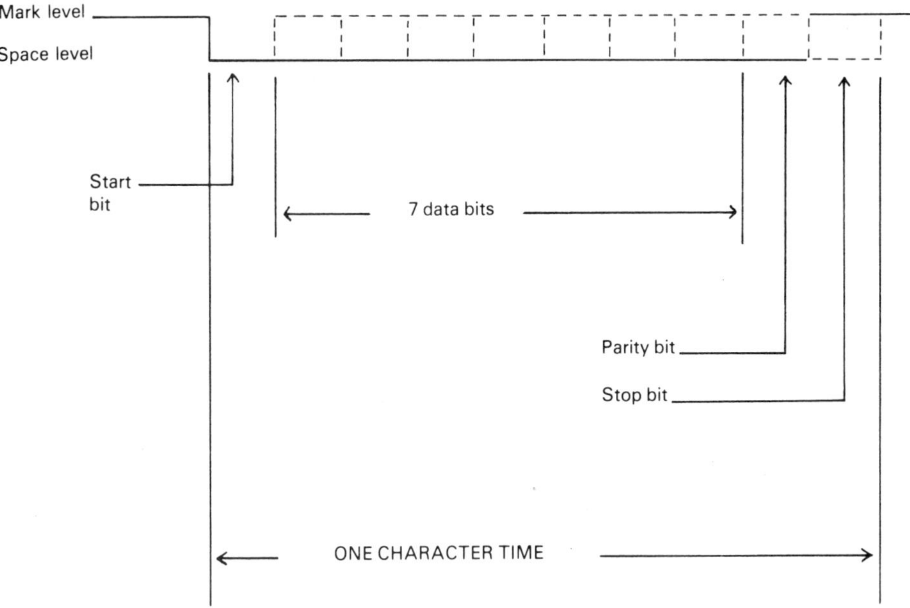

Fig. 6.12 The format of serial data

received. During the next 7 time slots (each of the same duration as the start bit) the output of the ACIA depends on the value of the character being transmitted. This format is called non-return to zero (NRZ). After the character has been transmitted a further two bits—parity and stop bit—are appended to the end of the character. The parity bit is the exclusive OR of all the preceding 7 data bits. That is, the parity bit $P = d_0 \oplus d_1 \oplus d_2 \cdots \oplus d_6$. This is called even parity because the total number of 1s in the word (including the parity bit) is even. Optionally, the complement of P may be transmitted to form an odd parity. The parity bit gives a measure of error protection to the transmitted data. At the receiver the parity bit is generated locally from the received data and then compared with the received parity bit. If the received and locally generated parity bits differ, an error in transmission is assumed to have occurred. Note that a simple parity bit cannot correct an error once it has occurred, nor detect a pair of errors in a character. The stop bit (or optionally two stop bits) signals the end of the word. At the end of the stop bit(s), the transmitter output is once more in its mark state and is ready to send the next character. Note that the whole word is composed of 10 bits but contains only 7 bits of useful information.

They key to asynchronous data transmission is that once the receiver has detected a start bit, it need maintain synchronization only for the duration of a single character. The receiver examines successive received bits by sampling the incoming signal at the center of each pulse. Because the clock at the receiver is not synchronized with the clock at the transmitter, each received data bit will not be sampled exactly at its center.

Let the ACIA transmit bits at a rate of T bits per second, and let the receiver's clock sample the incoming bits every $T + t$ seconds, where t is the difference between the clock rates at the receiver and transmitter. In the example of Fig. 6.12, the stop bit of the received word is no longer sampled at its center, but $9\frac{1}{2}t$ seconds after it. If no errors are to occur in the detection of the received data pulses, the value of $9t$ must be less than half a pulse width. Therefore $9\frac{1}{2}t < T/2$ or $t < T/19$. That is, the receiver's clock must be no more than approximately 5.3% faster or slower than the transmitter's clock. If both transmitter and receiver clocks are crystal controlled, any difference between their frequencies is likely to be a small fraction of one

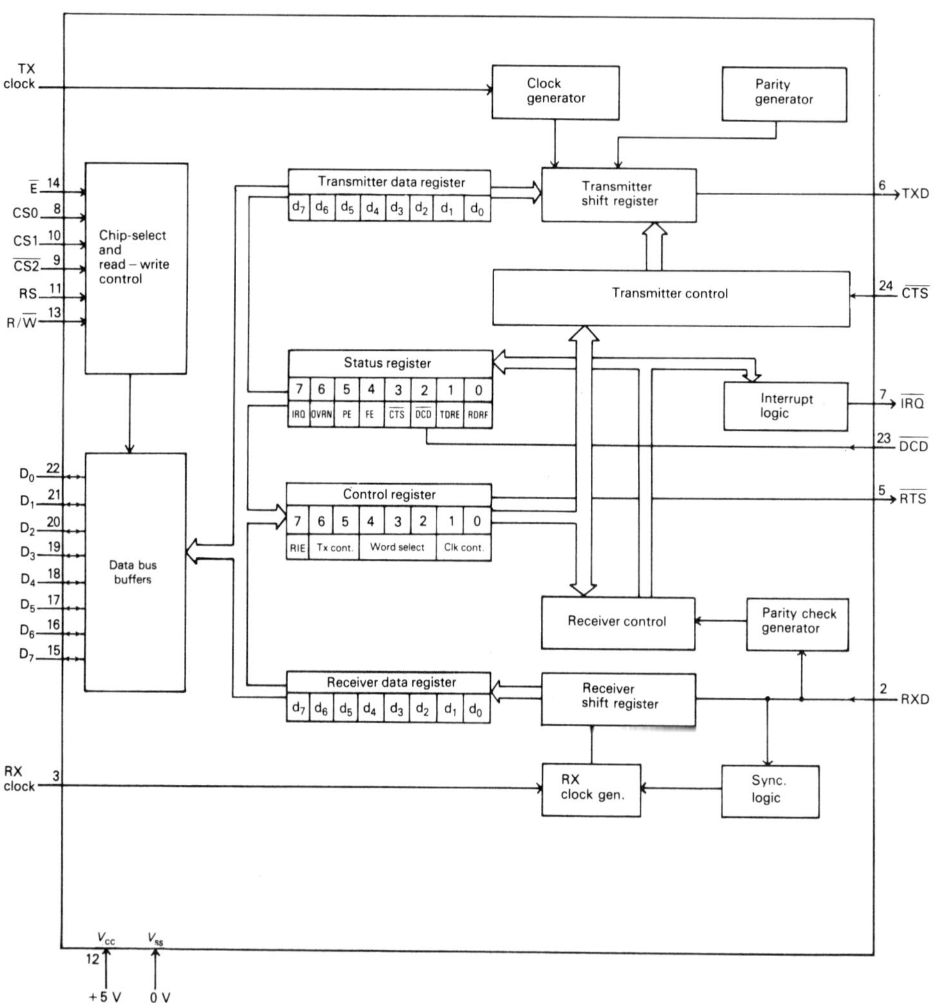

Fig. 6.13 The internal arrangement of the 6850 ACIA

percent. However, if both transmitter and receiver clocks are RC oscillators, satisfactory operation can be obtained only if the oscillators are carefully set up. Even so, thermal drift may lead to erratic operation of the data link.

The internal arrangement of the 6850 ACIA is given in Fig. 6.13. The ACIA is in many ways more complex than the PIA and is also less flexible. Unlike the PIA, whose interface pins can be defined as inputs or outputs, the ACIA has a single receiver input and a single transmitter output. The only flexibility in the ACIA is the ability to define the format of the transmitted (or received) data, and to control generation of interrupts by the ACIA.

The "CPU side" of the ACIA is very much the same as that of the PIA. There are only two significant differences between the PIA and ACIA's interface to the CPU. Firstly, the ACIA has only a single interrupt-request output, and secondly, the ACIA does not have a hardware reset facility. The ACIA must be reset under the software control by writing the appropriate code into its control register. According to the 6850's data sheet it is held in a reset state after power is first applied to it by means of its internal power-on reset logic which monitors the power turn-on transition. This turn on must be clean (the power supply monotonically rising from 0 to V_{cc}) if the internal reset logic is to function satisfactorily.

The "Peripheral Side" Lines of the ACIA

The ACIA has seven lines with which it communicates with a peripheral. These seven lines may be divided into three groups: receiver, transmitter, and modem control.

Receiver The receiver clock input is used to sample the incoming data bits. The signal at the clock input to the ACIA may be 64, 16, or 1 times that of the bit rate of the received data. If the receiver clock is operated in the ÷1 mode, the clock and received data must be synchronized externally. The receiver's serial data input receives data from the peripheral to which the ACIA is connected via (normally) an RS232C (V24) or 20 mA current loop interface. These interfaces match the TTL levels at the ACIA to the signal levels found on popular data links. The idle (mark) level at the input to the ACIA's receiver is a logical 1.

Transmitter The transmitter has a clock input, from which it generates the timing of the transmitted data pulses. As in the case of the receiver, the transmitter clock may be operated at 64, 16 or 1 times the rate of the data. In many cases the transmitter and receiver clocks are derived from the same oscillator. The transmitter output provides a serial signal, at TTL levels, which may operate a modem or some other peripheral.

Modem control The ACIA has three pins (two inputs and one output) with which it can communicate with terminal equipment—in particular the modem. The request to send $(\overline{RTS})$ output of the ACIA may be set or cleared under software control and is used by the ACIA to tell the terminal that it is ready to transmit data to the terminal. The $\overline{RTS}$ output is often used to switch on remote paper-tape punches or cassette recorders. The two active-low control inputs to the ACIA are clear-to-send ($\overline{\text{CTS}}$) and data-carrier-detect ($\overline{\text{DCD}}$). The $\overline{\text{CTS}}$ input is a signal from the modem to the ACIA and inhibits the ACIA from transmitting data if the modem is not ready for the data. If the $\overline{\text{CTS}}$ input is high, a bit is set in the ACIA's status register, indicating that the modem (or other terminal equipment) is not ready for data. The $\overline{\text{DCD}}$ input of the ACIA is employed by the modem to indicate to the ACIA that the carrier has been lost and that valid data is no longer available at the receiver's input. A low-to-high transition at the $\overline{\text{DCD}}$ input sets a bit in the status register and may also initiate an interrupt if the ACIA is so programmed. In the majority of simple applications of the ACIA, the $\overline{\text{CTS}}$ and $\overline{\text{DCD}}$ inputs are connected to ground.

The ACIA's Internal Registers

The ACIA has four internal registers: a transmit data register (TDR), a receive data register (RDR), a control register (CR), and a status register (SR). As the ACIA has a single register-select input, only two internal registers can be directly accessed by the CPU. As, however, two of the registers (RDR and SR) are always read from, and two of the registers (TDR and CR) are always written to, the $R/\overline{W}$ input of the ACIA is used to distinguish between the two pairs of registers. The addressing arrangements of the ACIA are given in Table 6.9.

Table 6.9 The Register Selection Scheme of the ACIA

RS	*$R/\overline{W}$*	*Type of register*	*ACIA register*
0	0	write only	control register
0	1	read only	status register
1	0	write only	transmit data
1	1	read only	receive data

The control register This write-only register defines the operational properties of the ACIA, particular the format of the transmitted or received data. The format of the control register is given in Table 6.10. The "counter division" field, CR_0 and CR_1, determines the relationship between the transmitter and receiver bit rates and their respective clocks (Table 6.11).

Table 6.10 The Format of the Control Register

Bit	7	6	5	4	3	2	1	0
Function	receiver interrupt enable	transmitter control		word select			counter division	

Table 6.11 The Relationship Between CR_1, CR_0 and the Division Ratio

CR_1	CR_0	*Division ratio*
0	0	÷1
0	1	÷16
1	0	÷64
1	1	master reset

When CR_1 and CR_0 are both one the ACIA is reset, and all internal status bits, with the exception of the $\overline{CTS}$ and $\overline{DCD}$ flags, are cleared. These two flags are entirely dependent on the signal level at their pins. The ACIA is initialized by writing ones into bits CR_1 and CR_0 of the control register, and then writing one of the three division ratio codes into these positions. In the majority of systems $CR_1 = 0$ and $CR_0 = 1$ for a $\div 16$ ratio.

The "word select" field, CR_2, CR_3, CR_4 defines the format of the received or transmitted data words. These three bits allow the selection of eight possible arrangements of number of bits per character, type of parity, and number of stop bits (Table 6.12).

Table 6.12 The "Word Select" Bits

CR_4	CR_3	CR_2	*Data word length*	*Parity*	*Stop bits*	*Total bits*
0	0	0	7	even	2	11
0	0	1	7	odd	2	11
0	1	0	7	even	1	10
0	1	1	7	odd	1	10
1	0	0	8	none	2	11
1	0	1	8	none	1	10
1	1	0	8	even	1	11
1	1	1	8	odd	1	11

The two most popular formats for the transmission of serial data are start bit + 7 data bits + even parity + two stop bits at 110 baud for teletypes and start bit + 7 data bits + even parity + one stop bit at 300 – 9600 baud for VDTs.

The "transmitter-control" field, CR_5 and CR_6, controls the level of the request to send ($\overline{RTS}$) output, and the generation of an interrupt by the transmitter portion of the ACIA. Table 6.13 gives the relationship between these control bits and their functions. The values of CR_6 and CR_5 are selected according to the operation of the system. The transmitter normally employs its $\overline{RTS}$ output to tell the terminal equipment (or modem) that the transmitted data is not valid. In many simple applications involving a link to a VDT or teletype, the level of the $\overline{RTS}$ output is unimportant.

Table 6.13 The Function of Transmitter Control Bits CR_5 and CR_6

CR_6	CR_5	$\overline{RTS}$	*Transmitter interrupt*
0	0	low	disabled
0	1	low	enabled
1	0	high	disabled
1	1	low	disabled—a break level is put on the transmitter output

Similarly, whether the transmitter interrupt is enabled or disabled depends on whether the CPU is operating in an interrupt-driven or in a polled-data mode. The operation of these two modes is described later. If the transmitter interrupt is enabled, a transmitter interrupt is generated whenever the transmit-data register (TDR) is empty, signifying the need for new data from the CPU. Note that if the ACIA's $\overline{\text{clear-to-send}}$ input is high, the TDR empty flag bit in the status register is held low, inhibiting any transmitter interrupt. The effect of setting both CR_6 and CR_5 to a one requires some explanation. If both of these bits are high a break is transmitted until these bits are altered. That is, the transmitter output of the ACIA is held at its active or space (logical zero) level. This condition may be used to generate an interrupt at the receiver because the asynchronous format of the serial data precludes the existence of a space level for more than about ten bit periods. The term "break" comes from the current-loop data transmission system (described later) when a break is effected by breaking the loop.

The "receiver interrupt enable" field consists of bit CR_7 which when clear inhibits the generation of interrupts by the receiver portion of the ACIA. Whenever bit CR_7 is set, a receiver interrupt may be generated by the receiver data register (RDR) flag of the status word going high, indicating the presence of a new data word ready for the CPU to read. As a receiver overrun (see later) sets the RDRF flag an overrun also forces a receiver interrupt. A receiver interrupt can also be generated by a low-to-high transition at the $\overline{\text{data-carrier-detect}}$ ($\overline{DCD}$) input, signifying the loss of a carrier. Note that CR_7 is a composite interrupt enable bit. It is impossible to enable either an interrupt caused by the RDR being empty or an interrupt caused by a positive transition on the $\overline{DCD}$ pin alone.

The Status Register

The status register has the same address as the control register, but is distinguished from it by being a read-only register. The format of the status register is given in Table 6.14.

Table 6.14 The Format of the Status Register

7	6	5	4	3	2	1	0
IRQ	PE	OVRN	FE	$\overline{CTS}$	$\overline{DCD}$	TDRE	RDRF

Bit 0—Receiver Data Register Full (RDRF) When set this bit indicates that the receiver data register is full, and a word has been received. Whenever bit 0 is set, the interrupt request flag, bit 7, is also set if the receiver interrupt is enabled. The RDRF bit is cleared by reading the data in the receiver data register. Whenever the $\overline{\mathrm{DCD}}$ input is high, the RDRF bit remains at a logical zero, indicating the absence of any valid input. The RDRF bit is cleared by a master reset.

Bit 1—Transmitter Data Register Empty (TDRE) This is the transmitter counterpart of bit 0. A logical 1 in bit 1 indicates that the contents of the transmit data register (TDR) have been transmitted and the register is now ready for new data. The IRQ bit is also set whenever the TDRE flag is set if the transmitter interrupt is enabled. The TDRE bit is at a logical zero when the TDR is full, or when the $\overline{\mathrm{CTS}}$ input is at a logical 1, indicating that the terminal equipment is not ready for data.

Bit 2—Data Carrier Detect ($\overline{DCD}$) The $\overline{\mathrm{DCD}}$ bit is high whenever the $\overline{\mathrm{DCD}}$ input is high, indicating that a carrier is not present. The $\overline{\mathrm{DCD}}$ pin is normally only employed in conjunction with a modem. When the signal at the $\overline{\mathrm{DCD}}$ input makes a low-to-high transition, the $\overline{\mathrm{DCD}}$ bit is set and the IRQ bit is set if the receiver interrupt is enabled. The $\overline{\mathrm{DCD}}$ bit remains set even if the $\overline{\mathrm{DCD}}$ input returns to a low state. To clear the $\overline{\mathrm{DCD}}$ bit, the CPU must read the contents of the ACIA's status register and then the contents of the data register. Alternatively, a master reset will clear the $\overline{\mathrm{DCD}}$ bit.

Bit 3—Clear to Send ($\overline{CTS}$) The $\overline{\mathrm{CTS}}$ bit directly indicates the status of the ACIA's $\overline{\mathrm{CTS}}$ input. A low level on the $\overline{\mathrm{CTS}}$ input indicates that the modem (tape punch, TTY, cassette, etc.) is ready for data. If the $\overline{\mathrm{CTS}}$ bit is high, the transmit data register empty bit is inhibited (clamped at zero), and no data may be transmitted by the ACIA.

Bit 4—Framing Error (FE) The framing error bit is set whenever a received character is incorrectly framed by a start bit and a stop bit. A framing error is detected by the absence of the first stop bit, and indicates a synchronization (timing) error, faulty transmission, or a break condition. The framing error flag is set or cleared during receiver data transfer time and is present throughout the time that the associated character is available.

Bit 5—Receiver Overrun (OVRN) The receiver overrun flag bit is set when a character is received by the receiver part of the ACIA but is not read by the CPU before a subsequent character is received, over-writing the previous character which is now lost. Consequently, the receiver overrun bit indicates that one or more characters in the data stream have been lost. The overrun bit is set in the midpoint of the last bit of the second character received in succession without a read of the RDR having occurred. Synchronization is not affected by an overrun error—the error is caused by the CPU not reading a character, rather than by a fault in the transmission process. The overrun bit is cleared after reading the data from the RDR or by a master reset.

Bit 6—Parity Error (PE) The parity error bit is set whenever the received parity bit does not agree with the parity bit generated locally at the receiver from the preceding data bits. Odd or even parity may be selected by writing the appropriate code into bits 2, 3 and 4 of the control register. If no parity is selected, then both the transmitter parity generator and the receiver parity checker are disabled. Once a parity error has been detected and the parity error bit set, it remains set as long as a character with a parity error is in the receiver data register.

Bit 7—Interrupt Request (IRQ) The interrupt request bit is a composite interrupt request flag because it is set whenever the ACIA wishes to interrupt the CPU, for whatever reason. The IRQ bit may be set by any of the following:

(1) receiver data register full (SR bit 0 set);
(2) transmitter data register empty (SR bit 1 set);
(3) $\overline{\text{DCD}}$ bit set (SR bit 2).

Whenever IRQ = 1 the $\overline{\text{IRQ}}$ pin of the ACIA is pulled low. The IRQ bit is cleared by a read from the RDR, or a write to the TDR.

Programming the ACIA

Although the ACIA performs all the functions necessary to transmit and receive serial data, the CPU must initialize the ACIA's control register, read data from the ACIA and write data to it. The software required to carry out these functions may vary from a few lines of assembly-level code to a relatively large program which deals with the recovery from transmission errors, and the control of a modem. The ACIA can be handled in one of two ways: interrupt driven or polled. When the ACIA is interrupt driven, it interrupts the CPU whenever it is ready for data or has data ready for the CPU to read. This is a very efficient mode of operation because the CPU does not waste time waiting for the ACIA. Remember that at a 110 baud rate (typical of the teletype) characters are transmitted at the rate of 10 per second, equivalent to 100 000 machine cycles per character. In the polled mode, the CPU operates in a loop, continually examining the status register of the ACIA for either permission to send new data or permission to read a new word from the ACIA. Although this mode is inefficient, the vast majority of small microprocessor systems poll their ACIA's because they have nothing better to do while waiting to input or output data. Clearly, efficiency is important only if the microprocessor has a background task to carry out while waiting for a response from the ACIA. Perhaps a more significant disadvantage of the polled mode of operation, from the point of view of the user of a small microprocessor system, is that the ACIA can receive data and transfer it to the CPU only when a program requests it. This makes it difficult (but not impossible) to interrupt a program while it is running. In the interrupt-driven mode a new character from the keyboard causes an interrupt whenever a key is pressed.

To illustrate how an ACIA is used, three examples are considered: a simple polled input/output routine, a more complex polled input routine, and an interrupt driven input/output routine.

Simple Polled Input/Output Routines

```
ACIAC   EQU    $F800     address of ACIA control/status register
ACIAD   EQU    ACIAC+1   address of ACIA data register

SETUP   LDA A  #3        contents of A=00000011
        STA A  ACIAC     master reset
        LDA A  #$19      set ACIA for ÷16 clock, disable interrupt
        STA A  ACIAC     8-bit word+even parity+1 stop bit
        RTS              return

INPUT   LDA A  ACIAC     get status register
        ASR A            shift bit 0 into carry (RDRF)
        BCC    INPUT     if carry clear data not ready: try again
        LDA A  ACIAD     carry set: read data into accumulator
        RTS              return

OUTPUT  PSH B            save the B register on the stack
OUT1    LDA B  ACIAC     get status register
        ASR B            shift bit 0 into carry
        ASR B            shift bit 1 into carry (TDRE)
        BCC    OUT1      if carry clear transmitter busy: try again
        STA A  ACIAD     store data in TDR for automatic transmission
        PUL B            restore B register
        RTS              return
```

A More Complex Input Routine

```
INPUT   LDA A  ACIAC     get the status register
        ASR A            shift RDRF bit into carry
        BCS    FRAME     if carry set data is ready check for errors
        ASR A            shift TDRE bit into carry
        ASR A            shift DCD bit into carry
        BCC    INPUT     if clear read status register again
        BRA    ERROR1    if set carrier loss go to error routine
FRAME   ASR A            shift TDRE bit into carry
        ASR A            shift DCD bit into carry
        ASR A            shift CTS bit into carry
        ASR A            shift FE bit into carry
        BCC    OVRN      if clear look for overrun error
        BRA    ERROR2    if set go to framing error routine
OVRN    ASR A            shift OVRN bit into carry
        BCC    PRTY      if clear look for parity error
```

```
        BRA   ERROR3     if set go to overrun error routine
PRTY    ASR A            shift PE bit into carry
        BCC   RXDATA     if clear get the received data
        BRA   ERROR4     if set go to parity error routine
RXDATA  LDA A ACIAD      get the received data
        RTS              return

ERROR1                   deal with loss of carrier
ERROR2                   deal with framing error
ERROR3                   deal with overrun error
ERROR4                   deal with parity error
```

An Interrupt-Driven Input/Output Routine

```
IRQ     LDA A ACIAC      get status register
        BIT A #$80       examine bit 7—IRQ
        BNE   OTHER      if not set ACIA did not generate IRQ
        ASR A            shift RDRF into carry
        BNE   TRANS      if RDRF clear assume transmit interrupt
        LDA A ACIAD      get the data
        LDX   POINT1     get pointer to data input buffer
        STA A 0,X        store the data in the buffer
        INX              point to next empty place in the buffer
        STX   POINT1     restore the pointer
        RTI              return from interrupt
TRANS   LDX   POINT2     get pointer to data output buffer
        LDA A 0,X        get the data
        STA A ACIAD      transmit the character
        INX              point to next character in the buffer
        STX   POINT2     restore the pointer
        RTI              return
OTHER                    deal with other interrupting devices

        RTI
```

The ACIA on the CPU Module

The circuit diagram of the two ACIAs on TS1's CPU module is given in Fig. 6.14. This circuit is entirely conventional, but the following notes may help the reader.

(1) The MC14411 baud rate generator (IC23) conveniently provides the common bit rates for the majority of serial interfaces. Appendix A3 gives some details on this device. The console ACIA requires a clock input at 4800 Hz which is sixteen times the 300 baud rate of the serial data to and from this port. The

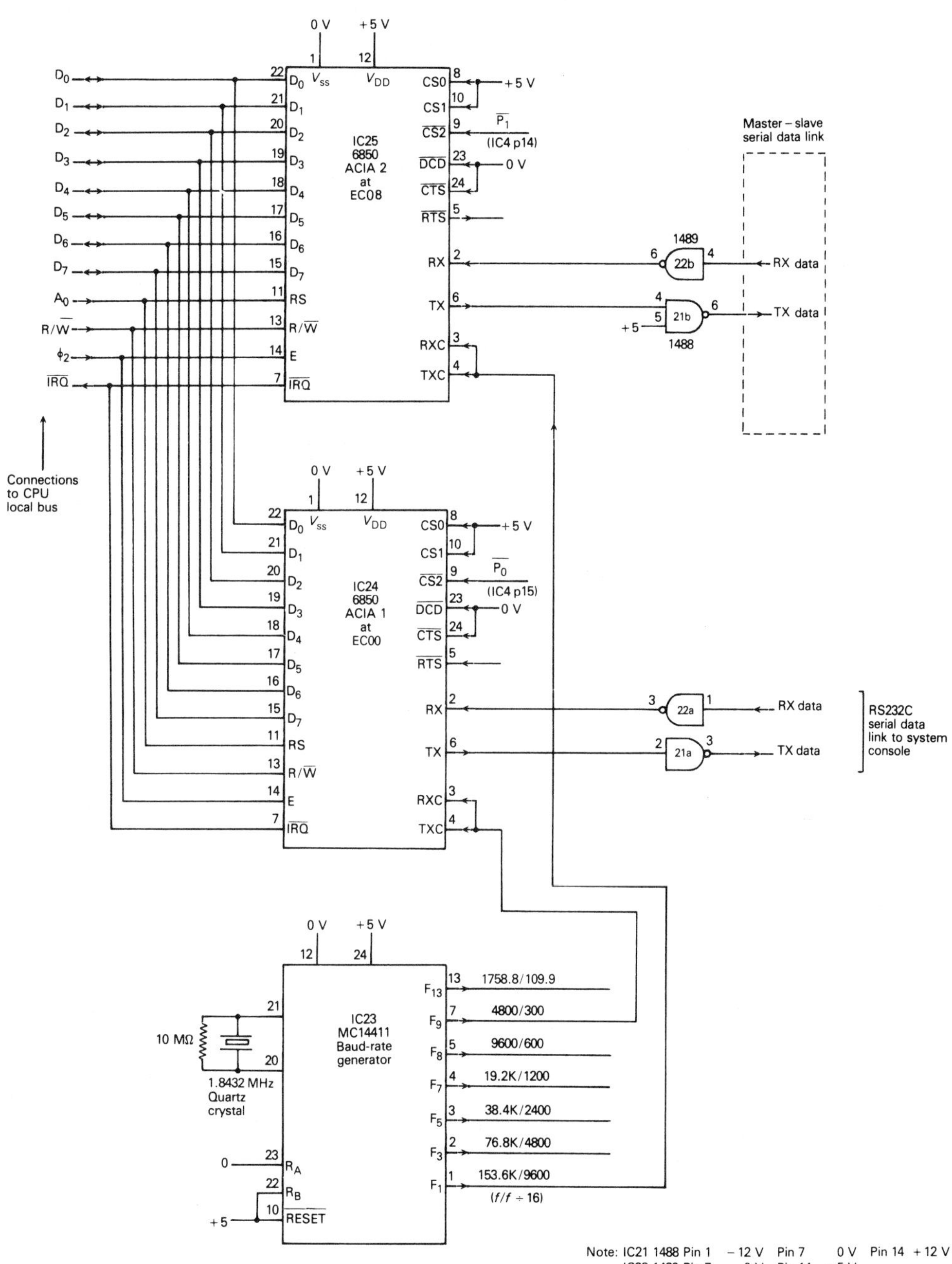

Fig. 6.14 The ACIA on the CPU module

only reason for choosing the relatively slow rate of 300 baud is that it matches that of the author's printer. The ACIA used as the master – slave link operates at 9600 Hz and requires a clock at 153.6 kHz. Note that the MC14411's output drive capability is only one low-power TTL load.

(2) Both ACIAs have their receiver and transmitter clock inputs strapped together. There is, of course, no reason why the transmitter and receiver sections of an ACIA cannot operate at different baud rates.

(3) The $\overline{\text{clear-to-send}}$ and $\overline{\text{data-carrier-detect}}$ inputs of the ACIAs are not required in the current application and are strapped to ground.

(4) The serial inputs and outputs of the ACIAs have their signal levels converted between TTL standards and RS232C standards by ICs 21 and 22. Section 6.3 deals with the RS232C standard for serial data, and Appendix A3 gives the details of the 1488 and 1489 line driver and receiver, respectively.

(5) The software to control the console ACIA (IC24) at EC00 is given in the monitor listing in Chapter 8.

(6) The ACIA dedicated to the master – slave link (IC25 at EC08) also has its serial I/O signal levels converted between TTL and RS232C standards. Such a step is not really necessary as the output of this ACIA can be connected directly to the input of this ACIA (and vice versa) on the slave CPU module (see Chapter 7). However, by employing RS232C signal levels, the ACIA may be connected to a cassette interface, paper-tape reader/punch, modem, or any other commercially available peripheral operating with a serial data link.

6.2.3 The 6840 PTM

The programmable timer module is the most complex of the three peripheral devices to be described in this section. The complexity of the PTM is increased by four factors. Firstly, like the PIA, it is a general-purpose device with a host of facilities. Secondly, in order to reduce the number of pins of the PTM a bit in one of the control registers is used to point to one of the other two control registers, saving one address line at the cost of increased programming complexity. Thirdly, programming the PTM is made difficult because the meaning of some of its control bits is modified by the particular mode in which the PTM is operating. Finally, the PTM has 16-bit internal timing registers, causing problems when interfacing it to an 8-bit bus.

The complexity of the 6840 PTM is so great that justice cannot be done to it in the space available here. In this section a basic description of the PTM is given together with an example of its operation. Fundamentally, the PTM consists of three independent 16-bit timers in a 28-pin DIL package and its purpose is to free the CPU of the tasks of maintaining timing loops or counting events. Figure 6.15 gives a block diagram of the internal arrangement of the PTM. The "CPU side" of the PTM is almost identical to that of the PIA except that the PTM has three register-select lines and a single, composite, interrupt-request output. There are nine "peripheral side" lines connected to the PTM, arranged into three groups of three.

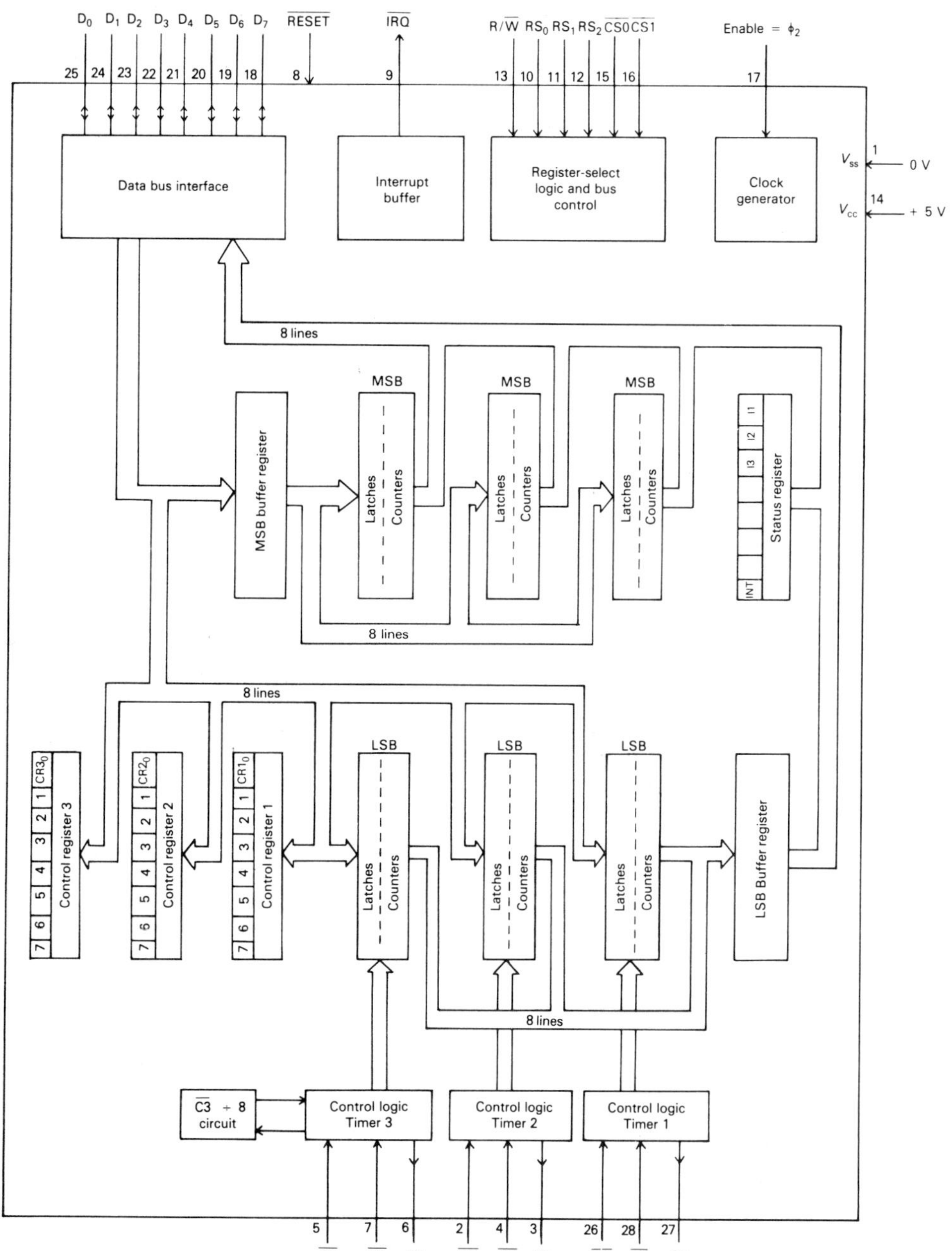

Fig. 6.15 The internal arrangement of the PTM

Each counter has a clock input, a $\overline{\text{GATE}}$ input which gates the clock pulses, and an output.

The PTM can be programmed to operate in four basic modes.

(1) A continuous mode in which a continuous square wave is generated at the timer's output. The PTM can be programmed to generate an interrupt at each transition of the output.
(2) A single-shot mode in which the PTM behaves as a monostable, producing one pulse at its output each time it is triggered. The PTM can also be programmed to generate interrupts in this mode.
(3) A period measurement mode which measures the period of a square wave.
(4) A pulse-width measurement mode which measures the period of a pulse.

From Fig. 6.15 it can be seen that the PTM has 18 internal registers. As there are only three register-select lines allowing 8 registers to be directly accessed, some considerable amount of ingenuity is required to get at these 18 registers. There are three 16-bit timer latch registers and three 16-bit timer counter registers, the former being write only and the latter read only. As with the ACIA the R/$\overline{\text{W}}$ input becomes, effectively, a register-select input. To write to a 16-bit timer latch the most significant byte of the data is written to the PTM and is latched internally into a write buffer. When the least significant byte is written to the PTM the LSB and the MSB in the buffer are transferred to the relevant timer latch. This procedure allows the index register to write to the PTM counter latches. The X register is loaded with a 16-bit value and then stored at the location of the requisite latch—this results in the MSB being transferred to the buffer, the LSB to the latch and then the MSB to the latch.

The timer counters are read in a similar fashion. On reading the MSB of a counter the LSB is moved to a buffer register so that a second read picks up the LSB. The addressing arrangements of the PTM are given in Table 6.15.

The PTM has a single read-only status register whose sole function is to indicate that a timer has generated an interrupt. Figure 6.16 gives the format of the status register. If any of timers 1, 2, or 3 generates an interrupt the corresponding interrupt flag is set together with the composite interrupt bit, bit 7. There are three ways of clearing an interrupt flag: by an external reset pulse, by a software reset (bit 1 of control register 1 set), by a read of the status register followed by a read of a timer counter.

The PTM has three write-only control registers, one for each of the counters. As these three registers occupy only two locations in the memory space, one control register (number 2) has a unique address (base + 1) while the other two control registers (1 and 3) have a common address (base + 0). To select control register 1, bit 0 of control register 2 must be set, and to select register 3 bit 0 of control register 2 must be clear.

Table 6.15 The Address Map of the PTM

Register select			*Read*	*Write*
RS_2	RS_1	RS_0	$R/\overline{W}=1$	$R/\overline{W}=0$
0	0	0	No operation	Control register 1 or 3
0	0	1	Status register	Control register 2
0	1	0	Timer 1 counter	MSB buffer register
0	1	1	LSB buffer register	Timer 1 latches
1	0	0	Timer 2 counter	MSB buffer register
1	0	1	LSB buffer register	Timer 2 latches
1	1	0	Timer 3 counter	MSB buffer register
1	1	1	LSB buffer register	Timer 3 latches

Example of Use of Timer Latches and Timer Counters

Base address of PTM = $9000
To put $1234 into timer latch 1
execute LDX # $1234
STX $9002 (i.e. base + 2)

The STX has the effect X_{high} → 9002 = MSB buffer register
X_{low} → 9003 = LSB timer 1 latch
MSB buffer reg → MSB timer 1 latch

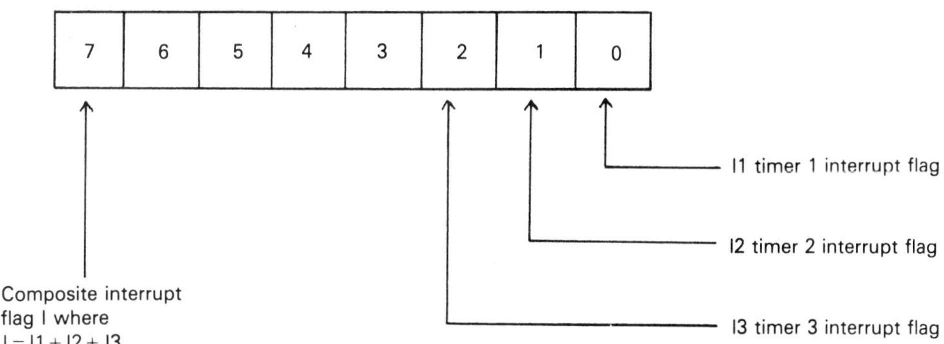

Fig. 6.16 The status register of the PTM

The Effect of the Control Registers

The structure of the three control registers is illustrated in Fig 6.17. This is a nasty looking diagram because, firstly, bit 0 of each control register has a different function and secondly, bits 2 – 5 do not operate independently—they must be considered as a group. It is best, perhaps, to explain the operation of the control register starting with the "easy" bits first.

CR_7 Timer output enable	CR_6 Interrupt mask bit	CR_5	CR_4	CR_3	CR_2 Counting mode 0 ← 16-bit mode 1 ← dual 8-bit mode	CR_1 Timer clock source 0 ← ext. clock 1 ← enable clock	$CR2_0$ Control register select
		0 continuous counting mode	0	0 initialize on $\overline{G}\downarrow + W + R$	$CR_2 = 0$ / $CR_2 = 1$		
		0 frequency comparison mode	0	1 interrupt generated if I/P period less than counter TO			
		0 continuous counting mode	1	0 initialize on $\overline{G}\downarrow + W$	$CR_2 = 0$ / $CR_2 = 1$		
		0 pulse width comparison mode	1	1 interrupt generated if I/P down time less than counter TO			
		1 single shot mode	0	0 initialize on $\overline{G}\downarrow + W + R$	$CR_2 = 0$ / $CR_2 = 1$		
		1 frequency comparison mode	0	1 interrupt generated if gate I/P period greater than counter TO			
		1 single shot mode	1	0 initialize on $\overline{G}\downarrow + W$	$CR_2 = 0$ / $CR_2 = 1$		
		1 pulse width comparison mode	1	1 interrupt generated if I/P down time greater than counter TO			

$CR1_0$ Internal reset bit

$CR2_0$ Control register select

$CR3_0$ Timer 3 prescale bit

G↓ Internal recognition of a negative-going input
W Write to timer latches command
R External reset ($\overline{RESET}$ low) or an internal reset ($CR1_0$ high)

Fig. 6.17 The control register of the PTM

Bit 0 In control register 1 this bit, when clear, allows all counters to operate, and when set holds the counters in a preset state. This bit is, effectively, a software reset. When a hardware reset occurs, all control-register bits are cleared with the exception of this bit which is set.

In control register 2 this bit, when clear, allows control register 3 to be selected by a write to the base address. When set, it allows control register 1 to be selected.

In control register 3 this bit when clear has no effect, and when set causes the clock input to timer 3 to be prescaled by 8.

Bit 1 This bit when clear causes the counter to use the external clock input and when set causes the PTM's enable input to act as the clock. In normal circumstances this is ϕ_2.

Bit 2 Bit 2 of each control register determines whether the counter operates in a "straight" 16-bit mode or in a "dual 8-bit" mode. When bit 2 is clear the 16-bit counting mode is selected and when it is set the dual 8-bit mode is selected. The meaning of these terms is illustrated in Fig. 6.18 which shows that either symmetric or asymmetric pulses may be generated by the PTM depending on the state of bit 2. In these examples it is assumed that bit 7 is set—otherwise the output is suppressed. The counters in the PTM count downwards and when their contents are zero a condition called "time out" (*TO*) is reached. A time-out condition causes an interrupt if the interrupt mask bit (CR bit 6) is set.

Bit 6 When clear bit 6 masks an interrupt generated by the counter and when set allows the interrupt to pull the $\overline{\text{IRQ}}$ pin low.

Bit 7 When this bit is clear the output of the counter is masked and when it is set the output of the counter is enabled. Of course, the status of this bit is relevant only for the continuous pulse-generation mode and the single-shot mode.

Bits 5, 4 and 3 These three bits control the function of the PTM as described in Fig. 6.17. A brief discussion of the PTM's modes of operation together with an example of one of its applications is given below. The reader wishing to learn more should consult the relevant data sheet.

Continuous Operating Mode

One of the most popular functions of the PTM is the generation of a continuous square wave, or the production of equi-spaced interrupts as a real-time

(1) Continuous operating mode $CR_3 = 0$, $CR_5 = 0$

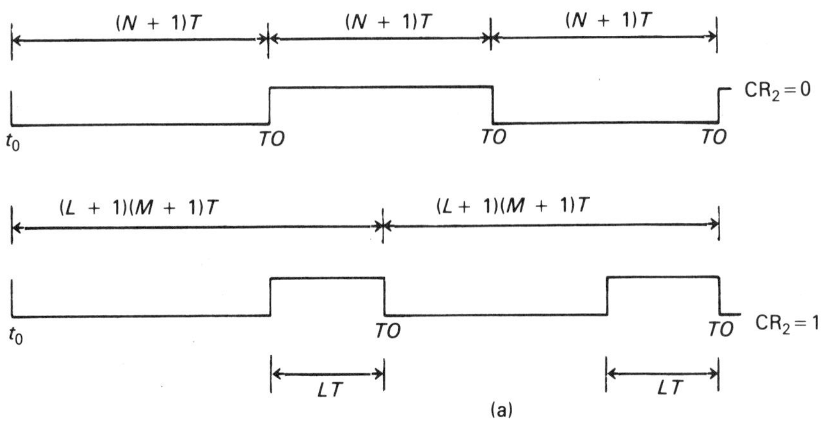

(a)

(2) Single-shot operating mode $CR_3 = 0$, $CR_5 = 1$

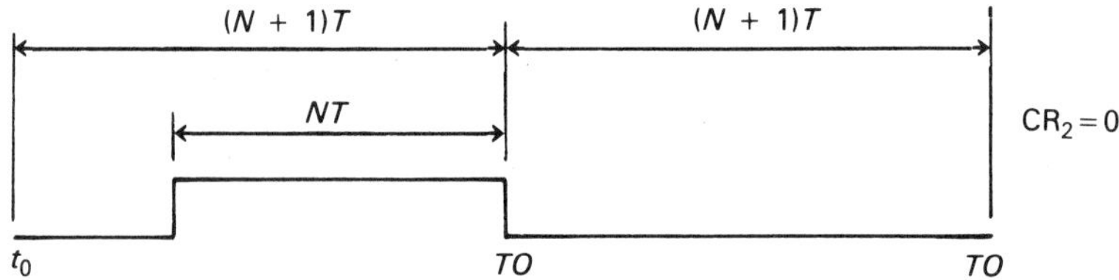

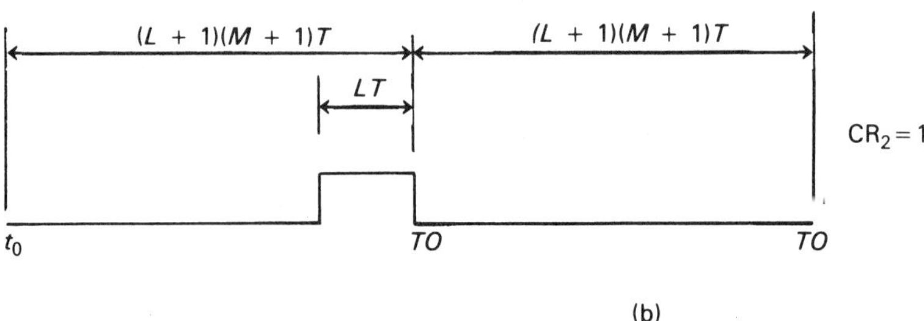

(b)

N = 16-bit number in counter latch
L = 8-bit number in LSB counter latch
M = 8-bit number in MSB counter latch
T = clock input negative transitions to counter
t_0 = counter initialization (start of the operation)
TO = counter time out (all zero condition)

Fig. 6.18 The effect of control register bit 2: (a) continuous operating mode, (b) single-shot mode

clock. In this mode CR_5 and CR_3 are both zero. To set up this mode the counter latch is first loaded with its value—in the 16-bit mode this will simply be the number of clock periods minus one between successive time outs. Remember that the latches are loaded by two successive transfers to the PTM (or one if an STX or STS operation is used).

Once the counter latch has been loaded, the counting must be started by means of a counter-latch initialization, which has the effect of transferring data from the latches to the counters and clearing the counter's interrupt flag. A counter initialization occurs after a hardware reset ($\overline{RESET} = 0$) or a software reset ($CR1_0 = 1$) has occurred. It can also occur when a negative transition takes place at the gate input or a "write timer latches" command is executed. These events are programmable. In the continuous operating mode an initialization occurs on a reset, a negative transition at the $\overline{GATE}$ input, or if bit 4 is clear, a write timer latch operation is executed. The $\overline{GATE}$ input must be low throughout the time the counter is operating in this mode.

Single-shot Operating Mode

This mode is similar to one cycle of the continuous mode—see Fig. 6.17. One difference between this mode and the continuous mode is that it is not necessary for the gate input to remain low throughout the duration of the single shot.

Frequency-comparison Mode

In both this mode and the pulse-comparison mode the status of the output signal is not defined. In the frequency-comparison (or period-measurement) mode with $CR_5 = 1$, if a time out occurs prior to the first negative transition of the $\overline{GATE}$ input after a counter-initialization cycle, the interrupt flag is set. The counter is disabled and a new counter initialization cannot begin until the interrupt flag has been cleared and a negative transition at the $\overline{GATE}$ input has been detected. That is, a negative transition at the $\overline{GATE}$ input starts the timing process and the interrupt flag is set if a time out occurs before the next negative transition at the gate. If bit 5 is clear an interrupt is generated if the $\overline{GATE}$ input goes low before the time out. If the counter time out occurs first, the counter is recycled and continues to decrement. Note that when the counter time out occurs first no interrupt is generated on successive cycles until a new counter initialization cycle has taken place.

Pulse-width Comparison Mode

This mode is virtually the same as that of the frequency-comparison mode except that a positive rather than a negative transition at the $\overline{GATE}$ input terminates the count.

An Example of the Use of the PTM

Suppose that timer 1 is to be used as a programmable frequency synthesizer. Assume that the timer will use the system clock as its source of timing pulses and that timer 1's $\overline{GATE}$ input is permanently grounded. The following sequence of operations must be carried out:

(1) Bit 0 of control register 2 must be set to allow control register 1 to be accessed.
(2) Control register 1 is set to operate in the continuous mode as a 16-bit counter, decremented by the enable clock. The interrupt mask bit is cleared, the output enable bit is set, and the counter initialization is programmed to occur on a write to counter latches.
(3) The index register is loaded with the number of clock pulses (less one) between successive transitions of the output. If this value is N, the frequency of the square wave at the output pin of timer 1 is $f = 1/2(N+1)T$, where T is the duration of the clock pulse. For a 1 kHz output $f = 1000$, $T = 1$ μs (assuming a 1 MHz system clock), $N = 499$.

The Program

```
PTM    EQU    $EC20          set up PTM's base address
       LDA A  #1             set bit 0
       STA A  PTM+1          set up control register 2
       LDA A  #%10000010     program control register 1
       STA A  PTM            set up control register 1
       LDX    #499           counter value
       STX    PTM+2          perform a 16-bit write to counter latch 1.
                             This also causes the latch initialization.
```

To modify the frequency it is only necessary to perform an STX operation to PTM+2.

The PTM on the CPU Module

The circuit diagram of the interface between a 6840 PTM and the CPU is given in Fig. 6.19. The "CPU side" of the PTM is entirely conventional and only the $\overline{IRQ}$ line requires comment. Although the TS1 has a vectored interrupt mechanism due to the 6828 PIC, it has not been applied to any devices on the CPU module. All peripherals capable of generating an interrupt have their $\overline{IRQ}$ lines wired to the CPU's $\overline{IRQ}$ input. Thus any interrupts generated by these peripherals must be dealt with by a software polling routine whose address is located at FFF8/9. The PIC has not been employed in conjunction with the on-board peripherals for two reasons. Firstly, at the time of designing the TS1 system no *a priori* level of interrupt prioritization could be applied to the peripherals. Secondly, the system is entirely general purpose and is not intended to have all peripherals simultaneously active, and therefore software interrupt polling is likely to be adequate to service the one or two peripherals active at any one time.

The "interface side" of the PTM consists of nine lines in three groups of three, one group associated with each timer. Each group has an output via which the PTM may transmit its various programmable waveforms, and two inputs. One input is a clock which acts as the "unit of counting" or is redundant if the PTM is programmed to operate with the system clock, ϕ_2. The other input is the $\overline{\text{GATE}}$ which may be programmed to initiate the generation of a waveform or to enable a pulse-width measurement (etc.) to take place. In the CPU module connections from the PTM are brought out to a seven-pin DIN connector which, after allowing for a ground connection, leaves only six pins to interface with the PTM's nine outputs. It may be seen from Fig. 6.19 that all lines to timer one, two lines to timer two and just one line to timer three are brought out to the front panel. Timer two cannot be operated with an external clock as its clock input is not used and timer three can be operated only as a non-gated counter or waveform generator.

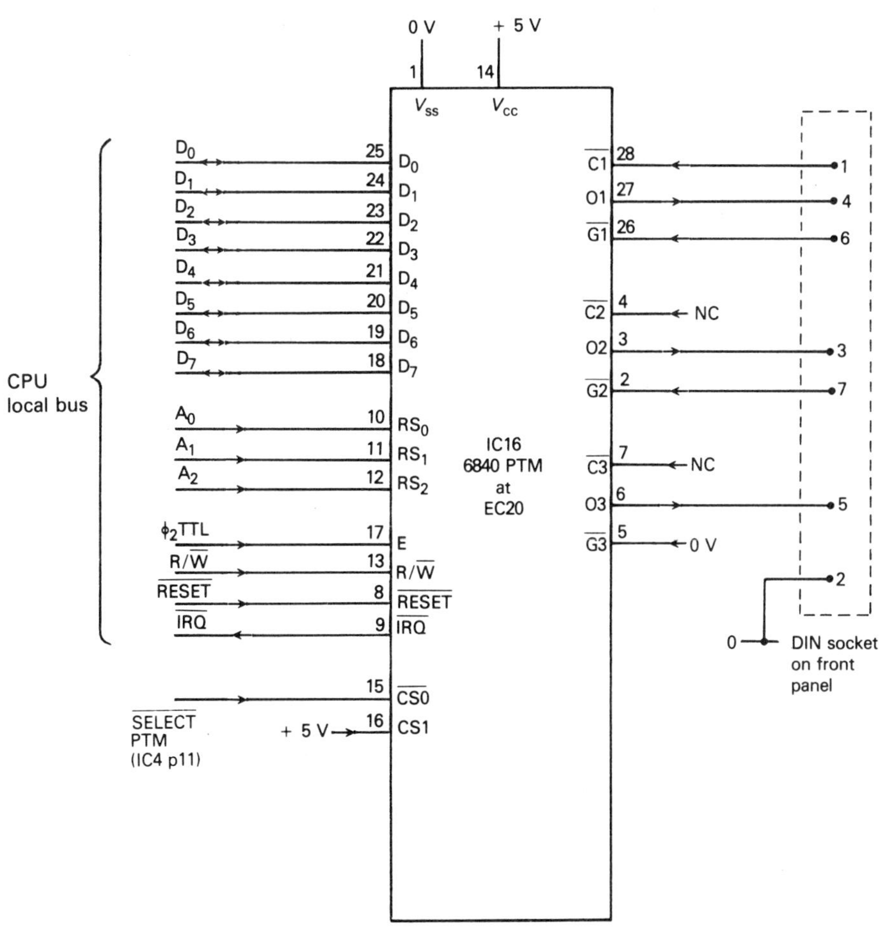

Fig. 6.19 The PTM on the CPU module

6.3 THE SERIAL DATA LINK

The principal input and output ports of the majority of general-purpose microprocessor systems handle data in a bit-serial format. That is, data is moved into, or out of, the port one bit at a time. In this context the term "principal port" refers to the port connected to the system's console. The only advantage in connecting the console device (VDT or teletype) to the CPU via a serial port and serial data link, as opposed to a parallel port and parallel data link, is the low cost of implementing a serial data link. Clearly a data link carrying eight bits of information simultaneously is approximately eight times the cost of a data link carrying only one bit of information at any instant. The penalty paid for a serial data link is the reduction in the rate at which information may be transmitted over the link compared with the corresponding parallel link. In general a serial link can transmit information at a rate of $1/n$ times that of an n-channel parallel link. In practice, the actual data rate over many serial links is somewhat slower than this because of the need to format serial data into units preceded by a start bit and terminated by a stop bit.

The basic components of a two-way serial data link are illustrated in Fig. 6.20. The arrangement in Fig. 6.20 is able to operate in a full duplex mode where information may be transmitted in both directions simultaneously. Systems operating in a simplex mode may transmit data in only one direction at a time. Consider the path from side A to side B in Fig. 6.20. At side A the 8-bit word to be transmitted is transformed into a stream of pulses by means of a parallel-to-serial convertor. This operation is initiated by applying a "data ready" strobe to the convertor.

A clock is required by the convertor to obtain the correct spacing between successive pulses. The serial output from the convertor is normally in the form of a TTL-compatible signal, and is translated to a suitable signal level with which to drive the data link by means of a line driver. The transmission path between side A and side B is normally composed of a co-axial cable or a twisted pair. At the receiver (side B) the signal from the data link is converted back into a TTL-compatible signal by means of a line receiver. A serial-to-parallel convertor transforms the stream of pulses into an 8-bit word and produces a "data ready" strobe to indicate that a word has been received. Although the arrangement of Fig. 6.20 could be constructed from standard MSI and SSI TTL components, all parts of this circuit may readily be obtained as functional units, fabricated with LSI techniques.

Where one end of a data link is a microprocessor system, the parallel to serial (and vice versa) convertor is best implemented by means of an ACIA, which is described in some detail in Section 6.2.2. It is assumed throughout this section that the data is transmitted asynchronously and that each character is delimited by a start bit and at least one stop bit. It is, of course, possible to transmit serial data synchronously. In a synchronous system the receiver's clock must be synchronized with the transmitter's clock if the received data is to be interpreted correctly. Such a system removes the inefficiency introduced by start and stop bits but at the cost of increased circuit complexity. Moreover, a synchronous system must continually transmit information if synchronism is to be maintained. This may be achieved by transmitting NUL or SYN characters which convey no information but provide the

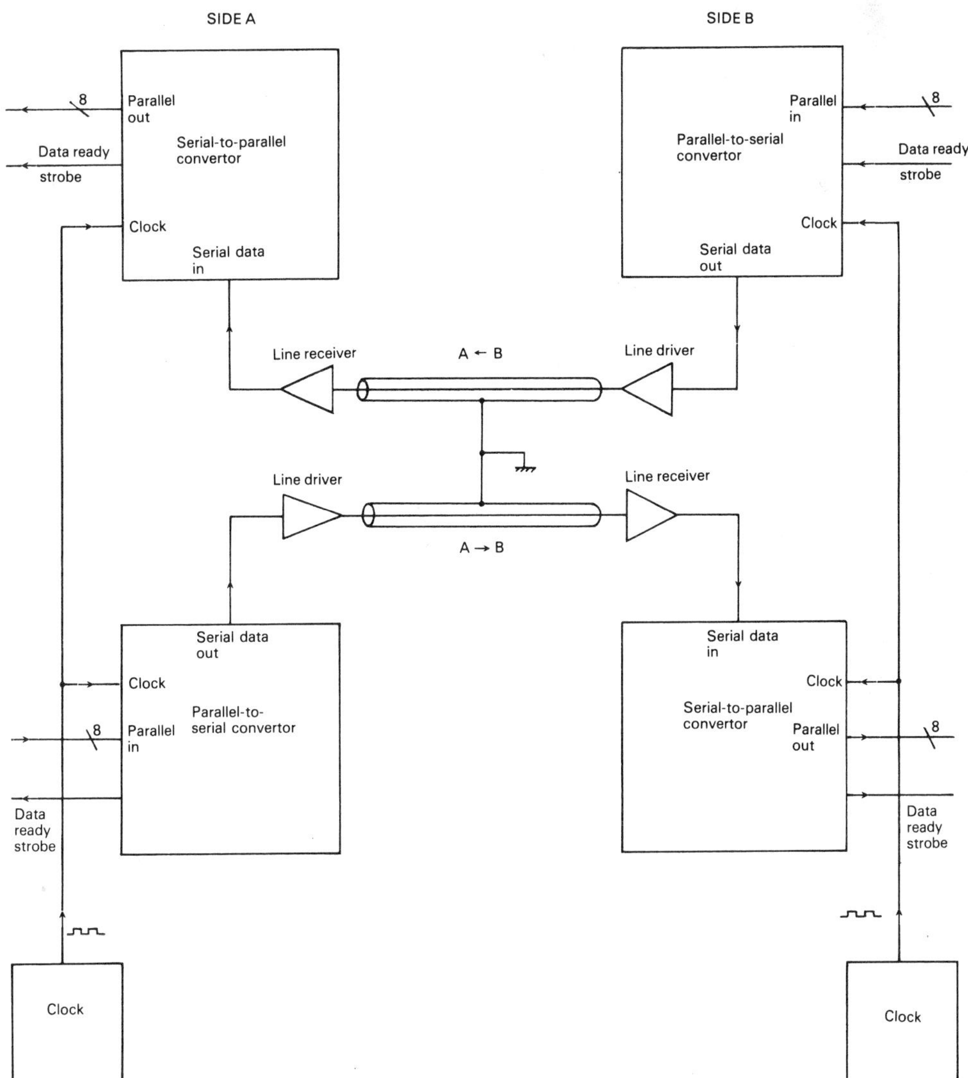

Fig. 6.20 A bidirectional serial data link

receiver with a stream of pulses from which they may extract timing information.

Unless the end of the data link remote from the microprocessor system is connected to a second microprocessor system it is not possible to use an ACIA at that end. An ACIA cannot be employed at the non-microprocessor end of the link because it operates under software control. Fortunately there exists a device, analogous to the ACIA, called a UART (Universal Asynchronous Receiver Transmitter), which may be controlled by hardware. That is, while the control bits

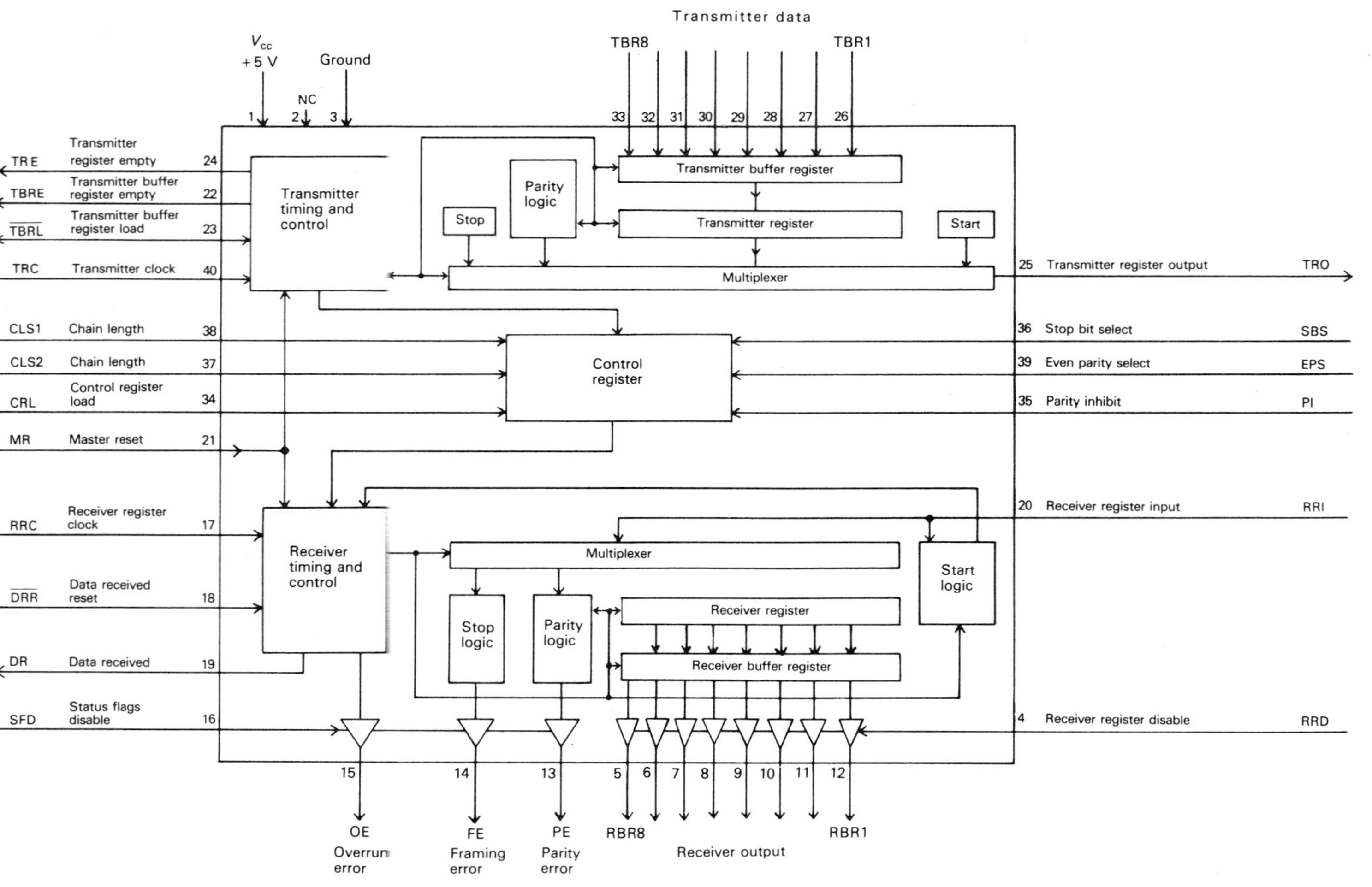

Fig. 6.21 The internal arrangement of the IM6402 UART

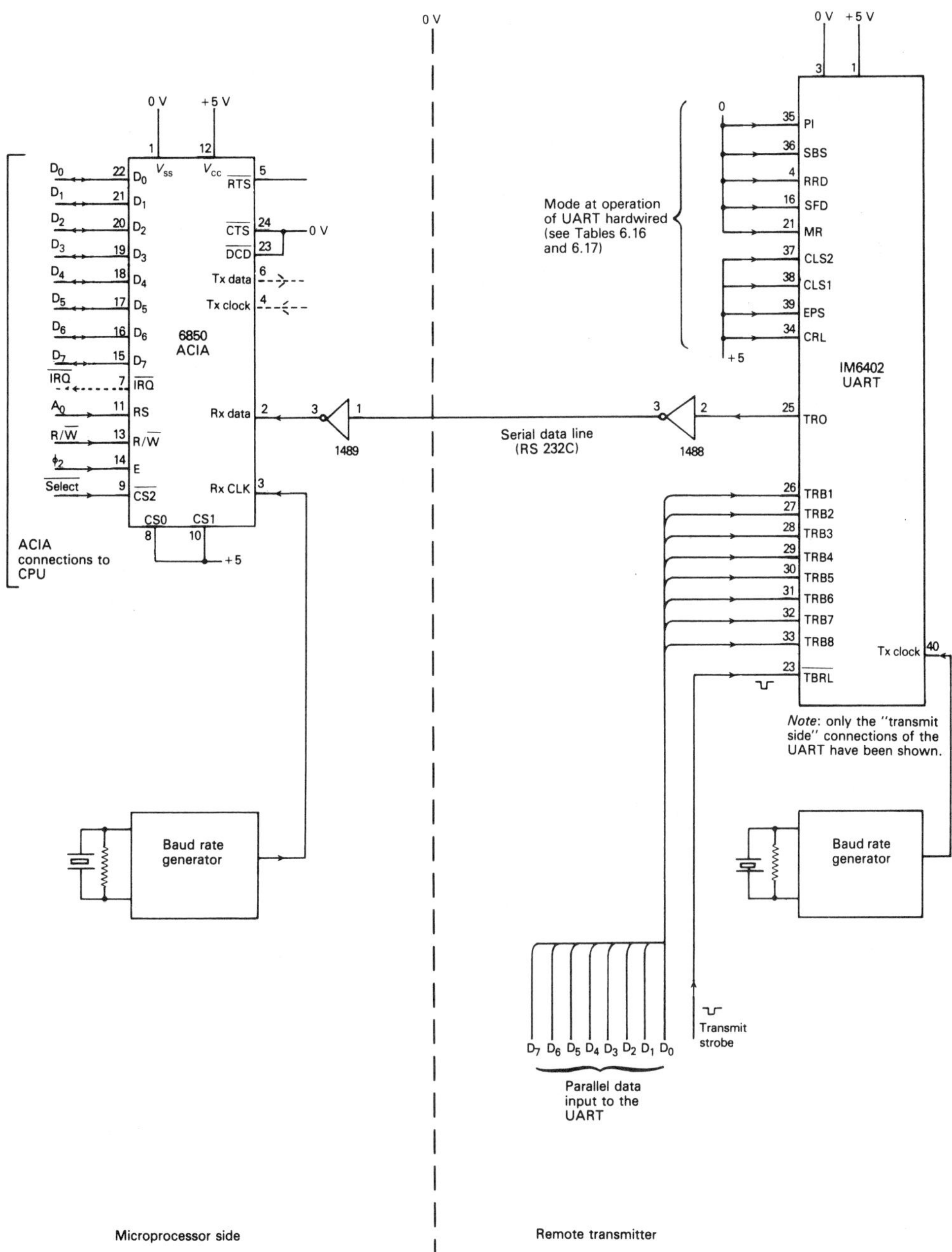

Fig. 6.22 The UART as a data transmitter

of an ACIA are written into it by means of a CPU-write cycle, the control bits of a UART are set up by hardwiring the appropriate pins to a logical 0 or 1. In a similar way, the status of an ACIA is read by the CPU while the status bits of a UART are physically connected to pins which may be used to control hardware directly. Consequently, a UART has a 40-pin package compared to the ACIA's 24 pins.

Because the operation of a UART is entirely independent of the host microprocessor the UART is second-sourced by a number of manufacturers. The most popular UARTs are the TMS6011 (Texas Instruments), AY-5-1013 (General Instrument Corporation), and the IM6402 (Intersil). Although these devices are functionally equivalent, both the TMS6011 and the AY-5-1013 require a supply of +5 V and −12 V, while the IM6402 operates from a single +5 V supply. The IM6402 has a further advantage over the other UARTs as it is fabricated with CMOS technology and consequently consumes very little power. The internal arrangement of an IM6402 UART is given in Fig. 6.21. As the operation of a UART is very similar to that of an ACIA only the most important details of a UART are given in this section. The actual circuit diagram of a link between an ACIA and a UART is given in Fig. 6.22. This link transmits data in only one direction (from the UART to the ACIA) and is intended to be operated in conjunction with a peripheral device having a parallel output. Such a device is the keyboard encoder described in Section 6.4. The salient features of the UART, as both a data transmitter and receiver, are given below.

The UART as a Transmitter

From Fig. 6.22 it can be seen that when a UART is operated as a transmitter, no more than three ICs are required. These are:

(1) A baud rate generator which provides the UART's transmitter with a clock at 16 times the required baud rate of the transmitted data.
(2) A line driver which matches the serial output of the UART to the data link between the transmitter and receiver
(3) The UART itself.

To transmit a character from the UART to the ACIA, the character code is applied to the parallel input of the UART, TRB1 − TRB8. Note that the UART may transmit character lengths of 5, 6, 7 or 8 bits and that the least significant bit of the character to be transmitted should be connected to TRB1. The definitions of the pins of the UART, corresponding to Fig. 6.21, are given in Table 6.16. The actual transmission process is initiated by strobing the $\overline{\text{TBRL}}$ (transmitter buffer register load) pin with an active-low pulse, whose width must be greater than 100 ns and whose rising edge must occur no sooner than 40 ns after the data at TRB1 − TRB8 has stabilized. The data must be held for at least 30 ns after the rising edge of $\overline{\text{TBRL}}$. The transmitter timing diagram is

Table 6.16 The Functions of the IM6402 UART's Pins

Pin	*Symbol*	*Type*	*Function*
1	V_{cc}	power	Positive power supply +5 V.
2			Not used (−12 V in TMS6011 and AY-5-1013).
3	V_{ss}	ground	Ground.
4	RRD	RX I/P	Receiver register disable. When high the receiver register outputs are floated.
5-12	RBR1 − RBR8	RX O/P	Receiver buffer register outputs, i.e. received data.
13	PE	RX O/P	A high level indicates that the received parity bit does not match the parity bit programmed by the control bits.
14	FE	RX O/P	A high level indicates the presence of a framing error.
15	OE	RX O/P	A high level indicates an overrun error—the data received flag was not cleared before the last character was transferred to the receiver buffer register.
16	SFD	control I/P	A high level on status flags disable forces the outputs PE, FE, OE, DR, TBRE into a high-impedance state.
17	RRC	RX I/P	The receiver register clock at 16 times the data rate.
18	$\overline{\text{DRR}}$	RX I/P	A low level on the $\overline{\text{data received reset}}$ clears the data received output (DR) to a low level.
19	DR	RX O/P	A high level on data received indicates a character has been received and transferred to the receiver buffer register.
20	RRI	RX I/P	The receiver register input.
21	MR	control I/P	A high level on master reset clears PE, FE, OE, DR, TRE and sets TBRE, TRO high.
22	TBRE	TX O/P	A high level on transmitter buffer register empty indicates the transmitter buffer register has transferred its data to the transmitter register and is ready for new data.
23	$\overline{\text{TBRL}}$	TX I/P	A low level on the $\overline{\text{transmitter buffer register load}}$ transfers data from inputs TBR1 − TBR8 into the transmitter buffer register. A low-to-high transition on $\overline{\text{TBRL}}$ requests data transfer to the transmitter register. If the transmitter register is busy, transfer is automatically delayed so that two characters are transmitted end to end.
24	TRE	TX O/P	A high level on transmitter register empty indicates the completed transmission (including stop bits) of the current character. TRE remains high until the next start bit.
25	TRO	TX O/P	The transmitter register output provides the serial output of the transmitter. The idle state of the O/P is high and a new character is signified by the high-to-low transition of a start bit.
26-33	TBR1 − TBR8	TX I/P	Character data is loaded into the transmitter buffer register via these pins. The least significant bit is designated TBR1 (pin 26).

Table 6.16 *(continued)*

Pin	Symbol	Type	Function
34	CRL	control I/P	A high level on the control register load input transfers the data control word on pins 35 – 39 into the control register.
35	PI	control I/P	A high level on the parity inhibit input prevents the generation of a parity bit.
36	SBS	control I/P	A high level on this pin selects 2 stop bits, a low level selects 1 stop bit.
37	CLS2	control I/P	Character length select 1 and 2 determine the number of bits per character.
38	CLS1	control I/P	
39	EPS	control I/P	A high level on the even parity select input generates an even parity. If EPS is low an odd parity is selected. Whenever PI is high the input at the EPS pin is a don't care condition.
40	TRC	TX I/P	The transmitter register clock at 16 times the data rate.

given in Fig. 6.23. Once started, the transmission process proceeds automatically. From Fig. 6.23 it can be seen that the rising edge of the $\overline{\text{TBRL}}$ pulse clears the TBRE (transmitter buffer empty) flag. In less than two clock cycles the data in the transmitter buffer register is moved to the transmitter register from which it is serialized, the TRE (transmitter register empty) flag is cleared and transmission starts. TBRE is reset to a logic one. A second pulse on $\overline{\text{TBRL}}$ now loads new data into the transmitter buffer register, and the TBRE flag is cleared. However, this data cannot

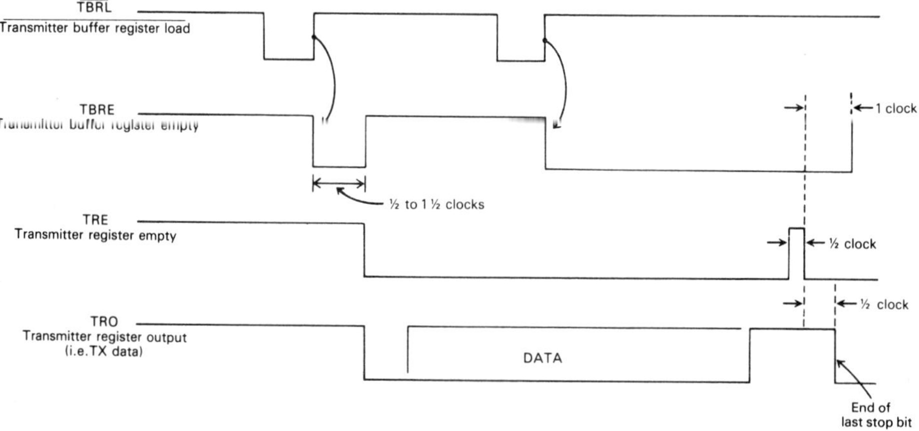

Fig. 6.23 The transmitter timing diagram of the UART

now be transferred to the transmitter register until the tranmission of the current character is complete. Once the current character has been serialized the TRE flag is set, the contents of the transmitter buffer register moved to the transmitter register, and the TBRE flag is set. The TRE flag is cleared as the transmitter register is now full.

From the above description of the operation of the UART as a transmitter it can be seen that data presented to the UART is double buffered and that TBRE and TRE provide a handshaking arrangement in conjunction with the $\overline{\text{TBRL}}$ strobe. In many applications of the UART a handshaking process is fortunately not necessary. As long as data to the UART from the keyboard encoder is not presented at an instantaneous rate greater than the clock rate multiplied by the total bits per transmitted character, no problems arise.

The UART is programmed by means of pins 35 – 39, which select the length of the character, the parity bit and its polarity, and the number of stop bits. These control bits operate on both the transmitter and receiver sides of the UART. Table 6.17 defines the effect of these pins on the format of the data handled by the UART.

Table 6.17 The Relationship Between the Control Word and the Character Format of the IM6402 UART

Control word								
Pin 37 CLS2	*Pin 38 CLS1*	*Pin 35 PI*	*Pin 39 EPS*	*Pin 36 SBS*	*Data bits per char.*	*Parity bit*	*Stop bits*	*Total char. length*
0	0	0	0	0	5	Odd	1	8
0	0	0	0	1	5	Odd	$1\frac{1}{2}$	$8\frac{1}{2}$
0	0	0	1	0	5	Even	1	8
0	0	0	1	1	5	Even	$1\frac{1}{2}$	$8\frac{1}{2}$
0	0	1	×	0	5	Disabled	1	7
0	0	1	×	1	5	Disabled	$1\frac{1}{2}$	$7\frac{1}{2}$
0	1	0	0	0	6	Odd	1	9
0	1	0	0	1	6	Odd	2	10
0	1	0	1	0	6	Even	1	9
0	1	0	1	1	6	Even	2	10
0	1	1	×	0	6	Disabled	1	8
0	1	1	×	1	6	Disabled	2	9
1	0	0	0	0	7	Odd	1	10
1	0	0	0	1	7	Odd	2	11
1	0	0	1	0	7	Even	1	10
1	0	0	1	1	7	Even	2	11
1	0	1	×	0	7	Disabled	1	9
1	0	1	×	1	7	Disabled	2	10
1	1	0	0	0	8	Odd	1	11
1	1	0	0	1	8	Odd	2	12
1	1	0	1	0	8	Even	1	11
1	1	0	1	1	8	Even	2	12
1	1	1	×	0	8	Disabled	1	10
1	1	1	×	1	8	Disabled	2	11

The input to these pins is called the control word and is gated into the UART by a logical 1 on the CRL (control register load) pin. In most applications of a UART the CRL pin is permanently connected to a logical 1, and the value of the control word is hardwired to pins 35 – 39.

Operation of the UART as a Receiver

It is possible to operate the UART as a transmitter or receiver, or both simultaneously. Both receiver and transmitter sections of the UART have their own clock input, making it possible to receive data at one baud rate and to transmit data at

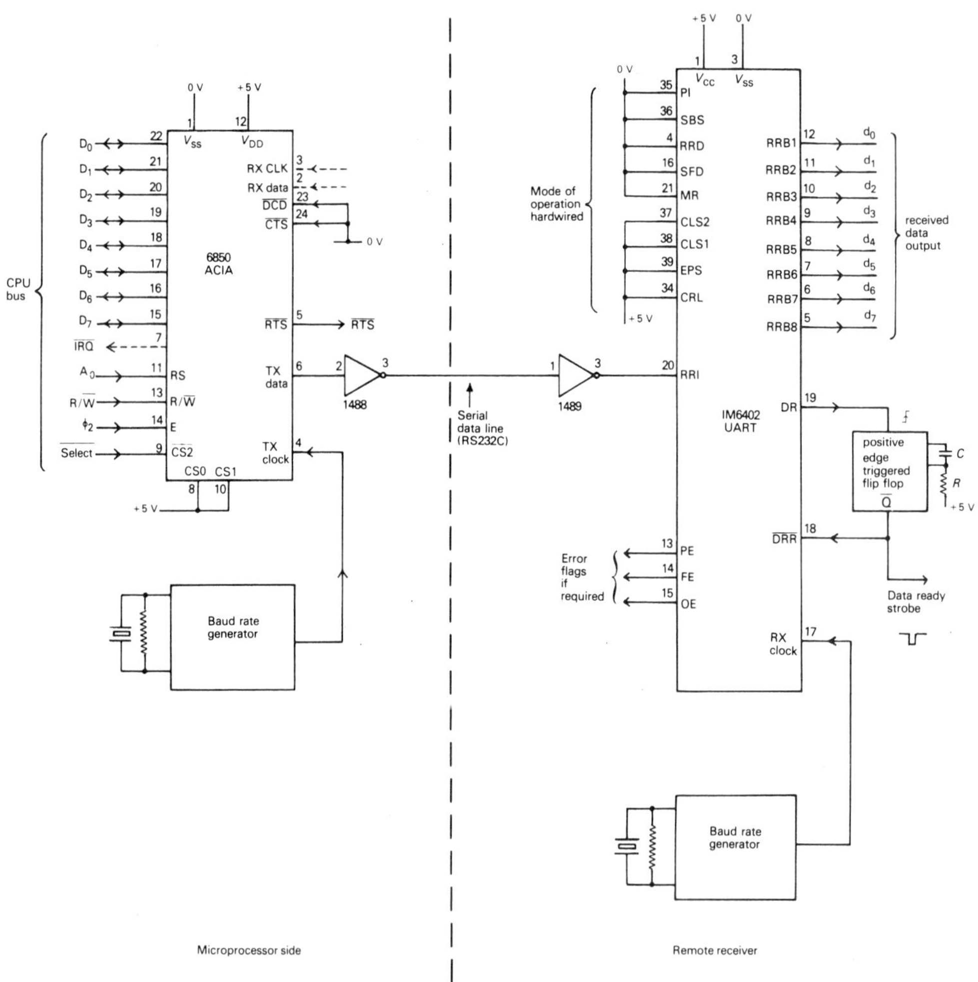

Fig. 6.24 The UART as a receiver

a different rate. Furthermore by multiplexing the control word between two different values, the UART can be made to transmit and receive characters in different formats. In the vast majority of cases, the receiver and transmitter sections of the UART operate at the same baud rate with the control word permanently hardwired.

The operation of the UART as a receiver is presented in Fig. 6.24, where serial data is converted into an 8-bit word and a data ready strobe. Note that the majority of the UART's pins are configured exactly as in the case where it is operated as a transmitter.

Serial data is received from the link by a line receiver and presented to the UART's receiver register input (RRI) in the form of a TTL-compatible signal. The serial data is clocked into the receiver register by the receiver register clock. Figure 6.25 gives the timing diagram of the receiver section of the UART. At point A a low level on the data received reset ($\overline{\text{DRR}}$) line clears the data received (DR) signal. At B during the first stop bit, data is transferred from the receiver register to the receiver buffer register. A logic high on the overrun error (OE) line indicates an overrun which occurs when data ready has not been cleared before the present character was transferred to the receiver buffer register. At C, half a clock cycle

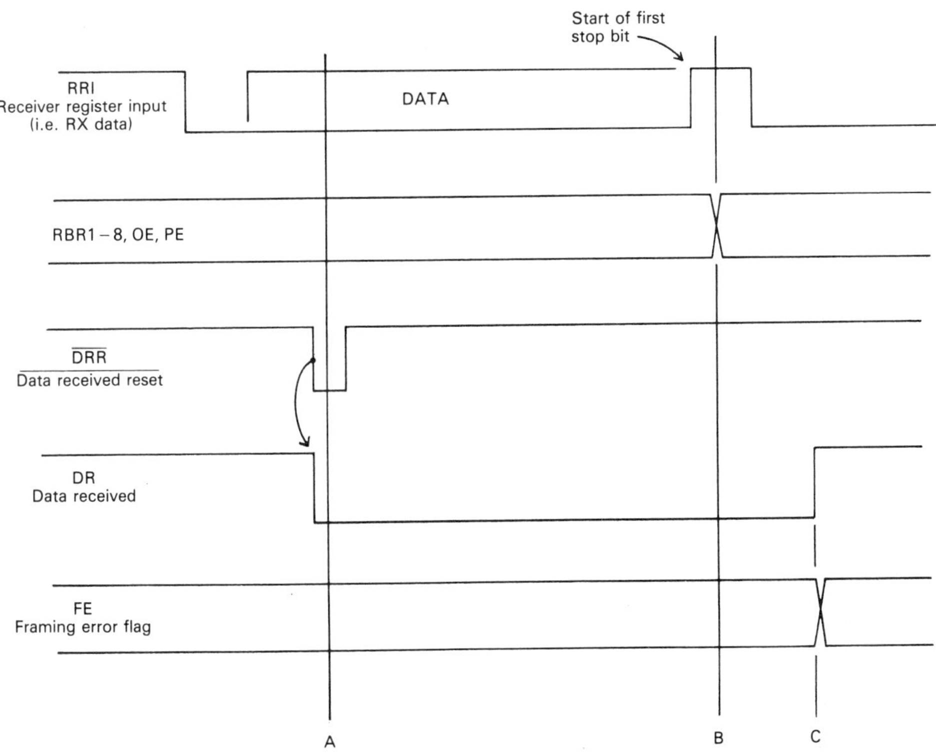

Fig. 6.25 The receiver timing diagram of the UART

after point B, the data received line is set to a logical one and the framing error (FE) is evaluated. A logic one on the FE line indicates that an invalid stop bit has been received. The receiver will not begin searching for the next start bit until a stop bit is received.

The timing requirements of the receiver section of the UART may be summed up by saying that after data has been received, the data received line goes high and must be reset by applying a negative going pulse to the data received reset line. In Fig. 6.24 this is done by using the DR output of the UART to trigger a monostable, and then connecting the $\overline{\text{Q}}$ output of the monostable to the UART's $\overline{\text{DRR}}$ input. Some designers simply connect the $\overline{\text{DRR}}$ input of the UART to the receiver register input so that the received data itself resets the receiver register. In many simple applications of a UART the error flags (PE, FE, and OE) are not used.

The Serial Data Link

As the receiver and transmitter ends of a data link are separated by some distance it is necessary to have some form of transmission path between the receiver and the transmitter. Over short distances (up to thousands of metres) this path is likely to be composed of a coaxial cable, a twisted pair of conductors, or a section of ribbon cable (very short paths only). The digital information is normally transmitted in the form in which it is generated (i.e. binary logic levels). Where the transmission path is very long, the public switched telephone network is often used to carry the information. In this case, it is no longer possible to transmit data as pulses—the binary information must be used to modulate a carrier (a continuous tone) at the transmitter. At the receiver end of the transmission path a demodulator recovers the digital data from the modulated carrier. The device which does all this (at least over telephone links) is called a MODEM (MODulator DEModulator).

One of the oldest forms of digital data transmission involves the concept of a current loop. That is, a current (normally either 20 mA or 60 mA) is generated at the transmitter and flows via one lead of the data link into the receiver and via the other lead out of the receiver and back to the transmitter. Hence, the current flows in a loop. This arrangement dates back to the electromechanical era when the current was used to open and close the contacts of a relay. The mark, or idle, state of the system is maintained by a 20 mA current flowing in the loop, and the space state is characterized by no current, or a break in the loop. By choosing the idle state of the circuit to be a continuous current of 20 mA, it is possible to detect a fault in the loop (an open-circuit) because the longest period for which a break may exist is often only eleven bit periods. The circuit diagram of a possible 20 mA current loop data link is given in Fig. 6.26.

Consider the transmitter section of Side A. When the output of the ACIA is in the idle or mark state (a logical 1) the output of invertor IC_1 is low (< 0.4 V) and a current flows through the diode in the opto-isolator. This is a light-emitting diode which when conducting generates (infra-red) light. The light illuminates photo-transistor T_1, turning it on. Consequently a current flows through T_1, round the data link and through diode D_2 in an opto-isolator at the receiver end of the link. D_2 emits

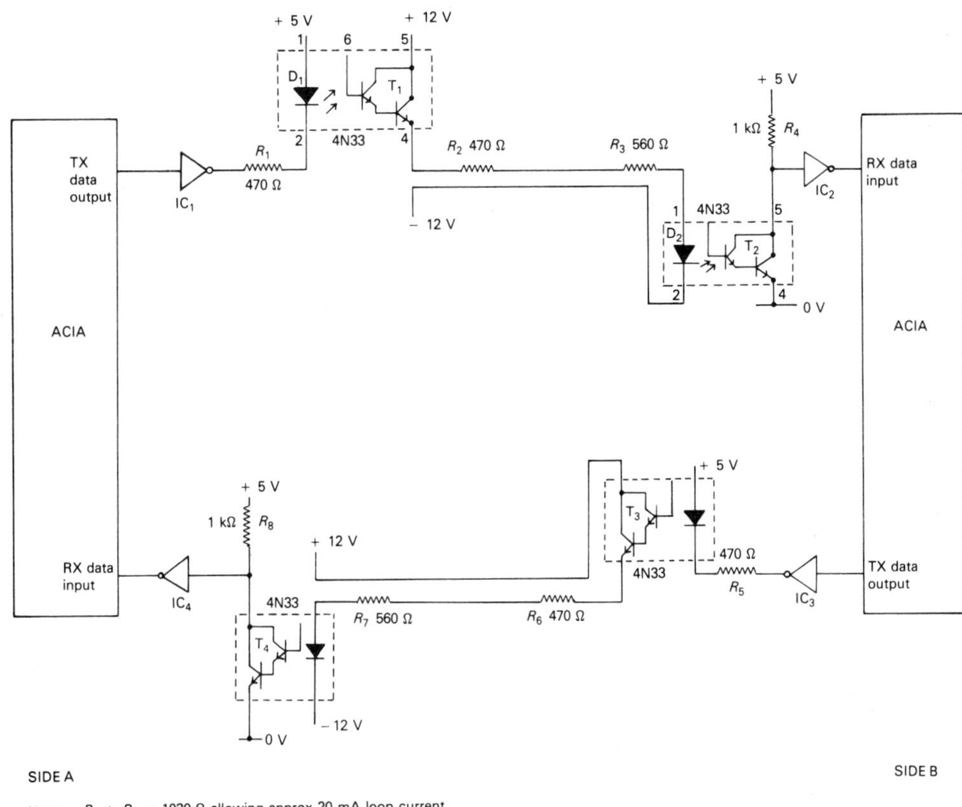

Fig. 6.26 The 20 mA current loop interface

light which turns on photo-transistor T_2, and produces a logical zero at the input of IC_2. The output of IC_2 is a logical 1, the same as the input to IC_1.

If the input to IC_1 now goes low (a space condition) no current flows through D_1, cutting off T_1. Consequently no current flows through D_2, T_2 is cut off and the input to IC_2 is pulled up to a logical one, causing a low level at its output. Thus, this circuit faithfully conveys the output of ACIA at side A to the input of the ACIA at side B.

The return path between sides A and B operates in a similar manner. There are two interesting aspects of this circuit. Firstly the opto-isolators physically separate the transmission path from the rest of the microprocessor system. In this way electrical disturbances applied to the loop do not harm the microprocessor and its peripheral components—opto-isolators can normally withstand up to 2 kV between their input and output. Secondly, the + 12 V and − 12 V driving the link need be provided at one end only (in this case side A). Note that the ±12 V supply may be isolated from the microprocessor's own supply.

The RS232C Interface

The most popular serial interface used to link VDTs and other such devices to computers is the Electronics Industries Association's RS232C interface. The CCITT equivalent of this interface is designated V24. This interface operates with a single-ended bipolar unterminated circuit. That is, the data link is single-ended because the binary information is referred to ground (one conductor carries the data while the other conductor is earthed as in Fig. 6.20). The circuit in unterminated, which means that there is no requirement to match the receiver to the characteristic impedance of the transmission path. Finally, the information is transmitted in a bipolar form with a negative voltage representing one logic level and a positive voltage representing the other. We shall see later how other types of interface standard have entirely different characteristics to the RS232C standard.

The basic characteristics of the RS232C interface are given in Table 6.18 from which it may be seen that this standard supports only transmission paths of less than 15 m (50 ft) at data rates of less than 20 kilobaud. These two limitations stem from the wide separation between the decision levels at the detector (space more positive than + 3 V and mark more negative than − 3 V), and the lack of a specific requirement for a low-impedance driver circuit.

The actual process of interfacing the TTL-compatible inputs and outputs of an

Table 6.18 The Characteristics of Three EIA Interfaces

Characteristic	*EIA RS232C*	*EIA RS423*	*EIA RS422*
Form of operation	Single ended	Single-ended	Double ended
Maximum cable length	15 m (50 ft)	600 m (2000 ft)	1200 m (4000 ft)
Maximum data rate	20 kilobaud	300 kilobaud	10 megabaud
Driver max output voltage open circuit	±25 V	±6 V	6 V between outputs
Driver min output voltage-loaded output	±5 V to ±15 V	±3.6 V	2 V between outputs
Driver min output resistance (power off)	$R_0 = 300\ \Omega$	100 μA between − 6 and + 6 V	100 μA between + 6 V and − 0.25 V
Driver max output short-circuit current	±500 mA	±150 mA	±150 mA
Driver output slew rate	30 V/μs max	Slew rate must be controlled based on cable length and modulation rate	No control necessary
Receiver input resistance	3 to 7 kΩ	⩾4 kΩ	⩾4 kΩ
Receiver max I/P threshold	− 3 to + 3 V	− 0.2 to + 0.2 V	− 0.2 to + 0.2 V
Receiver max I/P voltage	− 25 to + 25 V	− 12 to + 12 V	− 12 to + 12 V

ACIA or UART with an RS232C data link is made relatively straightforward by the use of the Am1488 quad RS232C line driver and the Am1489 quad RS232C line receiver. These devices are produced by a wide range of manufacturers, and are available in 14-pin DIL packages. The 1488 driver requires supplies of + 12 V and − 12 V and the 1489 receiver operates from a single + 5 V supply. Each of the 1489 receivers has a data input pin and an additional pin which may be used to set the input switching threshold. In the TS1 this facility is not used; the input threshold voltage adjustment pin is left floating which results in a switching threshold of approximately 1 V. Data on these two integrated circuits is given in Appendix A3.

Almost all equipment operating with an RS232C interface uses a 25-way connector between the two pieces of equipment communicating with each other over the serial data link. Normally, this equipment may be a VDT, microprocessor I/O port, or modem. Table 6.19 gives the input/output connections of a typical RS232C modem. Note that in many simple applications only pins 2 (data output), and 3 (data input) and 7 (ground) are used.

It should be noted that the RS232 interface is the cause of many headaches. The EIA RS232C standard defines the electrical and mechanical interface between data terminal equipment (DTE) and data communications equipment (DCE). This interface has been adapted by many manufacturers to connect printers and VDTs to microprocessor systems. Unfortunately, problems have arisen where, for example, the computer supplies ground, transmitted data and received data to a VDT, but the VDT requires, say, a request to send signal. In this case the user has to strap the VDT's RTS pin to a logical 1 if the system is to work. Where the RS232C standard is implemented between DTEs and DCEs pin 2 of the DTE is connection to pin 2 of the DCE, and similarly for pin 3. However, when VDTs are connected to microprocessor equipment, pin 3 of one connector is wired to pin 2 of the other connector. For these reasons, the specifications of both ends of the data link should be carefully checked before they are connected together.

Modern high-speed computer systems require data rates considerably higher than those provided by the RS232C standard. Two new standards have been introduced by the EIA, the RS423 and the RS422, to overcome the limitations of the RS232C standard. The basic characteristics of all three standards are given in Table 6.18.

The RS423, like the RS232C, is a single-ended (unbalanced) bipolar unterminated interface which can operate at data rates of 3000 baud up to 1200 m (4000 ft) or at rates of up to 300 kilobaud over a maximum distance of 12 m (40 ft). The RS422 is a differential balanced-voltage interface and is able to operate at very much higher data rates over longer distances than unbalanced interfaces. Data rates of up to 100 kilobaud over 1200 m (4000 ft) may be accommodated. Over shorter distances the data rate may be as high as 10 megabaud. In a balanced arrangement the transmission path is isolated from ground noise currents. It is also relatively immune from random potential differences between system ground references, and to common-mode electromagnetic interference.

Table 6.19 The RS232C Interface
(The specifications of a commercially available modem)

Pin	*Name*	*Function*
1	Protective ground	Electrical equipment frame and a.c. power ground
2	Transmitted data	Serial binary data generated by the DTE
3	Received data	Serial binary data generated by the modem
4	Request to send	An on condition indicates that the DTE is ready to transmit primary data.
5	Clear to send	An on condition indicates that the modem is ready to transmit primary data.
6	Data set ready	An on condition indicates that the modem is not in a test, voice or dial mode, that all initial handshake answer tone and timing delays have expired.
7	Signal ground	Common ground reference for all circuits except protective ground
8	Receiver line signal detector	An on condition indicates that data carrier signals are being received from remote equipment
9	Data modem testing	+12 V
10	Data modem testing	−12 V
11	New sync.	An on condition for at least 0.4 ms simulates loss of received line signal. Used only in special polling applications where system timing is carefully controlled.
12	Secondary received line signal detector	An on condition indicates that secondary channel data carrier signals are being received from remote equipment
13	Secondary clear to send	An on condition indicates that the modem is ready to transmit secondary data
14	Secondary transmitted data	Low-speed serial binary data generated by the DTE
15	Transmitted signal element timing	Signals on this line provide the DTE with signal element timing information
16	Secondary received data	Low-speed serial binary data generated by the modem in response to data signals received from remote equipment
17	Receiver signal element timing	Signals on this line provide the DTE with signal element timing information
18	Not used	Not used
19	Secondary request to send	An on condition indicates that the DTE is ready to transmit secondary channel data
20	Data terminal ready	Not used
21	Signal quality detector	An on condition indicates no errors. An off condition indicates the probability of error
22	Ring indicator	Not used
23	Data signal rate selector	An on condition causes the modem to operate at 4800 bits/s. An off condition selects the 3200 bits/s fallback rate
24	Transmit signal element timing	Signals on this line provide the modem with signal element timing
25	Not used	Not used

Note: DTE = data terminal equipment

6.4 THE KEYBOARD INTERFACE

The most popular method of entering data into a digital computer is the keyboard. A keyboard is composed of two distinct parts: a number of keys (usually push-buttons) which detect the pressure of a finger, and an encoder which converts a signal from a key into a unique code representing that key. The design of keyboards has been much influenced by the typewriter, and many computer keyboards are almost indistinguishable from those found on typewriters.

The keyswitches which detect the pressure of a finger, a keystroke, are normally mechanical devices. A typical mechanical keyswitch uses a plunger which is moved by a finger against the pressure of a spring. At the end of its travel the plunger forces two gold-plated wire contacts together, making a circuit. Between the plunger and the wires is a small stainless steel "snap-disk" which, because of its mechanical hysteresis, produces a click when it is bowed downwards by the plunger, and a similar click when the plunger is released. In this way the act of depressing a switch has a positive feel because of the tactile feedback and the audible click. Another form of mechanical switch has a small magnet in the plunger, which is designed to open and close the contacts of a reed relay. Although the mechanical switch has superb ergonomic qualities, it is less good from an electrical point of view. In particular, when the contacts first touch they tend to bounce, producing a series of pulses at their output rather than a clean make. This effect is common to all mechanical switches but is not normally important in analog circuits.

Three alternative forms of switch are: the Hall-effect switch, the elastometric switch, and the capacitive switch. The Hall-effect switch consists of a magnet which is pushed against a spring towards a Hall cell. The Hall cell is a semiconductor device through which a current flows. When a magnetic field is applied at right angles to the current, a voltage is produced across the terminals of the cell at right angles to both the field and the current flow. This type of switch has no contact bounce and is the most expensive of the switches described here.

The capacitive switch relies on the change in the capacitive coupling between two metallic "contacts" when a finger is pressed against them. The great advantage of the capacitive keyboard is its extremely low cost and its small size—it is often nothing more than a printed-circuit board, the contacts being etched on the surface. Unfortunately, this form of keyboard has no tactile feedback and is rather unpleasant to use. Some designers alleviate the lack of tactile feedback by providing audio feedback. Each time a keystroke is made a short audio bleep is sounded.

The keyboards relying on elastometric techniques use certain types of material which change their electrical resistance when subjected to pressure. As a finger is pressed against the material the drop in its resistance may be detected by a suitable interface. Once more, this type of switch has a less than positive feel—the response being described as "mushy and ill-defined" by one author.

Because of the influence of the typewriter, the layout of most electronic keyboards closely follows that of the QWERTY keyboard. Some electronic keyboards have a separate numeric keypad containing the digits 0 – 9, decimal point, and some cursor control characters (backspace, line feed, carriage return etc). Such an arrangement is often helpful to the "casual" user—the non-professional typist.

In order to reduce the total number of keys, and hence the size and the price, many of the keys have two or three functions. This is achieved by introducing the special purpose keys, *shift* and *control*, whose action modifies the normal operation of the remaining keys. The *shift* key behaves in a fashion entirely analogous to the corresponding key on a typewriter and either converts a lower-case character into its upper-case equivalent, or selects one of two symbols (e.g. ":" or "*"). The action of the *control* key is to allow the normal alphanumeric keys to be used to generate the non-printing ASCII control characters—pressing a "G" while the *control* key is down produces the code corresponding to the "ring bell command".

The ASCII Code

We shall later examine one of the techniques by which the closure of a keyswitch may be converted into a seven-bit code; here it is worth considering some of the properties of the ASCII code. Although there are other character codes than the ASCII code, this code is used by almost all VDTs, Teletypes and small

Table 6.20 The ASCII Code

$d_3d_2d_1d_0$ \ $d_6d_5d_4$		*0* *000*	*1* *001*	*2* *010*	*3* *011*	*4* *100*	*5* *101*	*6* *110*	*7* *111*
0	0000	NUL	DLE	SP	0	@	P	'	p
1	0001	SOH	DC1	!	1	A	Q	a	q
2	0010	STX	DC2	"	2	B	R	b	r
3	0011	ETX	DC3	#	3	C	S	c	s
4	0100	EOT	DC4	$	4	D	T	d	t
5	0101	ENQ	NAK	%	5	E	U	e	u
6	0110	ACK	SYN	&	6	F	V	f	v
7	0111	BEL	ETB	'	7	G	W	g	w
8	1000	BS	CAN	(	8	H	X	h	x
9	1001	HT	EM	)	9	I	Y	i	y
A	1010	LT	SUB	*	:	J	Z	j	z
B	1011	VT	ESC	+	;	K	[	k	{
C	1100	FF	FS	,	<	L	\	l	|
D	1101	CR	GS	–	=	M	]	m	}
E	1110	SO	RS	.	>	N	^	n	~
F	1111	SI	US	/	?	O	_	o	DEL

microprocessor systems. The relationship between the ASCII characters and their 7-bit codes is given in Table 6.20. Some basic points of interest are as follows:

(1) Character codes between 00 and 1F are non-printing control characters.

(2) The numeric characters 0–9 have codes 30_{16} to 39_{16}, which makes the conversion of an ASCII code into a binary number (or vice versa) an easy task.

(3) Some systems, particularly Teletypes, display only the 64-character subset of the ASCII code from 20_{16} (space) to $5F_{16}$ (–). This subset excludes the lower-case characters.

(4) The difference between the codes of a lower-case and upper-case letter is that bit 5 is clear in an upper-case letter and set in a lower-case letter. For example "A" is represented by 100 0001 and "a" by 110 0001.

Because of the popularity of Teletext display systems, some character generators (see Section 6.5 on VDTs) intended for Teletext applications have found their way into microprocessor systems. The (slight) difference between the alphanumeric characters of the ASCII and Teletext character sets is given in Table 6.21.

Table 6.21 The Difference between the ASCII and Teletext Code

Code	*ASCII*	*Teletext*	*Code*	*ASCII*	*Teletext*
23	#	£	5F	—	#
5B	[	←	7B	{	¼
5C	\	½	7C	|	▌▌
5D	]	→	7D	}	¾
5E	^	↑	7E	~	÷

The non-printing characters of the ASCII set may be subdivided into two types. There are those that are universally used to control the operation of a printer or VDT (e.g. line feed, carriage return, etc.) and those that, although they have a formal definition, are often employed in an *ad hoc* way in any given application. The actual definitions produced by the CCITT of the 32 control characters are:

NUL (null). This is a fill-in character which may be added to or removed from a data stream without affecting the information content of the data stream.
SOH (start of heading). This is the first character of a heading of an information message.
STX (start of text). A character which precedes a text and which is used to terminate a heading.
ETX (end of text). A transmission control character which terminates a text.
EOT (end of transmission). A transmission control character which indicates the conclusion of the transmission of one or more text.
ENQ (enquiry). A transmission control character used as a request from a remote station.
ACK (acknowledge). A transmission control character transmitted by a receiver as an affirmative response to the sender.
BEL (bell). A control character that rings a bell signalling the need for attention.
BS (backspace). A format effector which moves the active position (the position at which the next character is to be printed) one character position backwards on the same line.

HT (horizontal tabulation). A format effector which advances the active position to the next predetermined character position on the same line.

LF (line feed). A format effector which advances the active position to the same character position of the next line.

VT (vertical tabulation). A format effector which advances the active position to the same character position in the next predetermined line.

FF (form feed). A format effector which advances the active position to the same character position on a predetermined line of the next form or page.

CR (carriage return). A format effector which moves the active position to the first character position on the same line.

SO (shift out). A control character used in conjunction with *shift in* and *escape* to extend the graphic character set of the code. It may alter the meaning of the bit combinations which follow it until a *shift in* character is reached. The characters *space* and *delete* are not affected by *shift out*.

SI (shift in). A control character which is used in conjunction with *shift out* and *escape* to extend the graphic character set of the code. It may reinstate the standard meanings of the bit combinations which follow it.

DLE (data link escape). A transmission character which changes the meaning of a limited number of consecutively following characters. It is used exclusively to provide supplementary data transmission control functions. Only graphic characters and transmission control characters can be used in DLE sequences.

DC_1 (device control 1). A device control character primarily intended for turning on an ancillary device. It may also be used to restore a device to its basic mode of operation.

DC_2 (device control 2). A device control character primarily intended for turning on an ancillary device. It may also be used to set a device to a special mode of operation (in which case DC_1 is used to restore the device to the basic mode), or for any other device control function not provided by other DCs.

DC_3 (device control 3). A device control character primarily intended for turning off or stopping an ancillary device. This function may be a secondary-level stop, e.g. wait, pause, stand-by or halt (in which case DC_1 is used to restore normal operation). If not used in this mode it may be used for any other device control function.

DC_4 (device control 4). A device control character primarily intended for turning off, stopping or interrupting an ancillary device. If not required for this purpose it may be used for any other device control function not provided by other DCs.

NAK (negative acknowledge). A transmission control character transmitted by a receiver as a negative response to the sender.

SYN (synchronous idle). A transmission control character used by a synchronous transmission system in the absence of any other character (the idle condition) to provide a signal from which synchronism may be achieved or retained between data-terminal equipment.

ETB (end of transmission block). A transmission control character used to indicate the end of a transmission block of data where data is divided into such blocks.

CAN (cancel). A character, or the first character of a sequence, indicating that the data preceding it is in error. As a result this data must be ignored.

EM (end of medium). A control character that may be used to identify the physical end of a medium, or the end of the used portion of a medium, or the end of the wanted portion of data recorded in a medium. The position of this character does not necessarily correspond to the physical end of the medium.
SUB (substitute character). A control character used in place of a character that has been found to be invalid or in error. SUB is intended to be introduced by automatic means.
ESC (escape). A control character used to provide an additional control function. It alters the meaning of a limited number of consecutively following bit combinations which constitute the escape sequence.

FS (file separator) GS (group separator) RS (record separator) US (unit separator)	Control characters used to qualify data logically—the specific meaning of any character has to be defined for each application. These characters delimit information in the form of a file, group, record and unit respectively.

The Keyboard Encoder

The most direct method of converting the closure of a keyswitch into a binary code (depending on its position on the keyboard) involves a static encoder. This basic form of static encoder has an input for each of the keys (more than 50) and simply operates as a 50-line to 6-line encoder. Such a device is obviously cumbersome to design and construct. Other more efficient forms of static encoder arrange their keys in the form of an $n \times n$ matrix (say 8×8 for 64 keys) and reduce the number of inputs to the encoder from n to approximately $2\sqrt{n}$. This type of encoder is not discussed here because of its complexity and need for analog circuitry.

The most popular form of keyboard encoder is known as the dynamic or scanning encoder. The block diagram of one such encoder, the AY-5-2376, is given in Fig. 6.27. This diagram shows that a keyboard encoder requires very little circuitry beside the encoder chip itself and the keyswitches.

The operation of the AY-5-2376 relies on the detection of a closure within the keyswitch matrix by monitoring the flow of current through the closed keyswitch. An eight-stage ring counter applies a pulse to each of the X output lines for $x_0 - x_7$ sequentially. At the same time an eleven-stage ring counter interrogates the eleven Y input lines one by one from y_0 to y_{10}. If a keyswitch is depressed so that line x_i is connected to line y_j, at some time the pulse put out on x_i will be detected on y_j. As the X and Y ring counters contain the value of i and j, respectively, it is possible to interrogate the (i, j)th location of the ROM matrix to obtain the required code for the key depressed. If the control or shift keys are depressed during this time, the code from the ROM is modified accordingly. Figure 6.28 gives the relationship between the X and Y lines from the encoder and the layout of the keys. Although this keyboard encoder generates an 8-bit code plus a parity bit, it is normal practice to use output bits $d_0 - d_6$ corresponding to the seven bits of the ASCII code. The most significant bit d_7 is zero. The AY-5-2376 generates a keypressed strobe which becomes active (logical 1) approximately 1 ms after a key is depressed. This delay is determined by R_1 and C_1.

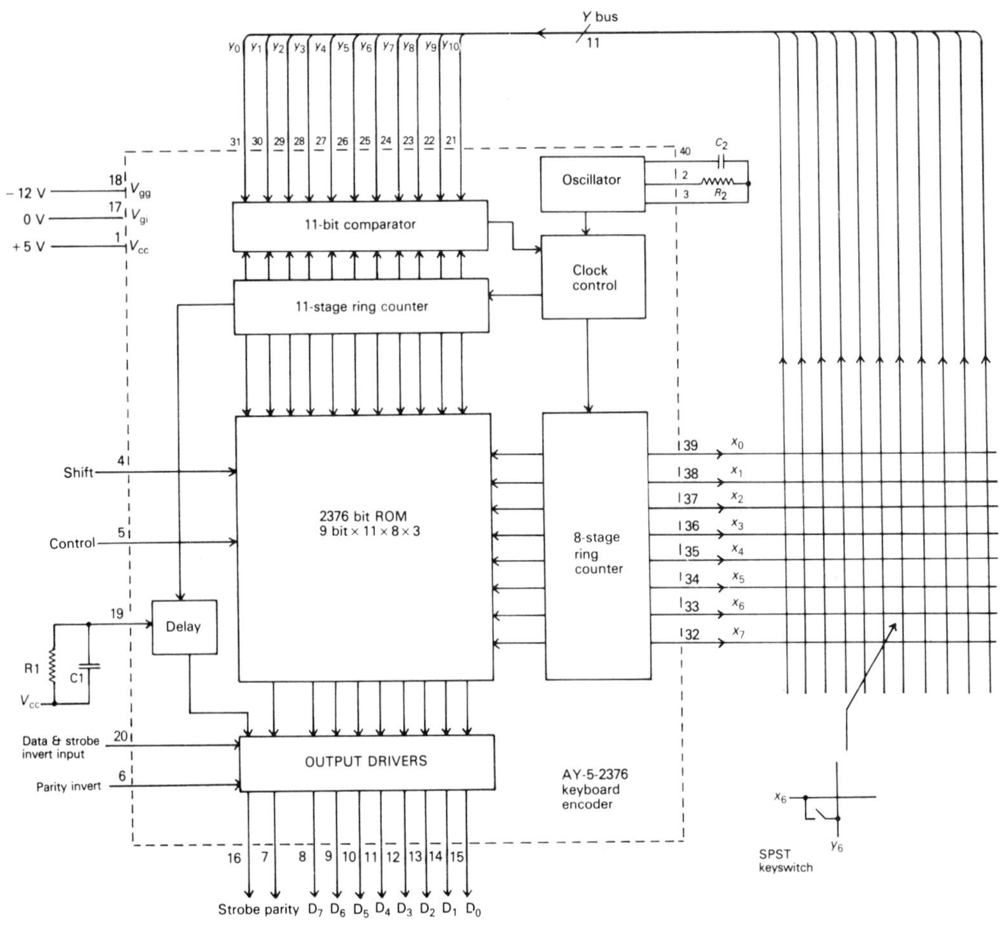

Notes

(1) $R_1 = 680\ \text{k}\Omega$ $C_1 = 0.001\ \mu\text{F}$ Strobe = 1.5 ms delay;

(2) $R_2 = 100\ \text{k}\Omega$ $C_2 = 50$ pF for approx. 50 kHz clock;

(3) data and strobe input (pin 20) inverts the output if it is wired to +5 V;

(4) the parity output at pin 7 is inverted if the parity invert input (pin 6) is wired to + 5 V;

(5) the "shift" and "control" inputs are connected to + 5 V by push-buttons to operate the shift and control functions of the keyboard.

Fig. 6.27 The AY-5-2376 keyboard encoder

The strobe remains active until the key is released.

This encoder also offers two important features—two-key roll-over and *N*-key lockout. When a key is depressed a strobe and the appropriate binary code are generated. If a second key is depressed while the first key is held down a strobe is not generated until the first key is released. This action is known as two-key roll-over and is very useful when typing at high speeds where the depression of two keys may occasionally overlap. In principle it is possible to arrange for *n*-key roll-over, but the additional complexity required to record the code for each key and transmit it at a later time is not often regarded as being cost effective. The n-key lockout facility is an arrangement whereby spurious strobes are avoided if more than two keys are pressed together. Whereas two-key roll-over preserves the value of the code generated by a second key depressed while one key is already down, n-key lockout causes all other codes to be lost if more than two key depressions overlap.

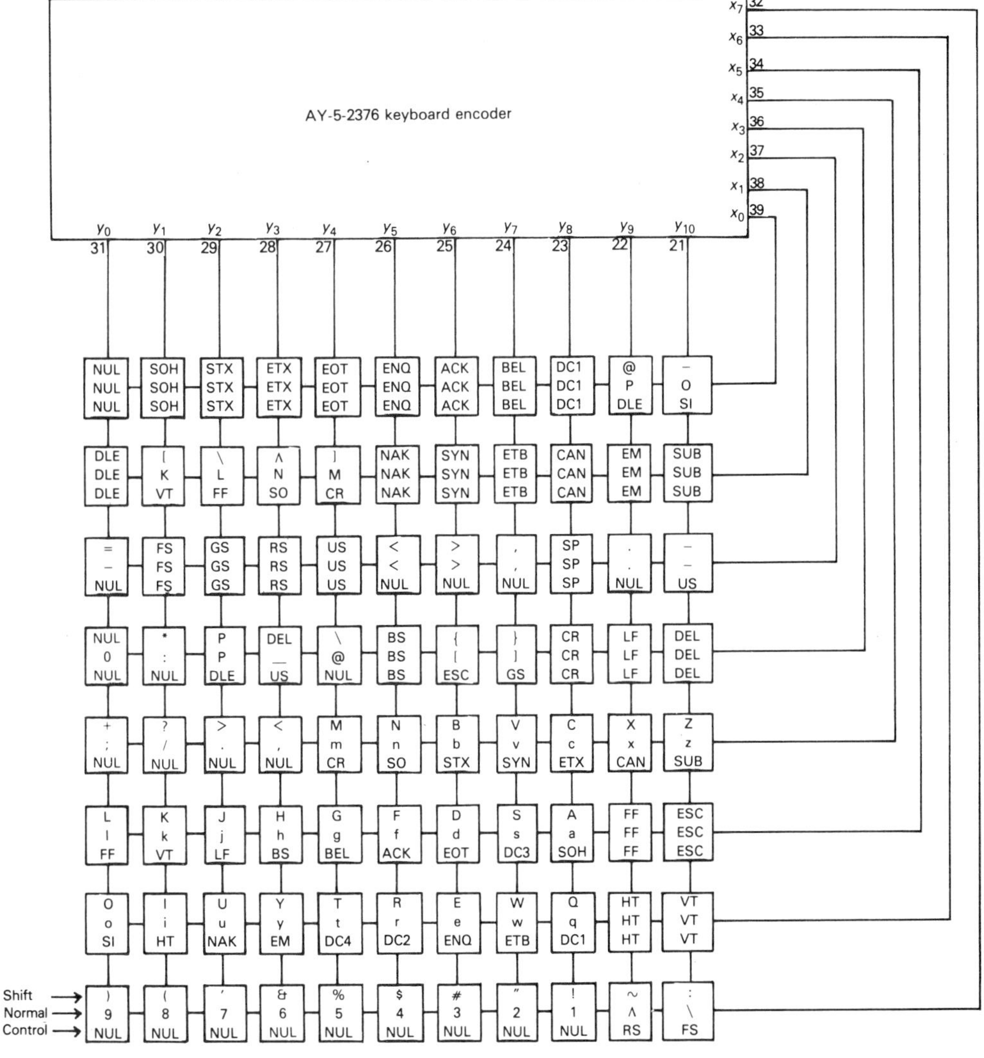

Fig. 6.28 The arrangement of keys with the AY-5-2376

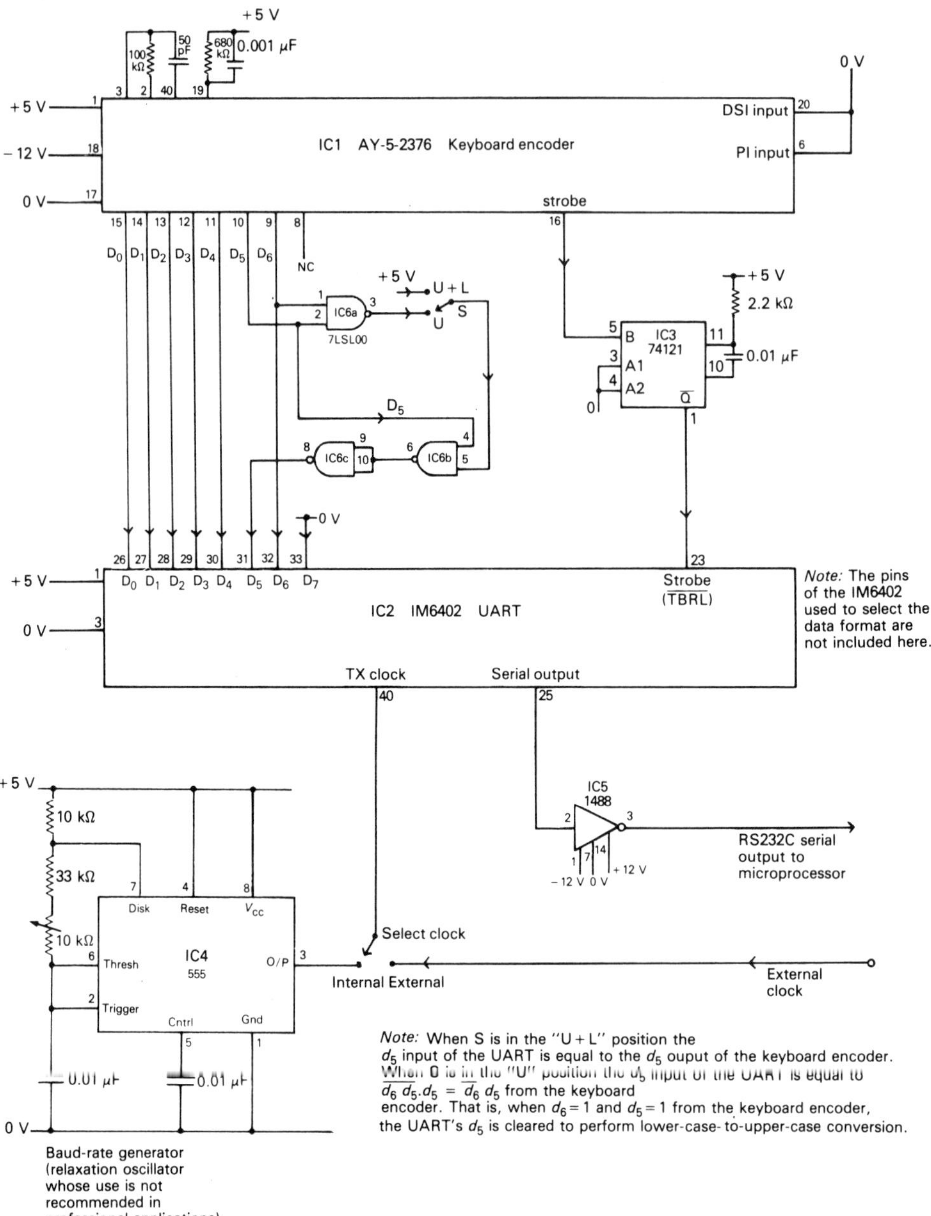

Fig. 6.29 Serializing the output of a keyboard encoder

Although the output of keyboard encoder is in a parallel format, some form of parallel-to-serial convertor is required if a connection to a microprocessor's RS232C-compatible input port is to be made. Figure 6.29 shows the additional circuitry required to interface an AY-5-2376 keyboard encoder with a microprocessor. This circuit is little more than the tandem connection of a keyboard encoder with a UART, both of which are described earlier in this section. However, two useful features have been included.

(1) The transmitter clock to the UART is obtained either from an external source (i.e. the host processor), or from an on-board oscillator. The internal oscillator is based on the popular 555 timer which is very cheap but does not give the type of accuracy expected of professional equipment. Relaxation oscillators of the type shown in Fig. 6.29 not only require setting up, but also suffer from aging and thermal drift.

(2) A method of providing automatic lower-case-to-upper-case conversion is included. Such an arrangement should be able to convert the code for an "a" into the code for an "A" without causing a shift for numbers and symbols. That is, an 8 should remain an 8 and not be shifted to a ")". When switch S is in the "U + L" position the keyboard operates normally. When S is in the "U" position, lower-case characters are automatically converted into their upper-case equivalents. A glance at Table 6.20 will show why this is so. Case conversion is carried out when bit 6 (the most significant bit) is 1, in which case bit 5 is cleared.

Note that the ASCII code is a 7-bit code with bit 6 the most significant bit. When an ASCII-encoded character is packed into an 8-bit byte, the character forms bits $d_0 - d_6$ of the byte and bit d_7 is cleared. Sometimes the most significant bit is set to the value of the character's parity.

The TS1 Keyboard Module

The keyboard used in the TS1 microprocessor system is a Claire Pender model obtained at a low cost from a second-hand dealer. As the reader will choose his own particular keyboard depending on his particular requirements, I have not given details of the keyboard module. The keyboard has been mounted in a steel case with its own power supply, a baud-rate generator based on the MC14411, a UART, and a 1488 TTL to RS232C convertor. The reader should have no difficulty in interfacing a standard keyboard to a microprocessor system using the techniques described in Section 6.3.4.

6.5 THE VIDEO DISPLAY TERMINAL

To make best use of the power and versatility of a general-purpose microprocessor system, the user must be able to extract data from it in the form in which it is easiest to assimilate. Because humans respond readily to visual images, the principal output medium of all general-purpose digital computers is either print on paper, or a picture on a screen. This situation may be expected to change only when the computer is able to receive input in the form of speech and generate a verbal output. The current state of the art allows the production of computer-generated speech with little difficulty, but is unable to produce a general-purpose, real-time, speech recognizer.

The main output device, sometimes called the console display, of many microprocessor systems is the video display terminal (VDT). The VDT is sometimes called "the glass Teletype" because it often replaces the ubiquitous Teletype in cases where a hard-copy printout is not absolutely necessary. The VDT has four important advantages over the Teletype.

(1) A VDT can normally display data at a much greater rate than all but the fastest mechanical printers. Typically, a VDT may be able to fill a screen (say 1024 characters) in less than one second.

(2) A VDT can be built at a very low cost with standard TTL components. By displaying the information on an ordinary domestic television the total cost can be limited to 10 – 40 ICs.

(3) The character set of a VDT, that is the letters, numbers and symbols capable of being displayed, can easily be expanded or modified by replacing a read-only memory in the VDT display generator circuit.

(4) The VDT, having no moving parts, is intrinsically more reliable than the mechanical printer with its print-head and moving carriage.

The VDT has only one drawback: it does not produce a permanent output. Once a screen is full of data, new output from the CPU can be accommodated only by erasing part of the display to make room. Consequently, a VDT is excellent for entering commands into a microprocessor system, or for editing text, but is a poor substitute for a mechanical printer if the whole of a program or file is to be examined. Apart from the above advantages of the VDT over the mechanical printer it must be remembered that a VDT may be constructed for under $80 while a crude printer costs $300 and a reasonably sophisticated printer costs over $800.

In this section two types of VDT are described. The first relies on the so-called memory-mapped display principle. That is, the data displayed on the screen corresponds to the contents of a block of the microprocessor's memory space. The second type of VDT appears to the computer as a serial port. The computer transmits data in a serial format to the VDT and the VDT itself is responsible for arranging the format of the data on the screen. In the former case, all formatting is performed by the computer under software control. Before describing these two VDTs in detail it is necessary to take a look at the operation of a raster-scan display system.

The Raster-scan Display

The vast majority of display systems are based on the cathode-ray tube (CRT), which may be operated in one of two modes: point-plotting or raster-scan. The operation of a point-plotting display is given in Fig. 6.30. There are three inputs to the CRT: an n-bit Y coordinate, an n-bit X coordinate and a blanking signal. The position of the spot on the screen is determined by the X and Y digital inputs which are converted into analog voltages to deflect the beam. To achieve an acceptable resolution, the X and Y digital-to-analog convertors must have an accuracy of at least 10 bits for a 1024 × 1024 display. Consequently this form of display is expensive. The blanking input to the CRT is used to switch off the beam between the points being plotted, if a line joining two successive points is not required.

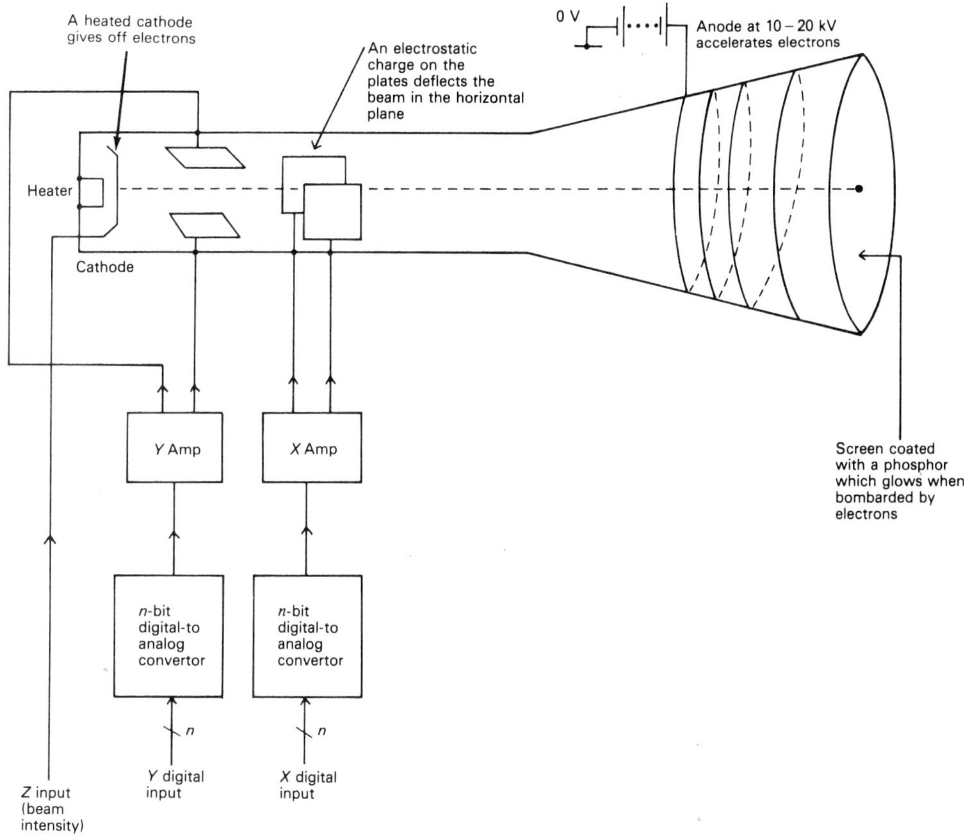

Fig. 6.30 The operation of a point-plotting display

The usual form of the CRT display operates in a raster scan mode in which the beam of electrons is periodically swept across the screen, line by line, so that the entire surface of the display is covered. In this mode the CRT controller does not have to specify explicit X and Y coordinates of the points it wishes to plot. Instead the CRT controller brightens up the display, to produce a dot, when the beam is at the appropriate X, Y location. The detailed operation of a raster scan display, which forms the principle of the television picture, is as follows.

	USA (EIA)	UK (CCIR)
Horizontal scan rate (Hz)	15 750	15 625
Vertical scan rate (Hz)	60	50
Lines per field	262½	312½
Lines per frame	525	625
Fields per frame	2	2
Frame rate (Hz)	30	30
Field rate (Hz)	60	60

A linearly rising sawtooth voltage is applied to the X deflection plates of the CRT. This causes the beam of electrons from the cathode to trace out a horizontal line across the display. In a television the intensity of the electron beam determines the brightness of the spot, while in a VDT the beam is normally turned fully on or off to produce a dot or a space. When the beam reaches the right-hand edge of the display it is turned off (i.e. blanked) and rapidly returned to its horizontal starting position (flyback), ready for the next scan. While the beam is scanning in the horizontal plane it is also scanned, at a much lower rate, in the vertical plane. In this way the moving dot covers the entire surface of the screen. By modulating the intensity of the electron beam a picture may be built up. In the EIA television standard implemented in the USA each horizontal scan, called a line, has a duration of 63.5 μs. This corresponds to a line repetition rate of 15.75 kHz. A vertical scan, called a field, has a duration of 16.667 ms, corresponding to a vertical repetition rate of 60 Hz. This is chosen for the field repetition rate because it is also the frequency of the mains power supply which avoids the wobble resulting from an interaction between the display and mains hum. It is not possible to have a field repetition rate at a submultiple of the mains frequency (say 30 Hz) because below about 30 Hz the display appears to flicker. At 60 Hz the human eye averages successive fields and perceives them as a smooth sequence.

The vertical resolution of the display is given by the field duration divided by the line duration, i.e. $16\frac{2}{3}$ ms/63.5 μs = 262.5. This number of lines per frame is too low to give the level of resolution required for the domestic television. The vertical resolution cannot readily be increased by speeding up the horizontal scan rate as this would require an excessively large video bandwidth. That is, if the time per horizontal scan is halved while keeping the horizontal resolution constant, then in any given period of time twice as much video information must be transmitted. A rather clever way of increasing the apparent vertical resolution is to transmit two successive fields, each of 262½ lines, to form a single frame of 525 lines by scanning odd lines in one field and even lines in the next field. This arrangement is known as interlacing. Figure 6.31 shows how a TV raster-scan display is arranged. In the majority of VDTs interlacing is not employed because it leads to an objectionable level of flicker as, in contrast to the case of a TV picture, successive fields contain radically different information. Most VDTs simply have 262½ pairs of lines per frame. This is sufficient for up to about 24 lines of text per frame.

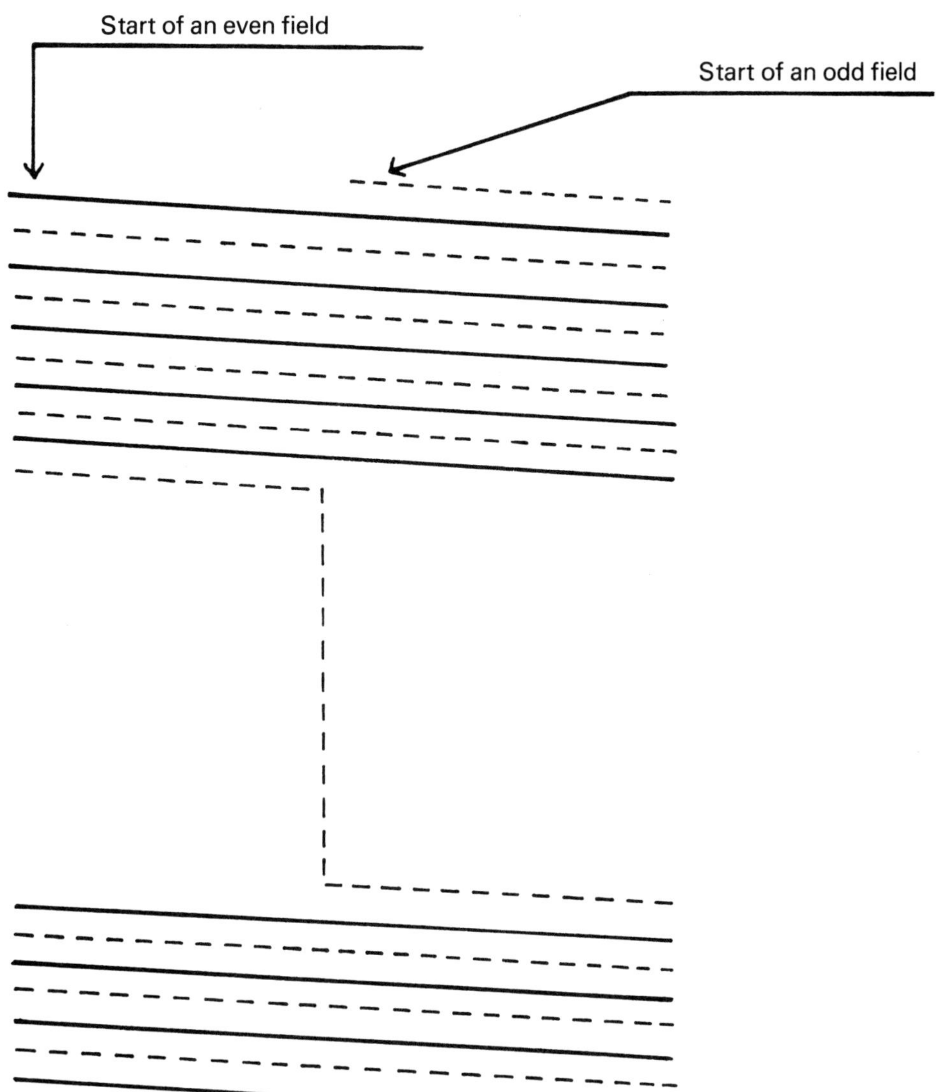

Fig. 6.31 Format of the interlaced display

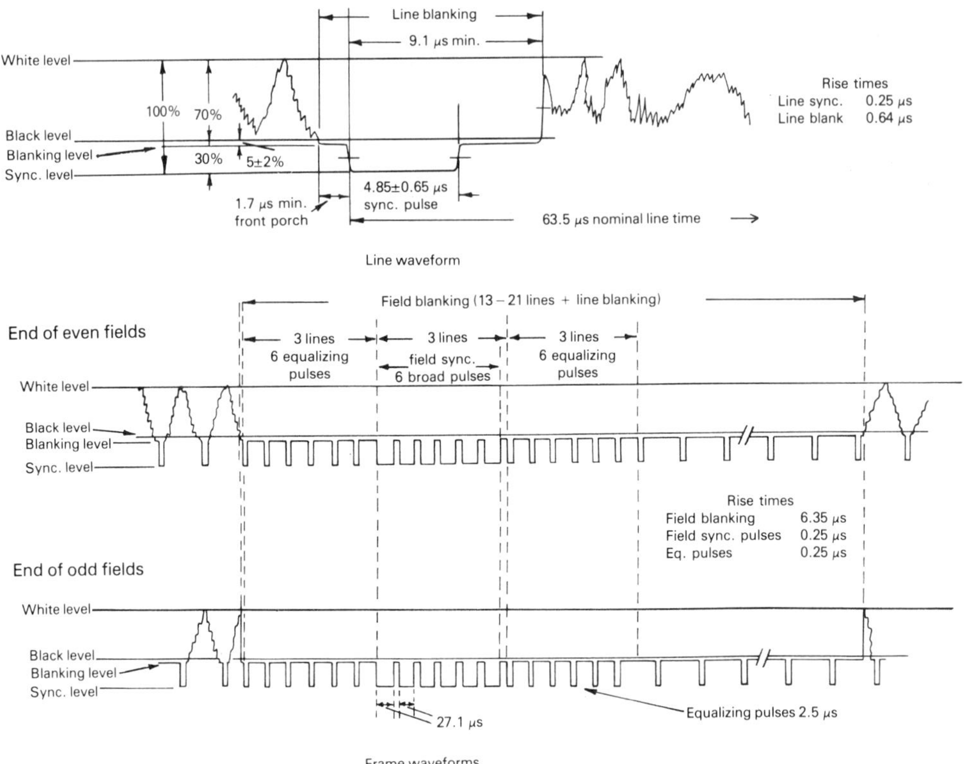

Fig. 6.32 Line and frame synchronizing waveforms (EIA)

In order to receive a stable display, the electron beam in the receiver must scan at exactly the same rate as the beam in the television camera. This is done by transmitting a line-synchronizing pulse at the start of each line, and a field-synchronizing pulse at the start of each field. These pulses are added to the video signal (the video signal determines the brightness of the dot at any point in time) to produce a composite video signal. In the TV receiver there are circuits which extract the synchronization pulses from the composite video signal and then use them to initiate vertical and horizontal scans. The arrangement of the horizontal and vertical synchronizing pulses is given in Figs. 6.32 and 6.33. Note that in a VDT the field-synchronization pulses do not have to be as complex as those described in Figs. 6.32 and 6.33 if interlaced fields are not required. Interfacing is almost never used in simple VDTs.

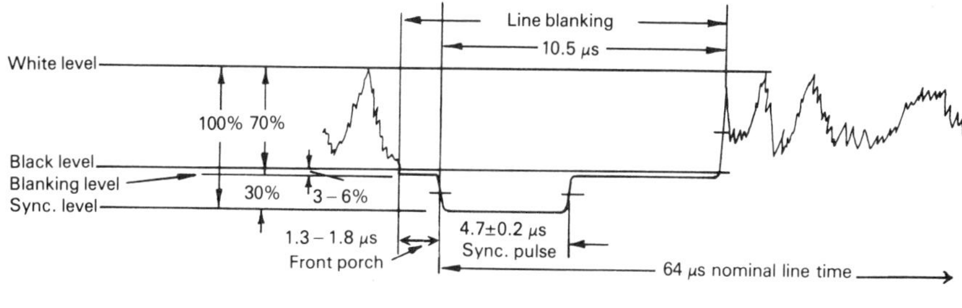

Line waveform

Field blanking (18 – 22 lines + line blanking)
2.5 lines 2.5 lines 2.5 lines
End of even fields
5 equalizing pulses
field sync. 5 broad bulses
5 equalizing pulses
White level
Black level
Blanking level
Sync. level
Rise times
Field blanking <6 μs
Field sync pulses 0.3±0.1 μs
Eq. pulses 0.3±0.1 μs
End of odd fields
White level
Black level
Blanking level
Sync. level
27.3 μs±0.2 μs
Equalizing pulses 2.2 – 2.4 μs

Frame waveforms

Fig. 6.33 Line and frame synchronizing waveforms (CCIR)

Basic Video Display Terminal Principles

The fundamentals of the operation of a VDT are remarkably simple. The CRT screen is divided into a matrix of rows and columns defining the display format. Typical VDT formats are 80 × 24, 40 × 24, 64 × 16, 32 × 16; the first figure in each pair gives the number of columns per frame. Figure 6.34 gives the format of a typical VDT display. Each character is displayed as a 5 × 7 dot-matrix, called a font, within a block of 6 dots × 8 lines.

The maximum number of characters per row is limited by the video bandwidth of the monitor. For example, consider a VDT displaying 64 characters per line with each character consisting of five horizontal dots, separated by three spaces* (i.e. blanked

* Here a space refers to an "undot" rather than the character called a "space" which consists of a group of undots and separates words of text.

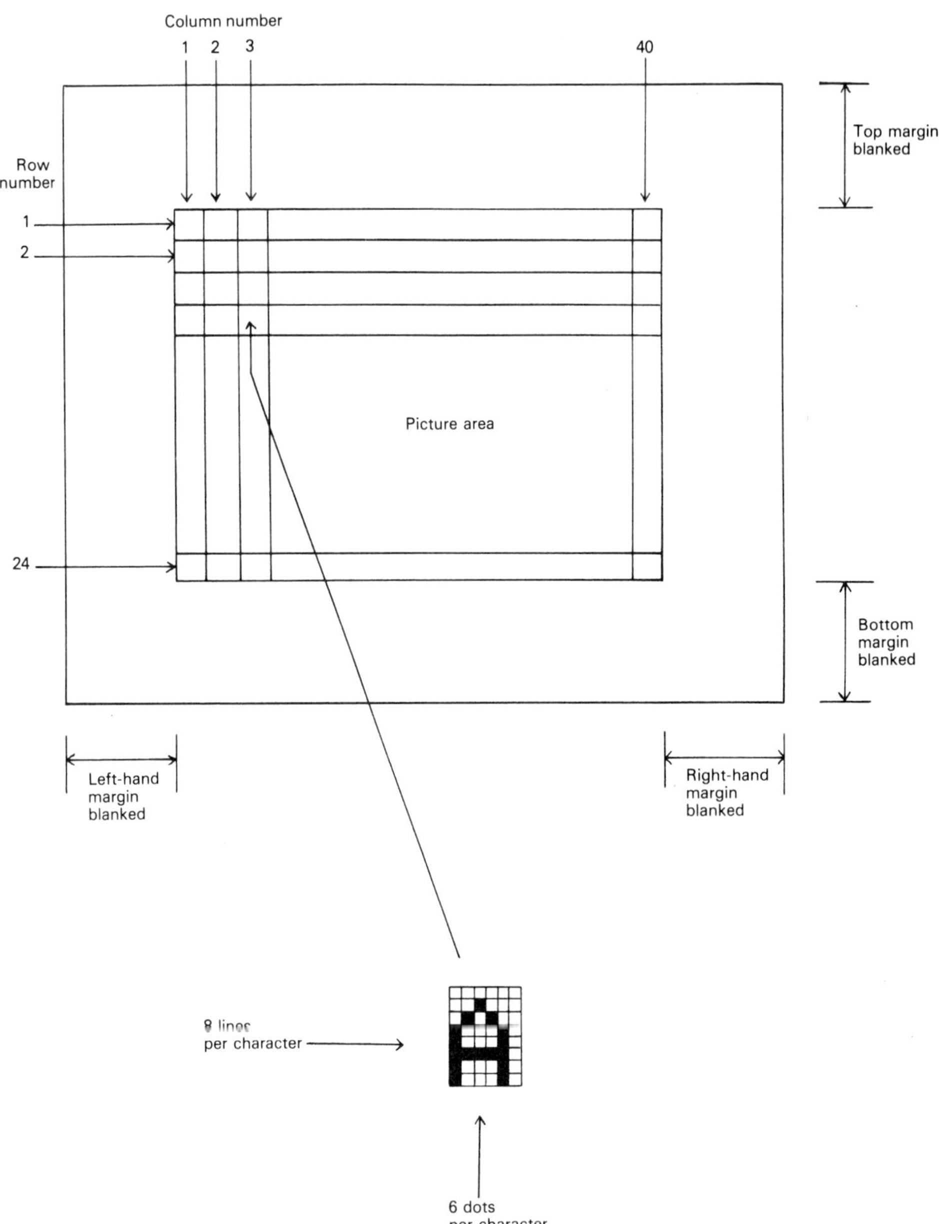

Fig. 6.34 The format of typical display

dots). If we assume that the displayed portion of the line is 48 μs out of the 63.5 μs line-scan period, the duration of a dot is therefore

$$\frac{1}{64} \times \frac{1}{8} \times 48\ \mu\text{s} = 0.09375\ \mu\text{s}.$$

That is, a dot has a duration of only 94 ns. The greatest video bandwidth is required when alternate dots and spaces are displayed, which in the above example corresponds to a dot frequency of ½ × 1/0.09375 μs = 5.3 MHz. For a reasonably high-quality display the monitor should have a bandwidth at least three times that of the maximum dot frequency, i.e. 3 × 5.3 MHz = 15.9 MHz. This implies that such a display cannot be obtained from a domestic TV, where a UHF modulator is used to inject the composite video from the display generator into the TV's aerial socket. Unfortunately, the video bandwidth of most TVs is limited by the IF amplifier to no more than 6 MHz. In practice it is just possible to obtain an acceptable display using an RF modulator, as long as there are no more than 64 characters per line. An alternative is to inject the composite video directly into the TV's video circuit. As many domestic TVs have a live chassis arrangement in which the ground of the receiver is connected directly to the mains neutral line to avoid the cost of an isolating transformer, it would be most unwise to attempt to make a connection between the display generator and the TV's video circuits. A possible solution to this problem is to impose an opto-isolator between the display generator and the TV, thus avoiding any direct connection to the "live chassis".

The block diagram of a basic 40 × 24 display generator is given in Fig. 6.35. (The block diagram of a similar display generator intended for use with the CCIR 625 line system is given in Fig. 6.36.) The key to the operation of the circuit is a chain of dividers which successively divide a 5.7024 MHz clock down to 60 Hz, to provide the field-synchronizing pulses. A clock operating at 5.7024 MHz generates dot pulses which are divided by six (one character = 5 horizontal dots plus a space) to give the character rate of 5.7024/6 MHz = 950.4 kHz. The character rate is divided by sixty to give sixty character slots per line. However, only 40 of these slots are used to display characters on the screen as one third of the line is allowed for flyback plus left and right margins. The output of the character counter at 950.4/60 kHz = 15.84 kHz is divided by 8 giving 8 lines per row of characters. Seven out of these 8 lines are used to form the character and the remaining line is blanked to give the space between adjacent rows. The output of the divide-by-eight circuit represents the row rate at 15.84/8 kHz = 1.98 kHz. The final counter in the chain divides the row rate by 33 to give 33 rows per field. As in the case of the character columns, only 24 of the 33 rows display characters, while the remaining 9 rows provide time for flyback plus top and bottom margins. The output of the row counter is at 1980/33 Hz = 60 Hz, which is, of course, the required value of the field rate, if a standard (i.e. unmodified) TV is used as a monitor. Note that the line rate is 15.84 kHz, which is approximately ½% higher than the EIA line rate of 15.750 kHz. This small difference is normally unimportant.

Having set up the timing chain it is a simple matter to generate the display itself. As the character counter and row counters sequentially step through all 960 character

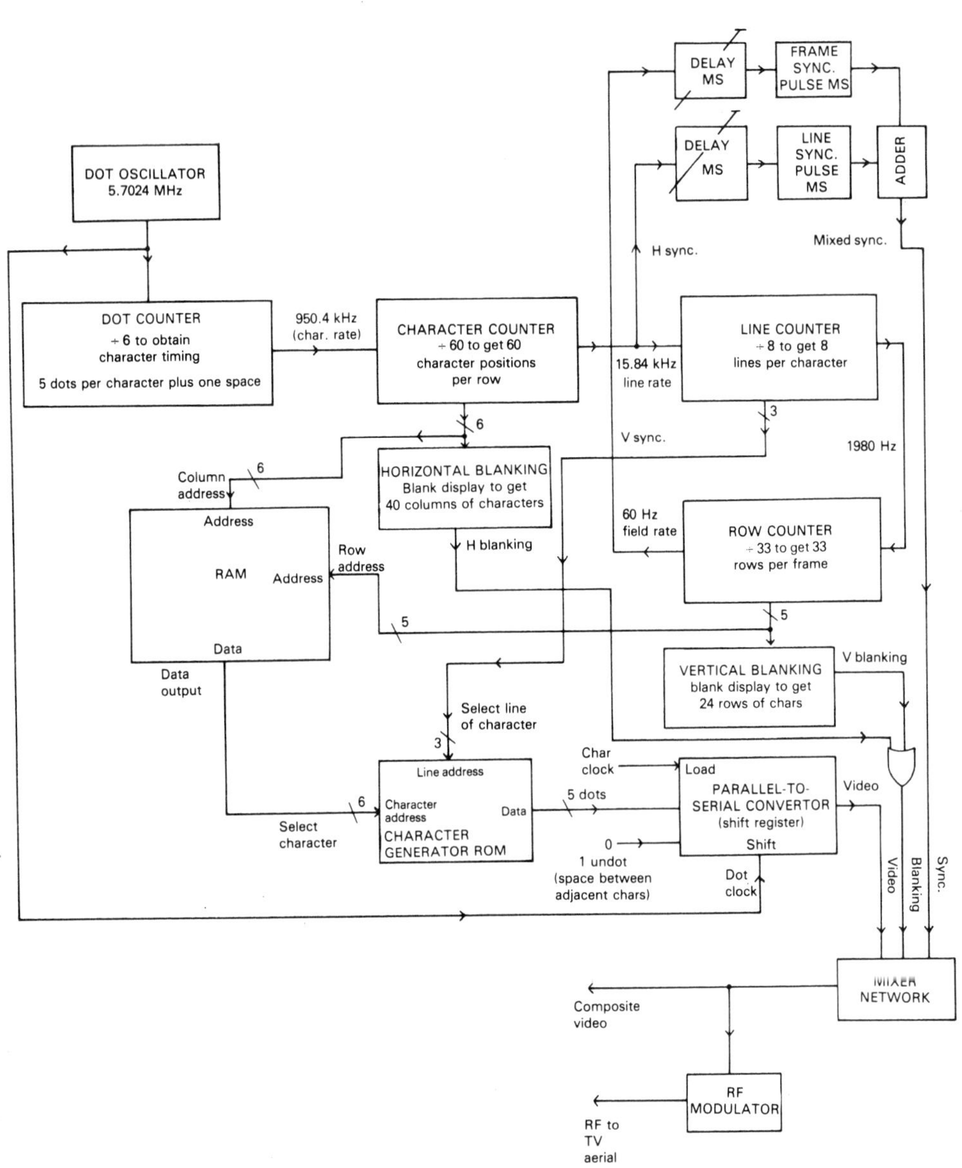

Fig. 6.35 A simplified block diagram of the display portion of a 40×24 display

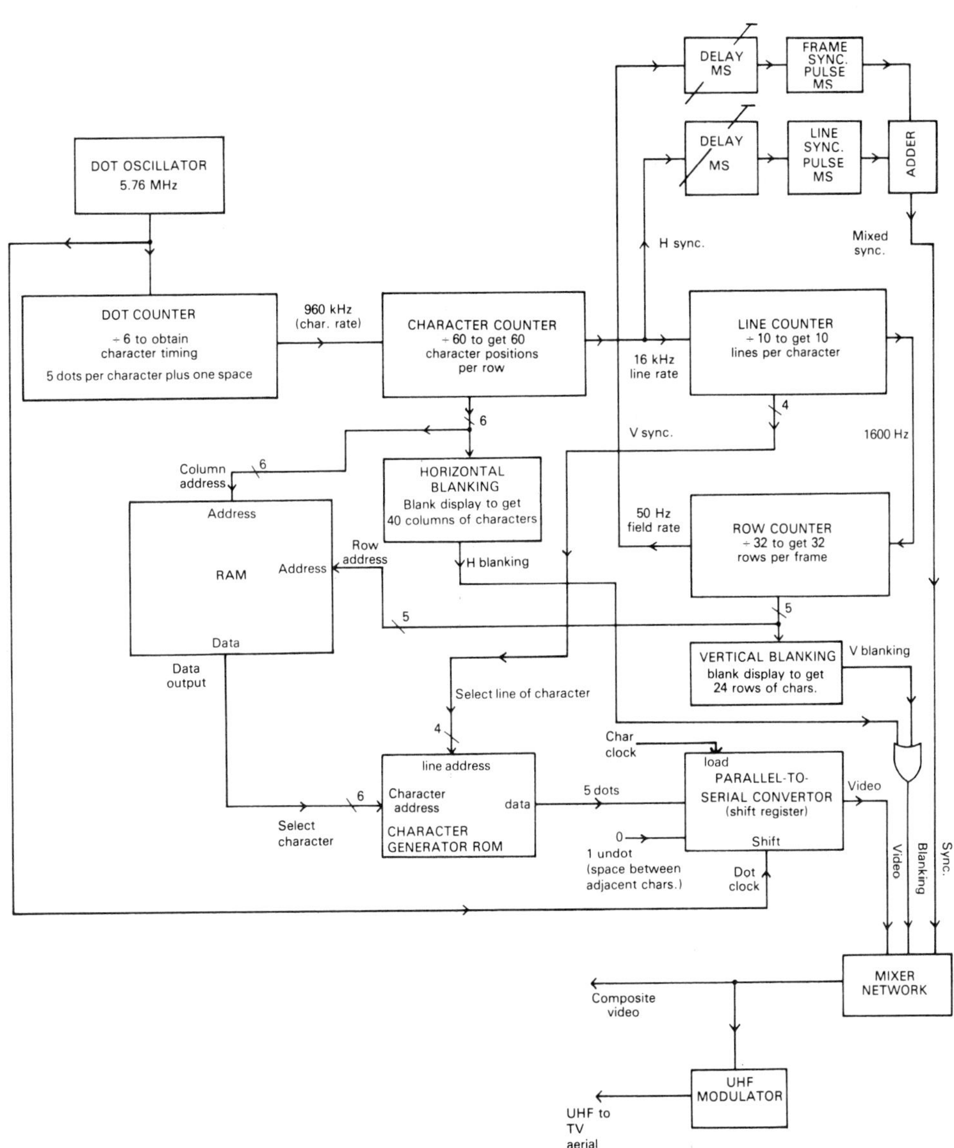

Fig. 6.36 A simplified block diagram of the display portion of a 40 × 24 display for a 625-line CCIR receiver. Note that the spacing between adjacent rows is 3 lines

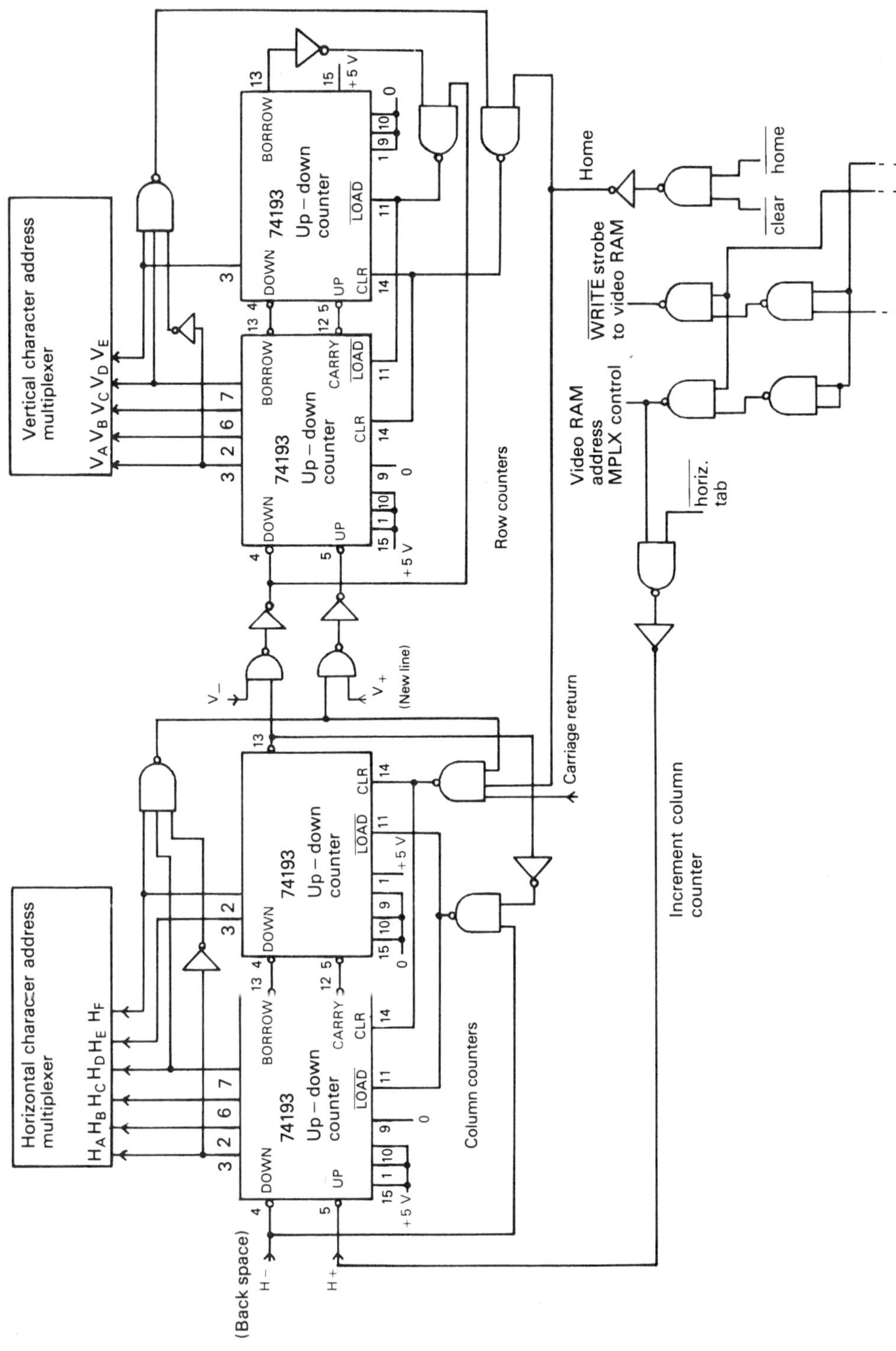
Vertical character address multiplexer
V_A V_B V_C V_D V_E
74193
Up – down counter
DOWN
UP
BORROW
CARRY
LOAD
CLR
+5 V
Row counters
Home
home
clear
WRITE strobe to video RAM
Video RAM address MPLX control
horiz. tab
V−
V+
(New line)
Carriage return
Increment column counter
Horizontal character address multiplexer
H_A H_B H_C H_D H_E H_F
Column counters
(Back space)
H−
H+

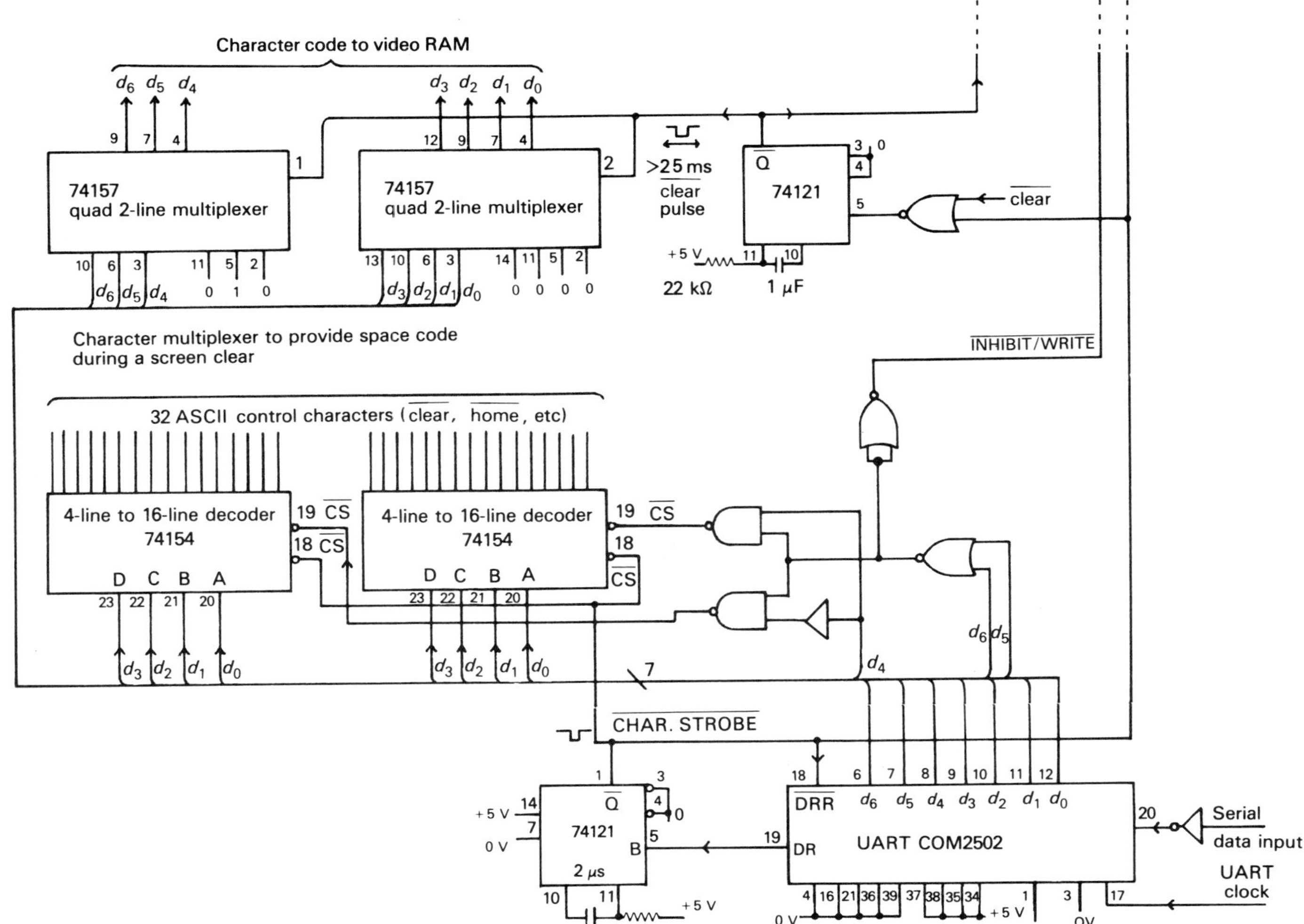

Fig. 6.37 Some of the logic necessary to control a display. This diagram illustrates the amount of logic necessary to control a 40×24 character generator. This is an eloquent demonstration of the advantage of a software-controlled memory-mapped display

positions (40×24), the outputs of these counters interrogate a block of RAM to produce an ASCII-encoded word for each character position. The data output of the RAM is fed into the address input of a ROM called a character generator which converts the character code into the actual dots making up the character. The ROM has an additional address input which selects one of the 7 lines of the character. Remember that the output of ROM (5 dots) is determined by the particular character selected and the line of the character currently being displayed. The output of the ROM is fed into a 6-bit shift register—one of the bits is permanently set to zero to give the required inter-character spacing. The data is moved out of the shift register by the 5.7024 MHz dot clock to form the video signal. Many character generator ROMs have six character-address inputs permitting the selection of one of 64 characters—normally the upper-case subset of the ASCII code. Other ROMs are available, some with high-resolution characters (7×9), and some with the full set of 96 ASCII characters. One range of ROMs even includes the Greek alphabet! Possibly the most widely used character generator is the 2513 which is produced by several manufacturers. This is a 64-character ROM with a 5×7 format. Some versions of the 2513 require a +5 and −12 V supply, while other versions need only a single +5 V supply.

The outputs from the column and row counters, respectively, are fed to two monostables to generate line and field synchronizing pulses. By giving the monostable a variable delay (i.e. user-adjustable delay) it is possible to center the display on the screen because the pulses determine the position of the display with respect to the edges of the screen. The synchronizing pulses are combined with the video signal from the shift register to create a composite video signal. Unless a commercial video monitor is used, the composite video must be fed into an RF modulator to produce a signal which can be injected into a TV's aerial socket and the TV tuned to this signal in the normal way.

The above arrangement may be called a display generator because it is capable of putting alphanumeric characters on to a raster-scan display. It is not yet a VDT because no method of getting the ASCII characters into the RAM has yet been examined. Incidentally, there is no reason why the character generator ROM must contain alphanumeric characters. Common alternatives to an alphanumeric display are:

(1) A set of patterns of the form ▪ ▙ ▀ ▜ █ ∷ etc. Such patterns may be put together to create pictures—maps or diagrams. This approach is found in the British Teletext system where the 64 possible patterns are generated directly from a 6-bit code without the need for a ROM.

(2) A set of special symbols which may be used in one of two ways. The symbols (e.g. electronic circuit elements) may be put together to form some type of plan or diagram. This arrangement differs from that above because line drawings may be depicted rather than regions of light or dark shading. Another application of special symbols is in the world of computer games in the entertainment industry. In this case the special symbol set may contain aircraft, spacecraft, etc. This allows an apparently high-definition display to be achieved

without incurring excessive memory costs. Furthermore, by rapidly moving the character code from one part of the video RAM to another, the effect of a dynamic display may be obtained.

If a display generator is to be turned into a VDT some means of entering data into the memory must be found. Figure 6.37 gives an idea of the type of additional circuitry required to convert a display generator into a VDT. A serial input is transformed into a character code plus a strobe by means of a UART. The character is then written into the display generator's RAM to display it.

The address of the next available location in the RAM is obtained from a pair of row and column counters which (unlike the corresponding counters in the display generator) do not constantly cycle through all possible memory locations but point instead to a location that is updated only after the receipt of a new character from the UART. When a new character is detected by the UART, the character-ready strobe momentarily switches the address input of the RAM from the display generator's row and column counters to the row and column counters pointing to the position of the next free character. Simultaneously, a write-strobe is generated and the new character is entered into the RAM, and hence displayed on the screen. After each character is received the counter pointing to the next free column is incremented so that the next character received is stored on the same row but in the next column to the right of the current character.

Virtually all VDTs have some form of cursor. A cursor is a special symbol (normally flashing) which is displayed on the screen and indicates the position into which the next character to be received will go. To generate a cursor the contents of the display generator's row and column counters are compared with the contents of the row and column counter pointing at the location of the next free space in the RAM. When the two contents are equal, the beam in the CRT must be at the next available position and a cursor character may therefore be displayed on the screen. In the case of a memory-mapped display it is not possible to generate a cursor by hardware (as above) so software techniques must be used to write the cursor directly into the video RAM.

Not all the ASCII characters received by the VDT are displayed on the screen. Some are control characters (e.g. carriage return, line feed, back space, tab, etc.) which act on the pointer row and column counters and therefore move the cursor.

6.5.1 A Memory-mapped Display

A memory-mapped display is one in which the memory holding the characters to be displayed also forms part of the microprocessors's address space. That is, the display memory (sometimes called refresh memory) is shared between the CPU and display generator. Figure 6.38 gives a block diagram illustrating how the shared memory is accessed by both the CPU and the display generator. For the vast majority of the time the display generator has control of the video RAM. The current values of the row and column counters are fed to the RAM's address input via a multiplexer and the output of the RAM (i.e. the code of the character to be displayed) is fed to

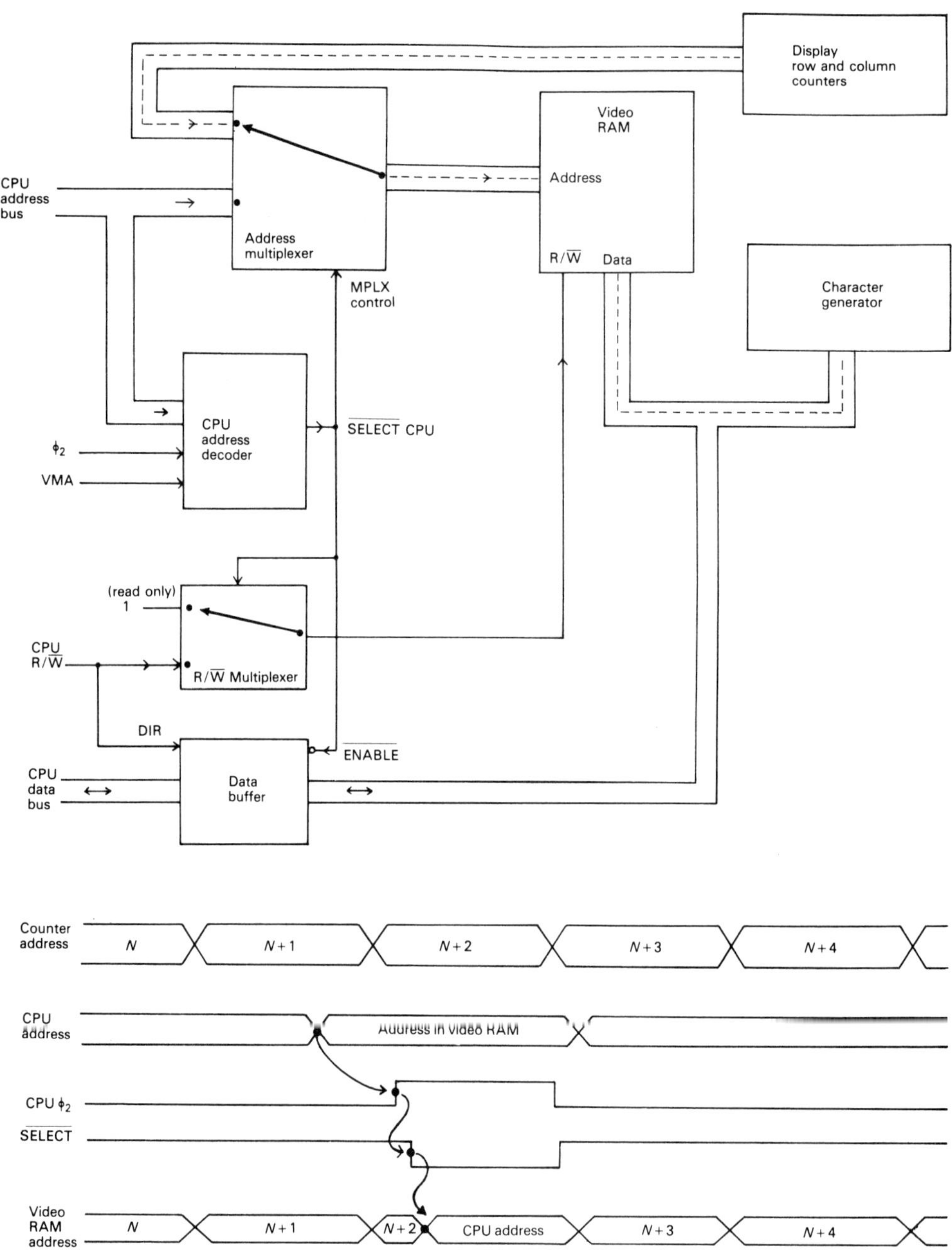

Fig. 6.38 The arrangement of shared memory

the character generator ROM. The path representing this flow of information is given by the short dashed line ------ in Fig. 6.38.

Now consider what happens when the CPU accesses the video memory. An address decoder detects a valid video RAM address during the ϕ_2 active-high phase of a CPU memory access. The active-low output of the address decoder switches the address input of the video RAM from the row and column counters to the CPU address bus. At the same time a data bus buffer is enabled between the CPU's data bus and the RAM output. Likewise the video RAM's read/write input is multiplexed from a permanent logical one (the display generator only reads the video RAM) to the $R/\overline{W}$ signal from the CPU. The CPU can therefore read from or write to the video RAM *at any time* because a CPU access always forces an unconditional access to the video RAM. There are two consequences of this action. Firstly, as the CPU has an unconditional access to the video RAM, the display generator is transparent to the CPU. That is, the CPU regards the video RAM exactly as any other block of RAM in its memory space. Secondly, the display generator can have its access to the video RAM cut off at any point by the CPU, consequently aborting the current access. Whenever this happens the data at the input of the character generator ROM is momentarily indeterminate and random dots or "speckles" are displayed on the screen. As, however, the display is refreshed, or renewed, sixty times a second, no problems occur in normal operation. If the CPU makes many accesses to the video RAM in rapid succession (such an event occurs when all the data in the video RAM is moved during a scroll-up operation) the effect of the speckles may be obtrusive. Much of this effect may be removed by blanking the display during (and slightly after) an access by the CPU to the video RAM. Alternatively, all access by the CPU may be restricted to the line or field flyback periods. The latter approach is not often adopted due to its greater complexity and the need for a handshaking arrangement between the CPU and the display generator.

The heart of the memory-mapped display system, the video display generator, is illustrated in Fig. 6.39 in block form. All important timing signals in the display generator are produced by a ZNA134 master timing generator. The ZNA134 is a 16-pin IC made by Ferranti and generates line- and field-synchronizing pulses, mixed synchronizing pulses, and video blanking pulses from a 2.5830 MHz quartz crystal. Further details of this chip are given in Fig. 6.40. Note that this IC is designed for professional use and contains more logic than is required in the present application. Moreover this chip may be operated in the 525-line EIA standard or in the 625-line CCIR standard found in the UK. The reason for selecting this integrated circuit rather than generating line- and field-synchronizing pulses as in Fig. 6.35 by means of a timing chain, is that by employing a master timing generator it is possible to modify the display generator so that different display formats may readily be obtained. If all timing signals are obtained from a chain of dividers, it is impossible to modify (say) the number of characters per line without greatly altering the whole system.

In the block diagram of a memory-mapped VDT (Fig. 6.39) an oscillator running at approximately 11.6 MHz generates pulses at the dot rate. The output of the dot clock is divided by 8 to give pulses at the character rate which load an 8-bit shift register with a line of seven dots and a space (the character font is 7×9) from the

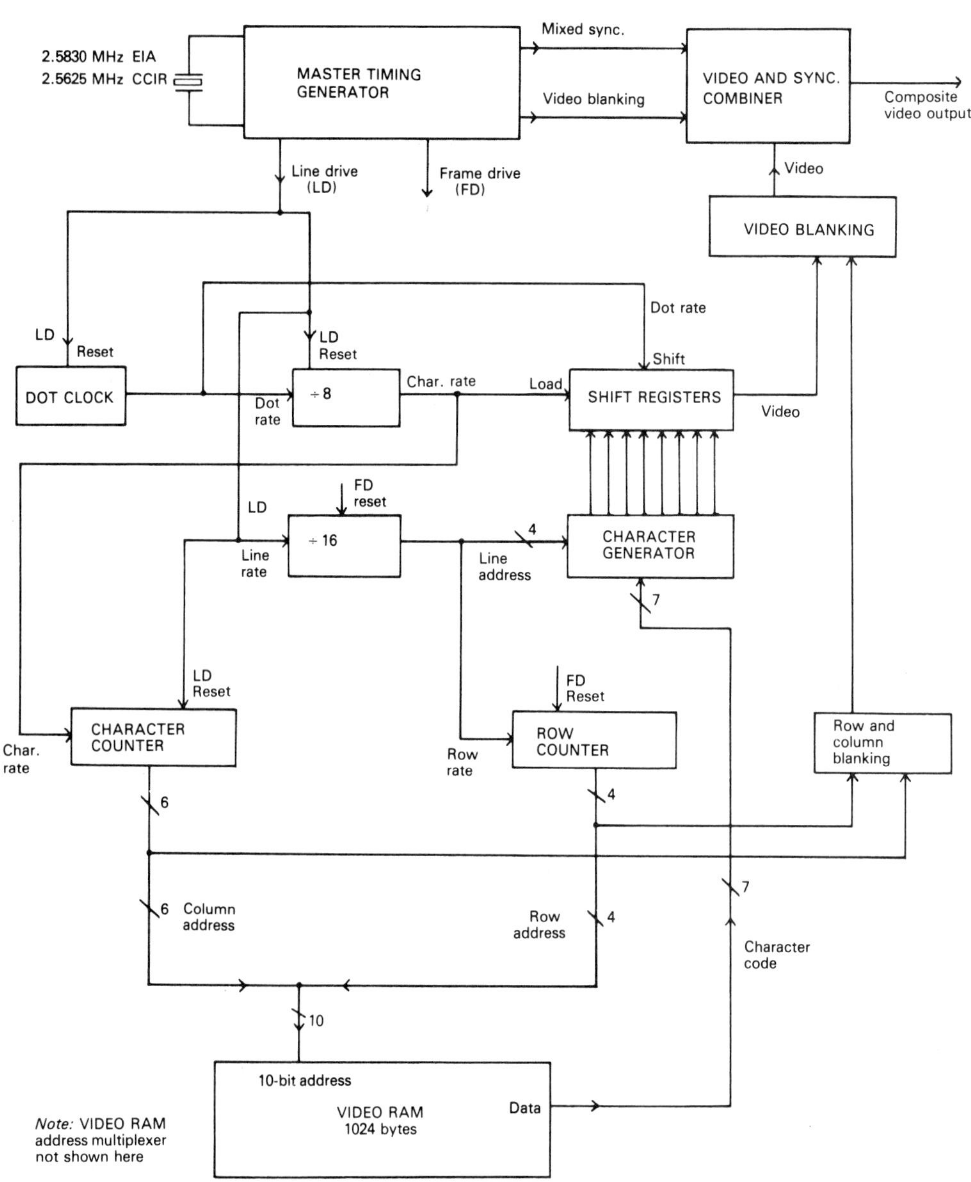

Fig. 6.39 Block diagram of the display generator

character generator ROM. The output of the shift register, which is shifted out at the dot-rate by the dot clock, is combined with the blanking signals and the synchronizing pulses to give a composite video signal. The purpose of the blanking signals is to turn off the display during line and field flyback periods and during the top, bottom, left and right margins.

The character generator ROM is an MCM66714 which generates the 96 upper- and lower-case ASCII characters in a 7-dot by 9-line matrix. This character generator has been selected for three reasons. Firstly it requires only a single +5 V power supply and, secondly, it is able to display lower-case characters with descenders. Certain characters (gjpqy) have tails which go "below" the line. Some character generators, and the majority of the low-cost dot-matrix printers, do not permit the display of tails below the line and hence a "g" is printed as g, making it almost indistinguishable from a 9. A disadvantage of the use of descenders is that at least four lines must be left for inter-row spacing as the tail extends three lines below the normal base line on which characters are displayed. Consequently, the total number of rows of characters is limited to approximately 16.

The third reason for the selection of the MCM66714 is that the first 32 values of the ASCII character set, normally reserved for control functions, are interpreted as the Greek alphabet plus a few additional symbols. Of course, if it is desired to display these characters, the CPU must be "told" that the following control character is to be interpreted as a Greek letter rather than a normal control character. Figure 6.41 gives the internal arrangement of the MCM66714 and its character set. Because of the additional lines required to display descenders, a divide by 16 counter has been used to generate the row pulse rate from the line rate and to provide a 4-bit line input to the character generator ROM.

The display generator has two separate oscillators—a crystal controlled master timing generator and a simpler RC-controlled dot clock. If these two oscillators were not synchronized in some way it would be impossible to obtain a stable display. In successive fields of the display, the dot oscillator has a random phase with respect to the start of a line, and hence the row of characters suffers from such severe jitter that it is entirely unreadable. This problem is readily solved by synchronizing the dot clock and all the counters with the master timing generator. In this case a character is in the same position in successive fields and the display is stable.

The full circuit diagram of the memory-mapped VDT is given in Fig. 6.42. The operation of this circuit is relatively straightforward but the following points may help the reader to appreciate some of the finer details.

(1) The composite video generator comprises D_1, C_1, R_1, R_2 and R_3. The mixed sync. pulses from IC3f have their positive peaks clamped to ground by D_1 and C_1. Three resistors R_1, R_2, R_3 form a passive mixer, adding the negative going sync. pulses to the positive going video pulses from IC5b.

(2) ICs 4a, 5a and 5b combine the video signal from the shift register (IC10) with the various blanking signals. This section could have been simplified but facilities have been included for additional blanking and video inputs. The video signal from IC10 is ORed with two external video inputs by IC5a. These inputs are

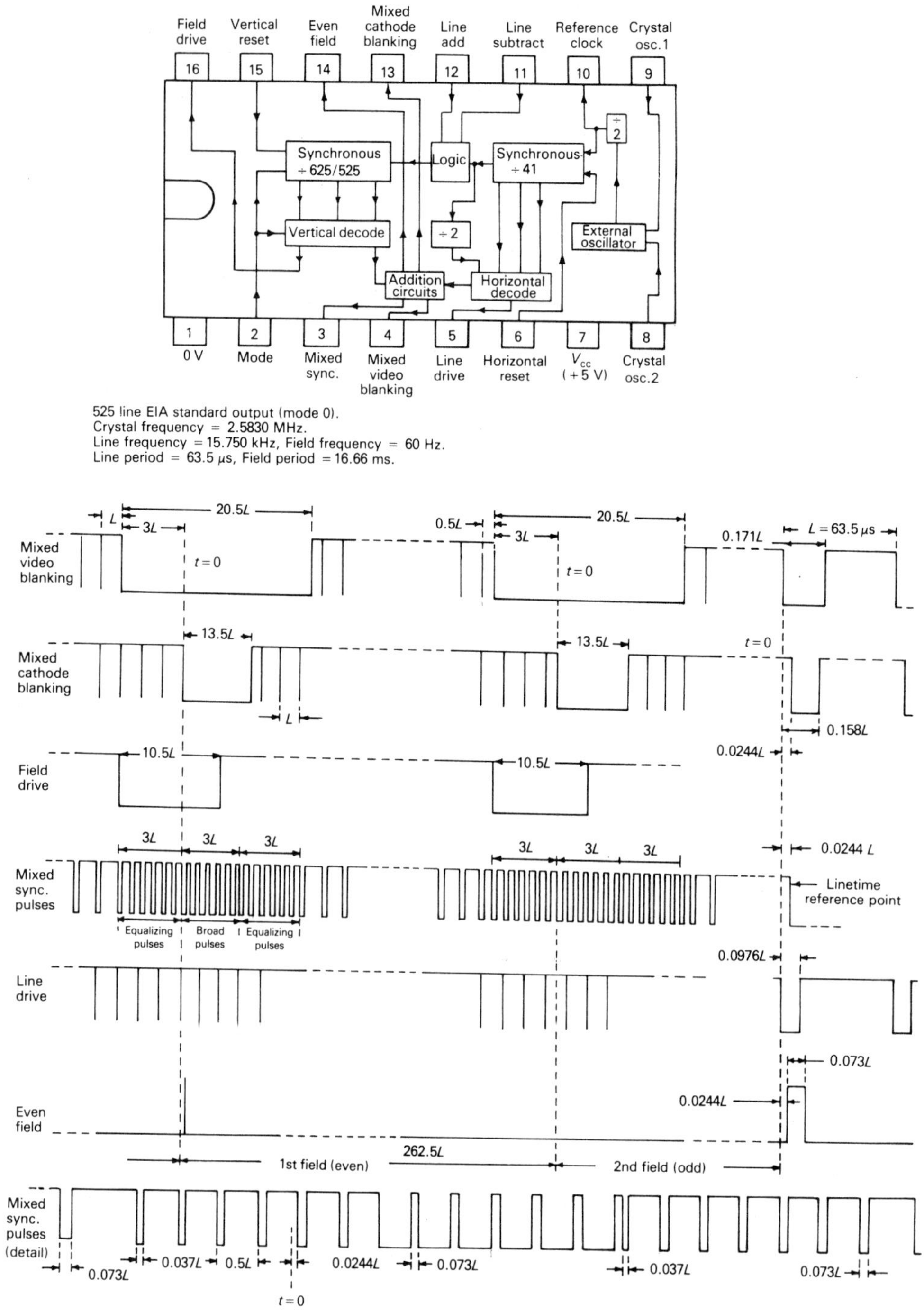

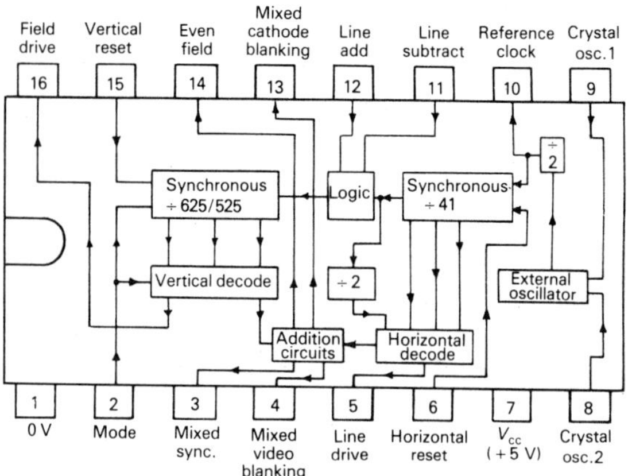

525 line EIA standard output (mode 0).
Crystal frequency = 2.5830 MHz.
Line frequency = 15.750 kHz, Field frequency = 60 Hz.
Line period = 63.5 μs, Field period = 16.66 ms.

Fig. 6.40 The Ferranti ZNA134 TV synchronizing pulse generator

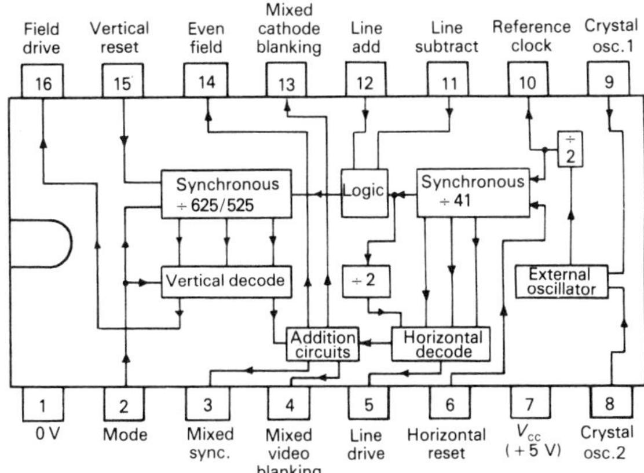

625 line CCIR standard output (mode 1).
Crystal frequency = 2.5625 MHz.
Line frequency = 15.625 kHz, Field frequency = 50 Hz.
Line period = 64μs, Field period = 20 ms.

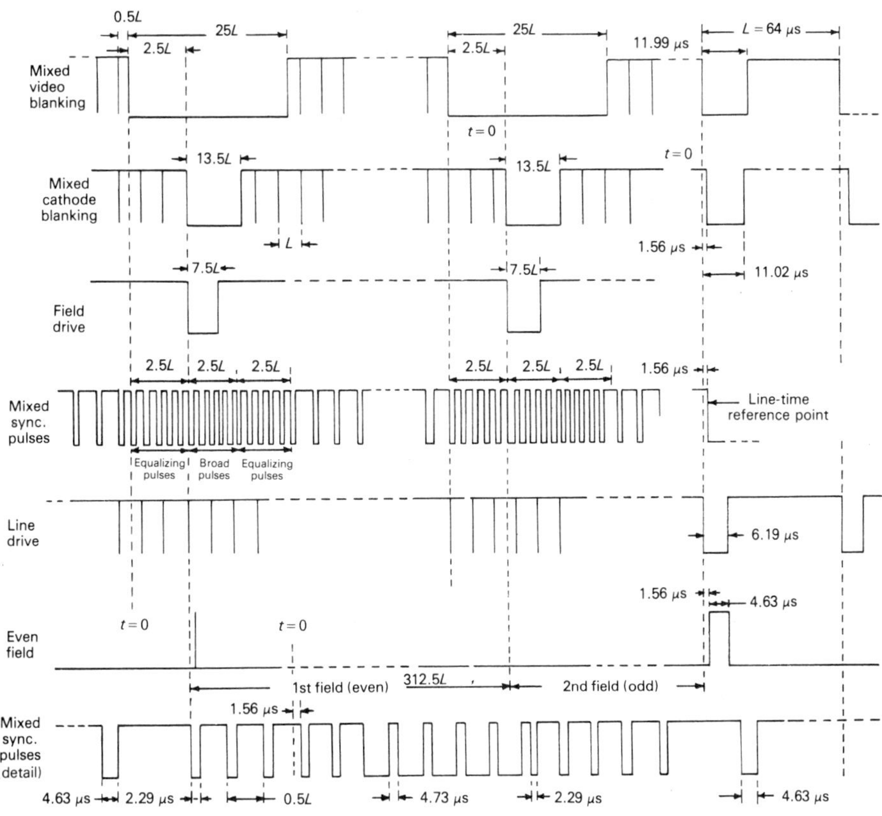

Fig. 6.40 (continued)

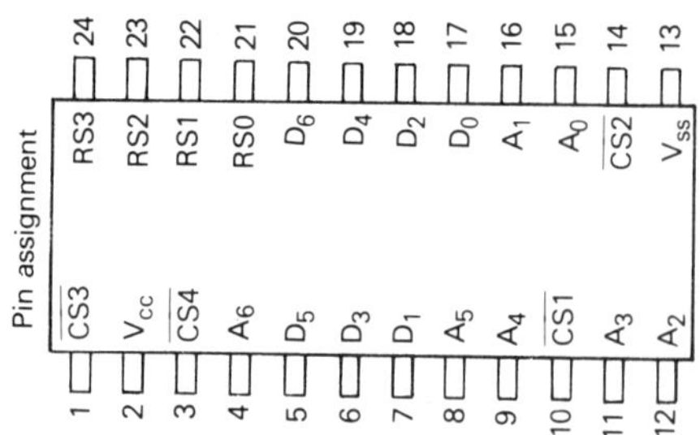
Pin assignment
1 CS3
2 Vcc
3 CS4
4 A6
5 D5
6 D3
7 D1
8 A5
9 A4
10 CS1
11 A3
12 A2
24 RS3
23 RS2
22 RS1
21 RS0
20 D6
19 D4
18 D2
17 D0
16 A1
15 A0
14 CS2
13 Vss

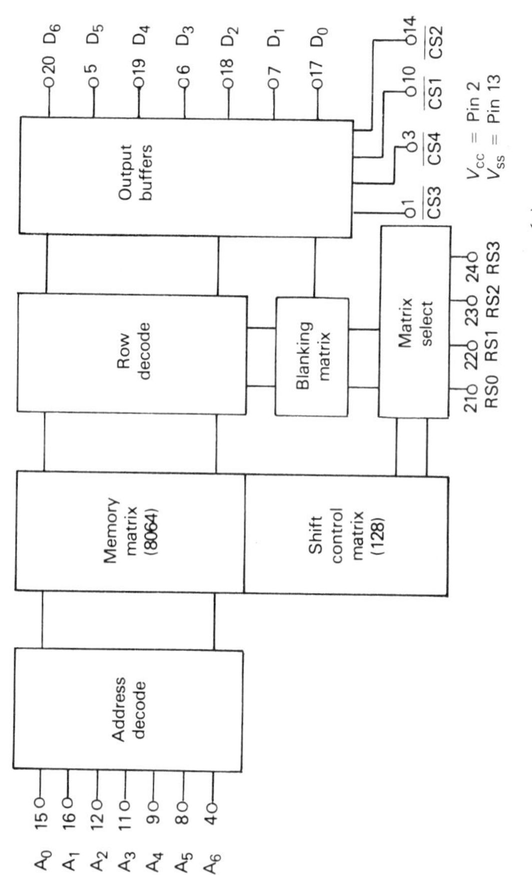
A0 15
A1 16
A2 12
A3 11
A4 9
A5 8
A6 4
Address decode
Memory matrix (8064)
Shift control matrix (128)
Row decode
Blanking matrix
Matrix select
Output buffers
20 D6
5 D5
19 D4
6 D3
18 D2
7 D1
17 D0
1 CS3
3 CS4
10 CS1
14 CS2
21 RS0
22 RS1
23 RS2
24 RS3
Vcc = Pin 2
Vss = Pin 13

(a)

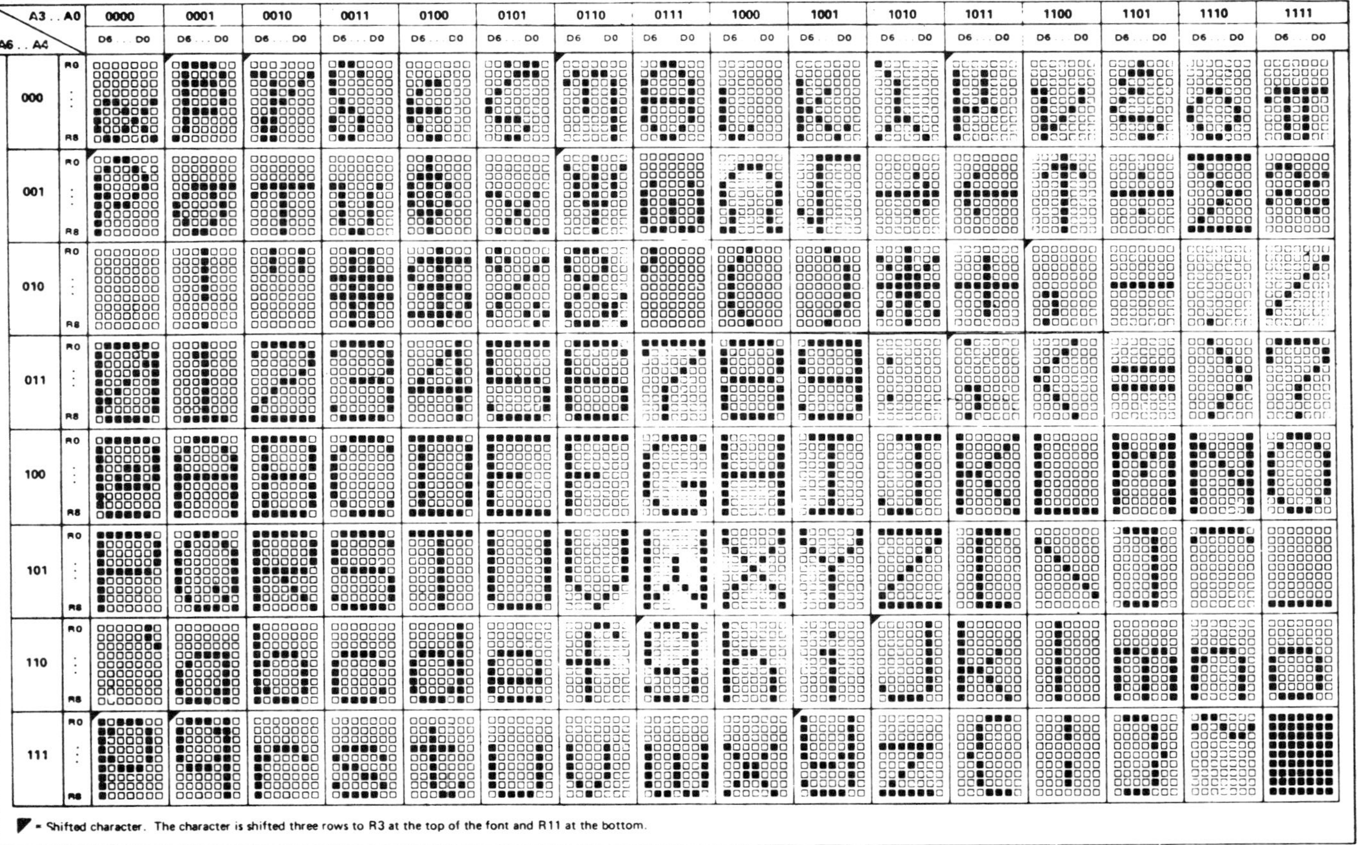

(b)

Fig. 6.41 The MCM66714 character generator: (a) block diagram; (b) character set

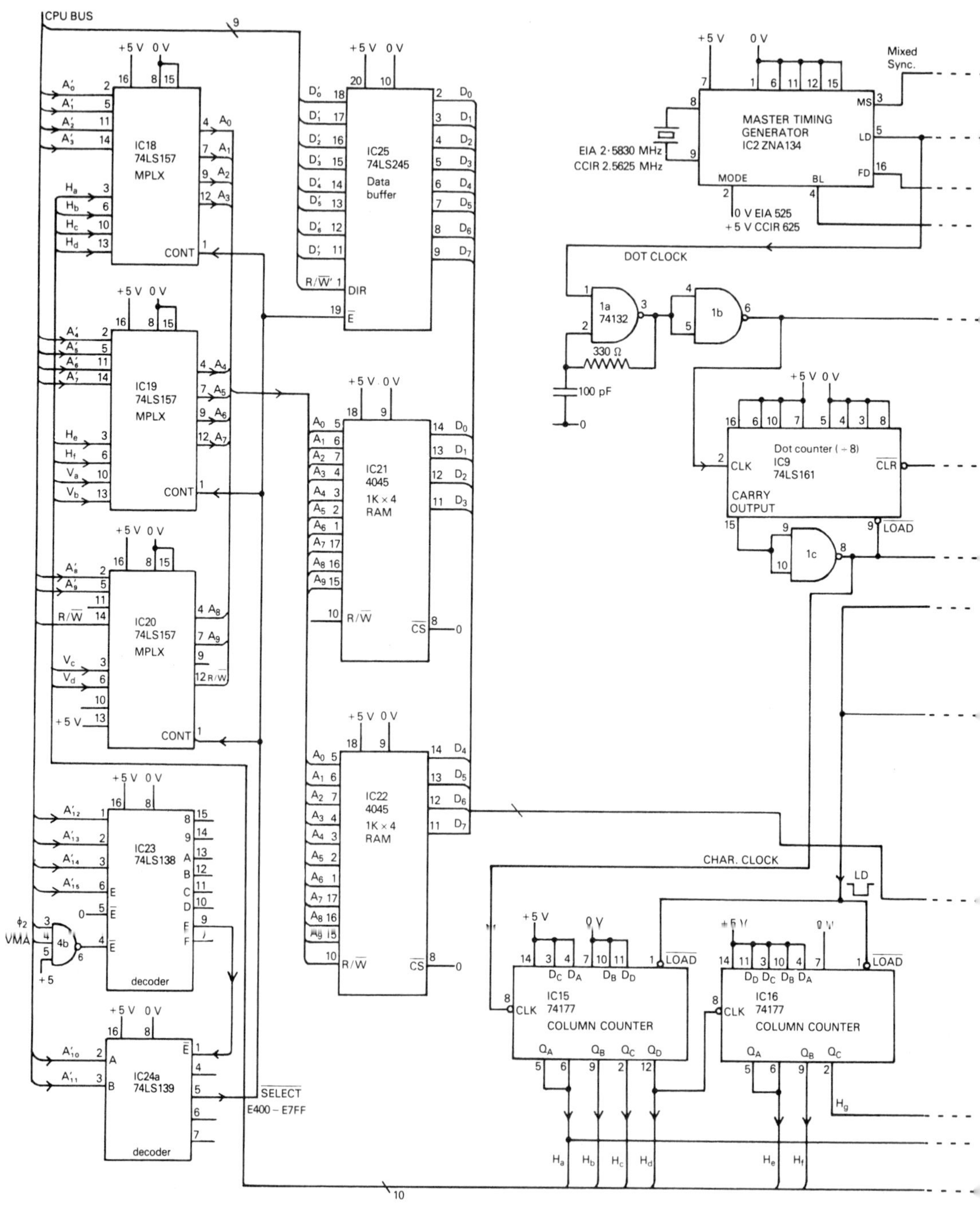

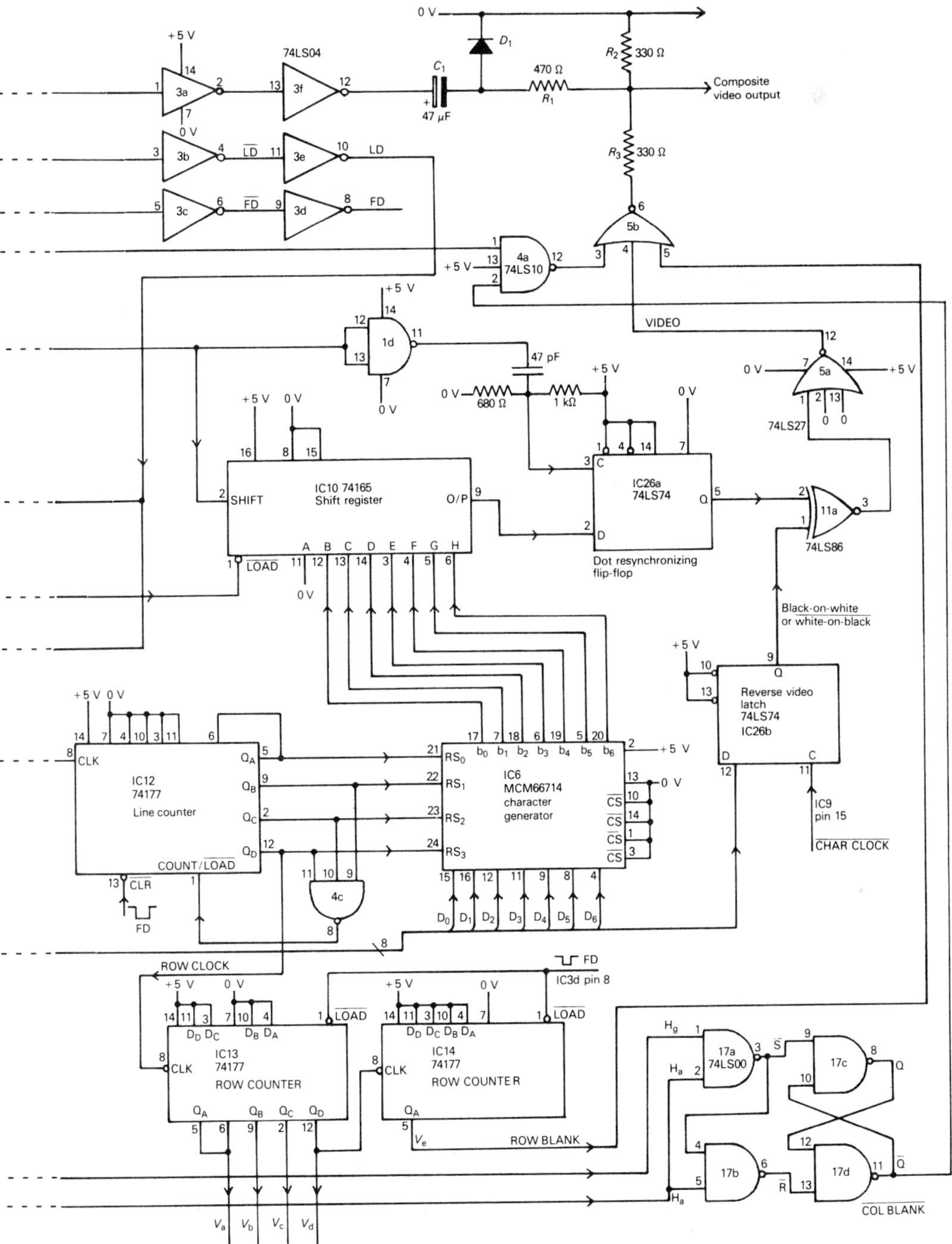

Fig. 6.42 Memory-mapped display

normally strapped to zero, but may be used to add graphics to the display by means of external logic. IC4a combines the mixed video blanking from the master timing generator (IC2) with the column blanking from IC17d, and IC5b takes care of the row blanking from IC14. Note that pin 13 of IC4a is normally strapped to +5 V and if brought low will blank the display.

(3) IC26a resynchronizes the video output from the shift register IC10. If the output of the shift register is connected directly to the video mixing circuits the eight dots forming a line of a character are not of equal widths. This effect occurs because of the high speed at which the system is clocked. In particular the load pulse to the shift registers has relatively long duration. By latching the output of the shift register in IC26a, a positive-edge triggered flip-flop, and then clocking out the data by means of a high-speed pulse (obtained by differentiating the dot clock pulses) an improved display may be obtained.

(4) The character clock is obtained from the dot clock by dividing the dot rate by eight in IC9. This IC is a divide-by-sixteen counter which is preset to eight after every eight dot pulses to give the effect of a divide-by-eight counter.

(5) The row counters are composed of two 74177 presettable binary counters (IC13 and IC14). These counters take their input from IC12, which generates a pulse for each new row of characters. The row counters are reset at the end of each field by the field-synchronizing pulse from IC2. The most significant bit of the row counter, V_e, goes high at the start of row 16 and is used to blank the display so that only rows 0 – 15 are displayed. If the row counters were to be preset to zero at the start of a field, the display would not be centered. The row counters are preset to 11100 by the field-synchronization pulses which ensure that the display is centralized.

(6) The column position counters, IC15 and IC16, operate in a similar manner to the row counters. The character rate clock is obtained from IC9, and the column counters are reset by the line-synchronizing pulse at the end of each line. The counters are preset to 1110101 by the line-synchronizing pulse, which defines the left- and right-hand margins. One interesting aspect of the column counter is the column-blanking arrangement. As it is desired to display columns 0 – 63 it may be expected that blanking be applied before column 0 and after column 63. Unfortunately when operating at a character rate of above 1MHz, system timing delays cannot be ignored. Figure 6.43 illustrates the problem by giving the timing diagram of the column counter – video RAM – character generator path. Consider the sequence of events at the start of the nth column position. Fcr a 64 characters per line display, the time available to each character is approximately 750 ns, allowing for left-hand and right-hand margins and the line flyback time. The video RAM does not yield its data for approximately 350 ns after the address from the column counter has stabilized. Data from the video RAM is presented to the character generator ROM which produces a dot output after not more than a further 350 ns. In this example the data from the ROM is not available for display until the end of the current character position. Consequently, the nth character is displayed during the $(n+1)$th column position. This effect simply shifts the whole display one

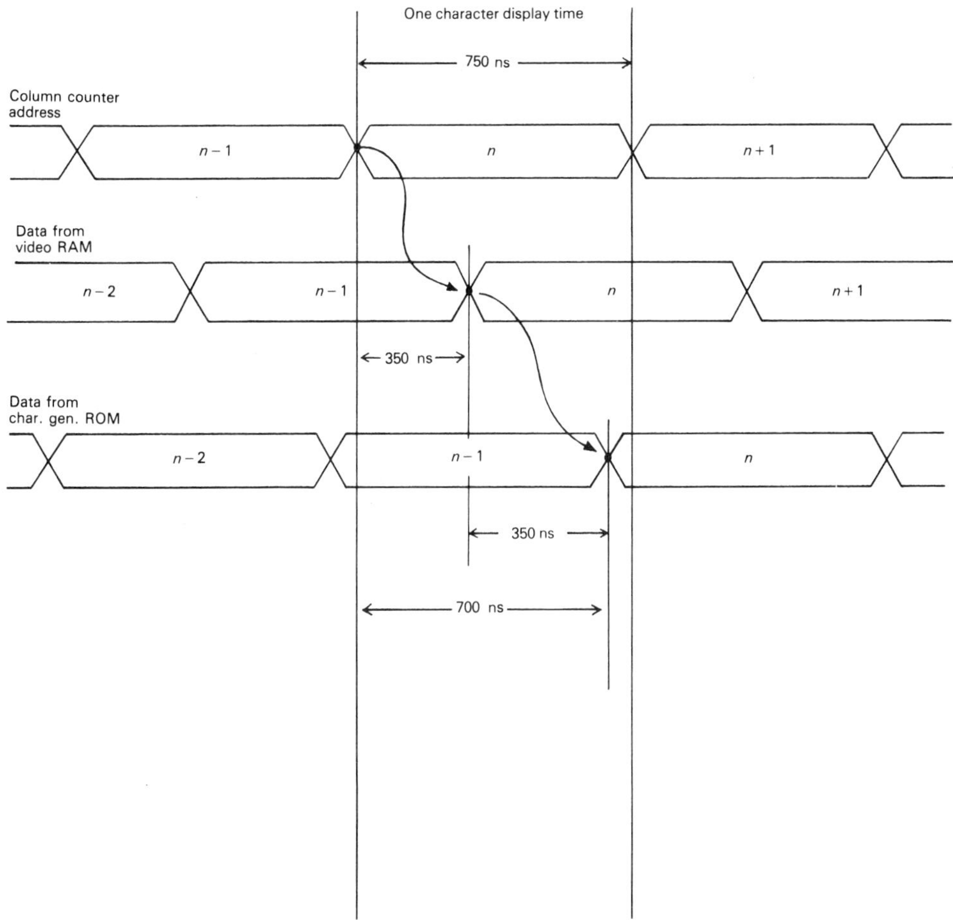

Fig. 6.43 Timing diagram of column counter

position to the right. However, if the display were unblanked from column zero, the leftmost column displayed would contain invalid data. To avoid this effect the display is blanked until the start of column 1. Similarly, the display is blanked from column 65 rather than column 64. The column-blanking circuitry generates an active-low column-blanking strobe by means of two cross-coupled NAND gates (IC17c and IC17d) which form an RS flip-flop. ICs 17a and 17b provide a gating arrangement so that when H_a first goes high (signifying column 1) the active-low column-blanking signal is set high and unblanks the display. When H_g and H_a are both high, the $\overline{S}$ input to the flip-flop goes low, setting Q and consequently blanking the display. The display is blanked from column 65 and remains blanked until column 1 on the next line.

(7) The composite video output from Fig. 6.42 may be converted into an RF signal by means of the circuit in Fig. 6.44. Any of the popular RF modulators may be

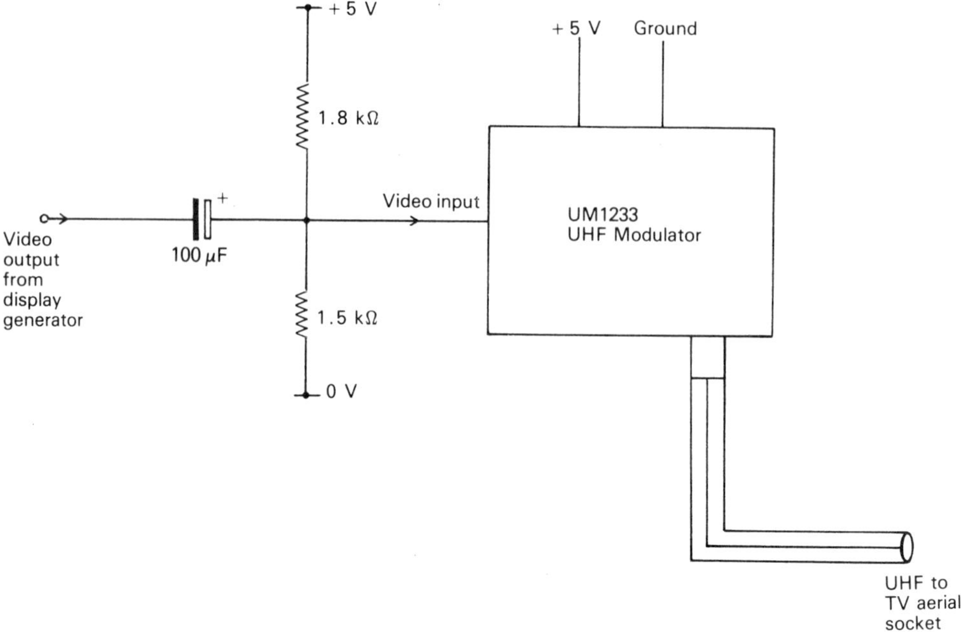

Fig. 6.44 The generation of a UHF signal from a composite video input

used in this application, provided the composite video signal is at the correct level and at the correct sense for the modulator.

(8) Only 7 bits per byte are used to generate characters. The remaining bit, d_7, is fed to one input of an exclusive-OR gate (IC11a) the other input being the video signal from IC26a. When $d_7 = 0$ the video is passed by the exclusive-OR gate and when $d_7 = 1$, the video is inverted. Hence d_7 determines whether a character is white-on-black or black-on-white. Because the video signal is delayed by one character time, the data input to the exclusive-OR is delayed one character time by a flip-flop IC26b.

The basic software necessary to drive the above type of memory-mapped display is given in Appendix A4.

6.5.2 A Stand-alone Display

A stand-alone display includes all the logic of the memory-mapped display, together with the circuitry necessary to convert serial data into parallel format, store characters in successive memory locations and interpret control characters. Such an arrangement may be based on the memory-mapped display described in the previous section plus approximately 20 MSI packages. Fortunately it is now possible to build a system with a low parts count and at a low cost, by using a CRT controller chip. The

Thomson-Efcis EF9364 CRT controller is a single NMOS chip and is able to replace the vast majority of SSI and MSI logic found in a VDT. While this CRT controller can save a great deal of design effort and dramatically reduce the cost of a VDT module, it suffers from a lack of flexibility. That is, the display format is fixed at 16 rows of 64 characters, and cannot readily be modified.

The block diagram of a VDT designed around the EF9364 CRT controller is given in Fig. 6.45. The CRT controller generates accurate system-timing pulses from a 1.018 MHz crystal. An external oscillator, operating at approximately 13 MHz, provides the dot timing. The output of the dot clock is divided by eight to give the character rate, which forms an input to the CRT controller as well as the load signal to the shift register. The CRT controller performs three functions:

(1) It continually scans the video RAM to obtain the ASCII character codes which are converted by the character generator ROM into the actual pattern of dots to be displayed on the CRT screen.

(2) It generates the line- and field-synchronizing pulses by means of an on-chip oscillator controlled by a quartz crystal. As in the case of the memory-mapped display described in the previous section, it is necessary to synchronize the external dot clock with the CRT controller's own clock if a stable display is to be obtained. The CRT controller provides an active-low output $\overline{\text{INI}}$ (= $\overline{\text{inhibit}}$) which generates an approximately 20 μs pulse at the end of each line of the display. This signal stops the external dot clock at the end of each line so that the displayed characters are always in the same relative positions in successive frames, ensuring a stable display. The CRT controller also provides the following display control outputs:

RO_0 to RO_2 These three lines provide a line-of-character address input to the character generator ROM. Note that the displayed characters cannot occupy more than 8 lines of the display. This restriction prohibits the use of high-resolution character fonts. RO_2 has a secondary role of jamming the space character (20_{16}) into all the video RAM's locations during the operation of a clear screen command.

PT This active-high output generates a flashing cursor which appears as a line beneath the position of the next character to be displayed.

SYNC The SYNC output provides the mixed line- and field-synchronizing signals and is normally combined with the video output from the external shift register to generate a composite video signal for direct connection to a monitor, or for feeding into a UHF modulator.

(3) The CRT controller keeps track of the position in which the next character from the input to the VDT is to be displayed. Whenever a normal (i.e. non-control) character is received and the CRT controller is strobed by an active-low pulse at its $\overline{\text{ST}}$ input, the CRT controller responds by generating an active-high 4 μs pulse which writes the new character into the video RAM.

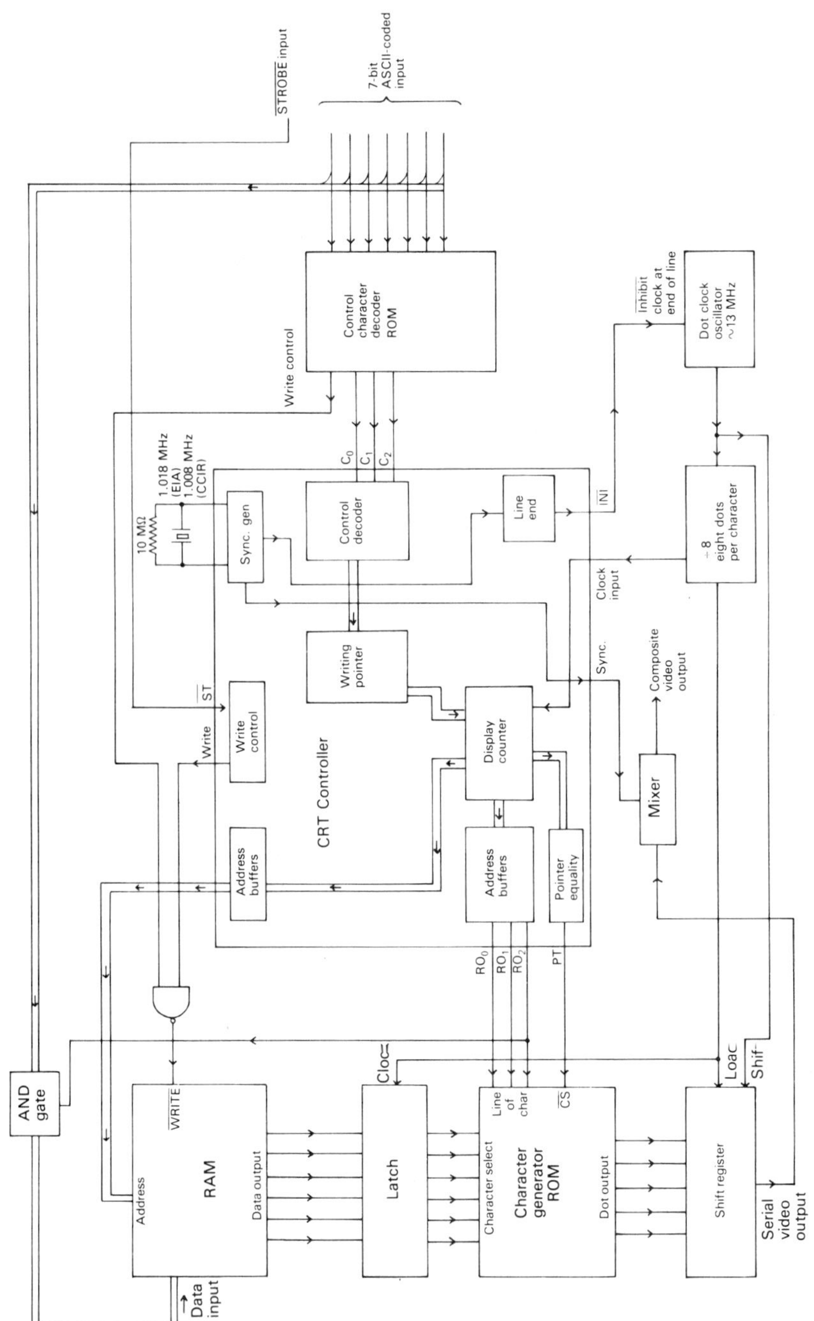

Fig. 6.45 The block diagram of a VDT using the Thomson-Efcis CRT controller

Whenever a non-printing (i.e. control) character is received, external logic converts the control character into a three-bit code (C_0, C_1, C_2), and the EF9364 interprets this code accordingly. The C_0, C_1, C_2 control inputs indicate the presence of a normal character, a non-printing control character (which is ignored), or a cursor control character. It is necessary to derive the value of these three lines from the 7-bit ASCII-encoded input by means of an external PROM decoder which may be obtained (ready programmed) from several sources. The CRT controller responds to a new input only when its $\overline{ST}$ input goes low, and requires that the minimum time between successive $\overline{ST}$ pulses should be no less than 8.3 ms. This corresponds to a rate of approximately 120 characters per second (i.e. 1200 baud). Unfortunately whenever a "clear screen" character is received a delay of 132 ms is required before a new character may be received. Hence, if the CRT controller is to operate at 1200 baud a delay of 125 ms must be inserted, at the transmitter, after each "clear screen" command is issued. This may be effected by a software-controlled timing loop in the computer's output routines.

The full circuit of a VDT built around the Thomson – Efcis CRT controller is given in Fig. 6.46 and corresponds to the block diagram of Fig. 6.45. This circuit is virtually identical to that published by Thomson – Efcis in their EF9364 data sheet. The input circuit receives a bit-serial data in an RS232C format and converts it into a 7-bit word and a data-ready strobe by means of a UART. A multifrequency baud-rate generator based on the MC14411 is included in the VDT to generate a stable clock for the UART's receiver. A DIL switch (IC17) has been provided to select the appropriate baud rate for the UART rather than hard-wiring a connection between the baud-rate generator and the UART. The DIL switch permits the selection of baud rates in the range 110 – 9600 baud, although at transmission rates above 1200 baud a delay must be inserted between successive characters at the transmitter (i.e. in the CPU module), if the minimum time between characters required by the CRT controller is not to be exceeded.

It may, at first sight, appear inefficient to connect the VDT module to the CPU module by means of a serial, asynchronous data link. Such an arrangement requires a UART at both the transmitter and receiver ends of the data link, plus baud-rate generators. A much more cost-effective organization would employ a PIA in the CPU module to transmit data, a strobe, and the cursor information directly to the CRT controller. In this way the UART's baud-rate generators, RS232C interfaces, and the PROM control character decoder could be dispensed with. Furthermore, it requires very little additional logic to convert the CRT controller chip into a memory-mapped display generator allowing the CPU to access the video RAM directly. Why then use a serial data link between the CPU and the VDT?

A serial data link has been chosen for two reasons:

(1) A stand-alone VDT module is required because it can be tested independently of the microprocessor system, and can be used with any microprocessor system having a serial output. The VDT module is particularly easy to interface because it has just four connections to the rest of the system—two power rails

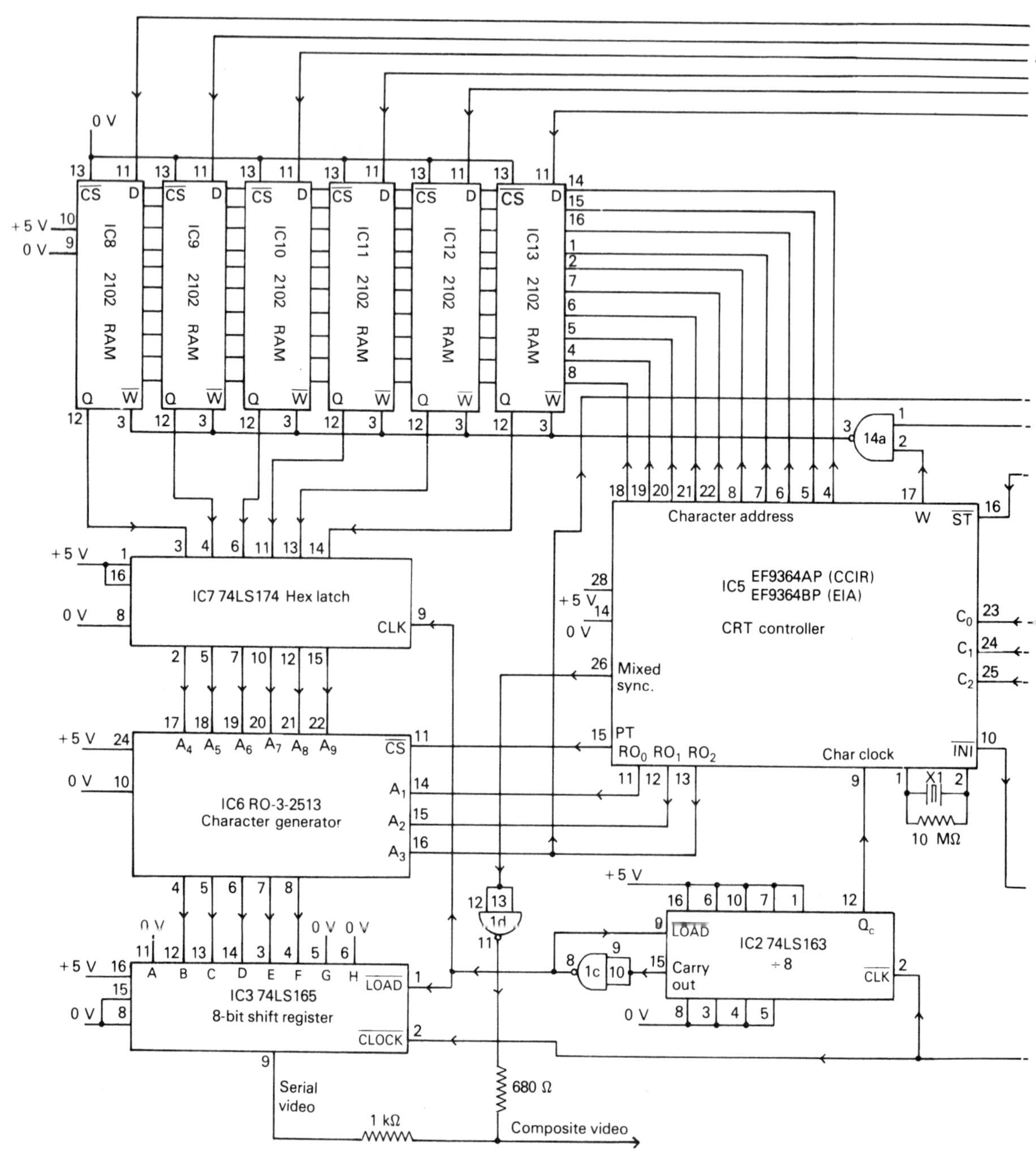

Fig. 6.46 A VDT using the Thomson-Efcis CRT controller

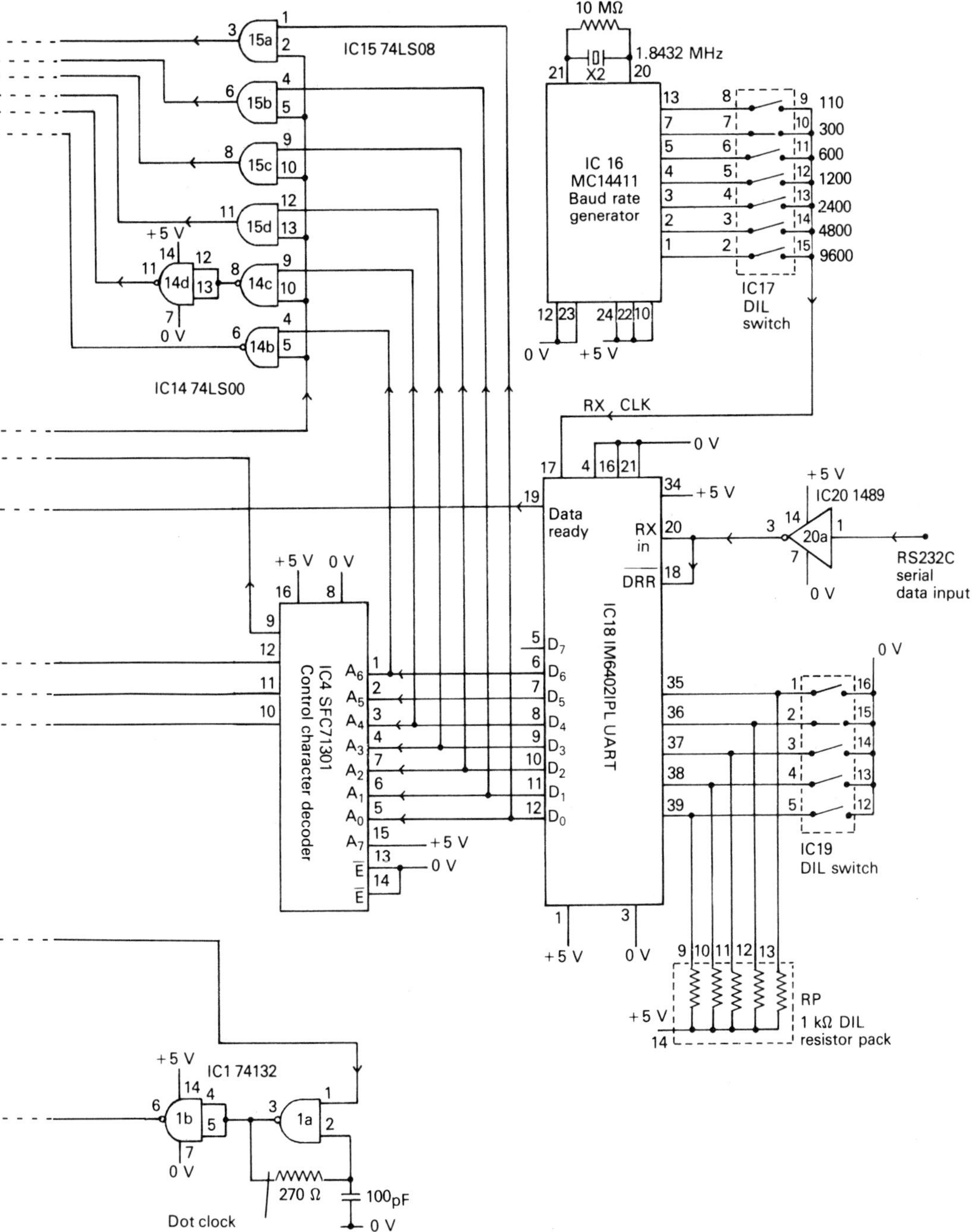
IC15 74LS08
15a
15b
15c
15d
14d
14c
14b
IC14 74LS00
+5 V
0 V
10 MΩ
1.8432 MHz
X2
IC 16
MC14411
Baud rate
generator
110
300
600
1200
2400
4800
9600
IC17
DIL
switch
RX CLK
Data
ready
RX
in
DRR
IC18 IM6402IPL UART
IC20 1489
20a
RS232C
serial
data input
IC4 SFC71301
Control character decoder
IC19
DIL switch
RP
1 kΩ DIL
resistor pack
IC1 74132
1b
1a
270 Ω
100pF
Dot clock

(0 V, +5 V), an RS232C serial input, and a composite video output.

(2) A VDT is normally connected to the microprocessor's console output port. As this port generates a serial output, teletypes, printers, tape punches, or cassette interfaces may also be connected to the port. If a memory-mapped display were dedicated to the function of console display, additional port would have to be provided for any other serial interfaces.

Although the circuit diagram of the VDT module closely follows the block diagram of Fig. 6.45, a few details require some further explanation:

(a) The dot clock is generated by a simple relaxation oscillator using a dual-input Schmitt trigger (IC1a 74132). One of the inputs of the Schmitt trigger is connected to the $\overline{\text{INI}}$ output of the CRT controller, enabling the controller to synchronize the dot clock with its own internal clock.

(b) The composite video output is formed by adding the inverted sync. pulses from the CRT controller to the video signal from the shift register (IC3 74LS165) by means of a simple resistor network.

(c) The character clock is obtained from the dot clock by dividing the output from IC1b by eight. The divider (IC2 74LS163) is in fact a presettable divide-by-sixteen counter which is loaded with eight by its carry-out pulse so that it counts from 8 to 15, equivalent to a count of 0 to 7. The output of this counter provides a character clock input for the CRT controller and a load pulse for the shift register which serializes the row of dots from the character generator.

(d) The character generator (IC6) is an RO-3-2513 which generates the 64 upper-case subset of the ASCII characters. This particular device requires only a single +5 V supply. The cursor display output of the CRT controller (PT) is connected to the active-low $\overline{\text{CS}}$ input of the character generator. When the cursor is to be displayed PT goes high, disabling the output of the character generator. The inputs to the shift register (the 74LS165 is a TTL device) float upwards to a logical 1 and a line of dots (the cursor) is produced.

(e) ICs 14 and 15 gate the data input from the UART into the video RAM. In normal operation all the gates are enabled and data from the UART is written into the RAM by a write pulse from the CRT controller (inverted by IC14a). The control input of the gates is the RO_2 output from the EF9364 and is normally high. Note that $D_0 - D_4$ from the UART are connected via the gates to $D_0 - D_4$ of the video RAM (ICs 8 – 13). D_5 from the UART is not connected to the video RAM (i.e. it is ignored) and D_6 from the UART is connected to D_5 of the RAM via IC14b, an inverting gate. This action has the effect of compressing the 7-bit ASCII code into a 6-bit upper-case subset of the ASCII code required by the character generator. When RO_2 is low, the data input to the video RAM is 010 000 = 20_{16} and represents the space code. Thus when the screen is cleared RO_2 goes low and a space character is written into each location of the video RAM.

(f) A DIL switch is used to program the UART so that the module may be operated with a wide variety of serial data formats. This refinement is not

Table 6.22 The Relationship between ASCII Characters, the Output of the Control Decoder PROM and the Action of the CRT Controller

Key	ASCII code Hex	ASCII code Decimal	Character	Control PROM address Hex	Control PROM address Decimal	Control PROM output O_3	O_2	O_1	O_0	Effect of control PROM output
—	—	—	—	00→7F	0→127	1	0	0	0	Clear screen/home cursor
	0→7	0→7	Non-printing control	80→87	128→135	0	0	1	1	Inhibit character
Back space	08	8	Back space	88	136	0	1	0	0	Cursor left
CNTRL I	09	9	Cursor right	89	137	0	1	1	1	Cursor right
Line feed	0A	10	Line feed	8A	138	1	0	1	0	Cursor down
CNTRL K	0B	11	Cursor up	8B	139	0	1	1	0	Cursor up
CNTRL L	0C	12	Clear screen and home	8C	140	1	0	0	0	Clear screen/home cursor
Return	0D	13	Carriage return	8D	141	1	0	0	1	End of line erase and C/R
	0E→19	14→25	Non-printing control	8E→99	142→153	0	0	1	1	Inhibit character
CNTRL Z	1A	26	Erasure of current line	9A	154	1	1	0	1	Erasure of current line
CNTRL [	1B	27	Line feed	9B	155	0	0	1	0	Cursor down
CNTRL \	1C	28	Home cursor	9C	156	0	0	0	0	Home cursor
CNTRL]	1D	29	Carriage return	9D	157	0	0	0	1	Carriage return
	1E→1F	30→31	Non-printing control	9E→9F	158→159	0	0	1	1	Inhibit character
	20→7E	32→254	Upper and lower case	A0→FE	160→254	1	1	1	1	Normal character
Delete	7F	255	Delete	FF	255	0	0	1	1	Inhibit character

normally necessary and pins 35 – 39 of the UART may be hard-wired to ground or +5 V as required.

(g) The UART is a CMOS device (IM6402IPL) and requires only a single +5 V supply unlike many other UARTs which, although functionally compatible with the IM6402, need a –12 V supply.

(h) IC4 is a control character decoder PROM and decodes the input characters into a three-bit code ($C_0 - C_2$) which controls the operations of the UART. A fourth output of the PROM gates the write strobe from the CRT controller into the video RAM by means of IC14a. The relationship between the ASCII code and the contents of the PROM is given in Table 6.22.

(i) There are two versions of the CRT controller: the EF9364AP which is compatible with the CCIR 50 Hz 625-line standard and the EF9364BP which is compatible with the EIA 60 Hz 525-line standard. The "A" version uses a 1.008 MHz crystal and the "B" version uses a 1.018 MHz crystal.

(j) The six 2101 1K × 1 RAMs may be replaced by two 1K × 4 RAMs to save board space.

6.6 THE BUS EXTENDER MODULE

The bus extender module fulfils two roles in the TS1 Microprocessor system. Firstly, it provides a termination for the system bus, and secondly it allows the bus to be extended beyond the physical housing of the TS1 to a second system. Terminating a bus by providing it with a resistive load reduces the noise on the bus and hence reduces the number of spurious errors.

Bus Termination

In Chapter 4 the electrical characteristics of a bus were dealt with from the point of view of static signal levels—a steady logical one or zero state. In this section the effects of changes of state on the bus are considered.

The electrical paths formed by the lines of a bus can be treated in terms of transmission-line theory. A transmission line may be considered to be two parallel conductors separated by an insulating medium. The theory of transmission lines regards the signal path as an infinite number of circuits of the form shown in Fig. 6.47, in series. In this diagram R is the resistance per unit length, L is the inductance per unit length, G is the leakage per unit length, C is the capacitance per unit length. Although these electrical properties are distributed throughout the transmission line, it is possible to consider an infinitely short length of the line, δx, and to regard these properties as being lumped together as in Fig. 6.47. The full treatment of transmission lines is a branch of radio engineering and the Bibliography points the more masochistic reader to the relevant sources of information.

The parameter of a transmission line of most interest to an engineer is its characteristic impedance. Typical random wire wrap wires have an impedance in the range 100 – 200 Ω, and the characteristic impedance of any transmission line is almost never less than 30 Ω or greater than 600 Ω.

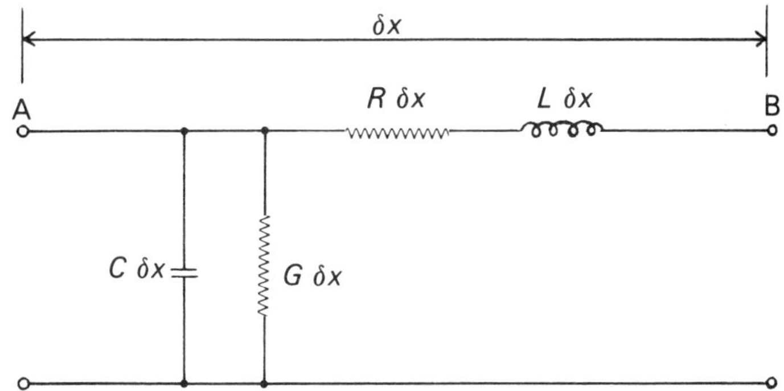

Fig. 6.47 The transmission line represented by lumped components

The principal effect of a transmission line on a pulse is to reduce the speed of its propagation from the 3 ns/m (1 ns/ft) value for free space to approximately 5 – 7 ns/m (1½ – 2 ns/ft). The aspect of transmission lines of greatest interest to the engineer is the behavior of pulses on reaching its ends. An infinitely long transmission line presents no problems as it does not have any ends! Figure 6.48 shows the effect of a pulse applied to a transmission line having an open circuit at its end.

The pulse from the transmitter travels along the line reaching the open circuit end after a delay of t_d seconds. Because the end is open circuit and there can be no current between the ends the current at the end of the line goes to zero only if at the moment the pulse is received a reflected pulse of amplitude V is reflected back down the line towards the transmitter. This causes a pulse of $2V$ to appear at the end and a pulse of V to be received at the transmitter after a further t_d seconds.

At the other extreme Fig. 6.49 illustrates the effect of a transmission line terminated by a short circuit.

In the case of a transmission line with a short circuit termination, the pulse travels down the line from the transmitter to the short circuit. On reaching the short circuit the voltage instantaneously becomes zero (as a potential difference cannot exist across the ends of a dead short). The effect is equivalent to a pulse of equal and opposite amplitude to the transmitted pulse being reflected from the terminated end of the line. When the inverted reflected pulse reaches the transmitter its output falls to zero as the incident and reflected waves cancel.

Figure 6.50 shows the effect of a line terminated by its own characteristic impedance. In this case the line is matched to its load and there is no reflection. In general, if the load impedance exceeds the characteristic impedance the reflection from the termination is positive and is added to the incident wave from the source, and if the load impedance is less than the characteristic impedance, the reflected

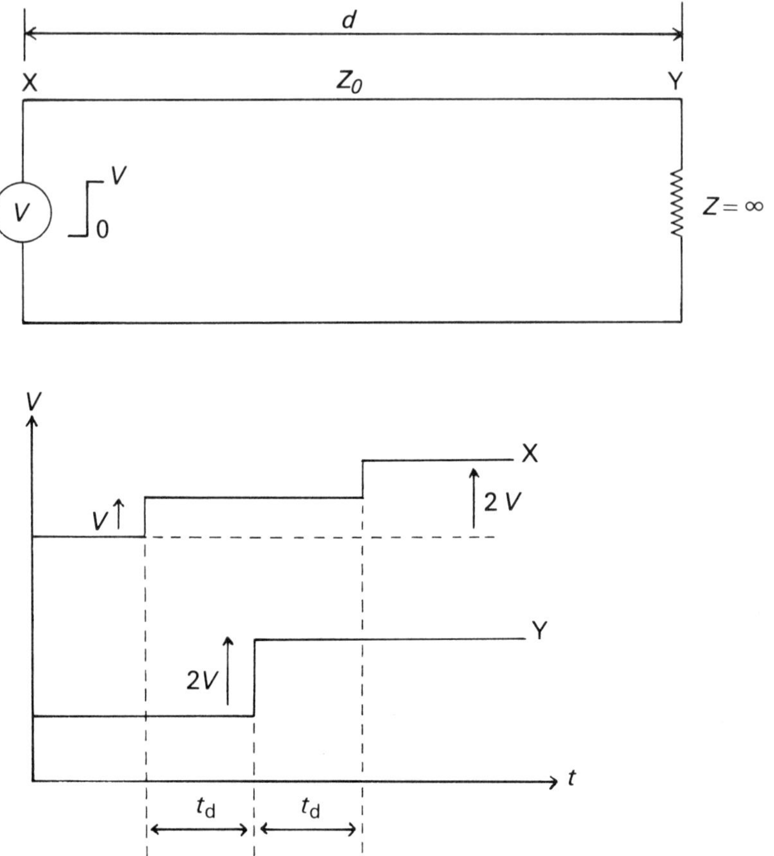

Fig. 6.48 A transmission line with an open circuit end

wave is negative and is subtracted from the incident wave. The reflection coefficient of the line is given by $\Gamma = (Z_1 - Z_0)/(Z_1 + Z_0)$, where Z_1 is the load impedance and Z_0 the characteristic impedance of the line. For example for a short circuit $Z_1 = 0$, and $\Gamma = -Z_0/Z_0 = -1$. The amplitude of the reflected signals is given by Γ times the incident signal.

A reflection occurs at any discontinuity (change of impedance) in the transmission line. Consequently, reflections also occur at the transmitter unless it too is matched to the line. Connections to the transmission line (called stubs) also cause reflections. The exact calculations of the reflections on any real transmission line can be quite complex—engineers often resort to graphical techniques.

There is insufficient space here to deal with the behavior of transmission lines in any detail. However, the reader should be aware of their effect on the operation of digital systems. The devices most susceptible to noise are clocked circuits (flip-flops, memory components, and peripherals with data latches) because any noise at their input during their set-up time may cause erroneous operation. For latches with a relatively long set-up time short noise pulses may have little effect, but for latches

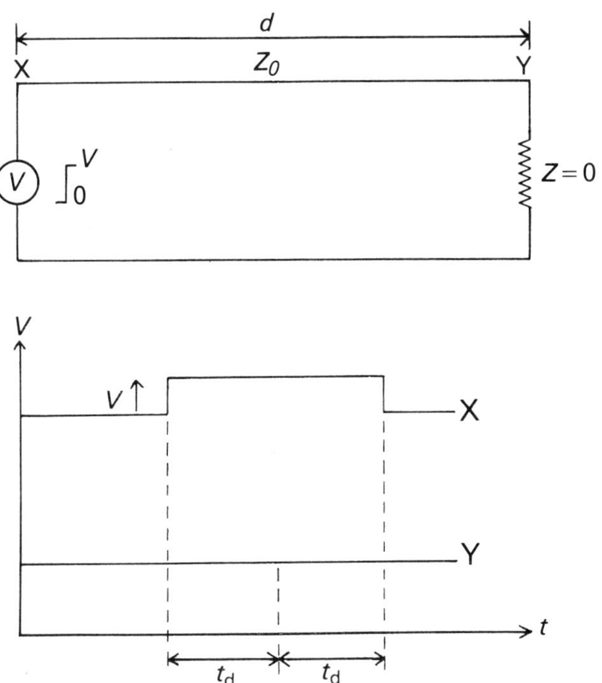

Fig. 6.49 A transmission line terminated by a short circuit

with short set-up lines (a 74S74 has a set-up time of only 3 ns) even short noise pulses may prove disastrous.

In order to reduce some of the noise on a system bus it is normal practice to provide a termination to the bus. It has been stated that the characteristic impedance of a random wire wrap is normally in the range 100 – 200 Ω. If we assume a worst case value of 100 Ω and terminate the bus with a 200 Ω resistor, the reflection coefficient is given by (200 – 100)/(200 + 100) = 100/300 = ⅓. Consequently, the reflected pulse is one third that of the incident pulse. If the characteristic impedance of the bus is 150 Ω, the reflection coefficient is only ⅕.

It is possible to terminate a bus by connecting a resistor between it and ground or V_{cc} (i.e. +5 V) as both ground and V_{cc} are common with respect to a.c. signals. While either of these forms of termination are suitable from the point of view of dynamic signals, both terminating the bus to ground and terminating it to V_{cc} are unacceptable from a static signal point of view. Terminating a bus to ground has the unfortunate effect of reducing the level of the signal when the bus is held in a logical one state. This in turn diminishes the high-level noise immunity of receivers

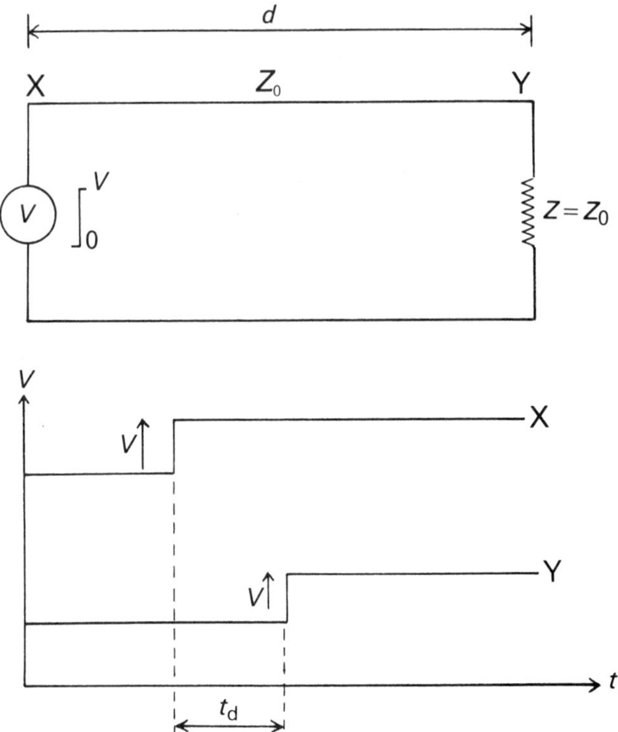

Fig. 6.50 A transmission line terminated by its characteristic impedance

connected to the bus. Similarly, terminating the bus to V_{cc} raises the level of the bus when it is in a low-level state, reducing the low-level noise immunity.

One of the most popular methods of terminating a bus in a microprocessor system is given in Fig. 6.51. The bus is pulled up to V_{cc} by a 360 Ω resistor and down to ground by a 390 Ω resistor. This network can be shown to be equivalent (by

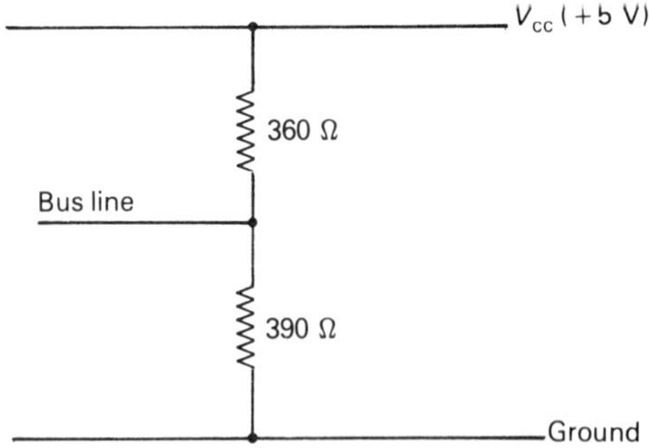

Fig. 6.51 A practical bus termination network

Thévenin's theorem) to a single resistor of approximately 187 Ω and a perfect voltage source of 2.6 V (Fig. 6.52). By employing this network the bus is approximately terminated by its characteristic impedance, while at the same time it is neither pulled up to V_{cc} nor down to ground. The principal disadvantage of this network is the current drain incurred by it. The average current taken by each termination is under 10 mA but there are often thirty or more lines to be terminated. An alternative to this arrangement is a single 180 Ω resistor connected between the line to be terminated and a constant voltage source of 2.6 V. This system is often called active termination and is found in some of the microprocessor systems based on the S100 bus.

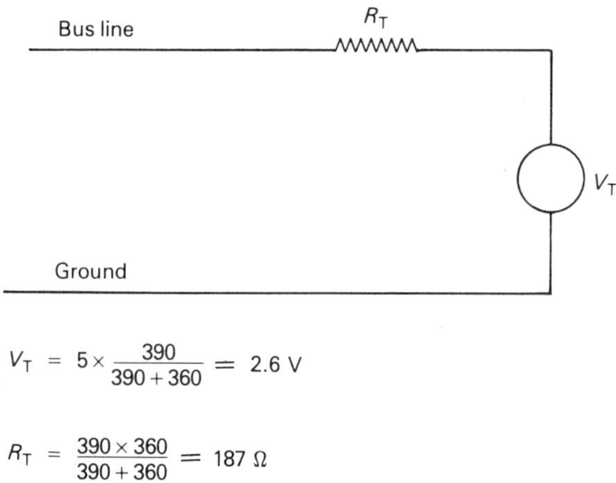

$$V_T = 5 \times \frac{390}{390 + 360} = 2.6 \text{ V}$$

$$R_T = \frac{390 \times 360}{390 + 360} = 187\ \Omega$$

Fig. 6.52 The Thévenin equivalent of Fig. 6.51

The Extender

The TS1 microprocessor system is able to support no more than eight modules because of the limitations of space in the rack. It is tempting to think that two systems can be joined together simply by connecting them by a few metres of ribbon cable. With a total bus length of three or more metres the effect of reflections and mismatches becomes more acute. The time taken by a pulse to travel to the end of the bus and to return is of the order of 30 ns. This is longer than the set-up time of many latches and can cause spurious errors.

A more reasonable solution is to provide a buffer between the bus of the TS1 and the extension cable. In this way reflections cannot travel along the whole length of the bus. Reflections are not the only problem arising from the interconnection of buses by ribbon cable. The capacitance between adjacent conductors or ribbon cable is in the region of 50 pF/m. This capacitance has the effect of inducing noise into the neighbors of a line undergoing a logic transition. The mutual coupling between conductors has no effect on static signal levels. One way of reducing this cross talk is

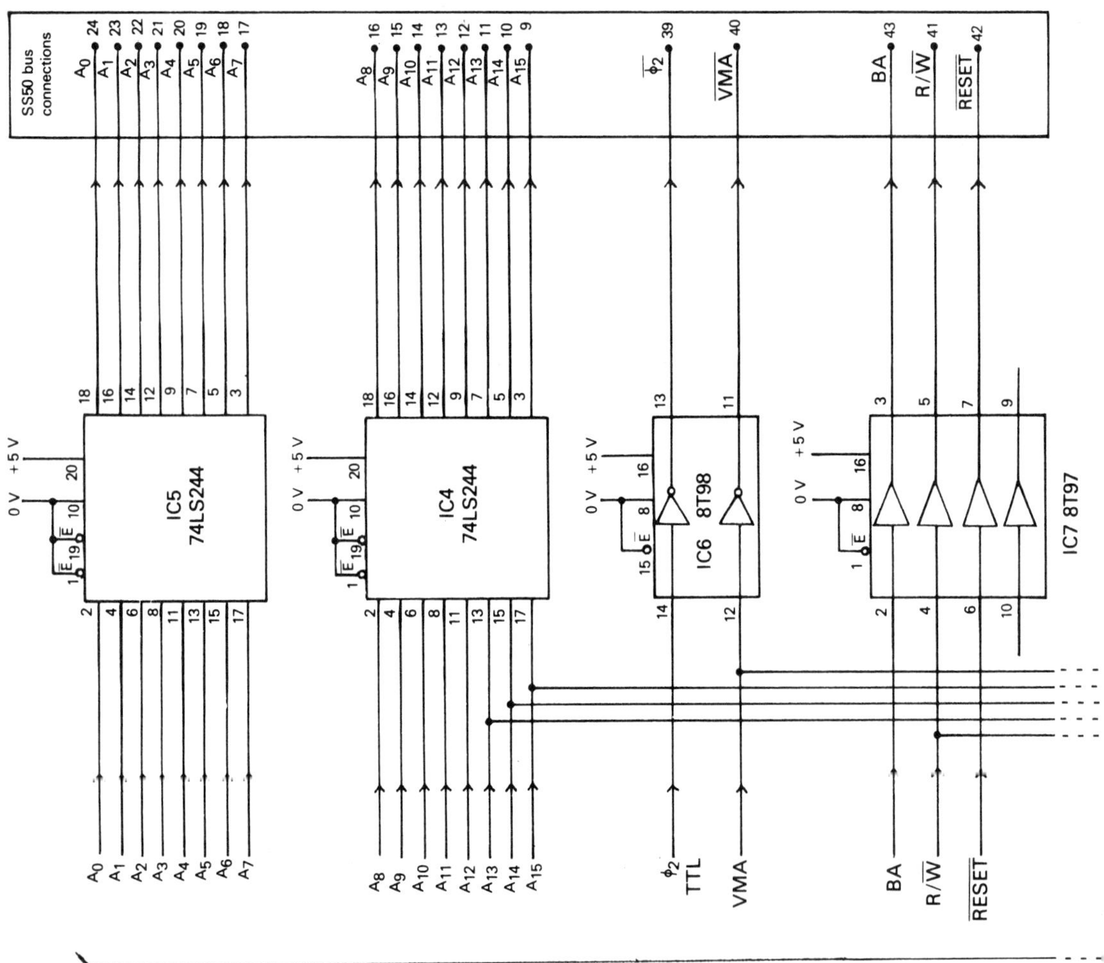
SS50 bus connections
IC5 74LS244
IC4 74LS244
IC6 8T98
IC7 8T97
0 V
+5 V
$\overline{E}$
A_0 A_1 A_2 A_3 A_4 A_5 A_6 A_7
A_8 A_9 A_{10} A_{11} A_{12} A_{13} A_{14} A_{15}
ϕ_2 TTL
$\overline{\phi_2}$
VMA
$\overline{VMA}$
BA
R/$\overline{W}$
$\overline{RESET}$

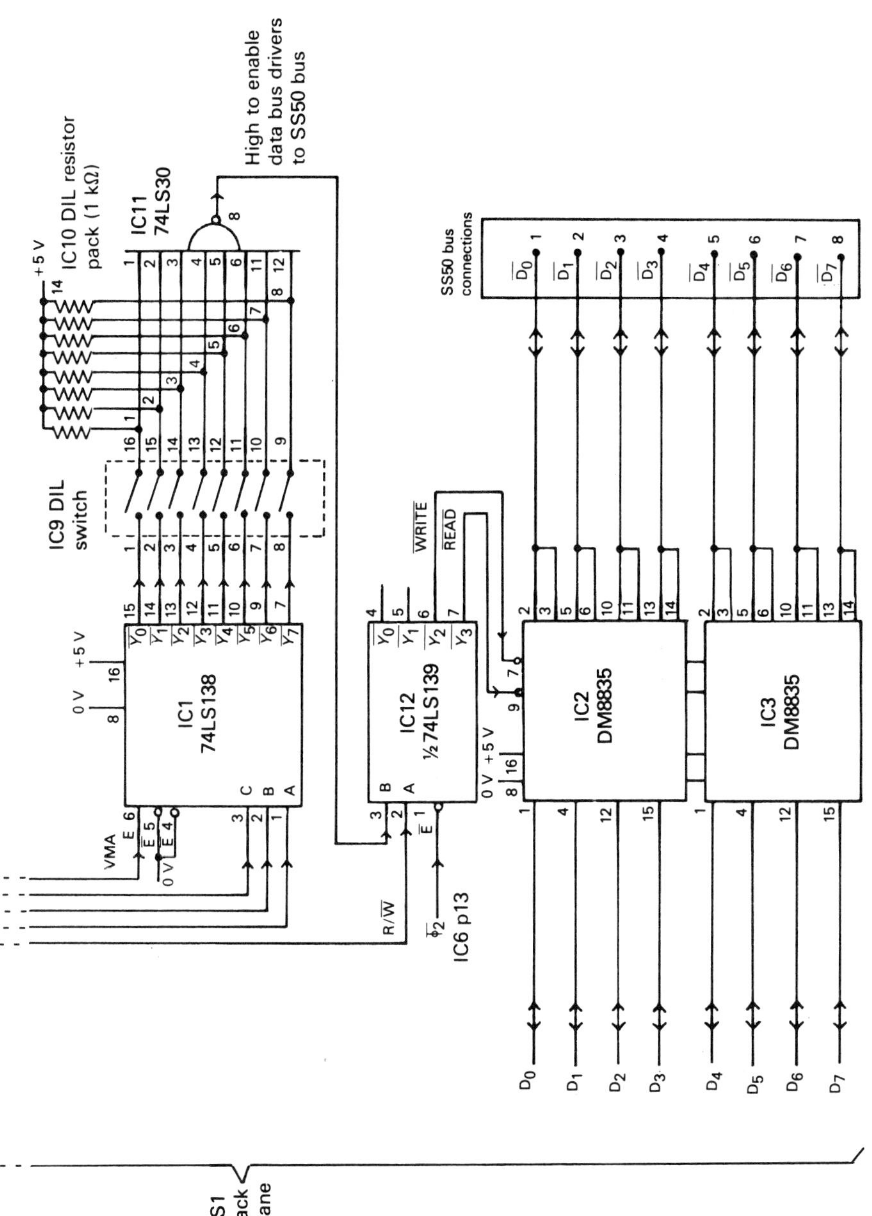

Fig. 6.53 The bus extender circuit

to ground every other conductor so that adjacent conductors are separated by a ground plane. It is now possible to obtain twisted-pair ribbon cable consisting of a number of parallel twisted pairs of conductors. By grounding one member of each of the twisted pairs, the lines carrying the digital signals are relatively isolated from each other.

The bus extender of the TS1 has been designed to allow the system to be interfaced to an SWTP 6800 computer system. This gives the TS1 access to the range of low-cost peripherals and memory boards of the SWTP system. In the author's system the SWTP computer is operated without its CPU board. That is, the SWTP acts purely as a passive system, merely increasing the number of peripherals which the TS1 microprocessor system can support.

The circuit diagram of the extender module is given in Fig. 6.53. This circuit is entirely conventional, but the following notes may help the reader.

(1) The address bus is buffered by two permanently enabled 74LS244 octal buffers.

(2) BA, $R/\overline{W}$, $\overline{RESET}$ are buffered by part of an 8T97 hex non-inverting buffer which is permanently enabled.

(3) ϕ_2 and VMA are buffered by part of an 8T98 inverting buffer which is permanently enabled. Data on these lines is inverted because the SS50 bus requires these signals to be active low. The definition of the SS50 bus is given in Table 6.23.

(4) Data bus buffering is provided by two quad bidirectional inverting bus drivers. These are DM8835s which have active-low receiver-enable and transmitter-enable inputs. The SS50 bus requires that the data lines $D_0 - D_7$ be active low. IC1, a 74LS138 3-line to 8-line decoder, divides the memory space into eight blocks of 8K. The decoder is enabled by VMA but not by ϕ_2. The outputs of the decoder may be connected to the respective inputs of a 74LS30 eight-input NAND gate. Unused inputs to the gate are pulled up to V_{cc} by the resistors of IC10. Whenever an address in the SWTP system is selected, the output of the NAND goes high (assuming the relevant DIL switch is closed). The output of the NAND gate is connected to the "B" address input of IC12, a 2-line to 4-line decoder. This decoder is enabled by ϕ_2. When the "B" input of IC12 is high and $\phi_2 = 1$, either the $\overline{Y_2}$ output or the $\overline{Y_3}$ output goes active-low depending on the state of the "A" input—the $R/\overline{W}$ signal. The $\overline{Y_2}$ and $\overline{Y_3}$ outputs of IC12 directly enable the data bus transmitters and receivers respectively.

(5) Not all the lines of the SS50 bus are required in this application. In particular the interrupt request lines and baud rates are redundant.

Table 6.23 The SS50 Bus

Pin number	*Signal*	*Description*
1 – 8	$\overline{D_0} - \overline{D_7}$	Active-low bidirectional data bus ($\overline{D_0}$ = pin 1, $\overline{D_7}$ = pin 8).
9 – 24	$A_0 - A_{15}$	Address bus (A_{15} = pin 9, A_0 = pin 24).
25 – 27	GND	The common ground return line
28 – 30	+8 V	The positive supply rail designed to drive on-board +5 V monolithic regulators
31	– 12 V	– 12 V rail (regulated) used for RS232C interfaces
32	+ 12 V	+ 12 V rail (regulated) used for RS232C interfaces
33	INDEX	Not used—an index plug prevents incorrect insertion of modules
34	$\overline{\text{M RESET}}$	An active-low input to a monostable which when triggered resets the system
35	$\overline{\text{NMI}}$	Non-maskable interrupt (negative-edge sensitive)
36	$\overline{\text{IRQ}}$	Interrupt request (active-low)
37	UD2	UD1 and UD2 are two user-defined lines
38	UD1	
39	$\overline{\phi_2}$	The logical complement of the ϕ_2 clock from the CPU module
40	$\overline{\text{VMA}}$	The logical complement of the valid memory address output from the CPU module
41	R/$\overline{\text{W}}$	Read/$\overline{\text{write}}$
42	$\overline{\text{RESET}}$	An active-low system reset from the CPU module which is triggered by a power-up condition or as a result of a pulse on the $\overline{\text{M RESET}}$ line
43	BA	Bus available which is normally low and goes high only when the CPU is halted
44	ϕ_1	The ϕ_1 clock
45	$\overline{\text{HALT}}$	An active-low input to the CPU module which when triggered halts the CPU. When $\overline{\text{HALT}}$ is active and BA is high, the address, data buses and R/$\overline{\text{W}}$ line are floated
46 – 50	Baud rates	Pins 46 – 50 provide baud rates of 110, 150, 300, 600 and 1200 from the CPU module. A supreme waste of pins!

In some ways the 6800 bus is relatively immune from the effects of reflections and cross talk. This is because the address lines, R/$\overline{W}$, and VMA change when ϕ_2 is low and have ample time to settle down before ϕ_2 goes high. For both read and write cycles the first few nanoseconds of the time for which the data from the CPU or the memory is valid may suffer from noise without affecting the operation of the CPU. It is really at the negative-going transition of ϕ_2 that the "action" takes place. Consequently, the ϕ_2 line (i.e. $\overline{\phi_2}$ in this arrangement) should be separated from its neighbors by grounded lines.

Some authorities suggest that resistors in the region of 470 Ω should be introduced in series with the ribbon cable conductors so that the rise times of pulses are severely reduced. By "rounding the edges" of pulses in this way the level of cross talk is diminished at the cost of the noise immunity of the bus receivers, because of the static voltage drop across these series resistors. Moreover, these resistors also damp any oscillation caused by reflections.

Terminating the TS1 Bus

The resistor networks used to terminate the TS1 bus have been placed on the same module as the bus extender circuitry, as this module has plenty of free space. Three 16-pin dual in-line packages, each containing 14 pairs of 330 Ω and 390 Ω resistors provide the necessary termination to the address, data, BA, R/$\overline{W}$, VMA, ϕ_2TTL, MClk, $2f_c$, DMAG, and $\overline{RESET}$ lines. Note that the chosen termination resistors are 330 Ω to V_{cc} and 390 Ω to ground, rather than 360 Ω and 390 Ω respectively as suggested earlier. This slight change in one of the resistors was made because Beckman Ltd who supplied the terminator packs do not produce a 360 Ω/390 Ω network. Figure 6.54 gives the circuit diagram of the terminator network applied to the TS1 bus.

When the behavior of one of the address bus lines is examined on an oscilloscope in both an unterminated and a terminated state, it is immediately apparent that the effect of termination is to reduce noise on the bus—in particular overshoots and undershoots are much reduced. A slight but undesired effect of termination is to raise the logical zero level of signals on the bus. This reduced the low-level noise margin of the signals. Another, and more useful, effect of termination is to define the signal level on any bus line when its drive is floated. For example, if the address bus drivers are turned off, and the address bus floated, then the termination network clamps the bus at approximately 2.7 V, which is interpreted by any TTL-compatible receivers as a logical 1.

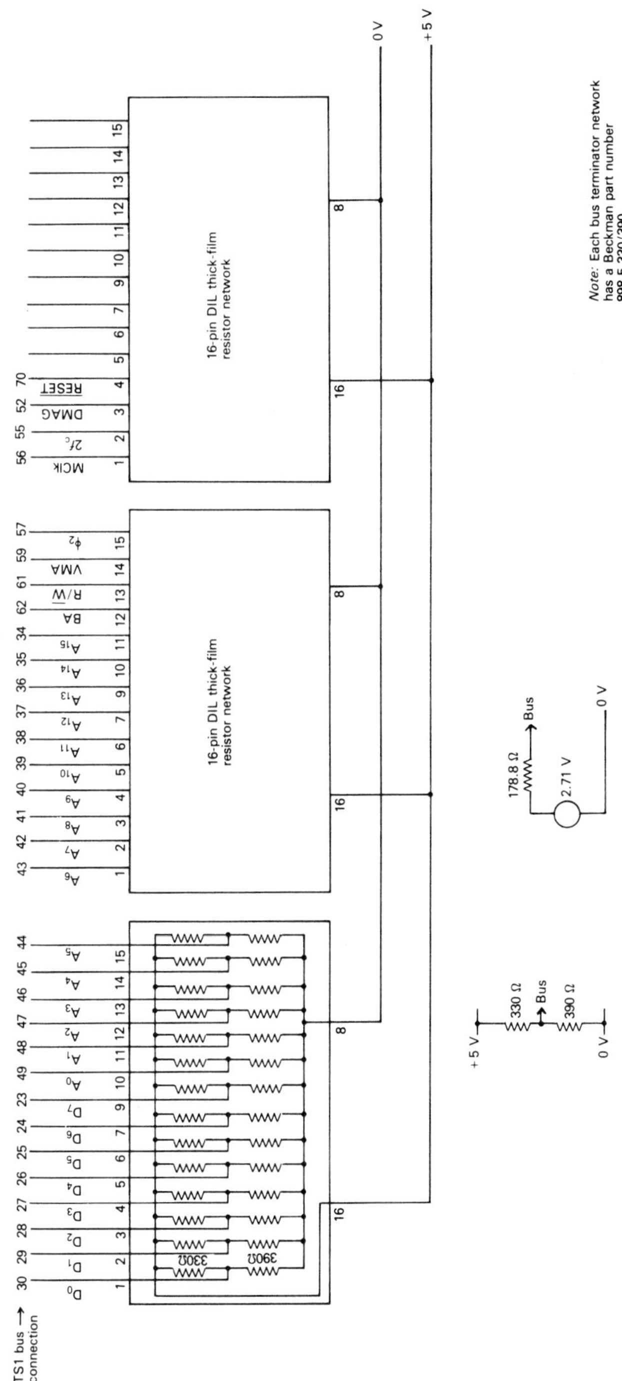

Note: Each bus terminator network has a Beckman part number 898-5 330/390.

Fig. 6.54 The TS1 bus terminator network

6.7 DIGITAL-TO-ANALOG CONVERSION

Introduction

Before describing the operation of analog-to-digital and digital-to-analog convertors, it is necessary to define the terms digital and analog, and to point out the fundamental difference between digital and analog systems. Signals may be classified as either digital or analog, and the distinction between these classes of signal may be illustrated by the following two examples.

A microphone is a device whose output, due to someone speaking into it, varies continuously over some arbitrary but finite amplitude range, depending on the loudness of the speech and the physical characteristics of the microphone. The instantaneous amplitude of the signal from the microphone can have any value within this range which is the characteristic of an analog signal. On the other hand, the electrical signal from a photoelectric cell corresponding to information represented as a pattern of holes along a paper tape can have only two amplitude levels: one representing a hole and the other representing the absence of a hole. Such a signal is known as a digital signal. An analog signal is one which can take any one of an infinite number of different values, while a digital signal may take only one of a set of discrete values.

Analog signals are generally continuous functions of time. The speech signal in the above example is a typical analog signal. The circuitry which processes analog signals is called analog circuitry and its most important feature is that it operates on continuous signals. Digital signals are always discrete in time. In the above example, the signal from the paper tape reader consists of a series of discrete pulses. The most important feature of a digital system is that it operates on discrete signals.

Analog signal-processing systems seek to preserve the nature or shape of the information-carrying signal. This criterion often requires that the operations carried out on the analog signal be linear. Therefore, one of the chief figures of merit of an analog system is its linearity or fidelity. A digital system operates on information in the form of symbols (e.g. the dots and dashes of Morse code). The most important property of a digital system is that as long as it can distinguish between the different symbols of which the information is composed, even moderate amounts of distortion and noise may be tolerated. The growing popularity of digital systems is partially due to the fact that digital information is made up of symbols chosen from an alphabet (0 or 1), and an error occurs only when one symbol is distorted so greatly that it is interpreted as a different symbol.

In many applications of a microprocessor the input is received in digital form, processed digitally, and the result displayed in digital form. The most obvious example of this is the combination of a keyboard, microprocessor system, and a printer. Many modern applications of the microprocessor and digital electronics in general involve the conversion of analog quantities into digital signals for processing by a microprocessor, and then the conversion of the digital results into analog signals.

A typical example of such a process may occur in an oil refinery. Suppose in a fractionating column the yield of a given fraction must be optimized. A transducer (i.e., a device which converts a physical property such as pressure, temperature or wind velocity into an electrical signal) measures the yield of the required product from one of its physical properties and produces a voltage proportional to the yield. An analog-to-digital convertor periodically transforms this voltage into a digital signal which is read by the microprocessor. The microprocessor can now perform calculations on the results from the yield-measuring device to compute the optimum values of control parameters (temperatures, pressure, rate of flow) for the fractionating column. These parameters are fed, in digital form, to a digital-to-analog convertor which generates the necessary control signals.

Before proceeding to the description of actual digital-to-analog (D/A) and analog-to-digital (A/D) convertors it is instructive to examine some of the terminology associated with these devices, and a little of the theoretical basis of A/D and D/A conversion. It has been stated above that a digital signal is discrete in both time and amplitude. Two obvious questions follow from this statement. Firstly how often do we need to sample an analog signal, and secondly, how many bits do we need to represent the analog signal?

The A/D convertor is often employed as part of an arrangement called a data-acquisition system. Figure 6.55 gives the block diagram of such an arrangement. The input to the system is a physical variable (temperature, pressure, humidity, weight, acceleration) and is coupled to a transducer which transforms it into a varying voltage. The function of the amplifier is to bring the range of the voltage up to a level capable of operating the rest of the system. The output of most transducers is exceedingly small—often in the microvolt or millivolt range. The purpose of the filter is to remove extraneous signals from the wanted signals. Such unwanted signals are noise components and frequencies outside the range of interest.

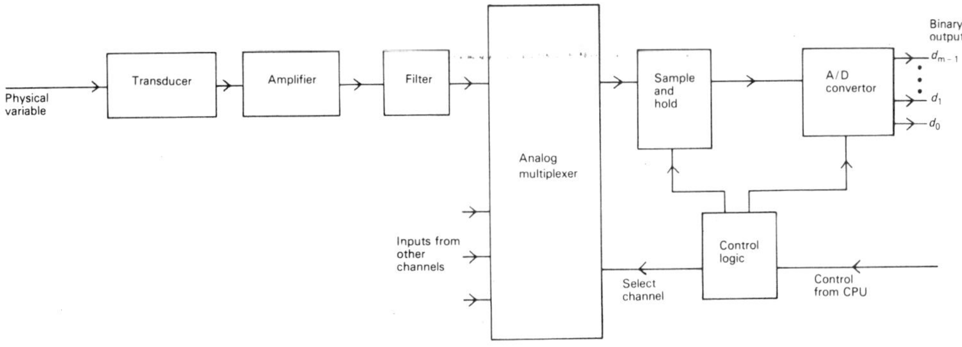

Fig. 6.55 The data acquisition system

The function of the analog multiplexer is to allow one A/D convertor to operate with several analog channels. The computer controlling the data-acquisition process selects which of the analog inputs is to be coupled to the A/D convertor. The output of the multiplexer is fed to a sample-and-hold circuit which samples the output of the multiplexer at some specific time (determined by the computer) and holds the signal constant until the analog-to-digital convertor has carried out its conversion. In many simple applications the full complexity of the system of Fig. 6.55 is not required.

Quantizing a Signal

To answer the question of the number of bits required to satisfactorily represent an analog signal, it is necessary to consider a little quantization theory. Figure 6.56 shows the operation of a simple, ideal, three-bit analog-to-digital convertor. Suppose that the output of the A/D convertor is a natural binary code from 000 to 111, and that the analog input is a voltage in the range 0 – 7.0 V. Now consider the effect of applying a linear ramp input to this convertor. Initially the ramp is at zero and the output is 000. As the ramp input rises the output remains at 000 until the input passes through 0.5 V, at which point the output jumps to 001. The output remains at 001 until the input passes through 1.5 V. Clearly, for each 1 V change in the input the output changes by one unit.

A graph of the error between the input and the voltage represented by the binary code is given below the graph of the transfer function of the convertor in Fig. 6.56. This graph is a sawtooth which oscillates between $+Q/2$ and $-Q/2$, where Q is the distance between decision levels. This error is known as the quantization error.

For an A/D convertor, Q represents the smallest analog difference that the convertor can resolve. The resolution of an A/D convertor is often expressed (indirectly) by the number of bits in the binary code. Table 6.24 gives the basic characteristics of A/D convertors from 4 to 16 bits. These figures are the ideal or optimum results, as any real A/D convertors suffers from a number of imperfections (e.g. non-linearity, drift, offset error). The performance of an A/D convertor is often described in terms of the error signal, and Fig. 6.57 illustrates how the performance of the A/D convertor may be measured. The D/A convertor should, of course, be very much better than the A/D convertor if its contribution to the error signal is to be neglected.

The quantization noise from an A/D convertor is inherent in the conversion process and cannot be reduced or eliminated. All that can be done is to increase the resolution of the convertor to reduce the quantization noise to an acceptable value. The signal-to-noise (S/N) ratio of an n-bit convertor is the ratio of the peak-to-peak signal to the r.m.s. noise, and is given by

$$\text{S/N (in dB)} = 10 \log_{10} \left[\frac{2^n Q}{Q\sqrt{12}} \right]^2 = 6.02\, n + 10.8.$$

The S/N ratio increases by approximately 6 dB for each additional bit of resolution.

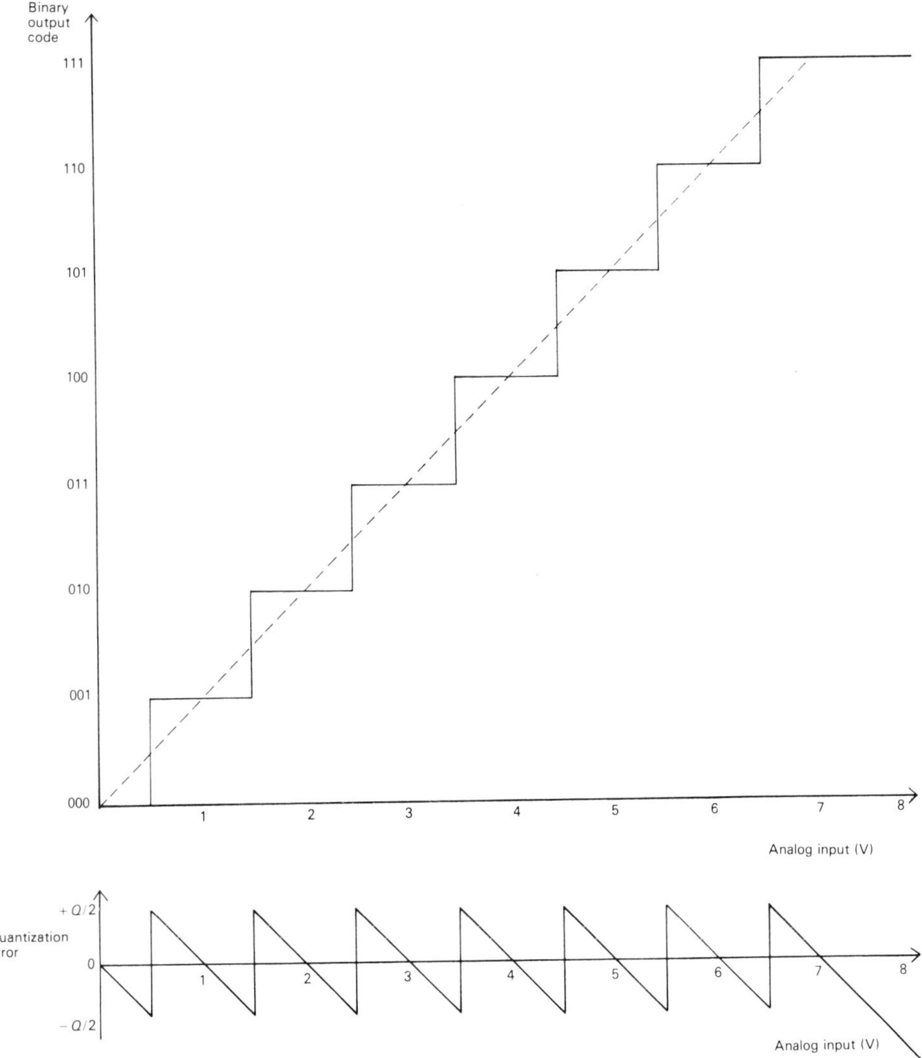

Fig. 6.56 The idealized transfer function of a 3-bit A/D convertor

This formula is due to Zuch (see Bibliography). Other authors get slightly different values for the offset (10.8 dB) as the calculation of the S/N ratio is subject to a number of assumptions. From Table 6.24 it can be seen that an 8-bit D/A convertor has a signal-to-noise ratio similar to some of the low-quality audio equipment, and a 10-bit convertor approaches the S/N ratio of high-fidelity equipment.

The dynamic range of a D/A convertor is given by the ratio of the full-scale range (FSR) to Q. The dynamic range in dB $= 20 \log_{10} 2^n = 20n \log_{10} 2 = 6.02n$.

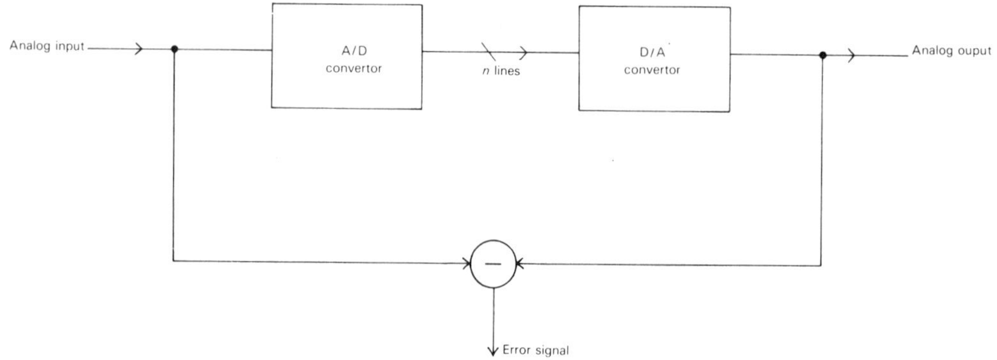

Fig. 6.57 The measurement of quantization noise

Once more, Table 6.24 illustrates than an 8-bit convertor gives barely acceptable results for audio work, but a 10- or 12-bit convertor is capable of high-fidelity performance.

Table 6.24 The Characteristics of A/D Convertors

Resolution bits n	*States 2^n*	*Binary weight 2^{-n}*	*Q for 10 V FS*	*S/N ratio (dB)*	*Dynamic range (dB)*
4	16	0.062 5	0.625 V	34.9	24.1
6	64	0.015 6	0.156 V	46.9	36.1
8	256	0.003 91	39.1 mV	58.9	48.2
10	1 024	0.000 977	9.76 mV	71.0	60.2
12	4 096	0.000 244	2.44 mV	83.0	72.2
14	16 384	0.000 061 0	610 μV	95.1	84.3
16	65 536	0.000 015 3	153 μV	107.1	96.3

Sampling a Signal

A/D convertors are not able to perform their conversions instantaneously and therefore the maximum rate at which a signal may be sampled is determined by the technology of the A/D convertor. Consequently, before designing (or buying) a convertor it is necessary to find out how often we need to sample the input. Intuitively, one would expect the answer to depend on how fast the input is changing. For example, one would measure the temperature of a swimming pool (say) hourly because the thermal inertia of the water does not permit sudden changes.

Fortunately, there is a simple rule (the sampling theorem) which states that a continuous signal may be completely recovered from a sampled signal provided that the sampling rate is at least twice that of the highest frequency component of the signal, including noise. Thus, if the input to an A/D convertor has a maximum frequency component of f_m Hz, the input must be sampled at least every $1/2f_m$ seconds. Note that even if we are not interested in frequencies as high as f_m, the interval between samples must still be less than $1/2f_m$.

If a signal, whose maximum frequency component is f_m, is sampled at less than $1/2f_m$ then some of the high-frequency components in the signal are folded back into the spectrum of the wanted signal. Once this "frequency folding" effect has occurred there is no way in which the original, wanted, signal may be recovered. To avoid this effect, the input must either be sampled at the appropriate rate or a filter used to remove unwanted high-frequency components from the input. Note that, unless the actual process of analog-to-digital conversion is very fast compared to the rate of change of the signal, a "sample-and-hold" amplifier must be used to hold the signal constant while it is being digitized.

The Digital-to-analog Convertor

The conversion of digital quantities to analog signals is dealt with first if for no other reason that the fact that D/A convertors are generally simpler and cheaper than the corresponding A/D convertors. One of the most easily understood D/A convertors is shown in Fig. 6.58. The current flowing into the inverting terminal of the operational amplifier is the linear sum of the currents flowing through each of the individual resistors. As each of the resistors can be connected to ground or to a reference voltage V_{ref}, the current flowing through the resistor is either zero or $V_{ref}/2^iR$, where $i=0,1,2,\ldots,\ n-1$. Thus by closing the appropriate switches (a 1 state) or opening them (a 0 state) the output of the operational amplifier is given by

$$V_o = -2\frac{V_{ref}}{R}R_f\left[b_{n-1}2^{-1} + b_{n-2}2^{-1} + \cdots + b_0 2^{-n}\right],$$

where b_i represents the state of the ith switch.

In a practical arrangement of Fig. 6.58 the switches are transistors which may be put into a conducting or a non-conducting state. This type of D/A convertor has the advantage of simplicity and speed but is not practical in applications where a high order of precision is required. It is relatively easy to produce matched sets of close-tolerance resistors, but it is difficult to produce accurate resistors over a very wide range of values. For example, if in a 12-bit D/A convertor the smallest resistor is 1000 Ω, then the largest value resistor must be $2^{12}\times 1000 = 4\ 096\ 000\ \Omega$.

A much better and more popular form of D/A convertor is described in Fig. 6.59. In this arrangement a network of matched resistors forms an $R-2R$ ladder. The shunt resitors ($2R$) may be switched between a voltage reference source or ground. The operation of the ladder network is based on the fact that as current flows down the ladder, from left to right, it is divided at each junction into two equal parts, one flowing down the ladder and one down the shunt resistor. As the network is linear, the output current is the sum of all the currents from the shunt resitors, which are binary-weighted, with the LSB at the left (of Fig. 6.59) and the

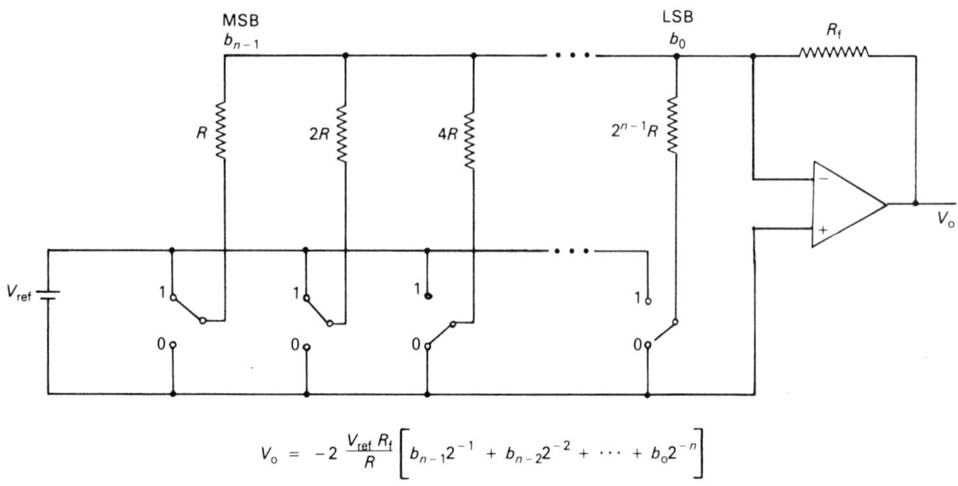

$$V_o = -2\frac{V_{ref}R_f}{R}\left[b_{n-1}2^{-1} + b_{n-2}2^{-2} + \cdots + b_o2^{-n}\right]$$

Fig. 6.58 The D/A convertor with binary weighted resistors

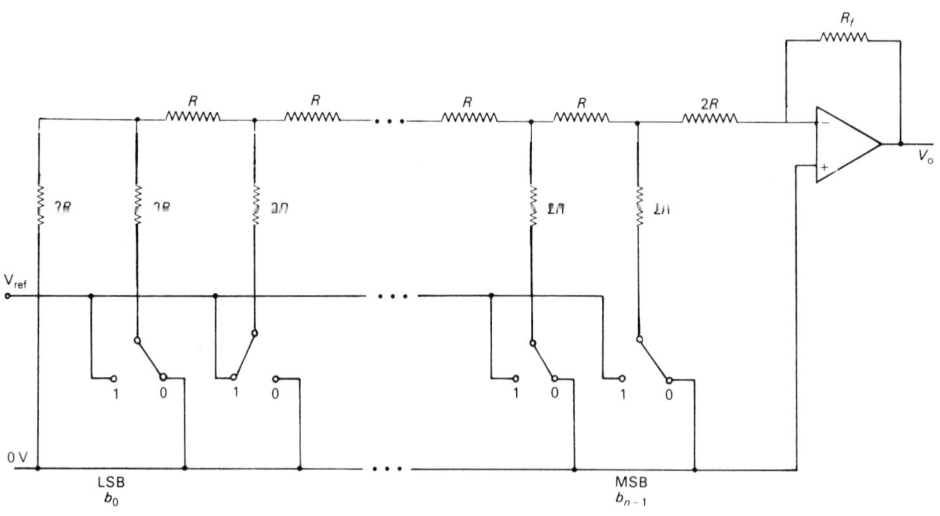

Fig. 6.59 The D/A convertor with an R – 2R network

MSB at the right. The output current from the ladder is fed into an operational amplifier to produce a suitable voltage output.

The advantages of the $R-2R$ type of D/A convertor are threefold:

(1) All resistors have a value of R or $2R$, resulting in easy matching and accurate temperature tracking. It is not the absolute values of the resistors that determine the accuracy of the convertor but their ratios.
(2) By selecting a relatively low value for R, the impedance of the network can be kept low and the response time of the device optimized.
(3) The output amplifier always sees a constant resistance value at its input.

Practical D/A convertors are available in a wide range of speeds and accuracies. Some convertors have an internal reference voltage while others require an external reference. The latter type of device is sometimes called a multiplying convertor because the analog output is proportional to the reference input voltage times the binary weighting of the switches. Many convertors do not include an output amplifier, leaving the user free to design his own output stage.

6.7.1 A Digital-to-analog Convertor Using the ZN425

There is a wide range of 8-bit digital-to-analog convertors suitable for use in a microprocessor system. A typical device is the Ferranti ZN425, which can also operate as an analog-to-digital convertor although this facility is not required in this application. Figure 6.60 gives the block diagram of the internal arrangement of the ZN425, chosen because of its single +5 V power-supply requirement, ease of interfacing with a microprocessor, and low cost.

The ZN425 is a monolithic 8-bit digital-to-analog convertor containing an $R-2R$ ladder network with precision bipolar switches, and an internal 2.5 V reference. The internal reference supply has a nominal output of 2.55 V±0.15 V, and a temperature coefficient of 40 parts per million/°C. It is possible to use an external reference with this chip by injecting the external V_{ref} into pin 16, otherwise pins 15 and 16 should be connected together.

A logic-input switch is incorporated on the ZNA425 so that the precision switches may be controlled from external inputs, (i.e. d_0-d_7) or from the outputs of an internal binary counter. In operation as a D/A convertor the "select input" (pin 2) is connected to ground to enable the external inputs.

The circuit diagram of the interface between the TS1 microprocessor system and two ZNA425s is given in Fig. 6.61. IC17 is a memory-mapped PIA located at address EC10. In this application, the PIA is configured as two eight-bit output ports and the four control lines CA1, CA2, CB1 and CB2 are not used. Similarly, the interrupt request outputs of the PIA ($\overline{\text{IRQA}}$, $\overline{\text{IRQB}}$) are also redundant. Of course, in some applications the designer may wish to put out an analog voltage, process it in an analog system and then, if necessary, generate an interrupt via one of the PIA's control inputs.

The operation of the ZN425 D/A convertor is straightforward. The reference

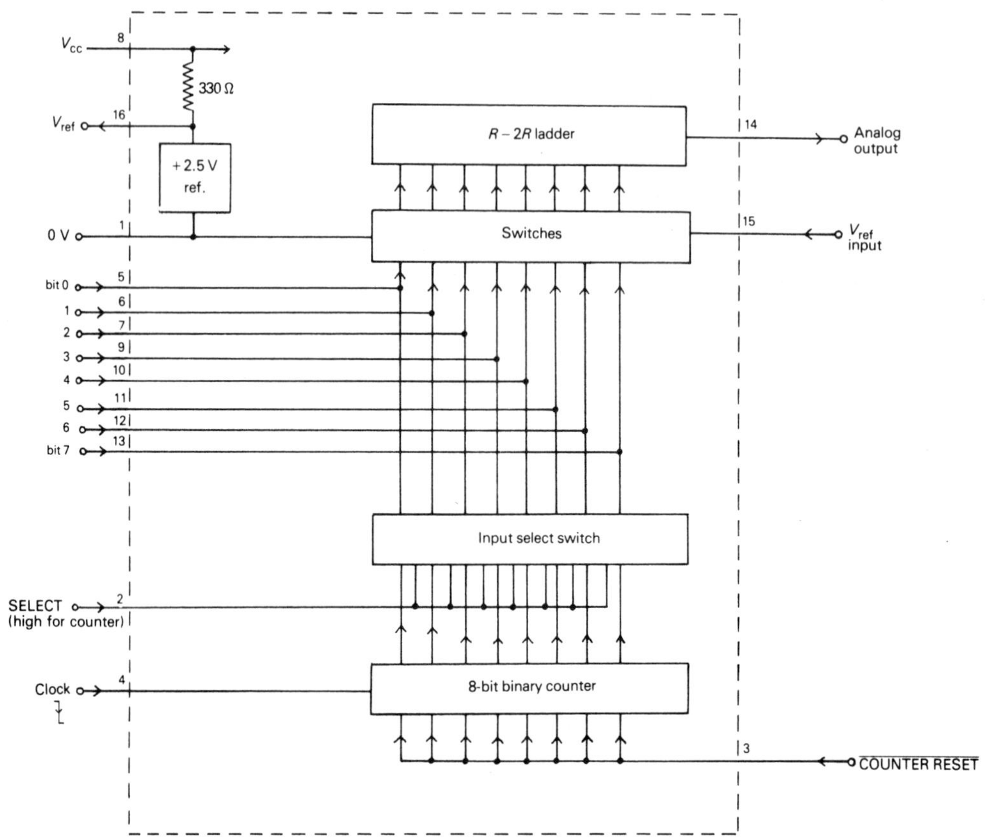

Fig. 6.60 The internal arrangement of the ZN425E (Note: When the ZN425E is operated as a D/A convertor it is necessary to connect the "select" pin to a logical zero. In this case the clock input and the $\overline{\text{COUNTER RESET}}$ pins are redundant and are wired to ground.)

voltage output (pin 16) is connected to the reference voltage input (pin 15), and the reference voltage is decoupled by a 0.22 μF capacitor connected to ground. The SELECT input of the ZN425 is connected to ground so that the D/A convertor is always converting the data from the PIA into an analog output on pin 14. The analog output is a signal in the range 8 mV (the zero level offset) to approximately 2.550 V, and has a source resistance of 10 kΩ. This output is brought to a DIN connector on the front panel of the TS1's CPU module.

Ferranti publish the circuit of a suitable buffer for their ZN425 DAC. This circuit is given in the dotted lines of Fig. 6.61. A ZN424P operational amplifier with a +5 and –5 V power supply removes the input offset of the analog output of the

ZN425, and allows the full-scale output to be set as desired. To calibrate the amplifier the following procedure should be carried out:

(1) Set all the ZN425's input bits to zero and adjust the 1 MΩ (set zero) potentiometer until $V_{out} = 0.000$ V.
(2) Set all the ZN425's input bits to one and adjust the 5 kΩ (set FSD) potentiometer until V_{out} = nominal full scale reading minus one LSB.
(3) Repeat steps 1 and 2.

The purpose of providing two outputs and calling them *X* and *Y* is to enable the TS1 microprocessor system to control the *X* and *Y* deflections on a cathode-ray tube. Most oscilloscopes have an external *X* input allowing them to be operated as $X-Y$ plotters. When data is displayed on a CRT in this way, the display must be continuously updated (refreshed) at a rate of at least 50 Hz if objectionable flicker is to be avoided.

A simple example of the use of the dual channel D/A convertor of Fig. 6.61 is given below. It is assumed that the analog outputs are connected to the *X* and *Y* inputs of an oscilloscope.

```
TABLE    EQU $1000              start of data table
TABEND   EQU $2000              end of data table
XPIAD    EQU $EC10              X-output data register
XPIAC    EQU $EC11              X-output control register
YPIAD    EQU $EC12              Y-output data register
YPIAC    EQU $EC13              Y-output control register
*        assume all PIA registers initially cleared (after a reset)
         LDA  A  #$FF           load A with all ones
         STA  A  XPIAD          set up XPIAD as outputs
         STA  A  YPIAD          set up YPIAD as outputs
         LDA  A  #4             set bit 2 high for data register access
         STA  A  XPIAC          set up XPIAC control register
         STA  A  YPIAC          set up YPIAC control register
*
LOOP     LDX     #TABLE         point to start of data table
LOOP1    LDA  A  0,X            pick up X value
         STA  A  XPIAD          give it to the X-axis DAC
         INX                    point to next value (i.e. Y value)
         LDA  A  0,X            pick up Y value
         STA  A  YPIAD          give it to the Y-axis DAC
         INX                    point to next pair of values
         CPX     #TABEND        end of table?
         BNE     LOOP1          if not end, display next point
         BRA     LOOP           start again at top of the table.
```

Note that this program involves a continuous loop which can be exited only by forcing an interrupt or a reset.

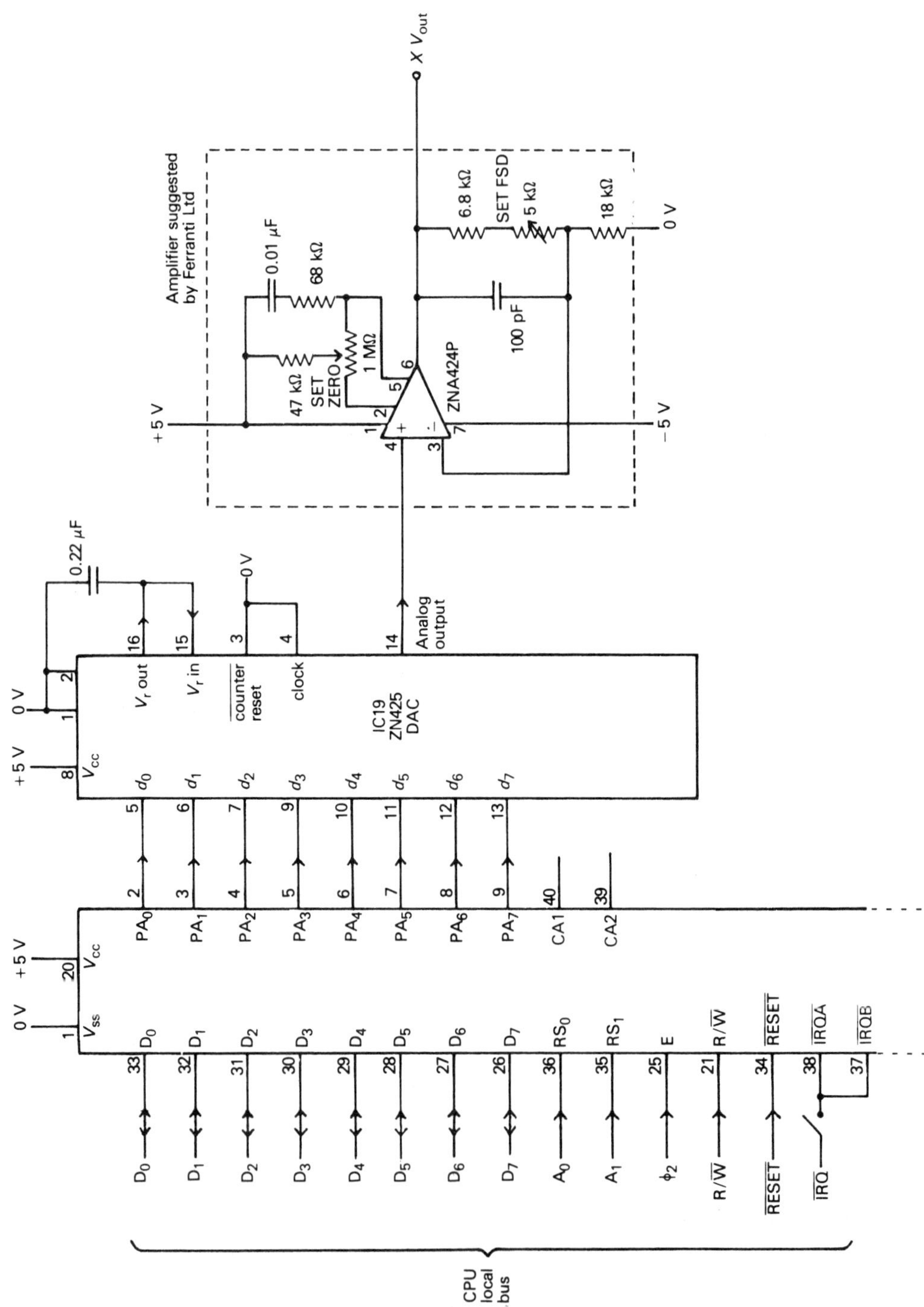
X V_{out}
Amplifier suggested
by Ferranti Ltd
0.01 μF
68 kΩ
6.8 kΩ
SET FSD
5 kΩ
18 kΩ
0 V
1 MΩ
47 kΩ
SET
ZERO
100 pF
ZNA424P
+5 V
−5 V
0.22 μF
0 V
+5 V
V_{cc}
V_r out
V_r in
counter
reset
clock
Analog
output
IC19
ZN425
DAC
d_0 d_1 d_2 d_3 d_4 d_5 d_6 d_7
PA_0 PA_1 PA_2 PA_3 PA_4 PA_5 PA_6 PA_7
CA1
CA2
V_{ss}
D_0 D_1 D_2 D_3 D_4 D_5 D_6 D_7
RS_0 RS_1
E
R/$\overline{W}$
$\overline{RESET}$
$\overline{IRQA}$
$\overline{IRQB}$
A_0 A_1
ϕ_2
$\overline{IRQ}$
CPU
local
bus

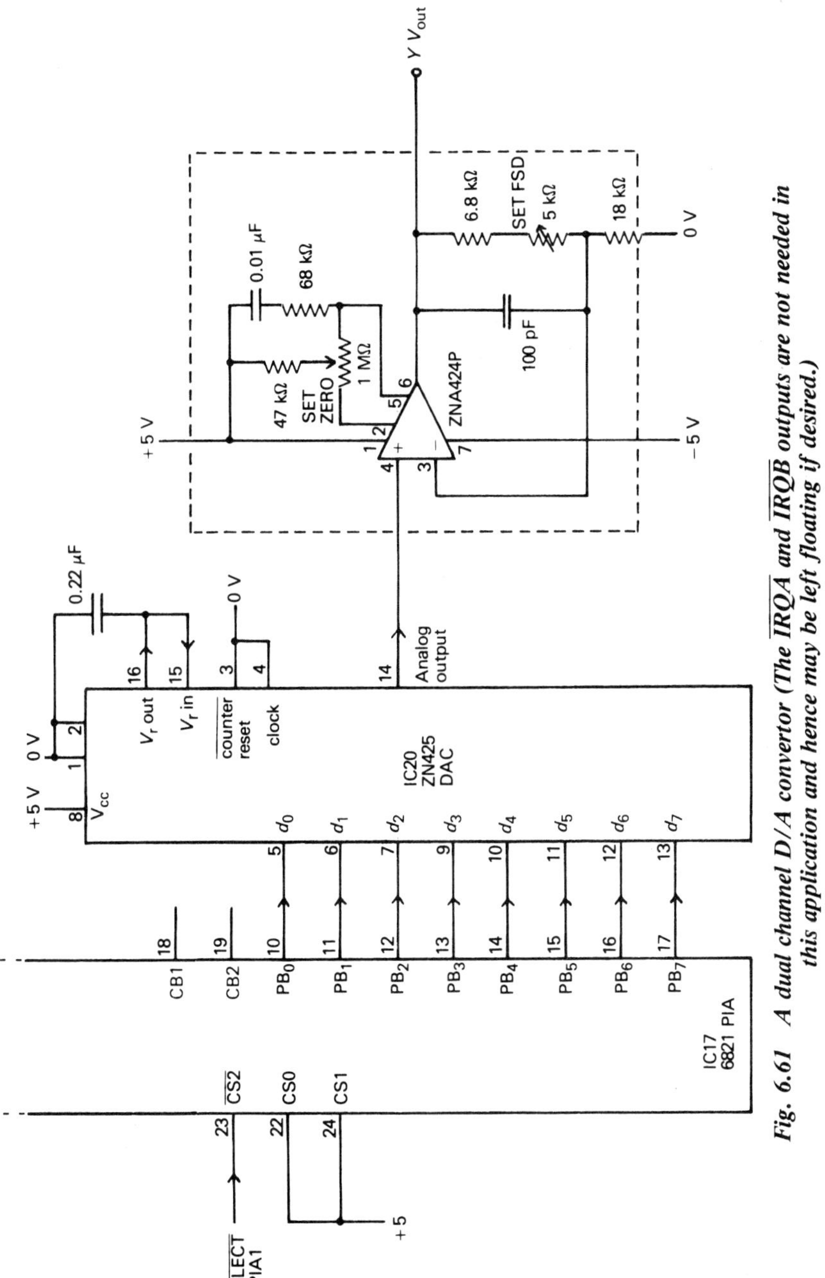

Fig. 6.61 A dual channel D/A convertor (The $\overline{IRQA}$ and $\overline{IRQB}$ outputs are not needed in this application and hence may be left floating if desired.)

6.8 ANALOG-TO-DIGITAL CONVERSION

Analog signals may be converted to digital form by one of several different processes. Analog-to-digital conversion techniques are generally more complex than those employed in D/A convertors of an equivalent resolution. Three types of A/D convertor described in this section are the parallel convertor, the feedback convertor, and the integrating convertor.

The Parallel Analog-to-digital Convertor

The parallel, or flash, A/D convertor is the fastest of all A/D convertors and operates by simultaneously comparing the analog input with $2^n - 1$ equally spaced reference voltages. Figure 6.62 gives the block diagram of TRW's TDC1014J 6-bit A/D convertor. The key to the operation of the TDC1014J is 63 high-speed differential comparators whose output depends on the sign of the difference between two analog voltages at their input. Each of the comparators has an input which is equal to the analog signal to be converted to binary, and an input obtained from a resistive divider. For any given analog input, the outputs of the comparators whose reference input is above that of the unknown analog input are logically zero, while the outputs of the comparators whose reference input is below that of the unknown analog input are logically one. The 63-input encoder converts the 63 binary inputs into a 6-bit code which forms the required digital output. The exclusive-OR networks and their control inputs are designed to enable this A/D convertor to operate with a natural binary or a 2s complement output.

The parallel A/D convertor is very fast—the TDC1014J can digitize an analog signal at up to 30 million samples per second. This phenomenal conversion rate is mandatory in the world of real-time signal processing in applications such as radar data processing and image processing. Unfortunately the price of parallel convertors reflects their very high performance. Furthermore it is difficult to design very high resolution parallel A/D convertors because the number of comparators doubles for each additional bit of resolution.

The Feedback Analog-to-digital Convertor

The feedback convertor transforms an analog signal into digital form indirectly by means of a D/A convertor. Figure 6.63 illustrates the basic principle of this type of A/D convertor. The analog signal is applied to the non-inverting input of an operational amplifier, and a locally generated analog voltage from a D/A convertor is applied to the inverting input. The output of the op-amp corresponds to an error signal and is employed by a digital network to adjust the input of the D/A convertor in such a way as to reduce the error signal from the amplifier. When the output of the op-amp is zero, or near to zero, the digital signal at the input to the D/A convertor is the required value of the analog input.

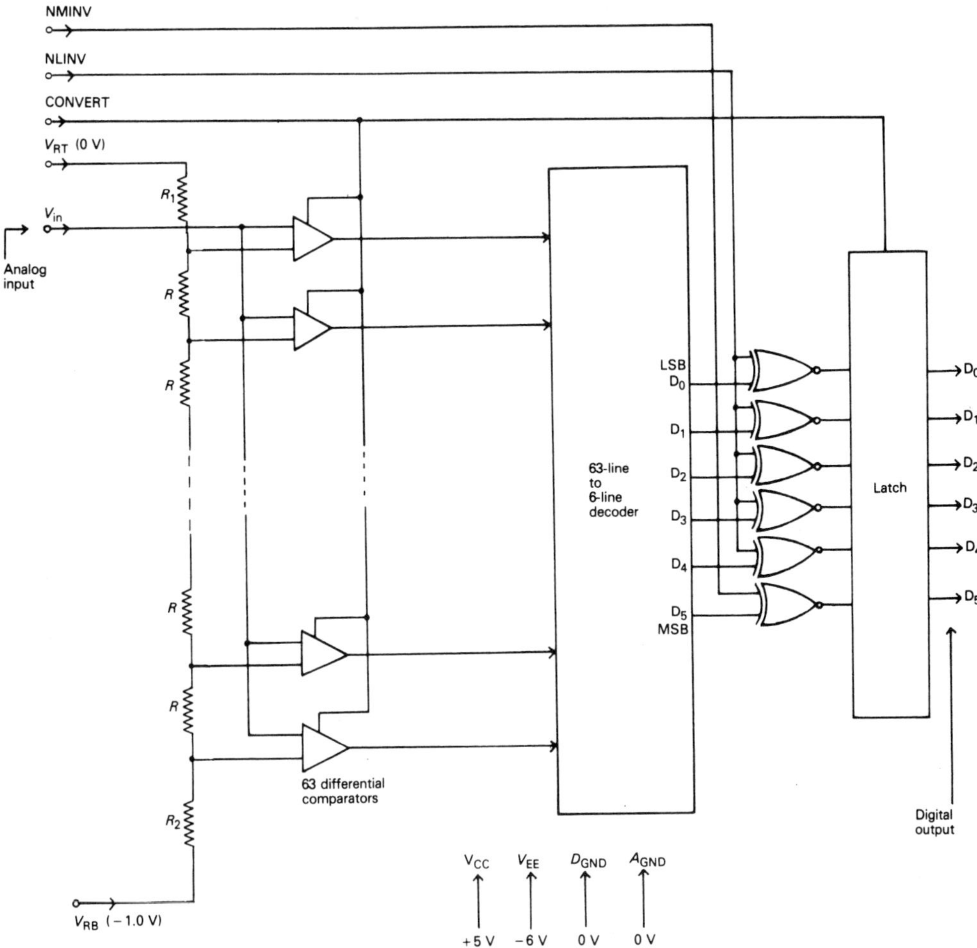

Note:

NMINV	NLINV	OUTPUT
1	1	Binary true
0	0	Binary inverted
0	1	2s complement true
1	0	2s complement inverted

Fig. 6.62 The TDC1014J Parallel A/D convertor

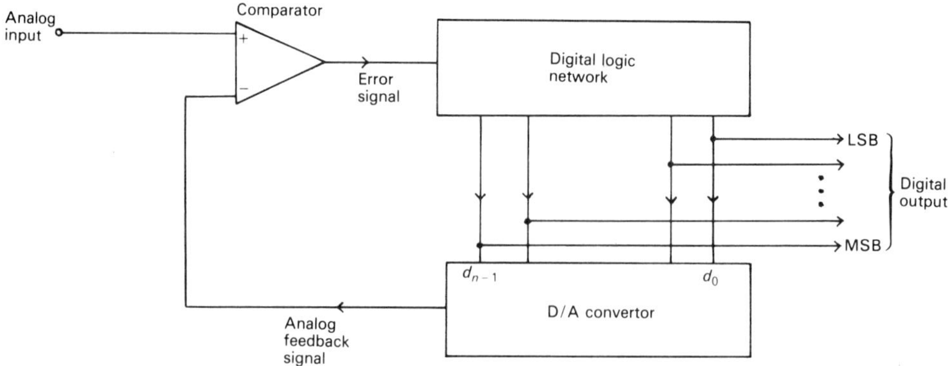

Fig. 6.63 The basic feedback A/D convertor

The simplest form of feedback A/D convertor is the ramp convertor in which the digital logic circuit controlling the D/A convertor is nothing more than a binary counter. At the start of a conversion the counter is set to zero. To effect a conversion the counter is clocked, resulting in a linearly rising ramp voltage from the D/A convertor. When this voltage is equivalent to or greater than the analog input, the counter is stopped and its contents read to give the required digital output. The ZN425 described in the last section contains an internal counter and needs only a clock and comparator to act as an A/D convertor. This type of A/D convertor is very cheap but is relatively slow, as the output must always be reached by stepping from zero to the final value in steps of the smallest unit. Intuitively, it would seem reasonable to take large steps early in the conversion process and then to reduce the step size as the conversion proceeds.

Such an A/D convertor is known as a successive-approximation convertor, and is able to perform a conversion in no more than n iterations, where n is the number of bits in the digital output. At the start of a conversion the digital logic (of Fig. 6.63) sets the MSB of the D/A convertor to 1, and the analog output is compared with the unknown analog input by the comparator. If the analog input is greater than half the full scale output of the D/A convertor, the MSB is retained at 1, otherwise it is switched off. On the second iteration the second most significant bit is set to one and retained at one if the D/A convertor output is less than the analog input, or cleared if it is not. This process is repeated until the LSB of the D/A convertor has been set and then retained or cleared. After the LSB has been dealt with in this way, the process is at an end and the result may be read. Figure 6.64 shows how a 4-bit successive-approximation A/D convertor, with a full scale range of 1.0 V, handles an input of 0.6400 V.

Practical successive-approximation A/D convertors may be bought off-the-shelf, implemented in software, or implemented in hardware. The A/D convertor to be described later in this section is, in fact, a single-chip successive-approximation A/D convertor with a 16-channel analog input. To implement a successive-

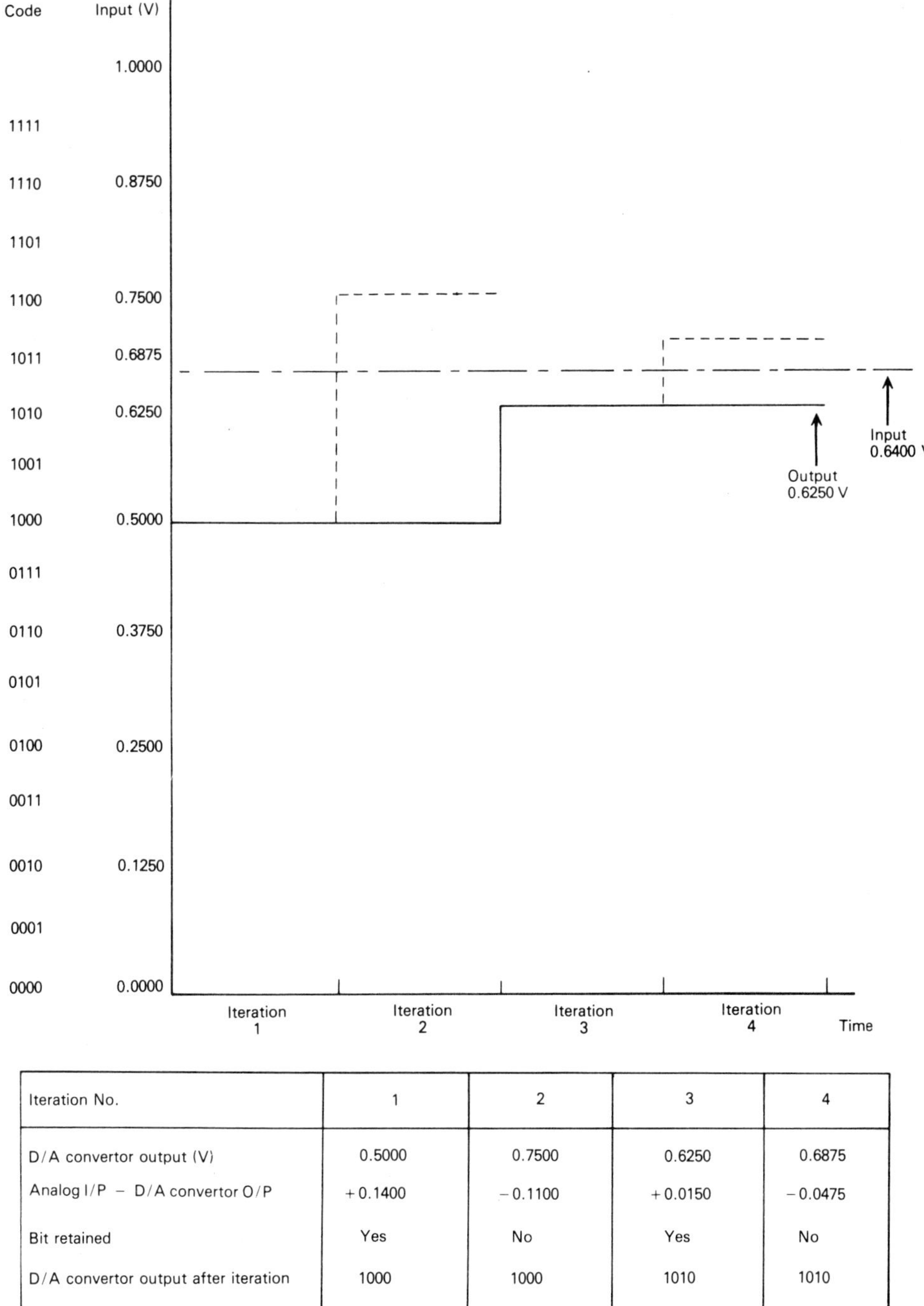

Iteration No.	1	2	3	4
D/A convertor output (V)	0.5000	0.7500	0.6250	0.6875
Analog I/P − D/A convertor O/P	+0.1400	−0.1100	+0.0150	−0.0475
Bit retained	Yes	No	Yes	No
D/A convertor output after iteration	1000	1000	1010	1010

Fig. 6.64 The operation of a 4-bit successive-approximation A/D convertor

approximation A/D convertor in software, no more than a D/A convertor and a comparator are required. As an example consider the arrangement of Fig. 6.61. The A-side of the PIA, at memory locations EC10 and EC11, forms the D/A convertor in the feedback loop. Figure 6.65 illustrates the additional logic necessary to convert the D/A convertor into a successive-approximation A/D convertor. The output of the D/A convertor (IC19) is compared with the unknown analog input in a comparator and causes a positive transition on the PIA's CA1 control input if the unknown input is greater than that from the D/A convertor. Note that the PIA can be programmed to set its IRQA1 flag on a positive transition of CA1 without generating an interrupt request to the CPU by setting control register bits CRA_1 and CRA_0 to 1 and 0, respectively. The program to carry out the conversion is given in Table 6.25.

The hardware approach to successive-approximation D/A convertors requires the use of a successive-approximation register (SAR) which replaces the digital logic section in Fig. 6.63. The SAR automatically performs the bit-shifting and testing functions required in this approach to analog-to-digital conversion.

Successive-approximation A/D convertors are very popular on account of their high speed (in the region of 100 000 conversions/s, allowing signals with a bandwidth of up to 50 kHz to be sampled), their moderate cost, and their reasonable accuracy.

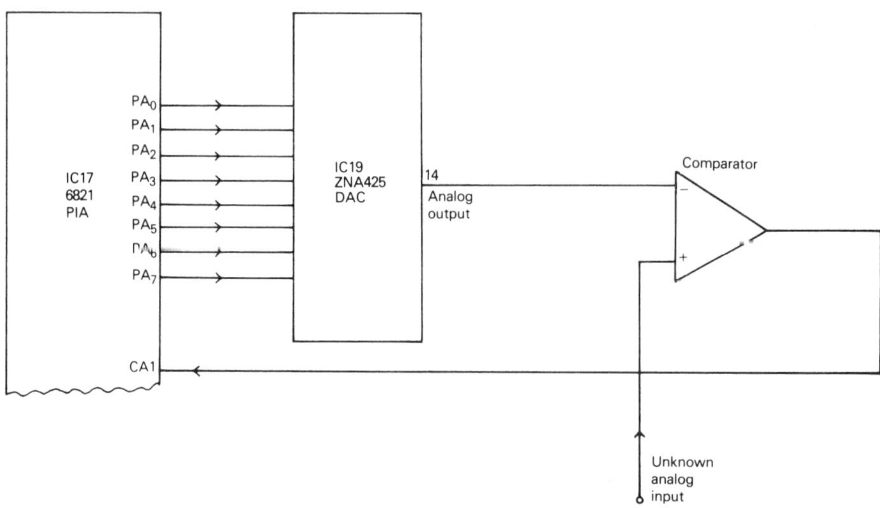

Fig. 6.65 The successive-approximation A/D convertor controlled by software

Table 6.25 Software-Controlled Successive-approximation Analog-to-digital Conversion

```
PIAD    EQU      $EC10    PIA data/DDR
PIAC    EQU      $EC11    PIA control/status
        ORG      $0000
        CLR   A
        STA   A  PIAC     select DDR
        LDA   A  #$FF
        STA   A  PAID     set up side A as output port
        LDA   A  #$06     select data reg and set IRQ1 on positive trans. of CA1
        STA   A  PIAC
CONV    LDA   B  #$80     set most significant bit of acc. B
        STA   B  PIAD     set half-scale voltage
        TBA               set A=B
AGAIN   LSR   B           shift B right
        BCS      END      conversion ends when carry set
        TST      PIAC     get status and test it
        BPL      BACK     if positive remove last increase
        ABA               add B to A (keep increase)
        STA   A  PIAD     output new value to D/A convertor
        BRA      AGAIN    continue
BACK    SBA               subtract B from A
        STA   A  PIAD     output new value to D/A convertor
        BRA      AGAIN    continue
END     EQU   *           end of conversion
```

The Integrating Analog-to-Digital Convertor

One of the most widely used types of integrating D/A convertor is the dual-slope convertor which transforms the problem from one of measuring a voltage to the more tractable one of measuring a period of time. The key to this transformation is the capacitor, which converts the analog input into a charge and then evaluates the charge by measuring the time taken to discharge the capacitor. Figure 6.66 gives the block diagram of a dual-slope A/D convertor, and Fig. 6.67 illustrates its operation.

The dual-slope A/D convertor operates in three phases: auto zero, integrate the analog input signal, and integrate the reference voltage. The first phase, auto-zero, is not dealt with here but it is a feature of some commercial integrating A/D convertors and serves to reduce offset errors. The "integrate the analog input signal" phase linearly charges the integrating capacitor for a period of t_1 to t_2 (in Fig. 6.67). This period of time is determined by an oscillator and is, say, of M pulses duration. At the end of phase 2, the capacitor is charged up to a level

$$V = \frac{1}{CR}\int_{t_1}^{t_2} V_{in}\, dt.$$

The third phase of the conversion process applies a negative reference voltage to the input of the integrator. Consequently, the voltage across the capacitor now falls

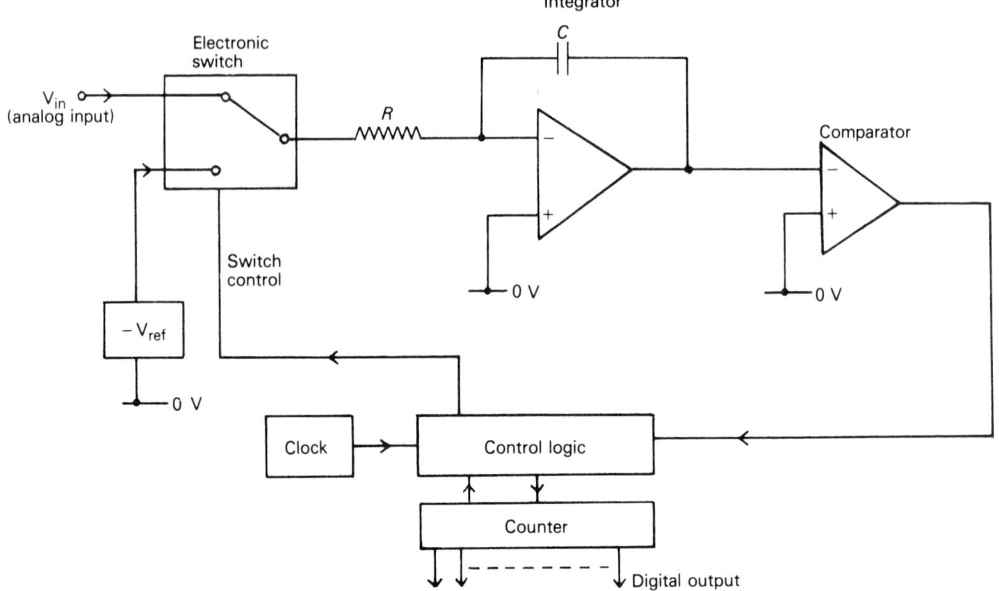

Fig. 6.66 The dual slope A/D convertor

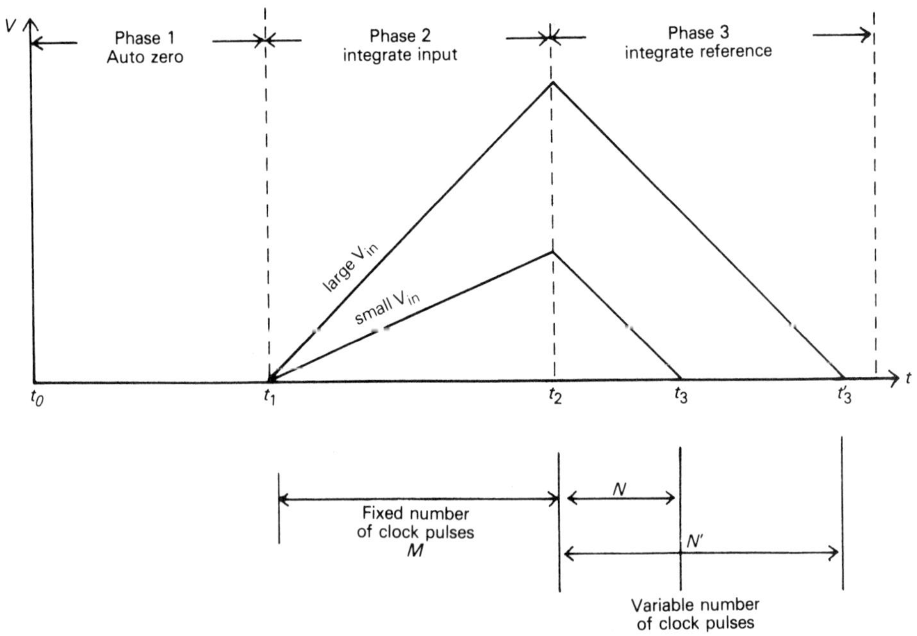

Fig. 6.67 The three phases of a dual slope conversion process

linearly towards zero, at a constant rate determined by $-V_{ref}$. When the voltage across the capacitor falls to zero, the conversion process has ended and the unknown analog input may be determined as follows.

The voltage rise in the second phase is equal to the voltage fall in the third phase, hence

$$\frac{1}{CR}\int_{t_1}^{t_2} V_{in}\,dt = \frac{1}{CR}\int_{t_2}^{t_3} V_{ref}\,dt,$$

or

$$\frac{1}{CR}\left[V_{in}t\right]_{t_1}^{t_2} = \frac{1}{CR}\left[V_{ref}t\right]_{t_2}^{t_3}.$$

If we assume $t_1 = 0$, $t_2 = MT$, $t_3 = (M+N)T$, where T is the period of the clock, M is the number of clock pulses in phase 2, and N is the number of pulses in phase 3, then:

$$\frac{1}{CR}\left[V_{in}t\right]_{0}^{MT} = \frac{1}{CR}\left[V_{ref}t\right]_{MT}^{(M+N)T}$$

or

$$V_{in}MT = V_{ref}NT;$$

hence

$$V_{in} = V_{ref}\frac{N}{M}.$$

Notice that the values of C and R do not appear in this result, and that the accuracy of the result depends only on the precision of V_{ref} and the stability of the clock. Even the simplest of clock circuits is very stable over short periods of time. To obtain the digital value of the analog input it is necessary to read the number of clock pulses in phase 3 (i.e. N) as the values of V_{ref} and M are constant.

The dual-slope analog-to-digital conversion technique is very popular because of its very low cost, high accuracy, and excellent noise-rejection properties. The only drawback of this form of A/D convertor is its very low conversion rate, often no more than tens of conversions per second. Consequently the dual-slope convertor is mainly found in digital voltmeters and similar instruments.

A particularly good example of the dual-slope integrating A/D convertor is Intersil's ICL7109 which is a 12-bit A/D convertor in a 40-pin package. This chip can readily be interfaced to a microprocessor system, or even a UART, with little additional logic.

6.8.1 An Analog-to-digital Convertor using the ADC0817

The choice of a suitable A/D convertor for the TS1 microprocessor system was made particularly easy by the availability of National Semiconductor's ADC0817 "Single Chip Data Acquisition System". This is a CMOS 8-bit successive-approximation A/D convertor together with a 16-channel multiplexer which can select one of 16 analog inputs, under software control.

Other basic features of the ADC0817 are:

(1) linearity better than $\pm\frac{1}{2}$LSB;
(2) no offset adjustment required;
(3) no additional external logic required;
(4) 100 μs conversion time;
(5) single +5 V power supply.

In addition to these features the ADC0817 has been designed as a microprocessor peripheral chip with minimal interfacing requirements. The block diagram of the ADC0817 is given in Fig. 6.68. This chip is split into two sections, the input multiplexer and the A/D convertor itself. The multiplexer is controlled by four address inputs, by which one of the 16 channels may be selected; an address latch enable (ALE) which clocks the address inputs into a latch; and an expansion control input which allows room for additional input expansion beyond 16 channels.

The convertor section of the chip receives its input either from the multiplexer or, if necessary, from an external source. The conversion process is started by a positive transition on the START input, and when the process is complete the end of conversion (EOC) output makes a positive transition. The result may then be read from the output latches by activating the tri-state control input. An external reference is required by the ADC0817, although in many applications the Ref (−) input may be connected to ground and the Ref (+) input to V_{cc}. Figure 6.69 gives the timing diagram of the ADC0817's operation.

A conversion begins at point A with the address of the requisite input channel being applied to the multiplexer. The address latch is enabled by a rising edge applied to the ALE input at B. The address must be held stable for 50 ns before B and 50 ns after B. The actual conversion process is started by a positive transition on the START input at C. The end of the conversion is signified by a positive transition of the EOC output which occurs typically 100 μs after C (640 kHz clock). The digital output may be read by raising the tri-state control input.

The circuit diagram of an interface between an ADC0817 and the TS1 microprocessor system is given in Fig. 6.70. A PIA has been selected to interface the ADC0817 to a 6800. The A/D convertor chip can be connected directly to the CPU's data bus, but this approach has not been adopted because of the additional logic which would be needed to perform the timing and control operations.

To operate the system of Fig. 6.70 it is necessary to transmit the address of the analog channel to be converted to the ADC0817. This is done with PB_0 to PB_3. The address is latched into the A/D convertor by a positive transition at the ALE input, which may be generated by programming CB2 as an output, or the B side of the PIA may be programmed with CB2 in an autohandshaking mode (i.e. CB2 is pulsed after the CPU writes data to the B side—see Section 6.2.1). In Fig. 6.70, the ALE input is wired to the START input so that the address latch is automatically strobed at the beginning of each data conversion.

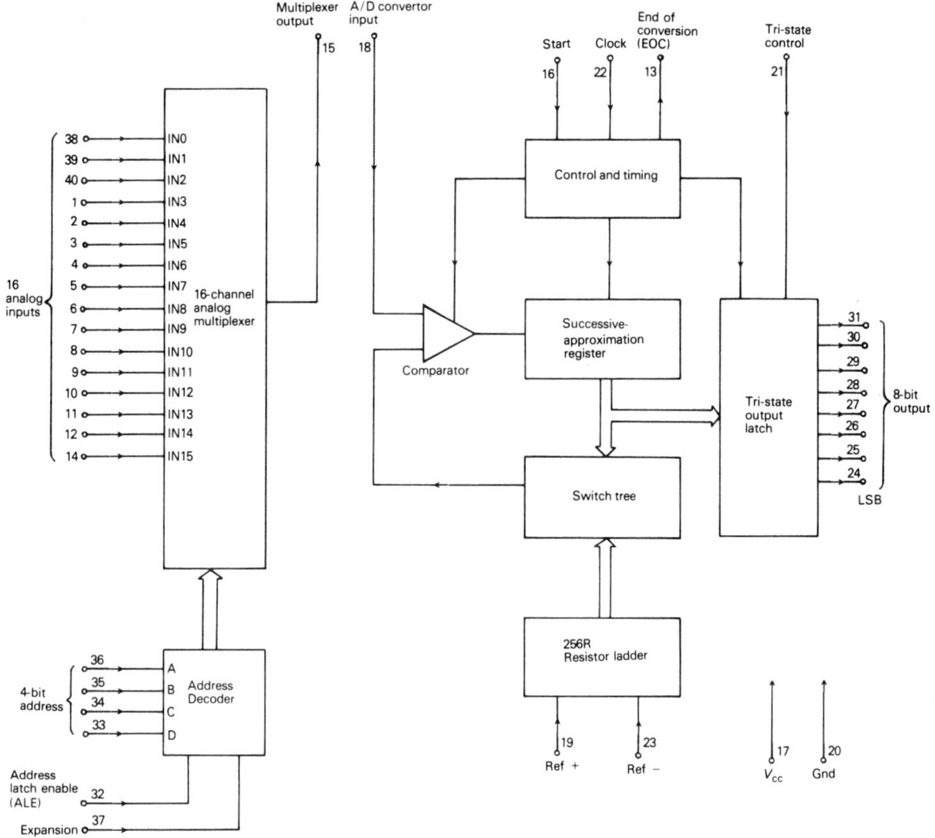

Fig. 6.68 The internal arrangement of the ADC0817

After the address of the input channel has been latched into the ADC0817, its START input must be pulsed high to clear the ADC's successive-approximation register on the rising edge of the START pulse, and low to begin the conversion on the falling edge. This operation is carried out by first setting CA2 (see Fig. 6.70), and then clearing it. The conversion process continues automatically and is complete when the EOC (end of conversion) output makes a positive transition. The EOC transition is detected by CA1, which may be programmed to set the IRQA1 flag. The transition of CA1 may be detected by the CPU by polling IRQA1, or CA1 may be programmed to generate an interrupt at the end of conversion, in which case the transition is detected automatically. The final step is to read the result with the PIA's A-side data lines. Note that in this application the ADC8017's tri-state control input is permanently enabled as it is not necessary to float the ADC's data output lines between successive conversions.

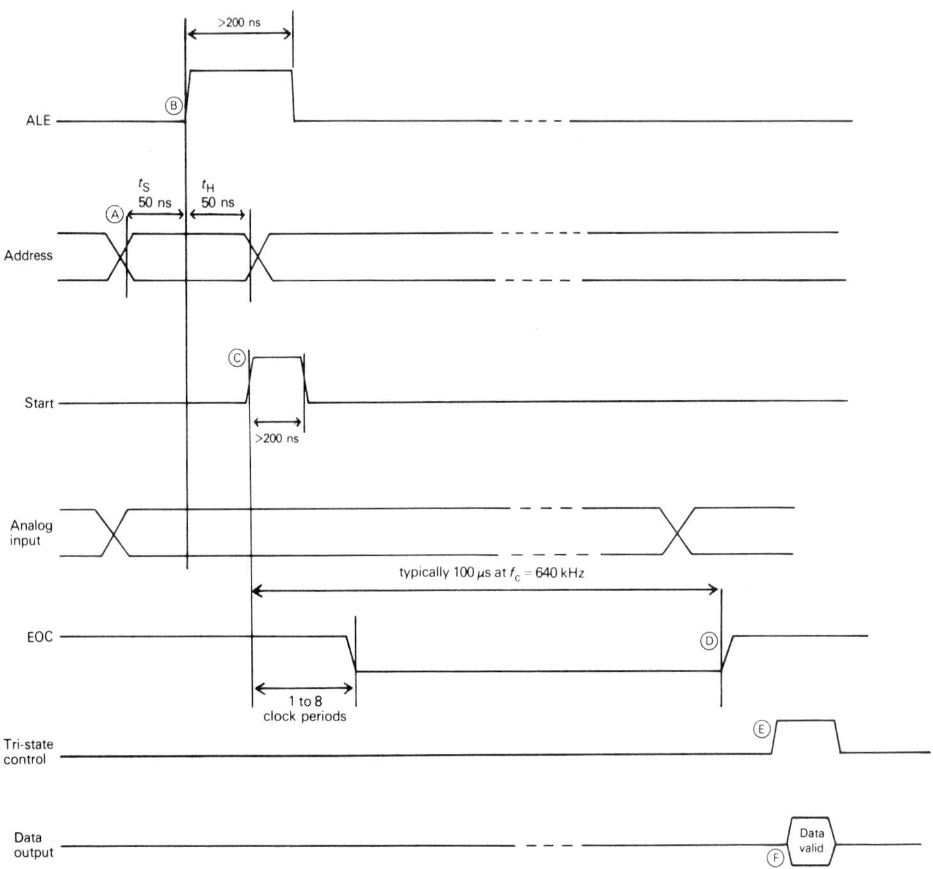

Fig. 6.69 The timing diagram of the ADC0817

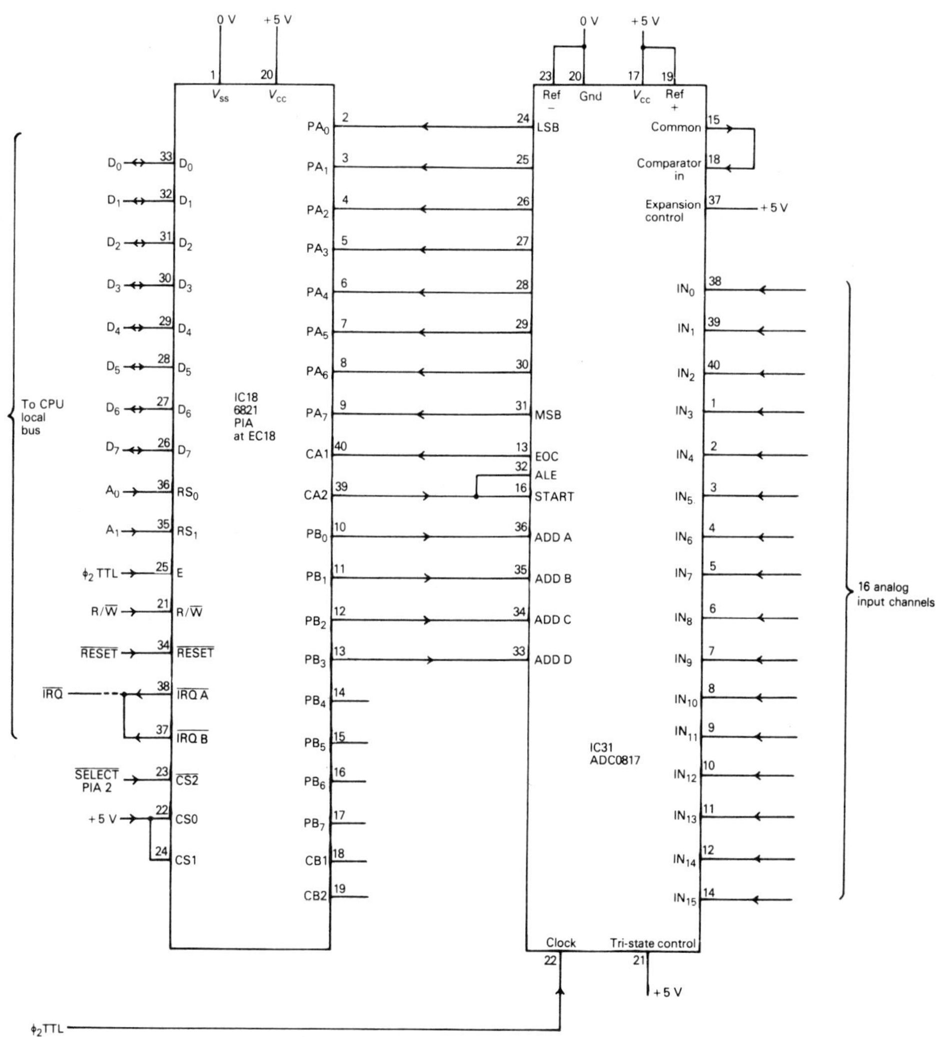

Fig. 6.70 The interface between the TS1 microprocessor system and the ADC0817 A/D convertor

6.8.2 An Example of the Use of the A/D and D/A Convertors

One of the most impressive ways of demonstrating the operation of A/D and D/A convertors is to convert speech or music into digital form, process it and then reconstitute it and feed it to a loudspeaker. Figure 6.71 gives the circuit diagram of TS1's A/D and D/A convertor sections (only one channel of the D/A convertor is shown in this diagram), together with an external analog interface. The analog circuitry is built on a piece of Veroboard (see Chapter 9) and is intended for demonstration purposes only.

The analog input circuit consists of two Sallen – Key low-pass filters in series. These filters have a cut-off frequency of approximately 3 kHz and an attenuation of 12 dB/octave so that their combined attenuation is 24 dB/octave. A 1 V output at 3 kHz is reduced to approximately 1/16 V if the frequency is increased to 6 kHz. The purpose of these filters is to reduce the effect of aliasing which occurs when the input signal is sampled at less than twice the rate of the highest frequency component in the signal. Choosing a cut-off frequency of 3 kHz permits sufficient fidelity for speech and requires a sampling rate of roughly 8 kHz, or one sample every 125 μs. As the A/D convertor operates on unipolar signals in the range $V_{ref}(-)$ to $V_{ref}(+)$, it is necessary to bias the bipolar speech signal by about $V_{cc}/2$. This is done by means of a resistive adder at the output of IC2, with VR1 providing the bias. To set up this circuit it is necessary to inject a sinewave into the analog input, while monitoring the output from the D/A convertor. This requires a simple program, of the type given in Listing 6.2, to read the input from the A/D convertor and to transfer it to the D/A convertor. The input signal is increased until it is just above the clipping level (i.e. the signal goes beyond the minimum and maximum values the A/D convertor is capable of handling) and VR1 is adjusted to make the clipping symmetrical about the positive and negative peaks.

The output circuit from the D/A convertor consists of a single Sallen – Key lowpass filter with a cut-off frequency of 3 kHz, followed by an audio amplifier driving a loudspeaker.

There are many ways of processing an audio signal—filtering, reverberation, and phasing. The demonstration program of Listing 6.2 simply reads a sample of the analog signal, quantizes it into a 256, 128, 64,... level signal and then converts it back into analog form. The quantization operation is carried out by the subroutine "QUANT" which masks off 0 – 7 of the least significant bits of the signal. It is positively amazing how few signal levels are required for recognizable speech or music.

The program begins at INIT with an initialization of the two PIAs. The main part of the program is an infinite loop which reads data from the A/D convertor, processes it and outputs the results to the D/A convertor. To read data from the A/D convertor IC18's CA2 line is pulsed by writing 3E into the side A control register followed by 36. At the end of the conversion process, the A/D convertor raises its EOC output which sets the IRQ1 flag of the control register. The MSB of the control register is continually tested until it goes true and then the data is read.

The signal-processing part of the program takes place in the subroutine

"QUANT", which simply performs a logical AND of the analog data with the constant "MASK". MASK is initially set at FF and may be reset to FE, FC, F8, F0 etc. to reduce the number of significant bits in the data.

Listing 6.2 An A/D – D/A Convertor Demonstration Program

```
PIAD1   EQU      $EC18        A/D convertor data side A
PIAC1   EQU      $EC19        A/D convertor control side A
PIAD2   EQU      $EC1A        A/D convertor data side B
PIAC2   EQU      $EC1B        A/D convertor control side B
PIAD3   EQU      $EC10        D/A convertor data side A
PIAC3   EQU      $EC11        D/A convertor control side A
        ORG      $0000
MASK    FCB      $FF
        ORG      $0100        Program entry point
INIT    CLR  A
        STA  A   PIAC1        select DDR (A/D convertor side A)
        STA  A   PIAC2        select DDR (A/D convertor side B)
        STA  A   PIAC3        select DDR (D/A convertor side A)
        STA  A   PIAD1        select A/D convertor side A as input
        LDA  A   #$FF         load A with all 1s
        STA  A   PIAD2        select A/D convertor side B as output
        STA  A   PIAD3        select D/A convertor side A as output
        LDA  A   #$04         set bit 2
        STA  A   PIAC1        select data reg. (A/D convertor side A)
        STA  A   PIAC2        select data reg. (A/D convertor side B)
        STA  A   PIAC3        select data reg. (D/A convertor side A)
        CLR  A
        STA  A   PIAD2        select channel zero (ADD = 0)
LOOP    BSR      INPUT        get an analog value
        BSR      QUANT        process it
        STA  A   PIAD3        transfer it to D/A convertor
        BRA      LOOP         continue
INPUT   LDA  A   #%00111110   set CA2 to start conversion
        STA  A   PIAC1
        LDA  A   #%00110110   clear CA2
        STA  A   PIAC1
REP     LDA  A   PIAC1        get status reg A/D convertor side A
        BPL      REP          loop until CA1 goes high
        LDA  A   PIAD1        get data
        RTS                   return
QUANT   AND  A   MASK         mask out unwanted bits of A
        RTS
```

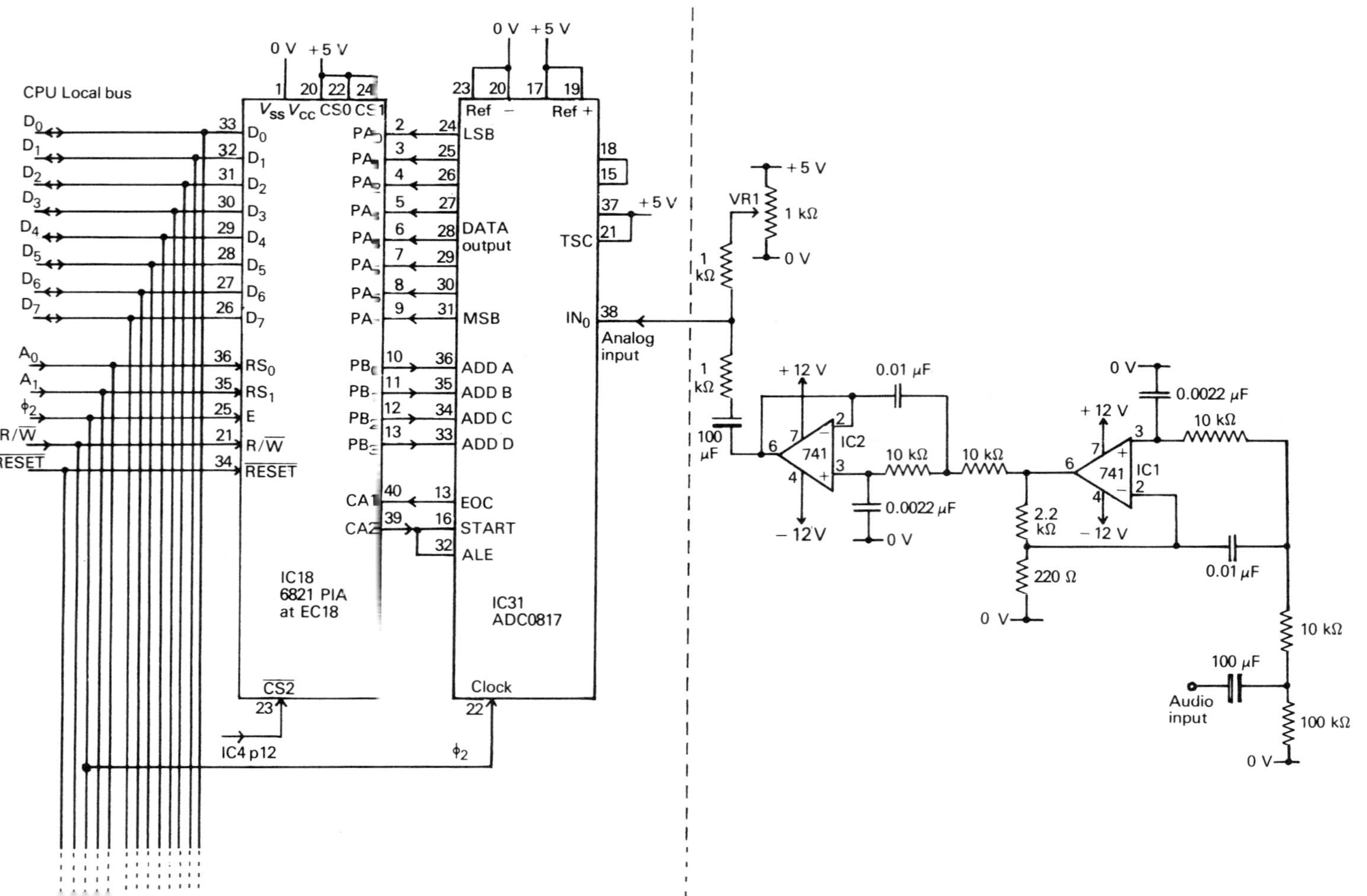
CPU Local bus
IC18
6821 PIA
at EC18
IC31
ADC0817
IC1
741
IC2
741
Audio
input
Analog
input
VR1
DATA
output
LSB
MSB
ADD A
ADD B
ADD C
ADD D
EOC
START
ALE
Clock
TSC
Ref +
Ref −
IC4 p12
10 kΩ
100 kΩ
100 μF
0.01 μF
0.0022 μF
2.2 kΩ
220 Ω
1 kΩ
+ 12 V
− 12 V
+ 5 V
0 V

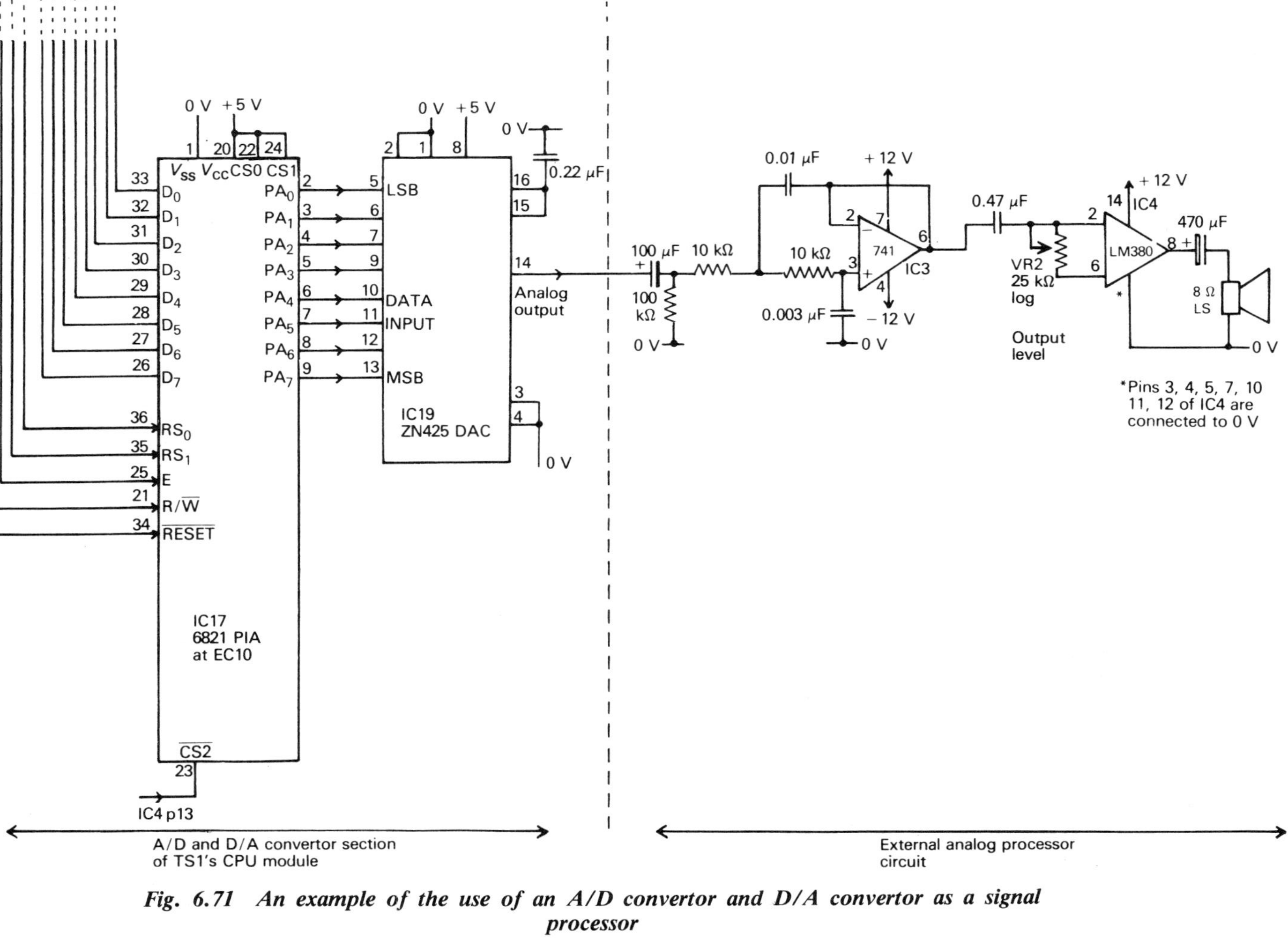

Fig. 6.71 An example of the use of an A/D convertor and D/A convertor as a signal processor

6.9 EXTERNAL PROCESSING

The majority of microprocessors are able to perform only primitive arithmetic operations. Typically, a microprocessor can do little more than add or subtract 8- or 16-bit binary integers. Some microprocessors have a limited multiplication facility—often no more than the ability to form the product of two 8-bit unsigned binary integers. Such a facility is very useful for calculating the address of an element in an array, but is of limited value when complex scientific operations, in floating-point arithmetic, are to be performed.

Although computers are widely thought of as "calculating machines" the majority of computers spend most of their time in data processing applications, rarely needing to perform a multiplication. Many microprocessor applications—text editors, text processors, assemblers, and compilers, involve little more than the movement of data from one place to another, together with the comparison of strings of characters. By far the most common applications of multiplication is in the calculation of address offsets when the elements of an array are accessed. For example, if A is an $n \times m$ array, the location of the element $A_{i,j}$ is given by $a+ni+j$, where a is the location of the first element of the array.

Sophisticated arithmetic operations, that is those involving floating-point numbers or trigonometric functions, are required in many applications from scientific calculations to signal-processing operations (filtering, speech recognition/synthesis, radar and sonar). While the average microprocessor user can easily write his own multiplication routine (for 8-bit integers), tackling floating-point trigonometric functions is a different matter. Before the advent of external processing devices the microprocessor user who wished to calculate transcendental functions such as sin (x), log (x) or $\sin^{-1}(x)$ had only two options open to him. He could either write routines to calculate them himself or buy a BASIC (or equivalent) interpreter. Writing custom software to generate transcendental functions is no mean task: an understanding of numerical methods is required. Although transcendental functions can be generated from simple polynomial functions of the form

$$F(x) = A_0 + A_1x + A_2x^2 + \cdots + A_nx^n,$$

problems arise when the modulus of x is large. More reliable techniques often involve Chebyshev polynomials which are able to minimize the maximum error of a function over a given interval. One of the early scientific calculators was able to calculate trigonometric functions to a precision of 5 decimal figures but, for certain angles, the error in the result was 20%, demonstrating the importance of selecting the "right" algorithm.

Generating complex arithmetic functions by means of a BASIC interpreter is fine if the microprocessor is acting as a scientific calculator, but if it is part of a dedicated computer system (e.g. for signal processing, or instrumentation) the speed of a BASIC interpreter may be far too slow. Furthermore, a commercial BASIC often requires a specific operating environment (disk system, large memory) which may be very expensive.

A possible solution to the microprocessor's limited mathematical power is to couple an existing microprocessor to an external arithmetic processor. An external processor is a device, or subsystem, which appears as a peripheral to the microprocessor and is able to perform arithmetic operations. Semiconductor manufacturers have now produced several devices capable of acting as an external processor. These devices range from simple multiplier chips to complex processors capable of generating a wide range of mathematical functions.

6.9.1 The Multiplier Chip

The multiplier chip is the simplest form of external processor and can form the product of two numbers in a very short time. Many of the currently available multiplier chips are fabricated with bipolar technology and are designed for high-speed real-time signal-processing applications. These chips are often intended for the aerospace market and other similar markets where high performance is mandatory. The speed of these multipliers is so great that they can usually form the product of two numbers in less time than a conventional NMOS microprocessor takes to add them.

The most basic form of multiplication consists of a process of shifting and adding. Consider the multiplication of two (unsigned) 4-bit binary numbers $X=13$ and $Y=9$. Let X be called the multiplier, and Y the multiplicand. Figure 6.72 illustrates the shift and add algorithm. Whenever the least significant bit of the multiplier x_i is 1 the multiplicand Y is added to the partial product Z_i. If x_i is 0 nothing is added to the partial product. After each addition both the partial product and the multiplier are shifted right one bit. Consequently, the multiplication of two n-bit numbers yields a $2n$-bit product.

$X = 13_{10} = 1101_2$ (multiplier)
$Y = 9_{10} = 1001_2$ (multiplicand)

$Z_0 = 0000$	initialize partial product
$+1001$	$x_0 = 1$ add Y
$Z_1 = 1001$	first partial product
01001	shift right
$+00000$	$x_1 = 0$ add 0
$Z_2 = 01001$	second partial product
001001	shift right
$+100100$	$x_2 = 1$ add Y
$Z_3 = 101101$	third partial product
0101101	shift right
$+1001000$	$x_3 = 1$ add Y
$Z_4 = 1110101$	fourth partial product (answer)
$Z_4 = 117_{10}$	

Fig. 6.72 Multiplication by shifting and adding

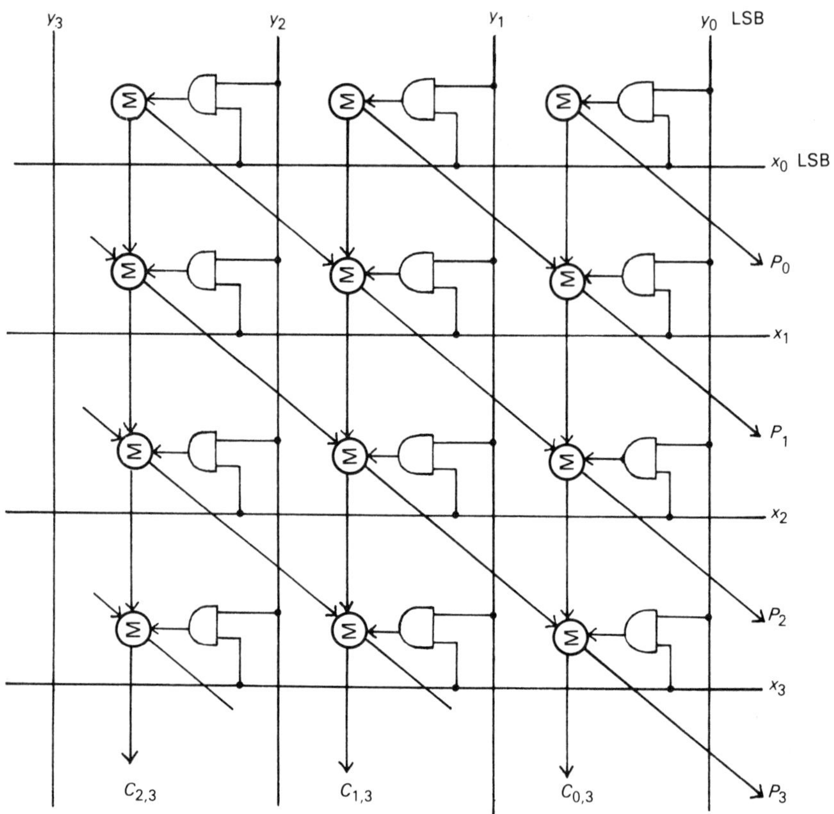

			y_3	y_2	y_1	y_0
....			x_3	x_2	x_1	x_0
....			y_3x_0	y_2x_0	y_1x_0	y_0x_0
....		y_3x_1	y_2x_1	y_1x_1	y_0x_1	
.....	y_3x_2	y_2x_2	y_1x_2	y_0x_2		
..... y_2x_3	y_1x_3	y_0x_3				
....			P_3	P_2	P_1	P_0

In the above array 1-bit products $x_i\ y_j$ are formed by AND gates. The partial products are summed in adders to give the result $P_0\ P_1 \ldots P_{2n-1}$. To each partial product is added one or more carries $c_{i,j}$ which result from the carries between the columns of the result. The long-hand multiplication on the left illustrates the operation of the array.

Fig. 6.73 The combinatorial logic multiplier

This multiplication technique may be carried out in software, or can be mechanized with a small amount of MSI and SSI logic. Only shift registers, an n-bit adder and a counter are required. The disadvantage of such a multiplier is that it is relatively slow (although fast compared with many 8-bit microprocessors) and requires a clock, causing problems of synchronization. A much better approach to multiplication is the combinatorial approach which forms all the partial products by combinatorial logic and sums their results in a similar way. Such an arrangement is asynchronous and requires no clock. The combinatorial approach has the advantage of speed—a typical multiplier of this type can form the product of two 16-bit words in 100 ns. The disadvantage of the combinatorial logic multiplier is its high power dissipation, caused by the very large number of gates on a bipolar chip. One of the early 16-bit multipliers dissipated as much as 5 W and required a special package with an integral heat sink. Figure 6.73 gives an illustration of the logic arrays found in some of these multiplier chips.

The MPY-8HJ 8-Bit Parallel Multiplier

A typical 8-bit by 8-bit multiplier chip, the MPY-8HJ made by TRW Inc., is illustrated in Fig. 6.74. This device is fabricated with bipolar technology and is capable of forming a 16-bit product of two 8-bit words in, typically, 65 ns. The multiplier is available in a standard 40-pin DIL package, is totally TTL compatible, and requires only a single +5 V power supply. One of its attributes, listed by TRW, is that it is "radiation hard" (i.e. it is insensitive to fairly high levels of ionizing radiation); this feature gives an indication of one section of the intended market for this device.

At the heart of the MPY-8HJ (Fig. 6.74) lies an asynchronous multiplier array of the type illustrated in Fig. 6.73. This particular chip performs signed multiplication on data represented in 2s complement form, and hence its array differs slightly from that of Fig. 6.73.

The multiplier and multiplicand are held in two 8-bit wide registers while the multiplication is taking place. The bytes to be multiplied are loaded into these registers from two 8-bit data highways. The input registers may be clocked independently by means of a positive-going edge at the respective clock inputs. The result of the multiplication is a 16-bit wide product which is clocked into two eight-bit output registers, composed of an 8-bit most significant product (MSP) register and an 8-bit least significant product (LSP) register. Two 8-bit wide tri-state bus drivers serve to put the MSP and the LSP data words onto their respective output buses.

The MPY-8HJ has two 8-bit input ports and two 8-bit output ports. All that is necessary to form the product of two numbers is to apply the multiplier and multiplicand to their respective inputs, clock the input registers, clock the product register, enable the output ports, and then read the product. In this configuration the MPY-8HJ can generate a new product every 65 ns (typically). The guaranteed worst-case multiplication time is 90 ns. Even higher multiplication speeds can be achieved by operating the MPY-8HJ in a pipeline mode. That is, time may be saved by clocking in a new pair of numbers and immediately reading the result of the product of the previous pair of numbers, while the current product is being generated. This mode will not, normally, be of interest to those who interface this chip to a microprocessor system.

Although the MPY-8HJ has separate input and output ports it is possible to operate it as if it had a single 8-bit port. This may be done by connecting all the four

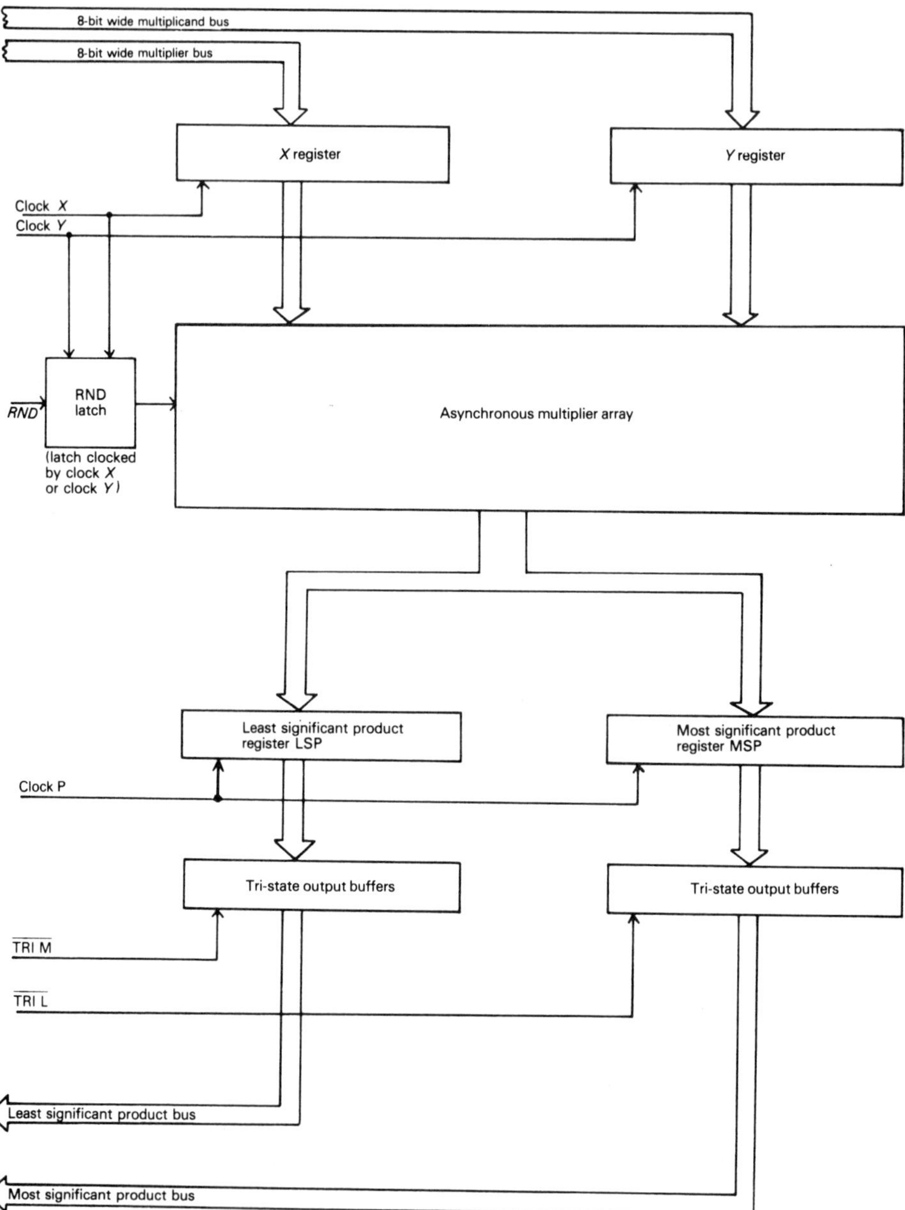

Fig. 6.74 A block diagram of the internal arrangement of the MPY-8HJ 8×8-bit parallel multiplier. (Note: $\overline{TRI\ L}$ and $\overline{TRI\ M}$ are active-low enable inputs. In TRW's own literature these are written TRI L and TRI M respectively. The negated form is used here for consistency with the convention adopted throughout this book.)

ports in parallel and then steering the data between the common 8-bit data bus and its destination by means of the multiplier's control signals (clock X, clock Y, $\overline{\text{TRI L}}$, $\overline{\text{TRI M}}$).* The multiplier is placed on the data bus and the X register clocked, and then the multiplicand is placed on the bus and the Y register clocked. After no less than 90 ns the product registers are clocked. The product is obtained by gating the most significant 8 bits of the result onto the bus by means of $\overline{\text{TRI M}}$ and reading the result. Similarly, the least significant product may be gated onto the data bus and read. In this mode, the MPY-8HJ is essentially acting as a memory-mapped peripheral. In a 6800 system with a 1 MHz clock, a product may be obtained in approximately 24 μs. This is, of course, much slower than the speed at which the multiplier is capable of generating products—but it is far faster than resorting to software multiplication.

As we have remarked above, the MPY-8HJ operates on signed data to produce a signed product. Figure 6.75 gives the format of the input and output data of the

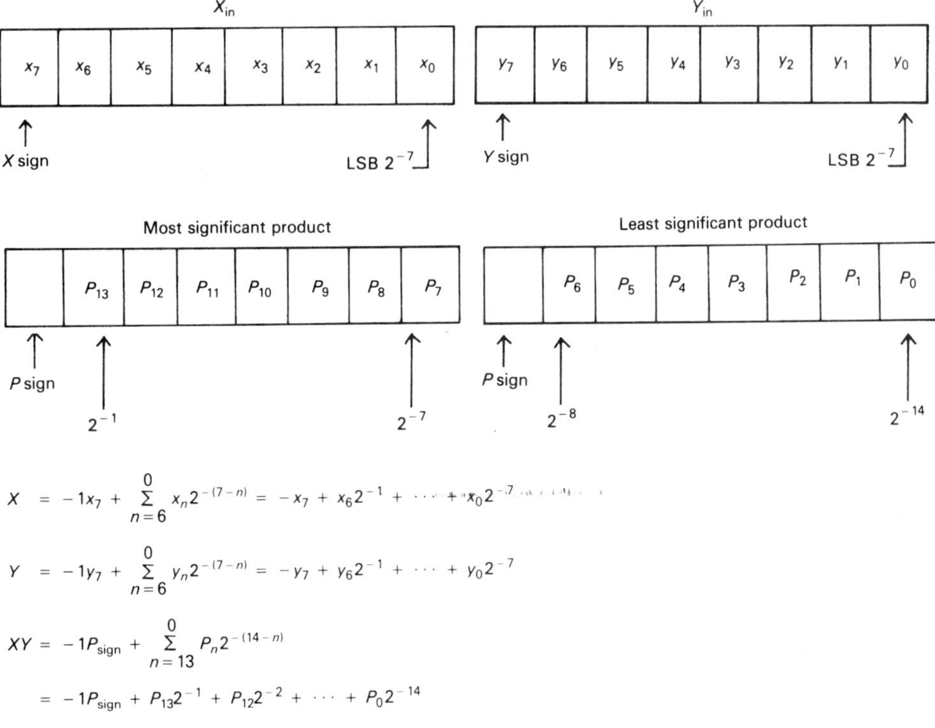

$$X = -1x_7 + \sum_{n=6}^{0} x_n 2^{-(7-n)} = -x_7 + x_6 2^{-1} + \cdots + x_0 2^{-7}$$

$$Y = -1y_7 + \sum_{n=6}^{0} y_n 2^{-(7-n)} = -y_7 + y_6 2^{-1} + \cdots + y_0 2^{-7}$$

$$XY = -1P_{sign} + \sum_{n=13}^{0} P_n 2^{-(14-n)}$$

$$= -1P_{sign} + P_{13}2^{-1} + P_{12}2^{-2} + \cdots + P_0 2^{-14}$$

If RND = 1 then 2^{-8} is added to the product

Fig. 6.75 The input and output formats of the MPY-8HJ multiplier
The X and Y operands are regarded as fractional binary numbers with a binary point between the sign bit and the rest of the number.

* $\overline{\text{TRI L}}$ and $\overline{\text{TRI M}}$ are active-low three-state control inputs which enable the LSP buffer and the MSP buffer respectively.

multiplier. When two m-bit numbers are multiplied together the resulting product is, at most, $2m$ bits wide. Because the multiplier and multiplicand are both 7-bit numbers (plus a sign bit), their product is a 14-bit number plus a sign. It can be seen from Fig. 6.75 that the most significant byte of the product is as one would expect, but the least significant byte also contains the sign bit in the most significant bit position. In most applications this second, redundant, sign bit may be removed by reading the LSP and executing an arithmetic left shift. It should be noted that the numbering of the bits in Fig. 6.75 is the reverse of that in TRW's own literature. The numbering of data bits has been modified to be consistent with Motorola's (and many other microprocessor manufacturers') convention that x_0 is the least significant bit and x_7 the most significant bit. It should also be noted that a property of the 2s complement algorithm employed by the MPY-8HJ is that the product of -1 and -1 gives the incorrect result of -1. This is caused by overflow and should be checked for by software or hardware. If both the sign bits of the operands are 1 and the sign bit of the product is 1, overflow has occurred.

The MPY-8HUJ

The MPY-8HUJ is a high-speed parallel multiplier capable of forming the 16-bit product of two 8-bit unsigned inputs. This device is very similar to the MPY-8HJ except that it operates on unsigned numbers while the latter treats its inputs and outputs as 2s complement numbers. One of the advantages of an unsigned multiplier is that it simplifies multiple-precision arithmetic. For example, consider the multiplications of two 16-bit unsigned numbers A and B, where

$$A = 2^8 A_u + A_l \qquad B = 2^8 B_u + B_l.$$

A_u and A_l are respectively the most significant and least significant bytes of A. The product of A and B is given by the expression:

$$AB = (2^8 A_u + A_l)(2^8 B_u + B_l) = 2^{16} A_u B_u + 2^8 (A_u B_l + A_l B_u) + A_l B_l.$$

From this result it is clear that the 32-bit product of two 16-bit numbers may be formed from four 8-bit multiplications, some shifting to multiply by 2^8 or 2^{16} and three additions.

The basic details of the MPY-8HUJ are given in Fig. 6.76.

The circuit diagram of a possible interface between the MPY-8HJ and a 6800 system is given in Fig. 6.77. Before designing an interface for the MPY-8HJ it is first necessary to examine its timing characteristics. Figure 6.78 and Table 6.26 define the most important parameters of the multiplier chip. From Fig. 6.78 it can be seen that the operation of the MPY-8HJ is straightforward and that the timing requirements are modest. The operation of the chip may be summarized as follows:

(1) Apply data to the X or Y input of the chip.

(2) Hold the data constant and clock the input register by a rising clock edge no sooner than 25 ns after the input has stabilized. It is not necessary to maintain the input after the occurrence of the clock edge (i.e. zero data hold time).

(3) The X and Y inputs may be clocked simultaneously or sequentially.
(4) The output registers should be clocked no sooner than 90 ns after the entry of the data.
(5) To read the result, the output buffers are enabled and the data becomes valid no later than 35 ns after the tri-state output has been enabled.

All the above times are very short compared with the clock rate of most microprocessors, so no problems arise because of the need to stretch the microprocessor's clock.

Table 6.26 Parameters of the MPY-8HJ

Parameter		*Value*
t_s	input register set-up time	25 ns min
t_h	input register hold time	0 ns min
t_{pw}	clock pulse width	25 ns min
t_{mc}	multiply time	90 ns min
t_d	output delay	35 ns max
t_{en}	output enable delay	35 ns max
t_{dis}	output disable delay	35 ns max
I_{IH}	high-level input current	75 μA max
I_{IL}	low-level input current	−0.4 mA max

In Fig. 6.77 the four data ports of the MPY-8HJ are connected together and buffered onto the CPU's data bus by means of a 74LS245 octal bus transceiver. The direction of data transfer is determined by the CPU's read/$\overline{\text{write}}$ signal. Two address decoders, IC3a and IC2, decode the high-order address lines $A_{10} - A_{15}$ and enable the transceiver when an address in the 1K range 8000 – 83FF is accessed during the ϕ_2-high portion of a valid memory-access cycle. The output from the address decoder also enables a 74LS139 two line-to-four line decoder (IC3b) which decodes A_0 and R/$\overline{\text{W}}$ into four signals as in Table 6.27. The X and Y registers are clocked by a positive edge which occurs at the end of a memory-write cycle when the $\overline{\text{ENABLE}}$ signal from IC3b returns to its inactive (high) state. When R/$\overline{\text{W}}$ = 1 the active-low outputs of IC3b enable the tri-state buffer of the multiplier and put data onto the data bus at the beginning of the ϕ_2-high part of the read cycle. In this way the MPY-8HJ is treated as any other memory-mapped peripheral.

Table 6.27

R/$\overline{W}$	*A_0*	*Function*
0	0	CLOCK *X* REGISTER
0	1	CLOCK *Y* REGISTER
1	0	$\overline{\text{ENABLE}}$ MSP ($\overline{\text{TRI M}}$)
1	1	$\overline{\text{ENABLE}}$ LSP ($\overline{\text{TRI L}}$)

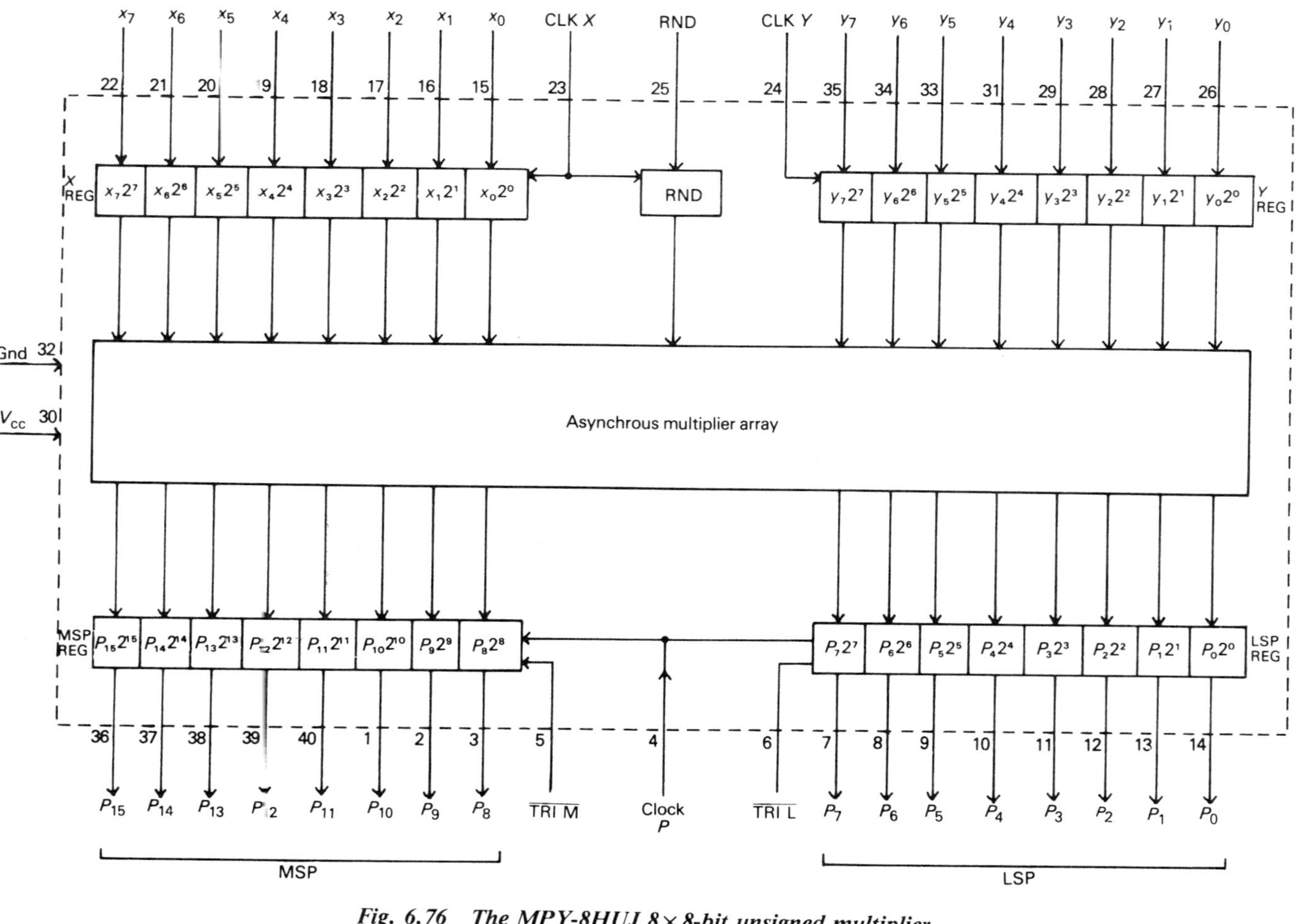

Fig. 6.76 The MPY-8HUJ 8×8-bit unsigned multiplier

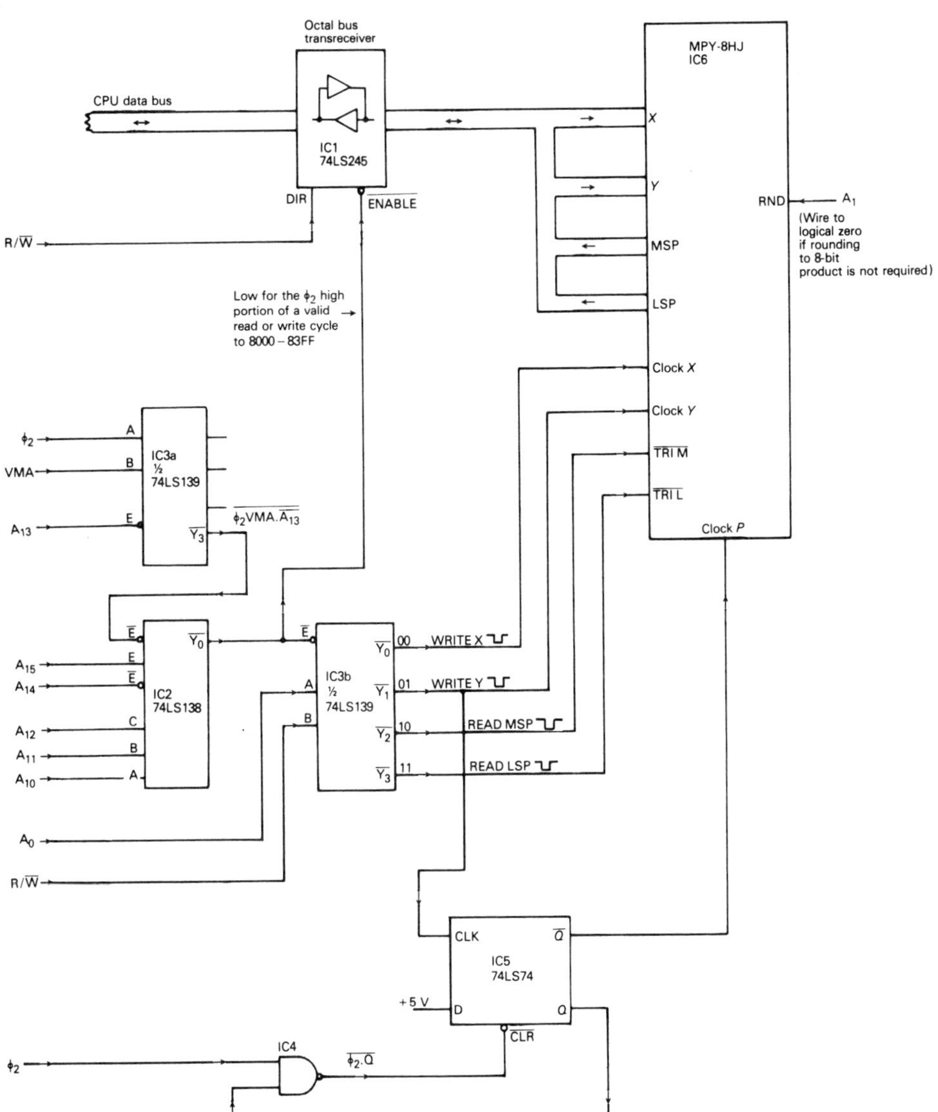

Fig. 6.77 The interface between an MPY-8HJ and a 6800 microprocessor

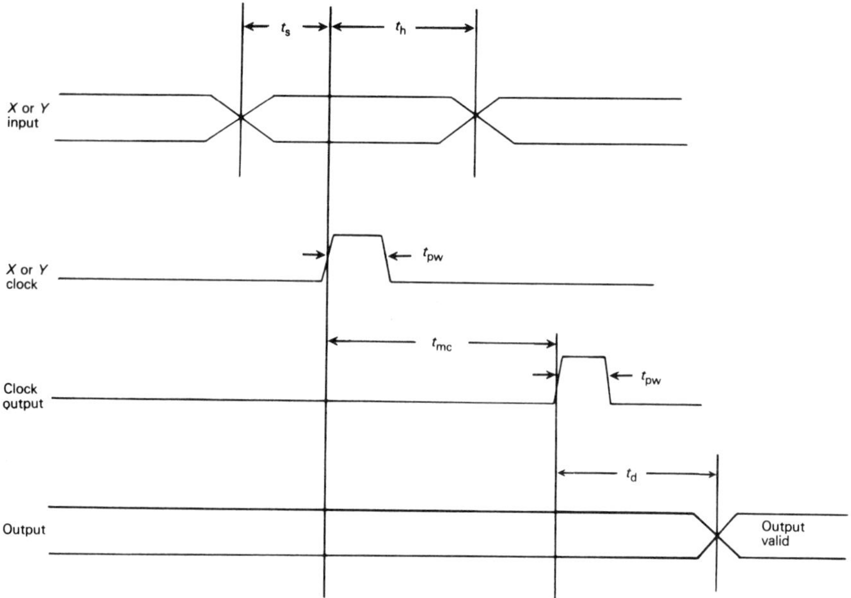

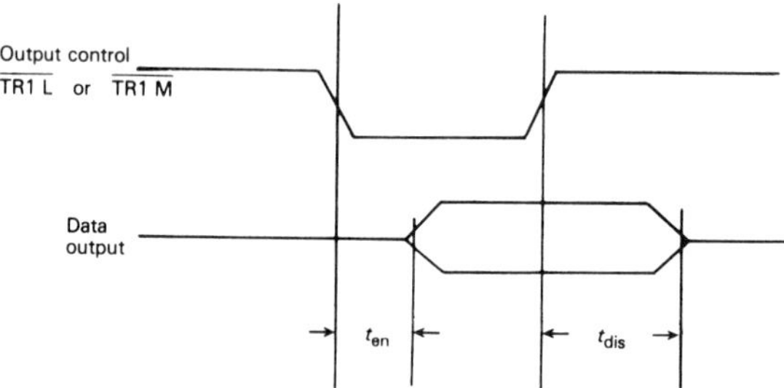

Fig. 6.78 The timing diagram of the MPY-8HJ

The only complexity introduced by the MPY-8HJ is its requirement that the product be clocked into the output registers no sooner than 90 ns after the data has been clocked into the input registers. The product register can be clocked by means of a dummy memory-reference operation after data has been entered into the multiplier, but such an operation wastes time. A much better approach is to clock the product register automatically after each write to the Y input register. Figure 6.77 shows how this may be done with a positive edge-triggered D flip-flop (IC5) (suggested by Bryant and Swasdee—see bibliography). The flip-flop is triggered at the end of a "clock Y" operation by the low-to-high transition of the output from the 74LS139 decoder. Figure 6.79 illustrates the operation of the flip-flop. As the D input of the flip-flop is tied to V_{cc}, the Q output of the flip-flop rises

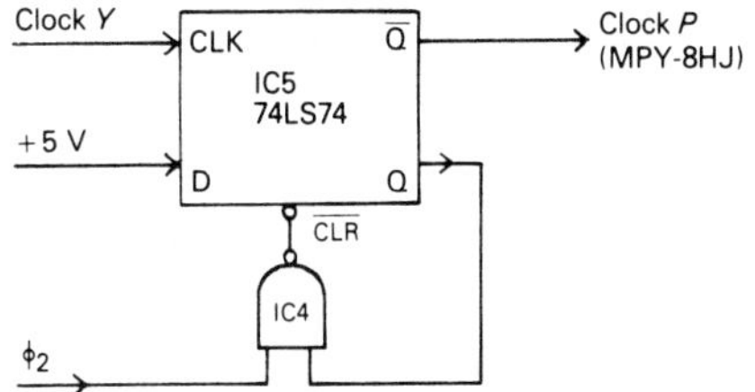

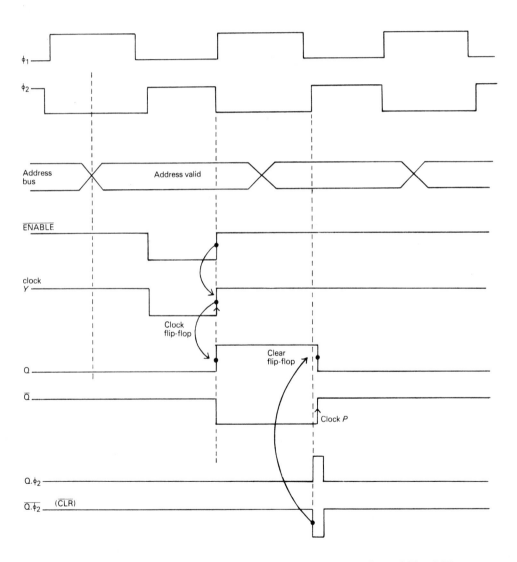

Fig. 6.79 The timing diagram of the MPY-8HJ 6800 interface of Fig. 6.77

to a logical one when it is clocked. The NAND gate, IC4, is now enabled by Q, and when ϕ_2 rises in the next CPU clock cycle the output of the NAND gate falls and clears the flip-flop. The $\overline{Q}$ output of the flip-flop is connected to the clock P input of the multiplier and when $\overline{Q}$ rises to a logical one, the product register is clocked. From Fig. 6.79 it can be seen that the rising edge of $\overline{Q}$ occurs half a clock cycle after the data has been written into the multiplier's Y register. Because half a cycle of the 6800 clock is approximately 500 ns, the timing requirement of the MPY-8HJ is more than satisfied.

In this application of the MPY-8HJ the RND input is permanently connected to ground. The RND input is employed only when the multiplier is being used to form 8-bit products. In such cases RND is connected to a logical one and has the effect of adding 2^{-8} to the result of a multiplication. This rounds up the most significant product byte if the value of P_6 is 1.

If it is desired to operate the MPY-8HJ as an 8×8 multiplier yielding an 8-bit product as well as a 16-bit product, it is necessary to control the state of the RND input. This may be done by latching a 1 or 0 into an external latch connected to the multiplier's RND input pin. A much better technique requiring no additional hardware in a memory-mapped I/O system is to connect the RND input to system address line A_1. Whenever the multiplier has data clocked into it the state of A_1 is clocked into the RND latch so that writing to address 8001 clocks 0 into RND when Y is written into the multiplier and writing to 8003 clocks 1 into RND when Y is written into the multiplier.

An Example of the Use of the Multiplier

If the multiplier (X), the multiplicand (Y), the most significant product (MSP), and the least significant product are stored consecutively in memory, the product of X and Y may be obtained in the following way:

```
LDX     #DATA    point to the data area.
LDA  A  0,X      pick up the multiplier.
STA  A  $8000    clock multiplier into X register.
LDA  A  1,X      pick up the multiplicand.
STA  A  $8001    clock multiplicand into Y register and clock the
                 product register.
LDA  A  $8000    read the most significant product.
STA  A  2,X      store the MSP in the result location.
LDA  A  $8001    read the least significant product.
ASL  A           shift the LSP left to remove the redundant sign
                 bit.
STA  A  3,X      store the LSP in the result location + 1.
```

The total time required to execute this code is 45 μs, which is considerably better than the 300 μs required to perform a software multiplication. The time taken to multiply the numbers could be reduced by avoiding the indexed addressing mode (5 μs per LDA X and 6 μs per STA X).

Although this section has dealt with the MPY-8HJ, TRW makes 12-bit, 16-bit and 24-bit multipliers. These larger multipliers are somewhat more sophisticated than the 8-bit multiplier. The 12- and 16-bit multipliers can perform signed and unsigned multiplication and the most significant product word may be shifted one place right to remove the second (redundant) sign bit in the least significant product word. The 24-bit multiplier, which can form a 48-bit product in only 200 ns, has several features making it suitable for floating-point operations. As these multipliers operate on words wider than eight bits it is necessary to provide a multiplexer between them and the 8-bit microprocessor bus.

Division by Multiplication

Microprocessors and computers perform division far less frequently than multiplication, and consequently commercial divider chips are not yet widely available. It is, however, possible to perform division with the aid of a multiplier chip. If we wish to divide a numerator N by a divisor D to obtain a quotient Q, so that $Q=N/D$, one possible approach is to obtain $1/D$ from a PROM and then obtain Q by multiplying the result by N. In practice, if Q is not needed to an accuracy of more than 8 bits a simple 256-word by 8-bit PROM is sufficient. The value of D is fed to the 8 address lines of the PROM and the output of the PROM, representing $1/D$, is fed directly to the input of an 8-bit multiplier. This approach becomes less attractive if accuracies greater than 12 bits are required.

An alternative way of performing division by multiplication is to employ an iterative technique, which assumes that the values of N and D have been scaled such that

$$\tfrac{1}{2} \leqslant D < 1.$$

A number Z is defined as $Z=1-D$ or $D=1-Z$. If the top and bottom of a fraction are multiplied by a constant the value of the fraction remains unchanged. Hence

$$Q=\frac{N}{D}=\frac{N(1+Z)}{D(1+Z)}=\frac{N(1+Z)}{(1-Z)(1+Z)}=\frac{N(1+Z)}{1-Z^2}.$$

If the resulting fraction is now multiplied by $(1+Z^2)/(1+Z^2)$, Q becomes

$$\frac{N(1+Z)}{1-Z^2}\,\frac{1+Z^2}{1+Z^2}=\frac{N(1+Z)(1+Z^2)}{1-Z^4}.$$

This process may be repeated n times with the result that

$$Q=\frac{N}{D}=\frac{N(1+Z)(1+Z^2)(1+Z^4)\ \cdots\ (1+Z^{2^{n-1}})}{1-Z^{2^n}}.$$

Since D is less than unity, Z is also less than unity and the value of Z^{2^n} approaches zero quite rapidly as n increases. Consequently, the approximate value of Q is given by

$$Q=N(1+Z)(1+Z^2)(1+Z^4)\ \cdots\ (1+Z^{2^{n-1}}).$$

For 8-bit accuracy n need be only 3, and if $n = 5$ this technique yields a quotient accurate to 32 bits.

6.9.2 The Number Cruncher

Number cruncher is the colloquial term applied to a device designed to perform arithmetic operations on numerical data. The most popular form of number cruncher is the pocket calculator which receives its input (data and instructions) from a keyboard and delivers its result to a bank of seven segment displays. The pocket calculator has the advantage of simplicity—the most complex of mathematical functions may be generated with no knowledge of computer programming.

With a little effort a pocket calculator may be interfaced to a microprocessor system. This allows the microprocessor to input and output data, store and manipulate it, but to delegate all complex arithmetic operations to the calculator. Interfacing a calculator to a conventional microprocessor is not a trivial task for three reasons.

(1) The voltage levels at which most calculators operate are rarely compatible with the TTL-level signals found in microprocessor systems.
(2) The output of the calculator consists of a 7-bit code (for a 7-segment display) and is rapidly multiplexed between the digits of the display. This arrangement simplifies the connection between the calculator chip and its display, but means that the microprocessor must demultiplex the output of the calculator.
(3) It is difficult to obtain detailed information about the circuit and characteristics of the majority of calculators.

The circuit diagram of a calculator employing the General Instrument Corporation chip C596L is given in Fig. 6.80. Data and operations are entered into the calculator by pressing a key which makes a connection between one of the K lines and one of the D lines. To enter data into such a system from a microprocessor, it is necessary to duplicate the effect of a key closure. This can be done with an electromechanical device (reed relay) or some form of electronic switch. Such a switch is the CMOS bilateral switch which is a three-terminal device, the resistance between two of its terminals being determined by the logic level at its third terminal. The CD4016A contains four of these switches in a 14-pin DIL package. Controlling the circuit of Fig. 6.80 by means of the CMOS bilateral switch would require a total of nine packages.

Data may be read from the calculator by sensing the state of the digit drivers and reading the value of the digit from the seven outputs a – g. Software may then be employed to convert the 7-segment value to its BCD equivalent. It is, of course, necessary to fit voltage-level shifters between the output of the calculator and the input of the microprocessor, possibly a PIA. This approach to number crunching with a microprocessor is suitable only for the enthusiast.

A more rewarding approach is to consider one of the number cruncher chips

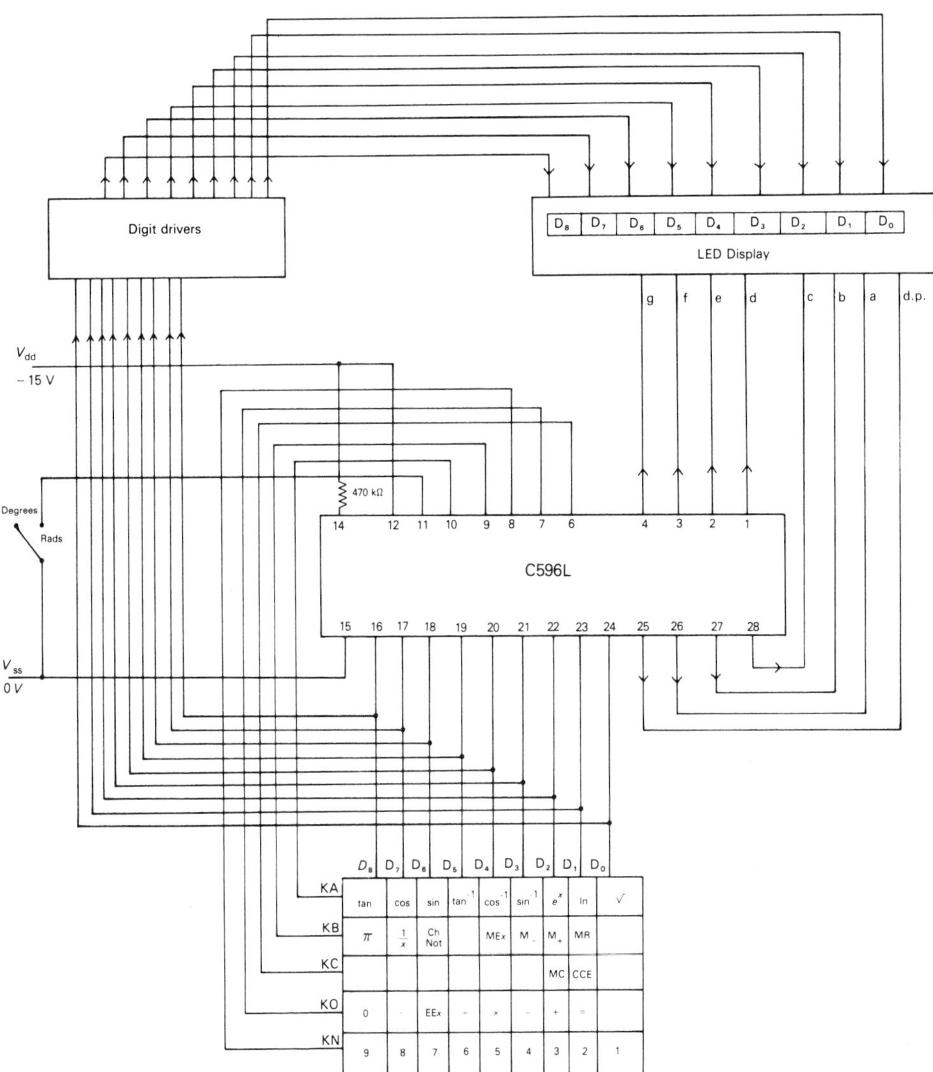

Fig. 6.80 The circuit diagram of a pocket calculator

specifically designed for the microprocessor market. The two number-cruncher chips discussed in this section are National Semiconductor Corporation's MM57109 and the Advanced Micro Devices, Inc. (AMD) Am9511, which is referred to by the manufacturers as an "arithmetic processor unit" (APU). These chips are similar in some ways but have such fundamental differences that it is obvious they have been designed for entirely different markets.

The MM57109

The MM57109 is described by National Semiconductors as "a number-oriented microprocessor intended for use in number-processing applications". This is a general-purpose chip and may be interfaced to a host microprocessor or operated as a microprocessor in its own right with some additional logic. In order to operate a number-cruncher chip, three things are necessary: the ability to enter numeric data, the ability to enter instructions, and the ability to read the result.

Before considering the details of the MM57109 it is instructive to examine the way the number-cruncher chips handle data. Conventional microprocessors have a one-address instruction format, the operation code being followed by the address of the data taking part in the operation. In order to operate on two words together (e.g. addition, subtraction, logical AND) or to move data from one place to another, a temporary resting place for the data is necessary. This is called the accumulator. Most number-cruncher chips and many pocket calculators have done away with the necessity of providing explicit addresses for data by employing a stack mechanism.

A stack is a data structure in which data is removed in the reverse order from which it is entered. Consequently, a stack is sometimes referred to as a "last in first out" (LIFO) queue. Two basic operations closely associated with the stack are:

PUSH: this places a new item of data on the top of the stack and pushes all the other items down one place.

PULL (or POP): this removes the item of data from the top of the stack and pulls all the other items up one place.

The stack may be realized in either hardware or software. In a software stack the data is not physically pulled or pushed but a pointer, the stack pointer, is incremented or decremented whenever an item is added to or removed from the stack. In this case the stack is actually a region of RAM. Number crunchers base their addressing mechanism on the stack because of the ease with which arithmetic expressions may be processed unambiguously, and without the need for parentheses or any explicit addressing facility. Consider the evaluation of the arithmetic expression $(A+B)(C-D)$ in a stack-based machine. Table 6.28 gives the sequence of operations carried out during the evaluation of this expression and Fig. 6.81 defines the state of the stack at each step of the calculation. Note that the operation ↑ after numbers A and C represents the operation "enter the number onto the stack". This operation is unnecessary if a function key is to be pressed following a number because the function key enters the last number from the keyboard before carrying out its intended action. The sequence of operations in Table 6.28 may be written as $AB+CD-*$ in what is called postfix notation, or reverse Polish notation, in honor of J. Lukasiewicz who investigated its properties.

It should now be clear that in a stack-based machine arithmetic (or logical) operations act on the data at the top of the stack if the operation is monadic, or on the top two items of data if the operation is dyadic. Data which takes part in an operation is removed from the stack (PULLED) and the result is put on the top of the stack (PUSHED). Both the MM57109 and the Am9511 have special operations which manipulate the order of data on the stack (in addition to PUSH and PULL).

Table 6.28 The Steps Involved in the Evaluation of the Arithmetic Expression $(A+B)(C-D)$

Step	*Key*	*Operation*
1	$A\uparrow$	PUSH *A*
2	*B*	PUSH *B*
3	+	PULL *A*, PULL *B*, ADD *A* + *B*, PUSH RESULT
4	$C\uparrow$	PUSH *C*
5	*D*	PUSH *D*
6	−	PULL *D*, PULL *C*, SUBTRACT *D* FROM *C*, PUSH RESULT
7	*	PULL (*C* − *D*), PULL (*A* + *B*), MULTIPLY (*C* − *D*) BY (*A* + *B*), PUSH RESULT

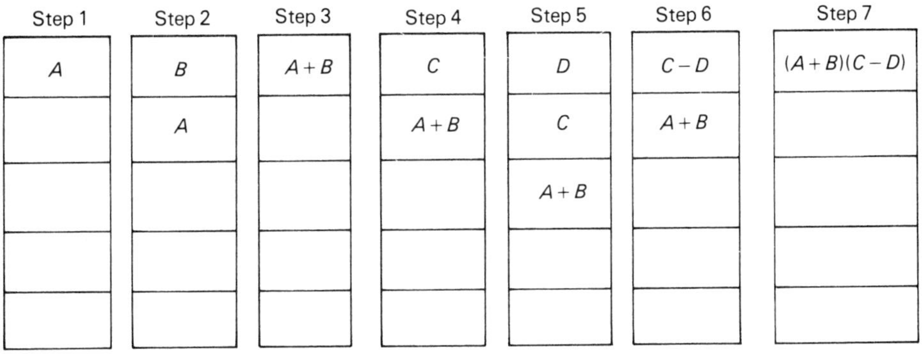

Step 1	Step 2	Step 3	Step 4	Step 5	Step 6	Step 7
A	*B*	*A* + *B*	*C*	*D*	*C* − *D*	(*A* + *B*)(*C* − *D*)
	A		*A* + *B*	*C*	*A* + *B*	
				A + *B*		

Fig. 6.81 The state of the stack during the evaluation of $(A+B)(C-D)$

For example, the Am9511 can rotate the stack—effectively a PULL except that the item pulled is transferred to the bottom of the stack.

The basic internal arrangement of the MM57109 is given in Fig. 6.82. This device requires a 9 V power supply, normally arranged so that the V_{ss} rail is at +5 V with respect to the host microprocessor's ground (i.e. V_{ss} of the MM57109 = V_{cc} of the CPU), and the V_{dd} rail is at the non-standard voltage of −4 V with respect to the microprocessor's ground. This unorthodox arrangement facilitates interconnection

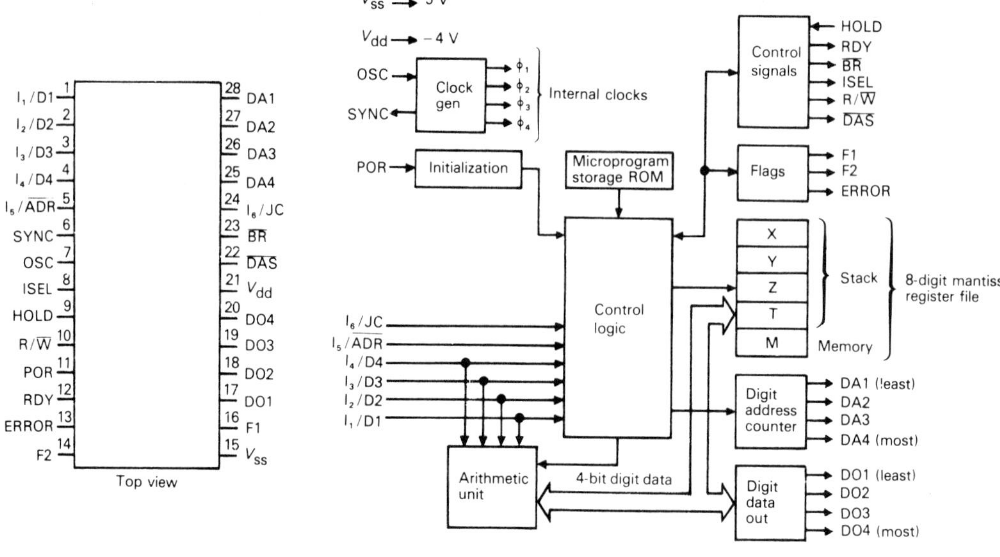

MM57109 pin description

Mnemonic	*Pin number*	*Functional name*	*Description*
V_{ss}, V_{dd}	15, 21	V_{ss}, V_{dd}	$V_{ss} = V_{dd} + 9$ V nominally (V_{ss} = Logic "1")
POR	11	Power on reset	Set high for at least 8 oscillator periods to power on. MM57109 will then set R/$\overline{W}$ = 1, other outputs = 0, and generate 3 ready pulses before reading first instruction. HOLD must be 0 to complete each ready pulse.
OSC	7	Oscillator input	Single phase clock with frequency 4× microcycle time. Typical frequency is 400 kHz.
SYNC	6	Sync output	Active low output pulse once each microcycle.
RDY	12	Ready	Rising edge indicates processor is ready to execute next instruction or get second word of 2-word instruction. If HOLD = 0, RDY goes low again and next instruction is executed. If HOLD = 1, RDY stays high until HOLD = 0. RDY can be used to clock an external program counter or to request an instruction from another CPU.
HOLD	9	Hold	When set high prior to or at the rising edge of RDY, RDY will be held high and instruction execution delayed until HOLD is set low.
$\overline{BR}$	23	Branch	A 1 microcycle active low pulse indicates a program branch. RDY goes high during this pulse. $\overline{BR}$ may be used as a load signal for an external PC or as a sense input to a microprocessor.
ISEL	8	Instruction select	Selects 6-bit instruction code (ISEL = 1) or JC, $\overline{ADR}$, D4 − D1 (ISEL = 0) on $I_6 - I_1$ (the 6 input lines).
R/$\overline{W}$	10	Read/$\overline{Write}$	Active-low pulses during OUT instruction to write data digits into a RAM or register. Address and data are valid at both edges. R/$\overline{W}$ is also pulsed during a PRW1 or PRW2 instruction.
I_6, JC	24	Input 6, Jump Condition	Most significant instruction bit when ISEL = 1. Jump condition for TJC instruction when ISEL = 0. (JC = 1 indicates jump condition true.)
I_5, $\overline{ADR}$	5	Input 5, AIN Data Ready	Instruction bit 5 when ISEL = 1. AIN Data Ready ($\overline{ADR}$) for AIN instruction when ISEL = 0. $\overline{ADR}$ = 0 for data ready.)
$I_4 - I_1$, D4 − D1	4, 3, 2, 1	Inputs 4 − 1, Data 4 − 1	Instruction bits 4 − 1, or mantissa digit count on second word of SMDC instruction, when ISEL = 1. Digit data (AIN or IN instructions) when ISEL = 0. Bit 4 is the most significant bit.

MM57109 pin description

Mnemonic	*Pin number*	*Functional name*	*Description*
DA4 – DA1	25, 26, 27, 28	Digit address 4 – 1	Digit address for AIN, IN, and OUT instructions. Used as multiplex selector (AIN) or as low-order address (IN, OUT) for RAM or other I/O device. Bit 4 is the most significant bit. Blanked (= 0) after each IN, OUT, or AIN instruction.
$\overline{\text{DAS}}$	22	Digit address strobe	Active-low pulse indicates digit address is changing. New address is valid on second (positive-going) edge.
DO4 – DO1	20, 19, 18, 17	Digit outputs 4 – 1	BCD digit output for OUT instruction. Blanked (= 0) after each OUT instruction. Bit 4 is the most significant bit.
F1	16	Flag 1	User-controlled flag can be set or pulsed (reset if high).
F2	14	Flag 2	User-controlled flag can be set or pulsed (reset if high). Active-low pulse (set if low) generated after each AIN data read. This can be used as an acknowledge signal to clear a flip-flop.
ERROR	13	Error flag	Set on an arithmetic or OUT error. Reset by ECLR instruction.

Fig. 6.82 The internal arrangement of the MM57109 and its pin functions

between the MM57109 number cruncher and the rest of the microprocessor system. The MM57109 should be thought of as a pocket-calculator chip designed to be interfaced to a microprocessor system.

Before dealing with the interface between the MM57109 and the microprocessor, it is necessary to look at the number cruncher's data format and the way in which data may be entered or removed from it. The MM57109, like all pocket calculators, has an internal architecture dedicated to BCD operations. Numbers may be entered into the MM57109 (or removed from it) in either a fixed-point or a floating-point format. Fixed-point numbers are represented by eight decimal digits plus a decimal point which may be located at any digit boundary. This results in a number in the range of 99999999 to 0.00000001.

Floating-point numbers are represented by an 8-digit fractional mantissa and a 2-digit exponent in the form

$$\pm 0.XXXXXXXX * 10^{\pm YY}$$

where X and Y represent any decimal digits. This representation gives a range of 10^{+99} to 10^{-99}, sufficient for the vast majority of scientific calculations. Although data may be moved into and out of the number cruncher in two different formats, all internal calculations are carried out in floating-point form. In their literature National Semiconductor call my fixed point format *floating point* and my floating point format *scientific notation.*

Because the MM57109 is such a general-purpose device it has three different ways in which data may be entered into it, although in each case the data is written into the top of the stack (the X register). The simplest way of entering data is to make the data part of the input instruction itself—this is akin to Motorola's inherent mode of addressing. The MM57109 has six lines labelled $I_1 - I_6$ which serve to input instructions into the device. There are 15 data entry instructions of the form:

Operation	op-code on $I_1 - I_6$
Enter 0	000000
Enter 1	000001
Enter 2	000010
Enter 3	000011
Enter 4	000100
Enter 5	000101
Enter 6	000110
Enter 7	000111
Enter 8	001000
Enter 9	001001
Enter decimal point	001010
Enter exponent	001011
Change sign	001100
Enter π	001101
Terminate number entry and push the current number onto the stack	100001

When the number cruncher is interfaced to a microprocessor, the above instructions represent the most convenient way (i.e. requiring the least amount of interface circuitry) of entering data into the chip.

There are two other modes by which data may be entered into the MM57109, although these modes are not well-suited to applications in which the chip is controlled by a microprocessor. The IN instruction inputs a multi-digit number, while the AIN instruction inputs a single digit each time it is executed. Both these instructions employ the number cruncher's digit input lines D1 – D4. These lines are also the instruction input lines $I_1 - I_4$. Whenever data is being read into the chip the ISEL (Instruction Select) output goes low, indicating that data, rather than an instruction, is requested. When an IN instruction is executed a 4-bit address is supplied by the chip on its DA1 – DA4 outputs together with an active-low pulse on the $\overline{\text{DAS}}$ (digit-address strobe) pin for each digit to be input. While the IN instruction is being executed the digit address line (DA1 – DA4) are sequenced through the values indicating which digit is to be input next.

The AIN instruction operates asynchronously and inputs a single digit. Once this instruction has been encountered the ISEL output goes low, indicating that data is required. The $\overline{\text{ADR}}$ (AIN DATA READY) pin is used by the interface to indicate that the contents of D1 – D4 contain a valid digit. As long as $\overline{\text{ADR}}$ is high, the chip remains in a wait state. When $\overline{\text{ADR}}$ goes low, the F2 flag output is pulsed low to acknowledge the receipt of the input. This instruction with its handshaking arrangement indicates just how general purpose this chip is.

All three input instructions have the same effect on the way data is stored in the number cruncher. When the first digit of a number is entered the stack is pushed and the X register is cleared: $Z \to T$, $Y \to Z$, $X \to Y$, $0 \to X$. Further digits are entered into the X register until the entry is terminated by any instructions other than 0 – 9, DP, EE, CS, PI, AIN or HALT. The number is then normalized.

The MM57109 has only one method of outputting its data. An OUT instruction transfers data between the number cruncher and its interface by means of the four output lines DO1 – DO4. The actual number of digits and the format of the data depend on whether the MM57109 is operating in a fixed-point or a floating-point mode. As each BCD digit is placed on DO1 – DO4 following an OUT instruction, the number cruncher's R/$\overline{W}$ line is pulsed low indicating the presence of a valid output to the interface circuit.

Interfacing the MM57109 to a Microprocessor

From an electrical point of view the MM57109 goes a long way to proving that semiconductor manufacturers have a sense of humor: its input lines have three different electrical characteristics, and its output lines also have three different characteristics. The clock input must swing between −2.5 V and +4 V, the HOLD and POR inputs must swing between −2.5 V and +2 V, and the $I_1 - I_6$ inputs must swing between +1 V and +4 V. Similarly, the R/$\overline{W}$, Sync, ISEL, and $\overline{BR}$ lines can drive one low-power TTL load, DO1 – DO4, F1, F2, ERROR, RDY lines can drive one TTL load, and DA1 – DA4, $\overline{DAS}$ can drive only a CMOS buffer.

The circuit diagram of the interface between an MM57109 and a 6800 system (based on an article by Nelson but untested by the author—see bibliography) is given in Fig. 6.83. This circuit is relatively simple and does not use all the facilities of the number cruncher. Although the electrical properties of the I/O lines of the MM57109 differ considerably, this chip interfaces easily to NMOS circuits—the outputs simply require 10 kΩ resistors connected to ground. Unfortunately the POR and HOLD inputs are not NMOS (or TTL) compatible and two operational amplifiers act as level shifters to convert the output of the PIA to a signal swinging almost between V_{dd} and V_{ss}.

The MM57109 requires a 400 kHz clock which is provided by a single CMOS oscillator. This clock is divided internally by 4 and all operations within the number cruncher are specified in terms of "microcycles" or units of 10 μs. The entry of a digit into the chip takes 238 microcycles (2.38 ms), while the worst case execution time for a tangent is 97 600 microcycles (0.976 s). The MM57109 is a very slow device indeed and its use can only be justified in terms of its low cost and convenience.

The basic operation of the MM57109 is relatively straightforward. Immediately after the application of power, the POR input must be raised to a logical 1 for at least 8 clock pulses. This is equivalent to a reset operation. After POR has returned low the number cruncher responds by outputting three RDY pulses of 8 microcycles duration. The first two RDY pulses are not required in a microprocessor system and are ignored. The third RDY pulse signifies that the chip is ready for an instruction to be placed on the $I_1 - I_6$ input lines. The interface must provide an op-code for the MM57109 before the falling edge of the RDY pulse. After RDY has made its high-to-low transition, the op-code on $I_1 - I_6$ is latched into the chip and the operation is executed. Sometimes, the host computer may not be ready to service the number cruncher before the RDY signal makes its active transition. In this case the interface must assert the HOLD signal which will keep RDY high until after HOLD makes a high-to-low transition. The HOLD signal must be set prior to or at the rising edge of the RDY pulse.

As the six instruction input lines $I_1 - I_6$ can specify at most 64 different operation codes, the MM57109 has resorted to two-word op-codes to furnish its 70 different operations. In such cases the RDY output is pulsed a second time for the second part of the op-codes.

Table 6.29 gives a list of the possible operation codes of the MM57109 and their effects. Some of these instructions are not relevant to the microprocessor-controlled operation of the MM57109. For example, branch instructions are available for those applications where the MM57109 can determine the order in which it receives instructions.

Table 6.29 The Op-Codes of the MM57109

An asterisk denotes a 2-word instruction.

Mnemonic	*Octal op-code*	*Full name*	*Description*
0	00	0	Mantissa or exponent digits. On first digit (d)
1	01	1	the following occurs: $Z \to T$
2	02	2	$Y \to Z$
3	03	3	$X \to Y$
4	04	4	$d \to X$
5	05	5	
6	06	6	
7	07	7	
8	10	8	
9	11	9	
DP	12	Decimal point	Digits that follow will be mantissa fraction.
EE	13	Enter exponent	Digits that follow will be exponent.
CS	14	Change sign	Change sign of exponent or mantissa. Xm = X mantissa Xe = X exponent CS causes $-X$m → Xm or $-X$e → Xe depending on whether or not an EE instruction was executed after last number entry initiation.
PI	15	Constant π	3.1415927 → X, stack not pushed.
EN	41	Enter	Terminates digit entry and pushes stack. The argument entered will be in X and Y. $Z \to T$ $Y \to Z$ $X \to Y$
NOP	77	No operation	Do nothing instruction that will terminate digit entry.
HALT	17	Halt	External hardware detects HALT op-code and generates HOLD = 1. Processor waits for HOLD = 0 before continuing. HALT acts as a NOP and may be inserted between digit entry instructions since it does not terminate digit entry.

Table 6.29 (continued)

Mnemonic	*Octal op-code*	*Full name*	*Description*
ROLL	43	Roll	Roll stack. (X → Y → Z → T → X)
POP	56	Pop	Pop stack. $Y \to X$ $Z \to Y$ $T \to Z$ $0 \to T$
XEY	60	*X* exchange *Y*	Exchange *X* and *Y*. $X \longleftrightarrow Y$
XEM	33	*X* exchange *M*	Exchange *X* with memory. $X \longleftrightarrow M$
MS	34	Memory store	Store *X* in memory. $X \to M$
MR	35	Memory recall	Recall memory into *X*. $M \to X$
LSH	36	Left shift *X*m	*X* mantissa is left shifted while leaving decimal point in same position. Former most significant digit is saved in link digit. Least significant digit is zero.
RSH	37	Right shift *X*m	*X* mantissa is right shifted while leaving decimal point in same position. Link digit, which is normally zero except after a left shift, is shifted into the most significant digit. Least significant digit is lost.
+	71	Plus	Add *X* to *Y*. $X+Y \to X$. On +, −, ×, / and YX instructions, stack is popped as follows: $Z \to Y$ $T \to Z$ $0 \to T$ Former, *X*, *Y* are lost.
−	72	Minus	Subtract *X* from *Y*. $Y-X \to X$
×	73	Times	Multiply *X* times *Y*. $Y \times X \to X$
/	74	Divide	Divide *X* into *Y*. $Y \div X \to X$
YX	70	*Y* to *X*	Raise *Y* to *X* power. $Y^X \to X$
INV + *	40,71	Memory plus	Add *X* to memory. $M + X \to M$. On INV +, −, × and / instructions, *X*, *Y*, *Z*, and *T* are unchanged.
INV − *	40,72	Memory minus	Subtract *X* from memory. $M - X \to M$
INX × *	40,73	Memory times	Multiply *X* times memory. $M \times X \to M$
INV/*	40,74	Memory divide	Divide *X* into memory. $M \div X \to M$
1/X	67	One divided by *X*	$1 \div X \to X$. On all *F* (*X*) math instructions *Y*, *Z*, *T* and *M* are unchanged and previous *X* is lost.
SQRT	64	Square root	$\sqrt{X} \to X$
SQ	63	Square	$X^2 \to X$
10X	62	Ten to *X*	$10^X \to X$
EX	61	*E* to *X*	$e^X \to X$
LN	65	Natural log of *X*	$\ln X \to X$
LOG	66	Base 10 log of *X*	$\log X \to X$
SIN	44	Sine *X*	$\mathrm{SIN}(X) \to X$. On all *F* (*X*) trig functions, *Y*, *Z*, *T*, and *M* are unchanged and the previous *X* is lost.

Table 6.29 (continued)

Mnemonic	*Octal op-code*	*Full name*	*Description*
COS	45	Cosine *X*	COS(*X*)→*X*
TAN	46	Tangent *X*	TAN (*X*)→*X*
INV SIN*	40,44	Inverse sine *X*	$SIN^{-1}(X)$→*X*
INV COS*	40,45	Inverse cosine *X*	$COS^{-1}(X)$→*X*
INV TAN*	40,46	Inverse tan *X*	$TAN^{-1}(X)$→*X*
DTR	55	Degrees to radians	Convert *X* from degrees to radians.
RTD	54	Radians to degrees	Convert *X* from radians to degrees.
MCLR	57	Master clear	Clear all internal registers and memory; initialize I/O control signals. MDC=8, MODE= floating-point.
ECLR	53	Error flag clear	0→Error flag.
JMP*	25	Jump	Unconditional branch to address specified by second instruction word. On all branch instructions, second word contains branch address to be loaded into external PC.
TJC*	20	Test jump condition	Branch to address specified by second instruction word if JC (I_6) is true (=1). Otherwise, skip over second word.
TERR*	24	Test error	Branch to address specified by second instruction word if error flag is true (=1). Otherwise, skip over second word. May be used for detecting specific errors as opposed to using the automatic error recovery scheme.
TX=0*	21	Test *X* =0	Branch to address specified by second instruction word if *X*=0. Otherwise, skip over second word.
TXF*	23	Test $\|X\|<1$	Branch to address specified by second instruction word if $\|X\|<1$. Otherwise, skip over second word, (i.e. branch if *X* is a fraction.)
TXLT0*	22	Test *X*<0	Branch to address specified by second instruction word if X<0. Otherwise, skip over second word.
IBNZ	31	Increment memory and branch if $M \neq 0$	*M*+1→*M*. If *M*=0, skip second instruction word. Otherwise, branch to address specified by second instruction word.
DBNZ	32	Decrement memory and branch if $M \neq 0$	*M*−1→M. If *M*=0, skip second instruction word. Otherwise, branch to address specified by second instruction word.
IN*	27	Multidigit input to *X*	The processor supplies a 4-bit digit address (DA4−DA1) accompanied by a digit address strobe ($\overline{DAS}$) for each digit to be input. The high-order address for the number to be input would typically come from the second instruction word. The digit is input on D4−D1, using ISEL=0 to select digit data instead of instructions. The number of digits to be input depends on the calculation mode (scientific notation or floating point) and the mantissa digit count. Data to be input is stored in *X* and the stack is pushed. (*X*→*Y*→*Z*→*T*). At the conclusion of the input, DA4−DA1=0.

Table 6.29 (continued)

Mnemonic	*Octal op-code*	*Full name*	*Description*
OUT*	26	Multidigit output from *X*	Addressing and number of digits is identical to IN instruction. Each time a new digit address is supplied, the processor places the digit to be output on DO4 – DO1 and pulses the R/$\overline{W}$ line active low. At the conclusion of output, DO4 – DO1 = 0 and DA4 – DA1 = 0.
AIN	16	Asynchronous input	A single digit is read into the processor on D4 – D1. ISEL = 0 is used by external hardware to select the digit instead of instruction. It will not read the digit until $\overline{ADR}$ = 0 (ISEL = 0 selects $\overline{ADR}$ instead of I_5), indicating data valid. F2 is pulsed active low to acknowledge data just read.
SF1	47	Set Flag 1	Set F1 high, i.e. F1 = 1.
PF1	50	Pulse Flag 1	F1 is pulsed active high. If F1 is already high, this results in its being set low.
SF2	51	Set Flag 2	Set F2 high, i.e. F2 = 1.
PF2	52	Pulse Flag 2	F2 is pulsed active high. If F2 is already high, this results in its being set low.
PRW1	75	Pulse R/$\overline{W}$ 1	Generates R/$\overline{W}$ active low pulse which may be used as a strobe or to clock extra instruction bits into a flip-flop or register.
PRW2	76	Pulse R/$\overline{W}$ 2	Identical to PRW1 instruction. Advantage may be taken of the fact that the last 2 bits of the PRW1 op-code are 10 and the last 2 bits of the PRW2 op-code are 01. Either of these bits can be clocked into a flip-flop using the R/$\overline{W}$ pulse.
TOGM	42	Toggle mode	Change mode from floating point to scientific notation or vice versa, depending on present mode. The mode affects only the IN and OUT instructions. Internal calculations are always in 8-digit scientific notation.
SMDC*	30	Set mantissa digit count	Mantissa digit count is set to the contents of the second instruction word (= 1 to 8).
INV	40	Inverse mode	Set inverse mode for trig or memory function instruction that will immediately follow. Inverse mode is for next instruction only.

Note: In this table National Semiconductor's own terminology has been used. "Scientific Notation" refers to the form: $\pm 0.XXXXXXXX \times 10^{\pm YY}$.

The circuit of Fig. 6.83 is given as an illustration of the way in which the MM57109 may be connected to a 6800 CPU, and has not been tested by the author. In order to implement this circuit a reasonable quantity of software is required to control the number cruncher as it has not been designed for ease of interfacing with a microprocessor. The principal advantage of this chip is that it operates in BCD arithmetic which means that decimal data may be entered from the keyboard,

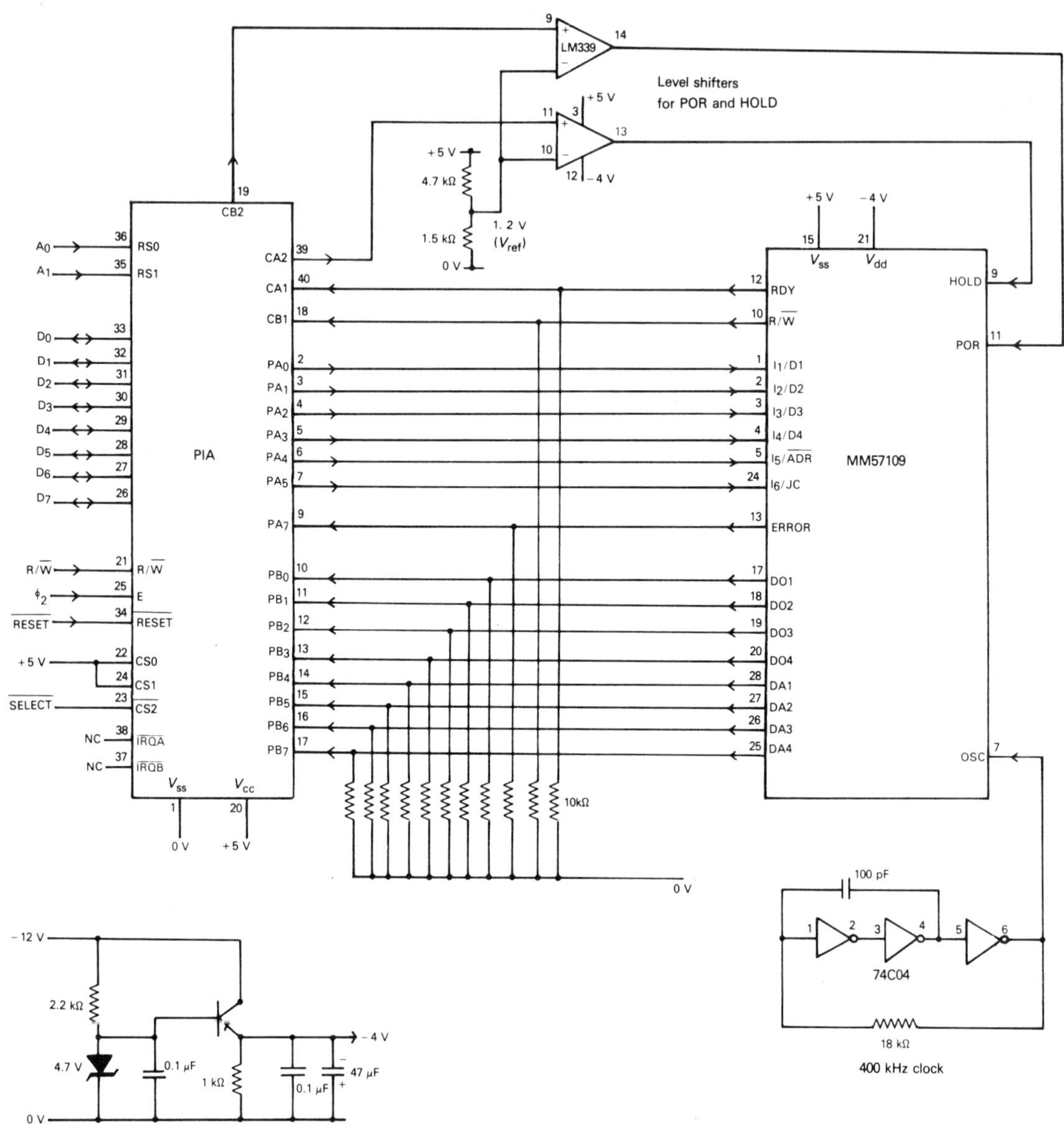

Fig. 6.83 The interface between an MM57109 and a 6800 system

processed and then displayed in decimal format. Arithmetic processor chips which operate in binary arithmetic require additional software to convert decimal data into binary format. Of course, where the calculations are not required directly by humans, for example in process control, there is no advantage in BCD arithmetic. It has been stated that the MM57109 is slower than the equivalent software run on a standard microprocessor. That is, replacing the MM57109 with a ROM containing the routines performed by the number cruncher will actually speed up the calculations. As remarked earlier in this section, the advantage of the MM57109 is that it does away with the need to write this software. At least one company produces an interface board containing the MM57109, a PIA, and the necessary software to drive the number cruncher at a very modest price.

The Am9511

Before looking closely at the Am9511 arithmetic processor unit (APU) it is worthwhile comparing it briefly with the MM57109. Both devices are external logic processors designed to relieve a host microprocessor of many arithmetic data processing duties. The principal differences between the Am9511 and the MM57109 may be summarized as:

Speed — The Am9511 is an NMOS device capable of operating at a clock rate of 2 MHz (3 MHz for the Am9511-1 version), and is approximately 200 times faster than the MM57109.

Electrical — The Am9511 is a TTL-compatible device and employs a standard +5 V and +12 V power supply.

Functional — The Am9511 looks, to the host microprocessor, like any other microprocessor support chip, while the MM57109 requires both special hardware and software to interface it to most microprocessors.

Operational — The Am9511 operates in single-precision, double-precision integer, and floating-point binary formats as opposed to the MM57109's fixed- and floating-point BCD formats.

Cost — The Am9511 is approximately ten times more expensive than the MM57109.

From the above list of differences, it should be obvious that the Am9511 is intended for the professional market in applications where complex fixed- and floating point operations must be performed very rapidly.

Like the MM57109, the Am9511 has a stack-based architecture although the width of the stack (that is, the number of bits representing an item of data on the stack) is dependent on the data type. Three types of numerical quantity are supported by the Am9511: a 16-bit single precision integer in the range −32 768 to 32 767, a 32-bit double-precision integer in the range −2 147 483 648 to +2 147 483 647, and a 32-bit floating-point number. The floating-point number is composed of a 24-bit fractional mantissa, a 7-bit, 2s complement exponent in the range −64 to +63, and a separate sign bit for the mantissa. Figure 6.84 illustrates the Am9511's floating-point format. A floating-point number is stored internally in a normalized form so that the most significant bit of the mantissa is always 1 and the mantissa is in the range ±(0.111...1 to 0.100...0), or is zero. The range of numbers

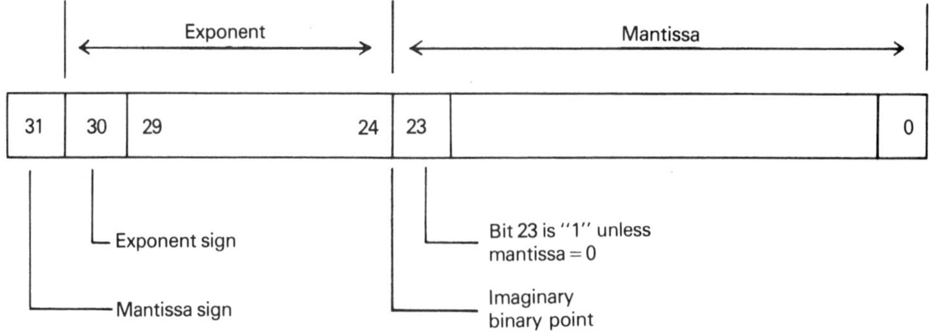

Fig. 6.84 Floating-point format of the Am9511

represented by the Am9511 is $\pm(2.7 \times 10^{-20}$ to $9.2 \times 10^{18})$ which is considerably lower than that of the MM57109. This may be very important in some applications.

Figure 6.85 illustrates the organization of the Am9511's stack. When dealing with 16-bit words the stack may be considered as 8 words deep, and when dealing with 32-bit words as effectively 4 words deep. The stack itself is really a 16-word deep, 1-byte wide stack and data enters or leaves the stack two or four bytes at a time, depending on the type of data being dealt with.

Data is written into the stack a byte at a time in the order B1, B2, B3, ..., and is

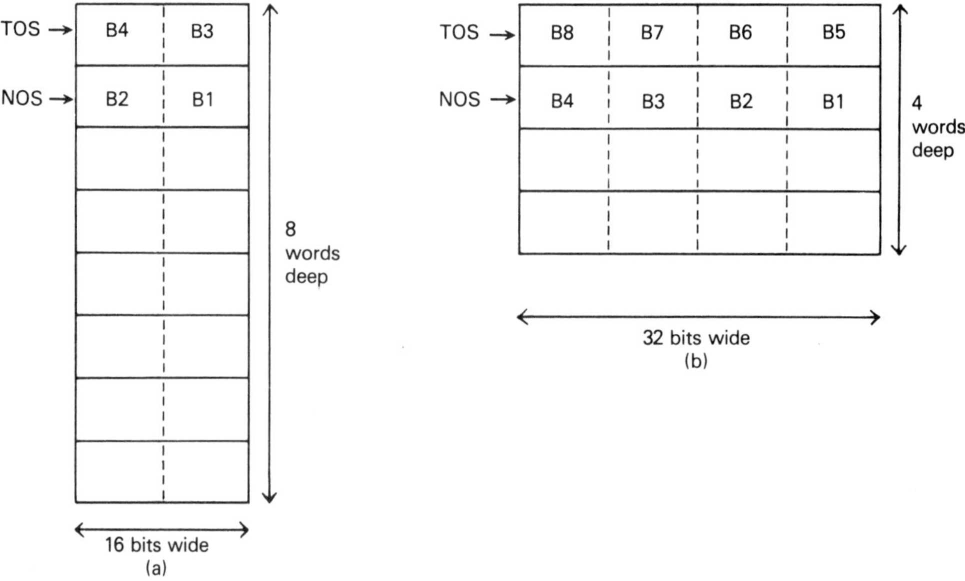

Fig. 6.85 The stack organization of the Am9511: (a) the stack configured for single-precision data; (b) the stack configured for double-precision data.

removed from the stack in the reverse order B8, B7, B6,.... Once more, it must be stated that it is the job of the programmer to enter or remove data from the stack in multiples of the number of bytes appropriate to the chosen data format. In contrast with the MM57109 the data locations within the stack do not have explixit names (X, Y, Z, T), but the top two locations on the stack are referred to (in AMD's literature) as TOS and NOS. TOS refers to the top of the stack and NOS refers to the next value on the stack.

Operation of the Am9511

The block of the internal arrangement of the Am9511 is given in Fig. 6.86. This device is really a special-purpose microprocessor designed to execute arithmetic operations. Its input/output lines are carefully tailored to make interfacing with a host microprocessor as easy as possible. This arithmetic processor has been designed specifically to interface with the 8080 microprocessor, although with a little extra logic it will interface with the 6800.

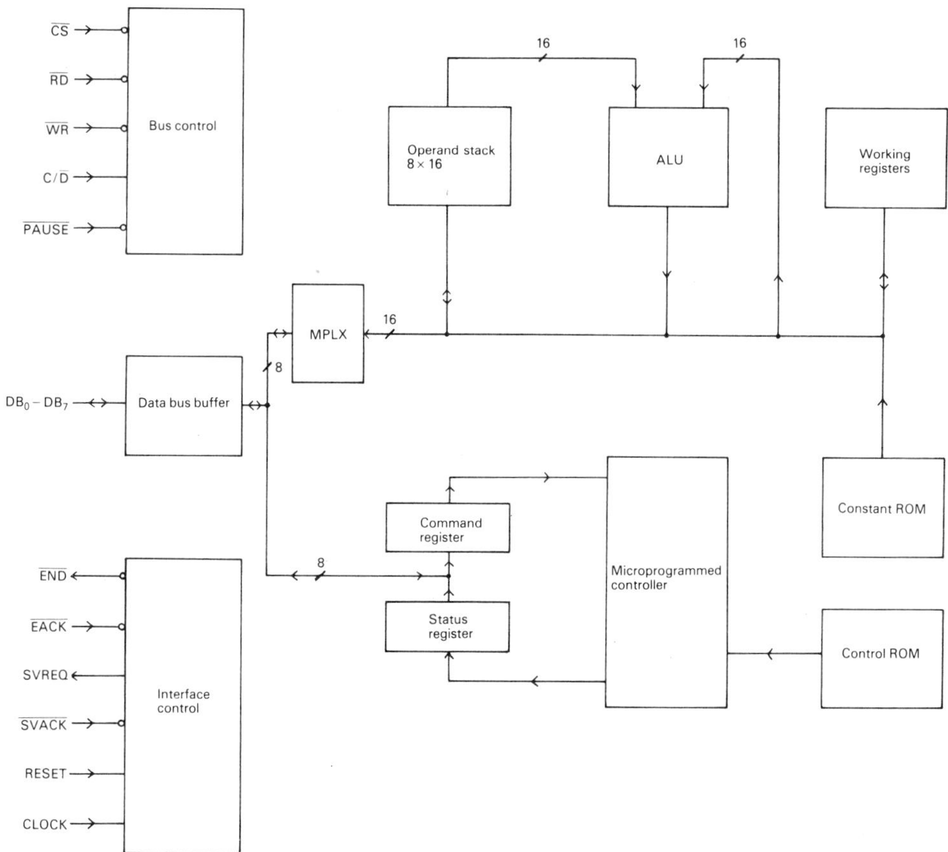

Fig. 6.86 The internal arrangement of the Am9511

From Fig.6.86 it can be seen that the Am9511 has three distinct groups of interface lines: bus-control lines, an 8-bit bidirectional data bus, and interface control lines. The first two groups of lines exist to move data, in an orderly fashion, between the Am9511 and the host processor. Their function is as follows:

$\overline{\text{CS}}$ The active-low chip select ($\overline{\text{CS}}$) input enables the chip during read or write operations. This input must make its active transition no later than the $\overline{\text{RD}}$, $\overline{\text{WR}}$, or C/$\overline{\text{D}}$ inputs become invalid, and it must not return high until 60 ns after $\overline{\text{WR}}$ has made a low-to-high transition in a write cycle.

$\overline{\text{RD}}$ The active-low read ($\overline{\text{RD}}$) input operates in conjunction with the ($\overline{\text{CS}}$) input to transfer information from the Am9511 to the data bus.

$\overline{\text{WR}}$ The active-low write ($\overline{\text{WR}}$) input operates in conjunction with the $\overline{\text{CS}}$ input to transfer information from the host processor's data bus to the Am9511. Both the $\overline{\text{RD}}$ and $\overline{\text{WR}}$ inputs must make their active-low transitions at the same time as, or after the active transition of the C/$\overline{\text{D}}$ input. The $\overline{\text{RD}}$ and $\overline{\text{WR}}$ signals must return high, at the end of a read or write cycle, before the $\overline{\text{CS}}$ or C/$\overline{\text{D}}$ signals.

C/$\overline{\text{D}}$ The command/data (C/$\overline{\text{D}}$) input operates in conjunction with the $\overline{\text{RD}}$ and $\overline{\text{WR}}$ inputs to select the type of information transfer between the Am9511 and the host processor. When C/$\overline{\text{D}}$=0 numeric data is transferred in a read or write cycle, and when C/$\overline{\text{D}}$ = 1 a command is entered in a write cycle, or the status register is examined in a read cycle. This input is functionally equivalent to the register select inputs of 6800-series peripherals and is normally connected to A_0 of the CPU's address lines. Table 6.30 summarizes the relationship between $\overline{\text{CS}}$, $\overline{\text{RD}}$, $\overline{\text{WD}}$ and C/$\overline{\text{D}}$.

$\overline{\text{PAUSE}}$ The active-low $\overline{\text{PAUSE}}$ output indicates that the Am9511 has not yet completed its information transfer with the host processor over the data bus. $\overline{\text{PAUSE}}$ is, effectively, a "busy" output and is a request to the host processor for a period of waiting before the current access can be completed. $\overline{\text{PAUSE}}$ goes low after each read cycle to the Am9511 for a duration of 800 ns to a maximum of 3.05 μs (at a clock rate of 2 MHz) For a write cycle the maximum duration of the $\overline{\text{PAUSE}}$ pulse is 50 ns.

The function of the above lines is straightforward and only the action of the $\overline{\text{PAUSE}}$ output needs further elaboration. If an existing command is still in the process of execution, and a write or a read access is requested, then $\overline{\text{PAUSE}}$ goes low and remains low for the duration of the existing command, plus any time needed to initiate a read operation. Whenever $\overline{\text{PAUSE}}$ is low the host processor must neither change any information to the Am9511 nor attempt to capture data from it. In an 8080 system the $\overline{\text{PAUSE}}$ line is connected to the 8080's RDY (ready) input. When $\overline{\text{PAUSE}}$ goes low the 8080 is held in a wait (idling) state until $\overline{\text{PAUSE}}$ returns high. Unfortunately the 6800 has no RDY facility and cannot be halted in mid-operation. The $\overline{\text{HALT}}$ input of the 6800 is useless in this application because an active transition of $\overline{HALT}$ has no effect until after the end of the current operation. The only way of employing the $\overline{PAUSE}$ signal in a 6800 system is to allow $\overline{PAUSE}$ to stretch the ϕ_2-high phase of the clock signal. Unfortunately, the 6800's clock may not be stretched beyond 9.5 μs without the 6800 losing its internal data. This is sufficient for normal read access to the Am9511—but it is not sufficient if the Am9511 is accessed before it has finished an arithmetic operation.

Table 6.30 The control of the Am9511

$\overline{CS}$	$C/\overline{D}$	$\overline{RD}$	$\overline{WR}$	Function
1	x	x	x	device de-selected
0	0	1	0	enter data byte into the stack
0	0	0	1	read data byte from the stack
0	1	1	0	enter-command
0	1	0	1	read status

The Am9511 has six interface control signals whose functions are as follows:

RESET The active-high RESET input initializes the Am9511. A reset, which should last at least 5 clock periods, terminates any operation in progress, clears the status register and places the chip in an idle state. There is no automatic, internal power-on reset in the Am9511. The RESET input may be obtained from the 6800's $\overline{RESET}$ line via an invertor.

CLK The Am9511 requires an external single-phase clock at up to 2 MHz. In a 6800 system the $2f_c$ output of a 6875 or a 6871A clock generator provides the necessary CLK input to the Am9511. Fortunately, the clock input of the Am9511 may be asynchronous with respect to the $\overline{RD}$ and $\overline{WR}$ control signals.

$\overline{END}$ The active-low end of execution ($\overline{END}$) output indicates that the execution of the previously entered command is complete. This output is open-drain, and can be connected directly to the 6800's $\overline{IRQ}$ input so that an interrupt may be generated after the Am9511 has finished a task. The $\overline{END}$ signal remains active-low until the host processor brings down the $\overline{EACK}$ input (a handshaking operation). $\overline{END}$ is also cleared by a reset or any read or write access to the Am9511.

$\overline{EACK}$ The end acknowledge ($\overline{EACK}$) is an active-low input which clears the end of execution signal ($\overline{END}$) after the completion of an operation. In many applications $\overline{EACK}$ may be permanently connected to ground, in which case the $\overline{END}$ output becomes self-clearing after no less than 400 ns.

SVREQ The active-high service request output (SVREQ) indicates that the execution of a command is complete and that post execution service was requested in the previous command byte. The difference between the SVREQ output and the $\overline{END}$ output (apart from the sense of the signals) is that SVREQ is programmed and makes its active transition only if the service request flag bit which forms part of each command is set. SVREQ is cleared by the $\overline{SVACK}$ input, a reset, or by the end of a subsequent command that does not request service.

$\overline{SVACK}$ The active-low service request acknowledge input ($\overline{SVACK}$) clears the service request output (SVREQ).

Note that the SVREQ and the $\overline{SVACK}$ signals are designed to operate in conjunction with direct memory access controllers.

Interfacing the Am9511 to a 6800 CPU

The circuit diagram of an interface between the Am9511 and a 6800 CPU is given in Fig. 6.87. The operation of this circuit is quite straightforward. The

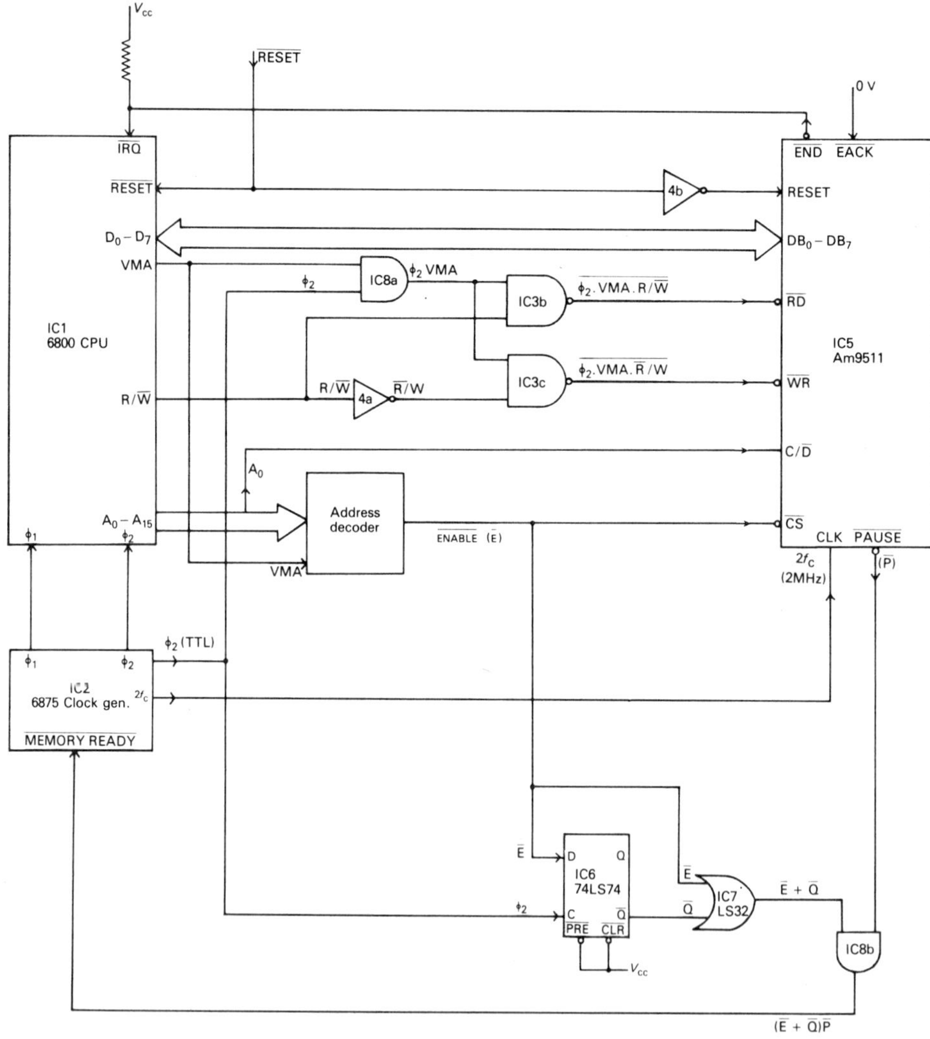

Fig. 6.87 Interfacing the Am9511 to a 6800 system

selection of the Am9511 is determined by the appropriate address decoding network which selects the Am9511 with an active-low signal $\overline{\mathrm{E}}$. The ϕ_2 signal is not needed by the address decoder because ϕ_2 takes part in the generation of the $\overline{\mathrm{RD}}$ and $\overline{\mathrm{WR}}$ strobes. By not enabling the address decoder with ϕ_2, the $\overline{\mathrm{E}}$ signal is available before $\overline{\mathrm{RD}}$ and $\overline{\mathrm{WR}}$ in accordance with the Am9511's timing requirements. The $\overline{\mathrm{RD}}$ and $\overline{\mathrm{WR}}$ signals are generated from VMA, ϕ_2 and R/$\overline{\mathrm{W}}$ by means of IC3, IC8a and IC4a.

The $\overline{\mathrm{EACK}}$ input of the Am9511 is connected to ground so that at the end of a command $\overline{\mathrm{END}}$ is pulsed low and generates an interrupt request, signifying a request for service from the 6800. The operation of the $\overline{\mathrm{PAUSE}}$ output of the Am9511 requires a little explanation. Whenever the Am9511 is accessed the $\overline{\mathrm{PAUSE}}$ output goes low, signifying that it is not yet ready to complete the read or write access. As the longest time for which $\overline{\mathrm{PAUSE}}$ may be low is 3.05 μs (assuming the APU is not busy), it is possible to connect the $\overline{\mathrm{PAUSE}}$ output of the Am9511 to the MEMORY READY input of an MC6875 clock generator. The MEMORY READY input of the MC6875 has the effect of stretching the ϕ_2-high state of the 6800 clock, as long as MEMORY READY input is low. Unfortunately a simple direct connection between $\overline{\mathrm{PAUSE}}$ and MEMORY READY is not possible.

In order to stretch ϕ_2, the MEMORY READY input must go low within the required minimum setup time, and be held low for the minimum hold time. The MEMORY READY input is sampled on the falling edge of $2f_c$, which corresponds to the rising edge of ϕ_2. Thus, if the following ϕ_2 phase is to be stretched MEMORY READY must go low approximately 60 ns before the rising edge of ϕ_2. As the $\overline{\mathrm{RD}}$ and $\overline{\mathrm{WR}}$ inputs of the Am9511 do not become active until ϕ_2 is high, the $\overline{\mathrm{PAUSE}}$ output from the Am9511 cannot satisfy the set-up requirements of the 6875. What is needed is an "interim" $\overline{\mathrm{PAUSE}}$ which anticipates the $\overline{\mathrm{PAUSE}}$ from the Am9511. An examination of Fig. 6.87 shows how this may be achieved. The $\overline{\mathrm{E}}$ output of the address decoder goes low about 300 ns after the start of a memory access cycle involving the Am9511, and is clocked into a positive edge-triggered flip flop on the rising edge of the following ϕ_2 clock pulse (approximately 200 ns later). Figure 6.88 gives the timing diagram corresponding to Fig. 6.87. The $\overline{\mathrm{E}}$ signal and the $\overline{\mathrm{Q}}$ output of the flip flop are ORed together to produce a single negative pulse ($\overline{\mathrm{E}}+\overline{\mathrm{Q}}$ in Fig. 6.88). The $\overline{\mathrm{PAUSE}}$ signal is in its inactive high state so that the result of ANDing ($\overline{\mathrm{E}}+\overline{\mathrm{Q}}$) with $\overline{\mathrm{PAUSE}}$ is a negative-going pulse. It is this signal that is connected to the MEMORY READY input of the 6875.

Because the ($\overline{\mathrm{E}}+\overline{\mathrm{Q}}$) $\overline{\mathrm{PAUSE}}$ signal goes low during the ϕ_1 portion of the clock cycle, the following ϕ_2 active-high phase of the clock is stretched for at least one half cycle. The $\overline{\mathrm{PAUSE}}$ signal goes low either at the beginning of a read cycle or 150 ns after the start of a write cycle, with the result that the ($\overline{\mathrm{E}}+\overline{\mathrm{Q}}$) $\overline{\mathrm{PAUSE}}$ signal is brought low once again and the MEMORY READY input of the 6875 is held low until the Am9511 has completed its read or write operation. Once more it must be stated that on no account must a read or write access be made while the Am9511 is busy executing a command, or $\overline{\mathrm{PAUSE}}$ will go low for the duration of the command, causing ϕ_2 to be stretched beyond its permissible limit and the program to crash. Fortunately, as the end of an operation is signified by an interrupt request from the Am9511, no problem should occur.

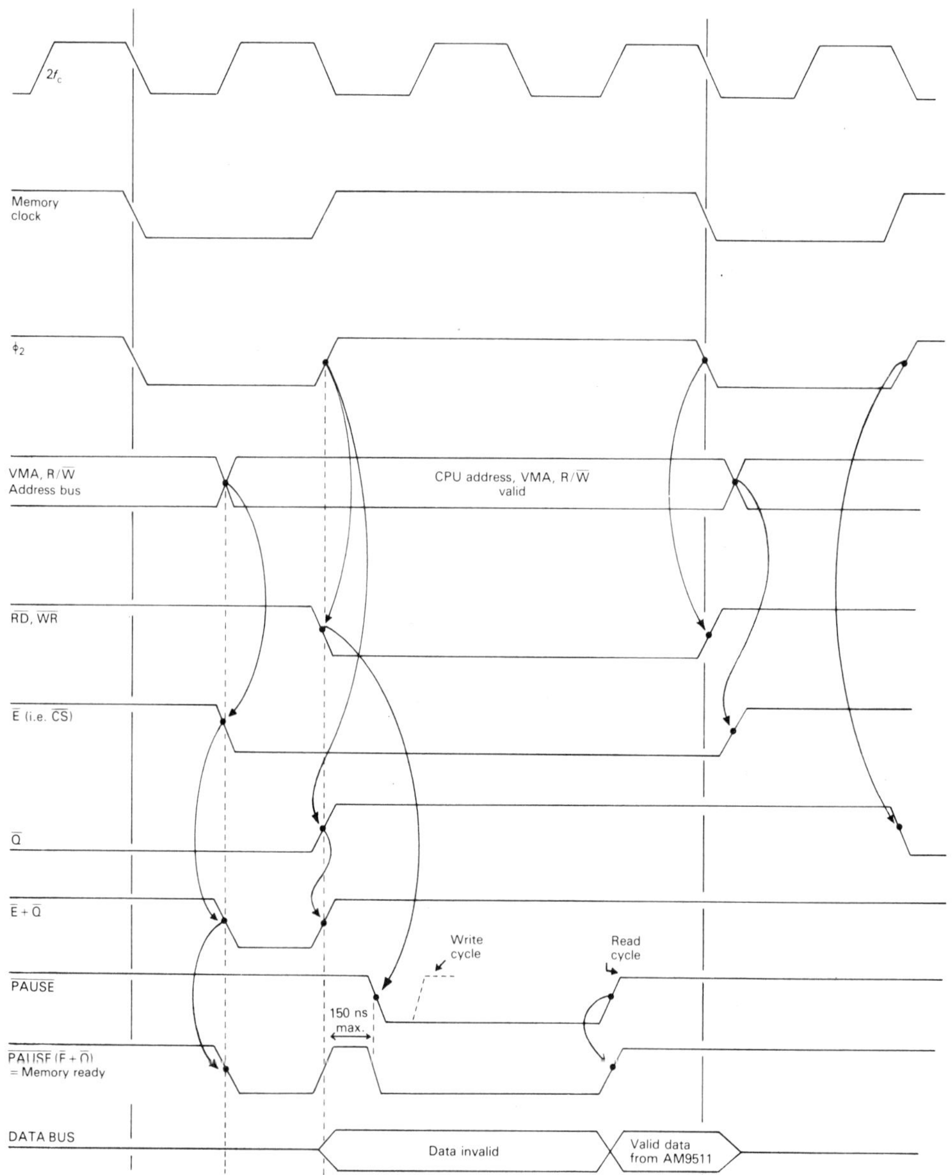

Fig. 6.88 The timing diagram of the Am9511 – 6800 interface circuit

The timing diagram of an Am9511 is given in Fig. 6.89, and Table 6.31 defines the parameters in the timing diagram.

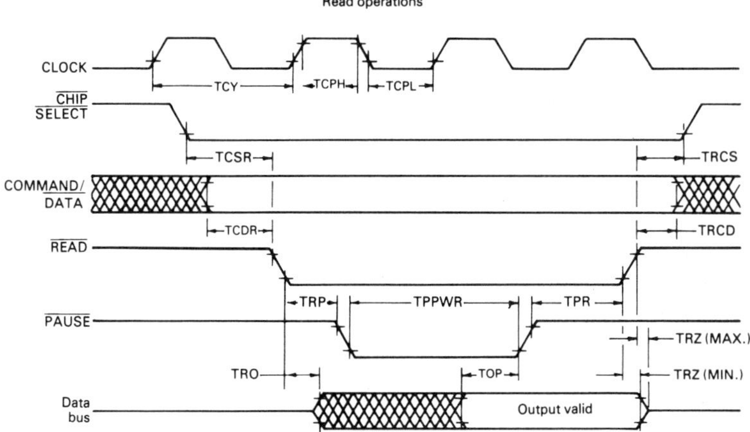

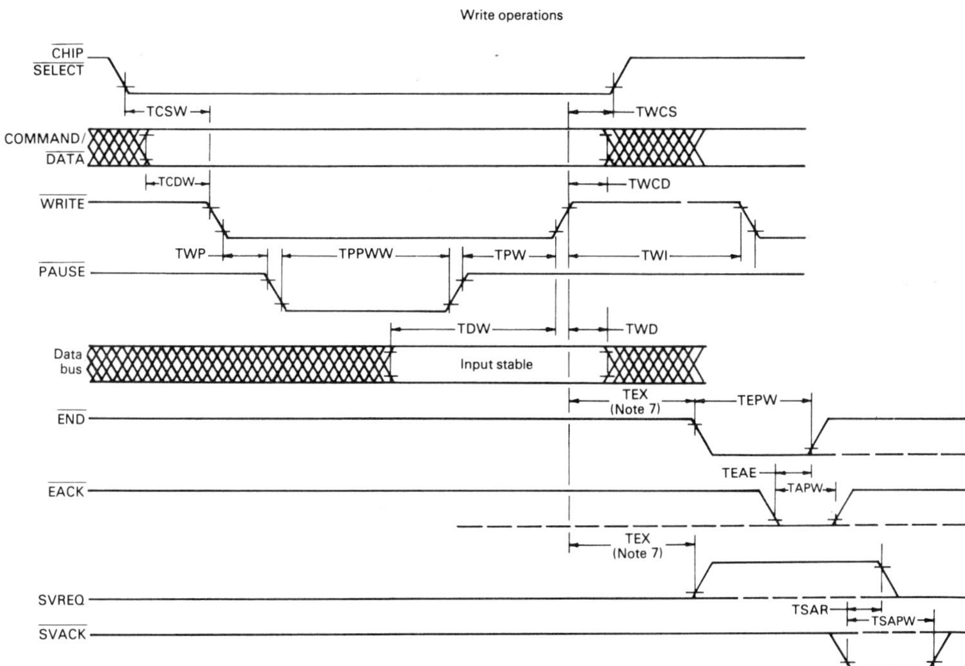

Fig. 6.89 Am9511 timing diagram (Copyright © 1980 Advanced Micro Devices, Inc. Reproduced with permission of copyright owner)

Table 6.31 The parameters of Fig. 6.89 (Copyright © 1980 Advanced Micro Devices, Inc. Reproduced with permission of copyright owner.)

Parameters	Description	Am9511 Min.	Am9511 Max.	Am9511-1 Min.	Am9511-1 Max.	Units
TAPW	$\overline{\text{EACK}}$ LOW pulse width	100		75		ns
TCDR	C/$\overline{\text{D}}$ to $\overline{\text{RD}}$ LOW set-up time	0		0		ns
TCDW	C/$\overline{\text{D}}$ to $\overline{\text{WR}}$ LOW set-up time	0		0		ns
TCPH	Clock pulse HIGH width	200		140		ns
TCPL	Clock pulse LOW width	240		160		ns
TCSR	$\overline{\text{CS}}$ LOW to $\overline{\text{RD}}$ LOW set-up time	0		0		ns
TCSW	$\overline{\text{CS}}$ LOW to $\overline{\text{WR}}$ LOW set-up time	0		0		ns
TCY	Clock period	480	5000	320	3300	ns
TDW	Data bus stable to $\overline{\text{WR}}$ HIGH set-up time		150		100	ns
TEAE	$\overline{\text{EACK}}$ LOW to $\overline{\text{END}}$ HIGH delay		200		175	ns
TEPW	$\overline{\text{END}}$ LOW pulse width (Note 4)	400		300		ns
TOP	Data bus output valid to $\overline{\text{PAUSE}}$ HIGH delay	0		0		ns
TPPWR	$\overline{\text{PAUSE}}$ LOW pulse width read (Note 5) Data	3.5TCY + 50	5.5TCY + 300	3.5TCY + 50	5.5TCY + 200	ns
	Status	1.5TCY + 50	3.5TCY + 300	1.5TCY + 50	3.5TCY + 200	
TPPWW	$\overline{\text{PAUSE}}$ LOW pulse width write (Note 8)		50		50	ns
TPR	$\overline{\text{PAUSE}}$ HIGH to $\overline{\text{RD}}$ HIGH hold time	0		0		ns
TPW	$\overline{\text{PAUSE}}$ HIGH to $\overline{\text{WR}}$ HIGH hold time	0		0		ns
TRCD	$\overline{\text{RD}}$ HIGH to C/$\overline{\text{D}}$ hold time	0		0		ns
TRCS	$\overline{\text{RD}}$ HIGH to $\overline{\text{CS}}$ HIGH hold time	0		0		ns
TRO	$\overline{\text{RD}}$ LOW to data bus ON delay	50		50		ns
TRP	$\overline{\text{RD}}$ LOW to $\overline{\text{PAUSE}}$ LOW delay (Note 6)		150		100	ns
TRZ	$\overline{\text{RD}}$ HIGH to data bus OFF delay	50	200	50	150	ns
TSAPW	$\overline{\text{SVACK}}$ LOW pulse width	100		75		ns
TSAR	$\overline{\text{SVACK}}$ LOW to SVREQ LOW delay		300		200	ns
TWCD	$\overline{\text{WR}}$ HIGH to C/$\overline{\text{D}}$ hold time	60		30		ns
TWCS	$\overline{\text{WR}}$ HIGH to $\overline{\text{CS}}$ HIGH hold time	60		30		ns
TWD	$\overline{\text{WR}}$ HIGH to data bus hold time	20		20		ns
TWI	Write inactive time (Note 8) Command	3TCY		3TCY		ns
	Data	4TCY		4TCY		
TWP	$\overline{\text{WR}}$ LOW to $\overline{\text{PAUSE}}$ LOW delay (Note 6)		150		100	ns

Notes:

1. Typical values are for $T_A = 25°C$, nominal supply voltages and nominal processing parameters.
2. Switching parameters are listed in alphabetical order.
3. Test conditions assume transition times of 20 ns or less, output loading of one TTL gate plus 100 pF and timing reference levels of 0.8 V and 2.0 V.
4. $\overline{\text{END}}$ low pulse width is specified for $\overline{\text{EACK}}$ tied to V_{SS}. Otherwise TEAE applies.
5. Minimum values shown assume no previously entered command is being executed for the data access. If a previously entered command is being executed, $\overline{\text{PAUSE}}$ LOW pulse width is the time to complete execution plus the time shown. Status may be read at any time without exceeding the time shown.
6. $\overline{\text{PAUSE}}$ is pulled low for both command and data operations.
7. TEX is the execution time of the current command (see Table 6.32).
8. $\overline{\text{PAUSE}}$ low pulse width is less than 50 ns when writing into the data port or the control port as long as the duty cycle requirement (TWI) is observed and no previous command is being executed. TWI may be safely violated as long as the extended TPPWW that results is observed. If a previously entered command is being executed, $\overline{\text{PAUSE}}$ LOW pulse width is the time to complete execution plus the time shown.

Arithmetic with the Am9511

Using the Am9511 is very easy. Data is entered into the stack by executing a write operation to the Am9511. Each data entry operation pushes all the old data down on the stack. Data at the bottom of the stack is lost. Conversely, data may be removed from the stack by executing a read data cycle to the Am9511. As data is removed from the stack the value of the NOS is moved to the TOS and the old value of TOS is not lost but is rotated to the bottom of the stack.

Commands are entered after the appropriate data has been put on the stack, so that the command can operate on the data stored on the stack. Commands requiring dual operands (e.g. ADD, MULTIPLY) operate on the TOS and NOS data words, while single operand commands (e.g. SIN, COS) act only on TOS. However, some commands do use the bottom of the stack as a scratchpad and overwrite the bottom one or two items on the stack.

The Am9511 has a status register which indicates the current status of the processor. The format of this register is given by:

BUSY	SIGN	ZERO	ERROR	CODE			CARRY
7	6	5	4	3	2	1	0

The BUSY bit indicates that the Am9511 is currently executing a command (the status register may be read while the Am9511 is busy). If BUSY is set, the other status bits are not defined.

The SIGN bit indicates that the value at the top of the stack is negative. The ZERO bit indicates that the value at the top of the stack is zero. The CARRY bit indicates that the previous operation resulted in a carry or borrow from the most significant bit.

The ERROR CODE field gives an indication of the validity of the result of the last operation, and the error codes are:

0 0 0 0	No error
1 0 0 0	Divide by zero
0 1 0 0	Square root or log of a negative number
1 1 0 0	Argument of inverse sine, cosine, or e^x too large
× × 1 0	Underflow
× × 0 1	Overflow

Table 6.32 gives the operation codes and execution times of all the Am9511's commands. AMD publishes a booklet *Algorithm Details for the Am9511 Arithmetic Processing Unit* which gives a considerable amount of information on the time taken to execute arithmetic operations, their effect on the stack, and their accuracy.

Table 6.32 The Am9511's instruction set

Command mnemonic	*Hex.code (sr = 1)*	*Hex.code (sr = 0)*	*Execution cycles*	*Summary description*
				16-bit fixed-point operations
SADD	EC	6C	16-18	Add TOS to NOS. Result to NOS. Pop stack
SSUB	ED	6D	30-32	Subtract TOS from NOS. Result to NOS. Pop stack
SMUL	EE	6E	84-94	Multiply NOS by TOS. Lower result to NOS. Pop stack
SMUU	F6	76	80-98	Multiply NOS by TOS. Upper result to NOS. Pop stack
SDIV	EF	6F	84-94	Divide NOS by TOS. Result to NOS. Pop stack
				32-bit fixed-point operations
DADD	AC	2C	20-22	Add TOS to NOS. Result to NOS. Pop stack
DSUB	AD	2D	38-40	Subract TOS from NOS. Result to NOS. Pop stack
DMUL	AE	2E	194-210	Multiply NOS by TOS. Lower result to NOS. Pop stack
DMUU	B6	36	182-218	Multiply NOS by TOS. Upper result to NOS. Pop stack
DDIV	AF	2F	196-210	Divide NOS by TOS. Result to NOS. Pop stack
				32-bit floating-point primary operations
FADD	90	10	54-368	Add TOS to NOS. Result to NOS. Pop stack
FSUB	91	11	70-370	Subtract TOS from NOS. Result to NOS. Pop stack
FMUL	92	12	146-168	Multiply NOS by TOS. Result to NOS. Pop stack
FDIV	93	13	154-184	Divide NOS by TOS. Result to NOS. Pop stack
				32-bit floating-point derived operations
SQRT	81	01	782-870	Square root of TOS. Result to TOS
SIN	82	02	3796-4808	Sine of TOS. Result to TOS
COS	83	03	3840-4878	Cosine of TOS. Result to TOS
TAN	84	04	4894-5886	Tangent of TOS. Result to TOS
ASIN	85	05	6230-7938	Inverse sine of TOS. Result to TOS
ACOS	86	06	6304-8284	Inverse cosine of TOS. Result to TOS
ATAN	87	07	4992-6536	Inverse tangent of TOS. Result to TOS
LOG	88	08	4474-7132	Common logarithm of TOS. Result to TOS
LN	89	09	4298-6956	Natural logarithm of TOS. Result to TOS
EXP	8A	0A	3794-4878	*e* raised to power in TOS. Result to TOS
PWR	8B	0B	8290-12032	NOS raised to power in TOS. Result to NOS. Pop stack
				Data and stack manipulation operations
NOP	80	00	4	No operation. Clear or set SVREQ
FIXS	9F	1F	90-214	Convert TOS from floating-point format to fixed-point format
FIXD	9E	1E	90-336	
FLTS	9D	1D	62-156	Convert TOS from fixed-point format to floating-point format
FLTD	9C	1C	56-342	
CHSS	F4	74	22-24	Change sign of fixed-point operand on TOS
CHSD	B4	34	26-28	
CHSF	95	15	16-20	Change sign of floating-point operand on TOS
PTOS	F7	77	16	Push stack. Duplicate NOS in TOS
PTOD	B7	37	20	
PTOF	97	17	20	
POPS	F8	78	10	Pop stack. Old NOS becomes new TOS. Old TOS rotates to bottom
POPD	B8	38	12	
POPF	98	18	12	

Table 6.32 (continued)

Command mnemonic	Hex.code (sr = 1)	Hex.code (sr = 0)	Execution cycles	Summary description
XCHS	F9	79	18	Exchange TOS and NOS
XCHD	B9	39	26	
XCHF	99	19	26	
PUPI	9A	1A	16	Push floating-point constant π onto TOS. Previous TOS becomes NOS

As an example, consider the evaluation of sine function, SIN.

SIN 32-bit floating-point sine

Binary coding

7	6	5	4	3	2	1	0
sr	0	0	0	0	0	1	0

Note: if sr is set a service request will be issued at the end of the command.
Execution time 3796 – 4808 clock cycles for $|A| > 2^{-12}$ radians, or 30 clock cycles if $|A| \leq 2^{-12}$ radians.
Description The 32-bit floating-point operand A at the TOS is replaced by R, the 32-bit floating point sine of A. Operands A, C, and D are lost.
Accuracy SIN exhibits a maximum relative error of 5.0×10^{-7} for input values in the range of -2π to $+2\pi$ radians.

Status affected Sign, zero.

Stack contents

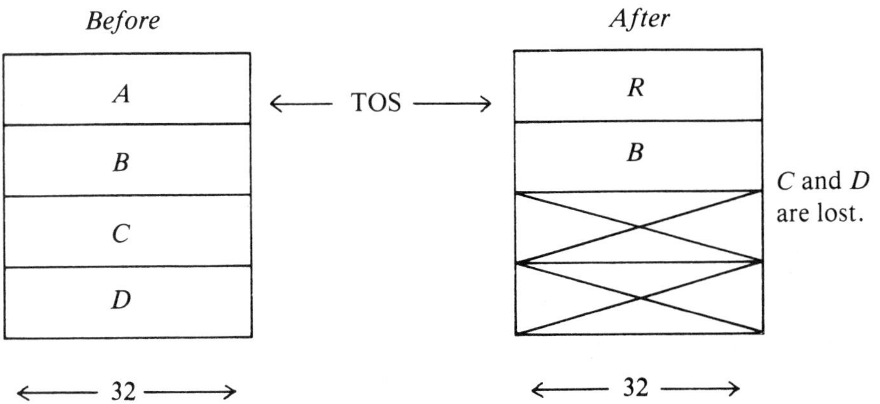

The Am9512 Floating-point Processor

Since the introduction of the Am9511 arithmetic processor, AMD has produced a so-called floating-point processor, the Am9512. The Am9512 has been created to handle floating-point operations in either single-precision (32-bit) or double-precision (64-bit) formats. Unlike the Am9511 with its wide range of arithmetic operations, the Am9512 can only add, subtract, multiply and divide floating-point binary numbers.

From an electrical point of view the Am9511 and Am9512 are virtually identical: the Am9512 has an error output (pin 6) which when high indicates that the execution of the current command resulted in an error, and the Am9512's "end of execution output" (END pin 24) is active-high while the corresponding output of the Am9511 is active-low. Apart from these details it appears that the Am9511 and Am9512 can be interchanged—providing, of course, that the "end of execution" output is not being used.

The Am9512 is used in a similar way to the Am9511. Data is written into the stack a byte at a time until either 4 bytes (single precision) or 8 bytes (double precision) have been entered. Operands are always entered into the stack with the least significant byte first. Once the operands have been entered a command is written to the Am9512 and the result removed from the stack (most significant byte first) by performing 4 or 8 read operations (as necessary).

The format of the data adopted by the Am9512 is compatible with the proposed IEEE floating-point format and differs from the arrangement used in the Am9511. The single-precision 32-bit data format is illustrated below.

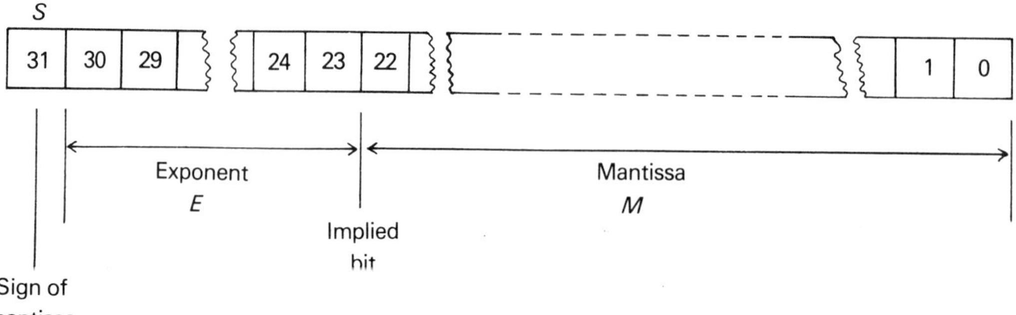

The mantissa is represented by a signed fraction with an "implied" 1 beyond the most significant bit (bit 22) of the mantissa. That is, the mantissa is a 24-bit word represented in 23 bits because the number is normalized in the range 1.00...0 to 1.11...1 so that the leading "1" may be dropped. In this notation a number N is given by:

$$N = (-1)^S 2^{E-(2^7-1)}(1.M)$$

(binary point)

The exponent is represented in a biased form where the stored exponent is 127 greater than the actual exponent.

A double-precision quantity is represented in a similar way, except that 11 bits are devoted to the exponent and 52 bits to the mantissa.

The commands available to the Am9512 and the results of some calculations using it are given in Table 6.33.

Table 6.33 The operation codes of the Am9512

Command bits 7 6 5 4 3 2 1 0	Mnemonic	Description
x 0 0 0 0 0 0 1	SADD	Add TOS to NOS single-precision and result to NOS. Pop stack
x 0 0 0 0 0 1 0	SSUB	Subtract TOS from NOS single-precision and result to NOS. Pop stack
x 0 0 0 0 0 1 1	SMUL	Multiply NOS by TOS single-precision and result to NOS. Pop stack
x 0 0 0 0 1 0 0	SDIV	Divide NOS by TOS single-precision and result to NOS. Pop stack
x 0 0 0 0 1 0 1	CHSS	Change sign of TOS single-precision operand
x 0 0 0 0 1 1 0	PTOS	Push single-precision operand on TOS to NOS
x 0 0 0 0 1 1 1	POPS	Pop single-precision operand from TOS. NOS becomes TOS
x 0 0 0 1 0 0 0	XCHS	Exchange TOS with NOS single-precision
x 0 1 0 1 1 0 1	CHSD	Change sign of TOS double-precision operand
x 0 1 0 1 1 1 0	PTOD	Push double-precision operand on TOS to NOS
x 0 1 0 1 1 1 1	POPD	Pop double-precision operand from TOS. NOS becomes TOS
x 0 0 0 0 0 0 0	CLR	CLR status
x 0 1 0 1 0 0 1	DADD	Add TOS to NOS double-precision and result to NOS. Pop stack
x 0 1 0 1 0 1 0	DSUB	Subtract TOS from NOS double-precision and result to NOS. Pop stack
x 0 1 0 1 0 1 1	DMUL	Multiply NOS by TOS double-precision and result to NOS. Pop stack
x 0 1 0 1 1 0 0	DDIV	Divide NOS by TOS double-precision and result to NOS. Pop stack

Command	*TOS*	*NOS*	*Result*	*Clock periods*
SADD	3F800000	3F800000	40000000	58
SSUB	3F800000	3F800000	00000000	56
SMUL	40400000	3FC00000	40900000	198
SDIV	40000000	3F800000	3F000000	228
CHSS	3F800000	—	BF800000	10
PTOS	3F800000	—	—	16
POPS	3F800000	—	—	14
XCHS	3F800000	40000000	—	26
CHSD	3FF0000000000000	—	BFF0000000000000	24
PTOD	3FF0000000000000	—	—	40
POPD	3FF0000000000000	—	—	26
CLR	3FF0000000000000	—	—	4
DADD	3FF00000A0000000	8000000000000000	3FF00000A0000000	578
DSUB	3FF00000A0000000	8000000000000000	3FF00000A0000000	578
DMUL	BFF8000000000000	3FF8000000000000	C002000000000000	1748
DDIV	BFF8000000000000	3FF8000000000000	BFF0000000000000	4560

Notes: x = don't care
Operation for bit combinations not listed above is undefined.
TOS, NOS and Result are in hexadecimal; Clock period is in decimal.

6.9.3 The Special Interface Module

The special interface module of the TS1 has been designed to investigate the properties of an 8-bit by 8-bit parallel multiplier chip and an arithmetic processor unit. In this sense the special interface module is an experimental module and its circuitry provides a test bed for the examination of the above devices. As the multiplier and the APU take up only a fraction of the space available on this module some other features have been included. One of these provisions is a 6821 PIA which has 20 I/O lines permitting other forms of arithmetic unit to be examined. A second feature is the inclusion of a 4K block of read/write memory, and a 4K block of ROM.

The first stage in designing the special interface module is to define its memory map. Figure 6.90 gives the memory map of the TS1 microprocessor system and the shaded portions are those blocks of memory situated on the special interface module. Note that this memory map is not to scale and that unused portions are free and available for use by new modules. The purpose of providing 4K of ROM on this module is to make room for resident programs and for any special software needed to the control multiplier and APU. This ROM is provided by two single supply voltage 2K EPROMs (Intel 2716 or Texas Instruments 2516) which are cheaper than a single 4K EPROM and have the advantage that they may be erased and reprogrammed independently of each other.

The ROM is located as close to the top end of the available memory space as possible—that is, D000 – DFFF. This leaves 0000 – CFFF (52K) of memory space for contiguous RAM. The 4K of read/write memory on this module is located at C000 – CFFF. This allows variables associated with programs involving the multiplier or APU to be kept out of the user memory space at the lower end of the memory.

The I/O memory space on the special interface module is located in two regions: EC80 – ED7F (256 bytes) for the multiplier and PIA, and EF00 – EFFF (256 bytes) for the APU. A separate I/O space is provided for the APU because of its special timing requirements (which are dealt with later).

Having determined the memory map of this module, the next step is to design the interface to the system bus and the address decoder circuits. Figure 6.91 gives these circuits. The address bus is buffered by two 74LS367 hex bus drivers which are permanently enabled. The data bus is buffered by an octal bidirectional transceiver (IC3 = 74LS245). This is controlled by the system $R/\overline{W}$ line (buffered by IC4a and 4b in series), and the $\overline{\text{ENABLE}}$ output from the address decoder circuitry (IC5 pin 12). The $\overline{\text{ENABLE}}$ signal is active low whenever an address in the ranges of C000 – CFFF, D000 – DFFF, EC80 – ECFF, ED00 – ED7F or EF00 – EFFF is present on the system address bus.

The primary address decoding is performed by IC6, a 3-line to 8-line decoder. This is enabled by $\phi_2.\text{VMA}.A_{15}$ so that it responds to a valid address in the range of 8000 – FFFF when ϕ_2 is active. The upper half of the memory map is divided into eight blocks of 4K. The block at C000 – CFFF is further subdivided into four 1K blocks by IC8a (because the RAM is provided by 1K × 4 memory components), and the block at D000 – DFFF is divided into two 2K blocks by IC8b.

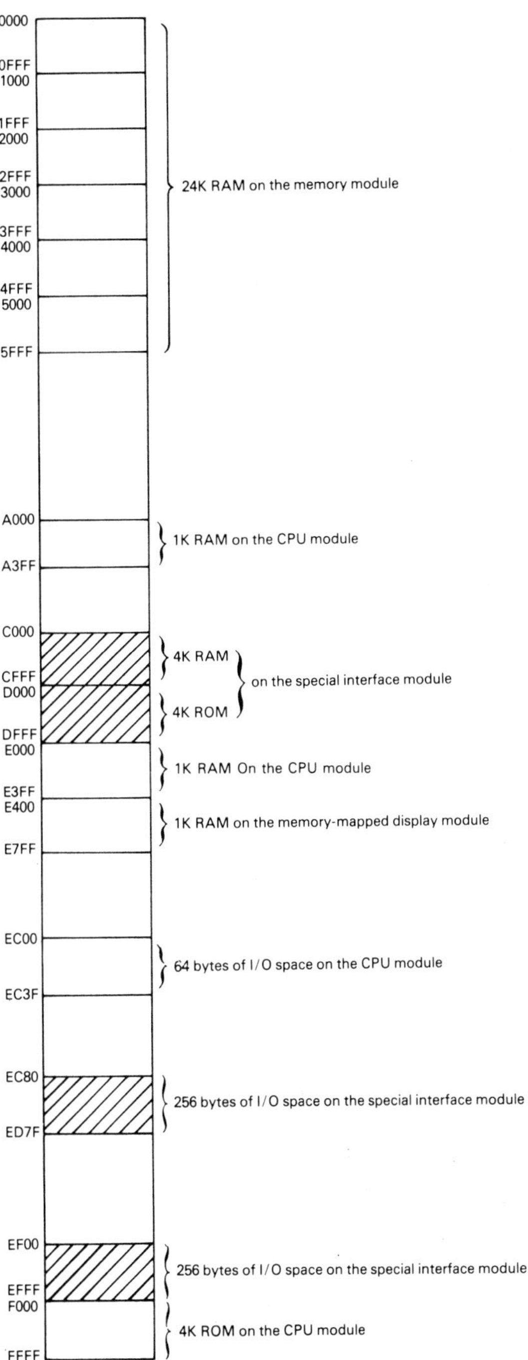

Fig. 6.90 The memory map of the TS1 microprocessor system

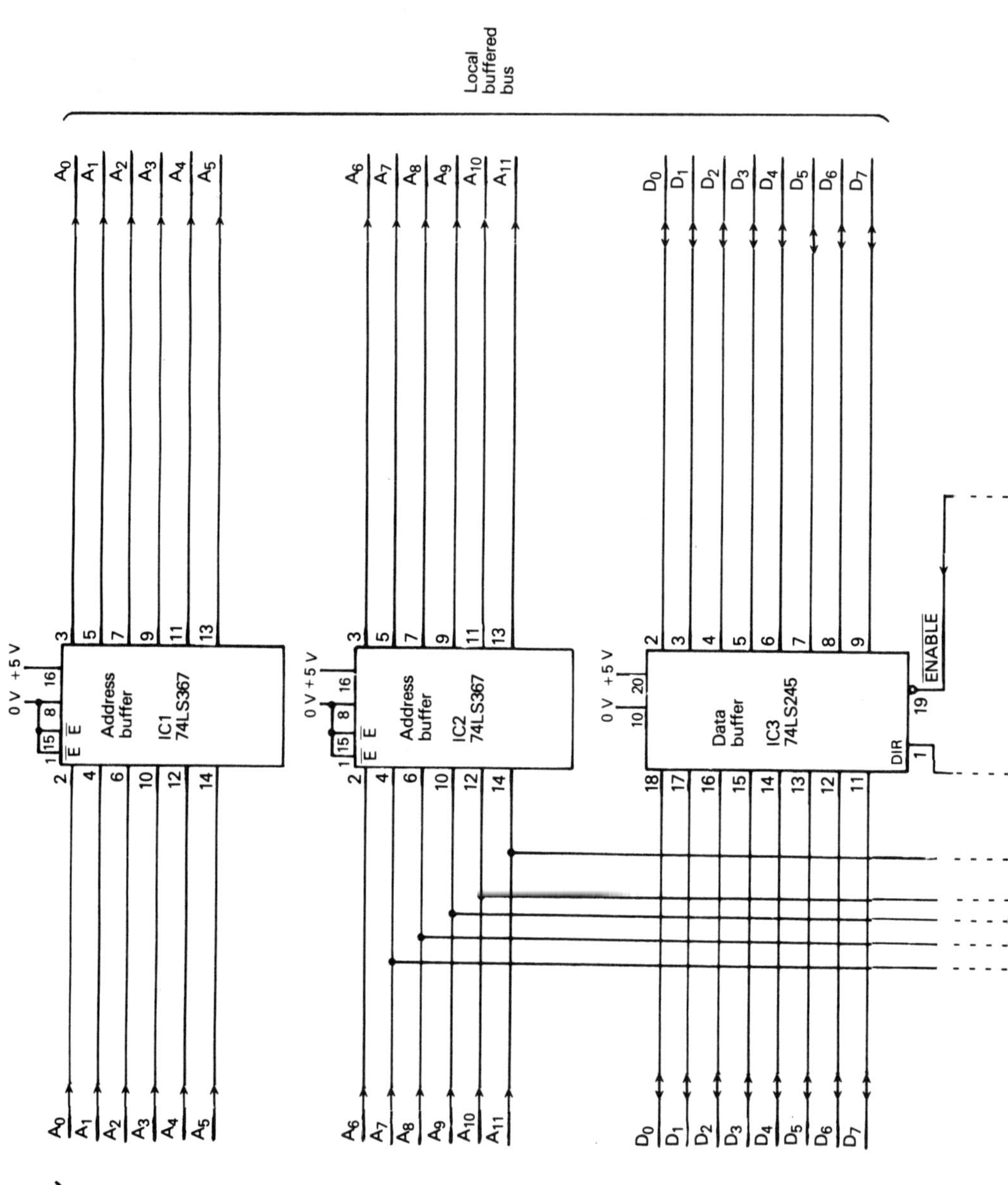
Local buffered bus
Address buffer
IC1 74LS367
Address buffer
IC2 74LS367
Data buffer
IC3 74LS245
0 V +5 V
ENABLE
DIR

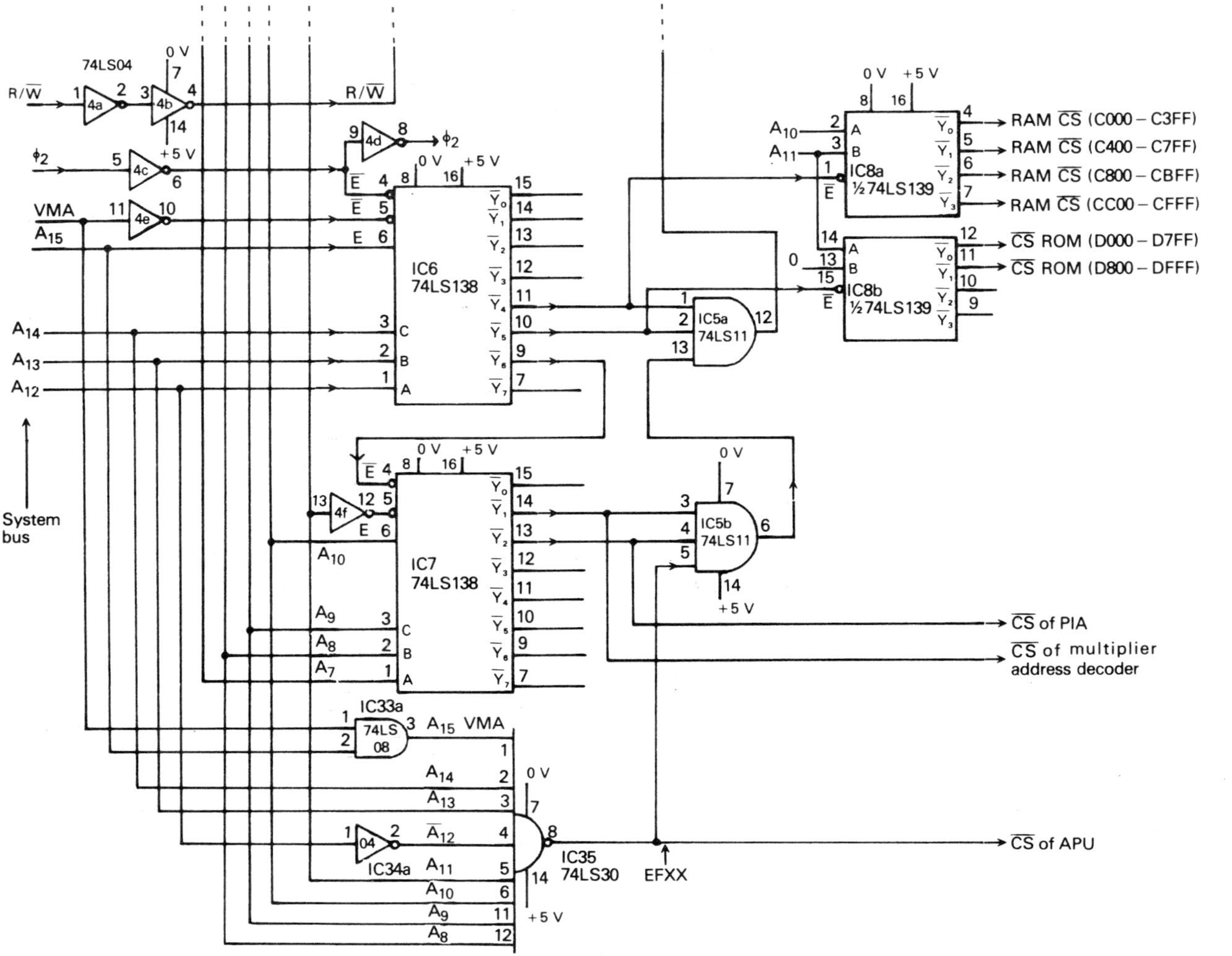

Fig. 6.91 The address decoder and bus interface circuits of the special interface module

The 4K block from E000 – EFFF is split into eight blocks of 128 bytes by a second 3-line to 8-line decoder IC7. This decoder is enabled by A_{11} and A_{10}. The 128 byte block at EC80 – ECFF is used to select the multiplier, and the block at ED00 – ED7F selects the PIA.

The APU has its own address-decoding circuitry (IC33a, IC34a, IC35) and is selected by an address in the range EF00 – EFFF. Further address decoding to limit the amount of memory space taken up by the APU could have been implemented, but was not felt to be worth the effort. The reader might wonder why one of the outputs IC7 was not used to select the APU. When examining the data sheet of the Am9511 APU it was found that its $\overline{CS}$ input must be activated before a write access is made. By not employing ϕ_2 to decode the address of the APU, its $\overline{CS}$ input may be brought low during the ϕ_1-high portion of the CPU cycle. This aspect is discussed in more detail later in this section.

All the device select outputs of decoders IC6 and IC7 are active-low so that these lines are normally in the logical 1 state. ICs 5a and 5b are used to AND together these lines so that if any of them goes low the output of IC5b goes low, enabling the data bus transceivers.

The arrangement of the RAM, ROM and PIA on the special interface module is given in Fig. 6.92. The only reason for choosing 1K × 4 RAM chips is that they were available at the time. If 4K × 1 RAM chips had been chosen all their chip-select inputs could have been connected together, removing the need for IC8a. The circuit diagram of the multiplier and APU sections of the special interface module is given in Fig. 6.93. The basic action of these circuits has been described earlier in this section. It is, however, necessary to say a few words about the timing arrangements of the Am9511. The Am9511 was designed as a peripheral for 8080 or Z80-based microprocessor systems. Consequently the logical and timing requirements of this chip have been made compatible with these microprocessors. When operating the Am9511 with a 6800 the logical differences present few problems—the reset input must be driven from the 6800's $\overline{RESET}$ line by an invertor, and $\overline{RD}$ and $\overline{WR}$ may readily be generated from VMA and $R/\overline{W}$. The only headache caused by the logical configuration of the Am9511 is its $\overline{PAUSE}$ output, which may be dealt with as described previously.

The principal difficulty in interfacing the Am9511 to a 6800 CPU is caused by timing incompatibilities between these chips. This is a general problem and arises whenever 8080-type peripherals are to be interfaced to a 6800. From the timing information on the Am9511 (Fig. 6.89) it can be seen that $\overline{CS}$ must go low before the $\overline{RD}$ or $\overline{WR}$ strobes become active. This is easily done: by not using ϕ_2 to generate a $\overline{CS}$ strobe, $\overline{CS}$ goes low during the ϕ_1-high clock phase shortly after the constants of the address bus and VMA have stabilized. The $\overline{RD}$ and $\overline{WR}$ strobes are derived from $\overline{CS}$, $R/\overline{W}$ and ϕ_2, ensuring an adequate set-up time for $\overline{WR}$ and $\overline{RD}$. Another timing problem is that in a write cycle $\overline{CS}$ should return high 60 ns before $\overline{CS}$ and $C/\overline{D}$ begin to change. Possibly the best way of solving this problem is to generate a $\overline{WR}$ signal from a monostable so that this "local" write strobe returns inactive-high at least 60 ns before the end of a write cycle. The actual solution adopted in the TS1 is to enable the $\overline{WR}$, $\overline{RD}$ strobe generator with ϕ_2.

Because of the address hold time of the 6800 and the delays incurred in the address decoders, the $\overline{CS}$ signal remains low for some time after $\overline{WR}$ or $\overline{RD}$ has made its low-to-high transition. An analysis of the TS1 system shows that the 60 ns hold time on the APU's $\overline{CS}$ input is not quite achieved although the circuit appears to function satisfactorily.

The special interface module has been constructed for purely experimental reasons. Consequently its circuit has been put together on an *ad hoc* basis and has never been rationalized. I leave that as an exercise for the reader who may redesign the circuit in a number of ways to achieve component economy. For example, consider the address decoder. As all addresses decoded by this module are in the range C000 – EFFF, the 3-line to 8-line decoder may be enabled by $A_{15} = 1$ and $A_{14} = 1$. This has the effect of dividing the memory space into eight blocks of 2K. Such an arrangement avoids the necessity for further address decoding for the EPROMs. If 4K $\times$ 1 RAM chips are used, then two 2K blocks must be combined to form a single 4K block; this may be done by means of an AND gate. Figure 6.94 gives some idea of how this address decoding may be carried out. Note that in this example the positions of the peripherals within the memory space differ slightly from those of the actual special interface module of Fig. 6.91.

The complete circuit diagram of the special interface module is given in Fig. 6.95.

Using the Am9511

In the lecture notes I hand out to my first-year students I say that floating-point arithmetic is not one of the great fun subjects of computer science. The Am9511 was clearly designed to illustrate this point. A few pages ago I remarked that "it is easy to use the Am9511". This is true only in the sense that moving data and operation codes to it, and extracting the result from it, is easy. The real problem lies in the format of the data. Unlike the MM57109, the Am9511 does not operate in a BCD mode so that if it is to be used as a calculater a considerable amount of software must be written to convert BCD data from the keyboard into the 32-bit binary floating-point format required by the processor chip. Moreover, the results of any calculation must be converted back to BCD.

Here, I am going to indicate, briefly, how the Am9511 may be used to perform calculations on binary numbers which have already been correctly formatted. The sequence of operations necessary to perform one calculation is:

(1) load the first operand onto the APU's stack;
(2) load the second operand onto the APU's stack;
(3) load the command;
(4) wait for the end of the calculation;
(5) test the APU status word for any errors;
(6) remove the result from the stack.

The above procedure is suitable for a dyadic operation. In any practical application

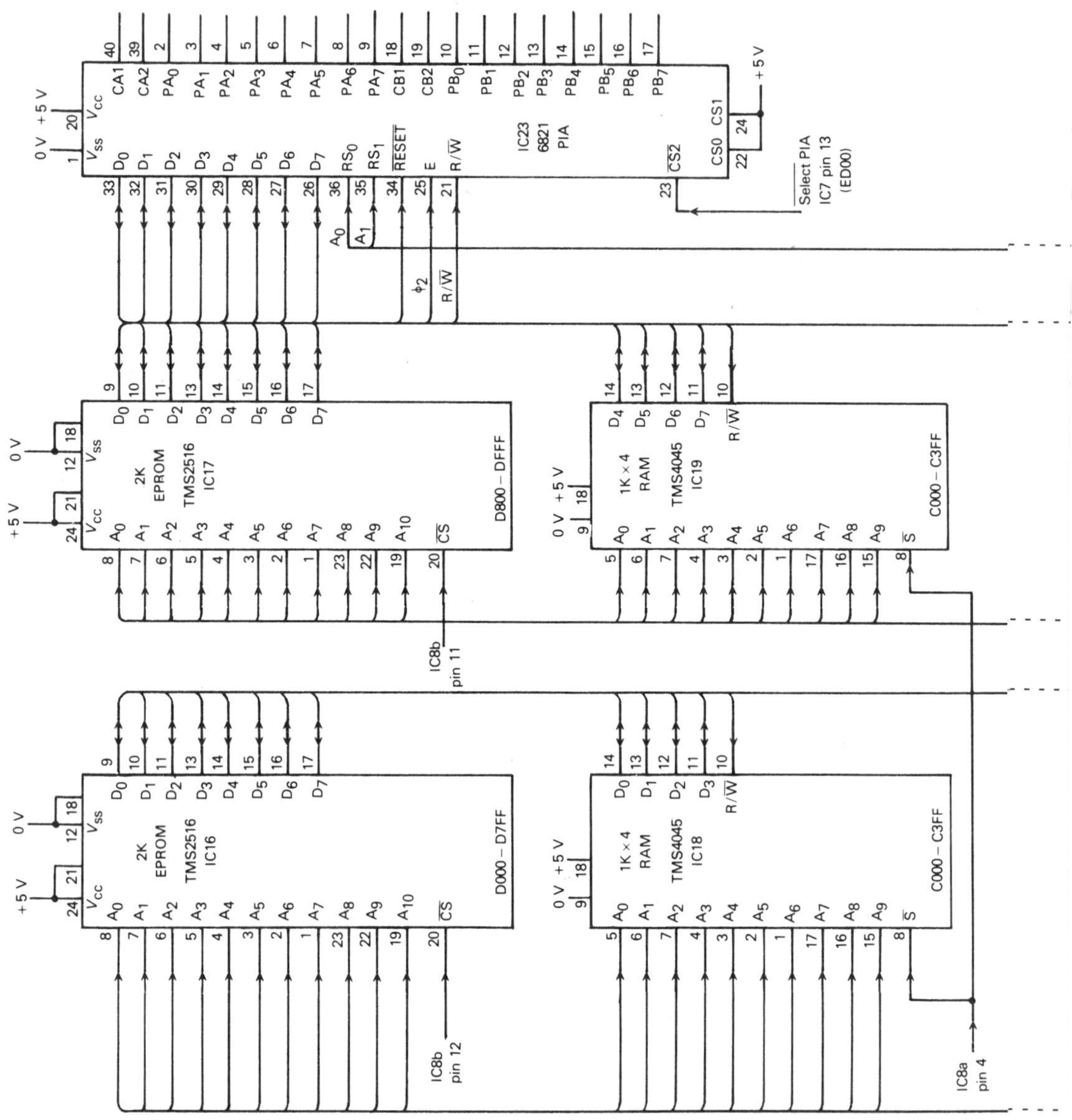
IC23
6821
PIA
0 V +5 V
+5 V
Select PIA
IC7 pin 13
(ED00)
CA1
CA2
CB1
CB2
RESET
E
R/W
CS0
CS1
CS2
RS0
RS1
φ2
2K
EPROM
TMS2516
IC17
D800 – DFFF
IC8b
pin 11
1K × 4
RAM
TMS4045
IC19
C000 – C3FF
2K
EPROM
TMS2516
IC16
D000 – D7FF
IC8b
pin 12
1K × 4
RAM
TMS4045
IC18
C000 – C3FF
IC8a
pin 4

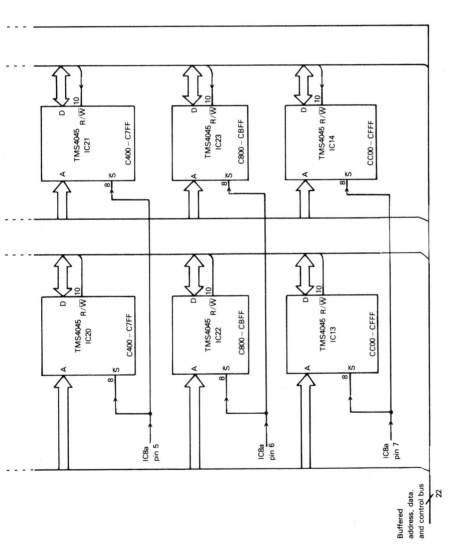

Fig. 6.92 The EPROM, RAM, and PIA on the special interface module

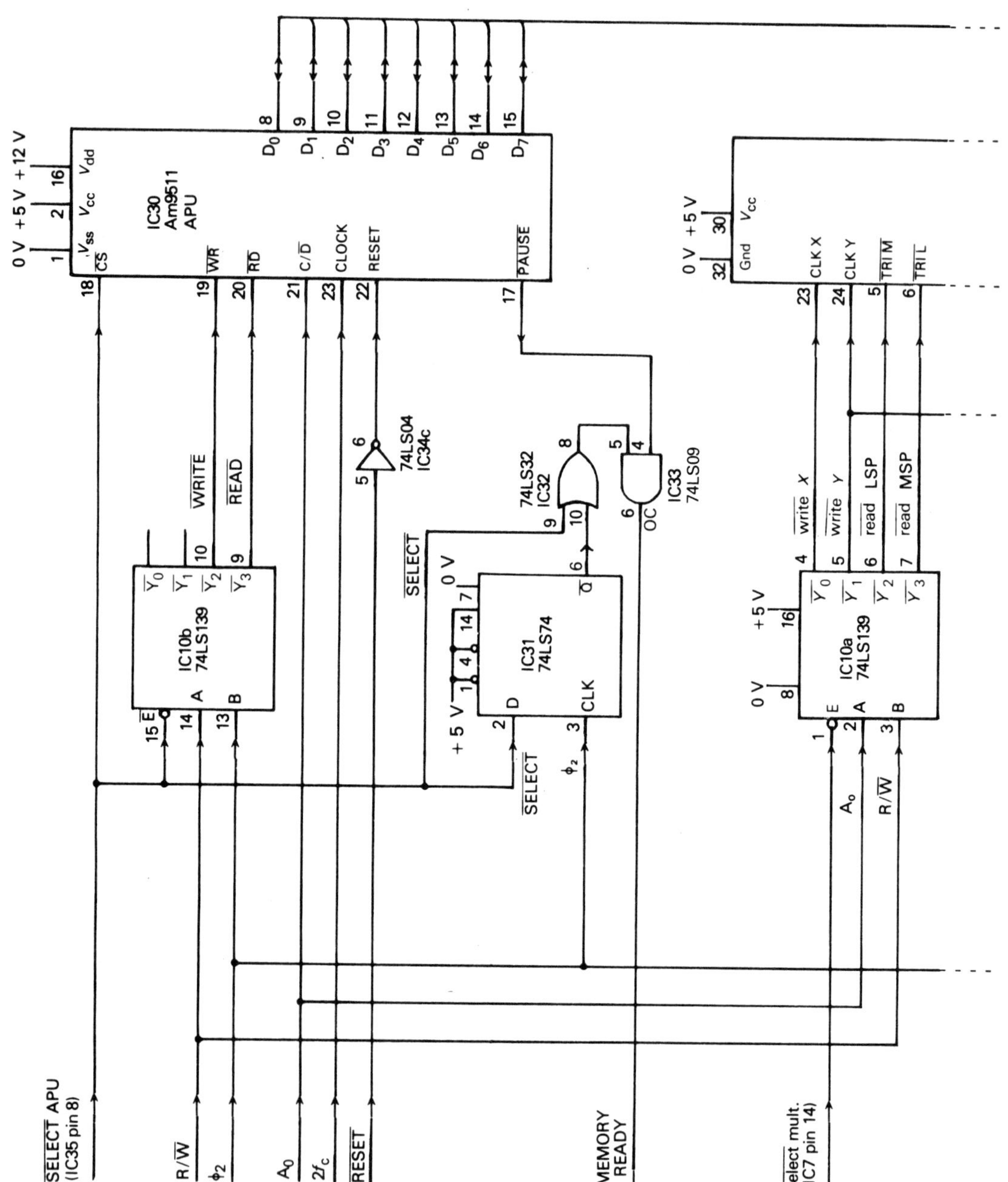
0 V +5 V +12 V
IC30
Am9511
APU
V_{ss} V_{cc} V_{dd}
CS
WR
RD
C/D
CLOCK
RESET
PAUSE
D_0 D_1 D_2 D_3 D_4 D_5 D_6 D_7
WRITE
READ
IC10b
74LS139
74LS04
IC34c
74LS32
IC32
IC33
74LS09
OC
SELECT
IC31
74LS74
+5 V
0 V
D
CLK
Q
ϕ_2
0 V +5 V
Gnd V_{cc}
CLK X
CLK Y
TRI M
TRI L
write X
write Y
read LSP
read MSP
IC10a
74LS139
E
A
B
A_0
R/W
SELECT APU
(IC35 pin 8)
R/W
ϕ_2
A_0
$2f_c$
RESET
MEMORY
READY
select mult.
(IC7 pin 14)

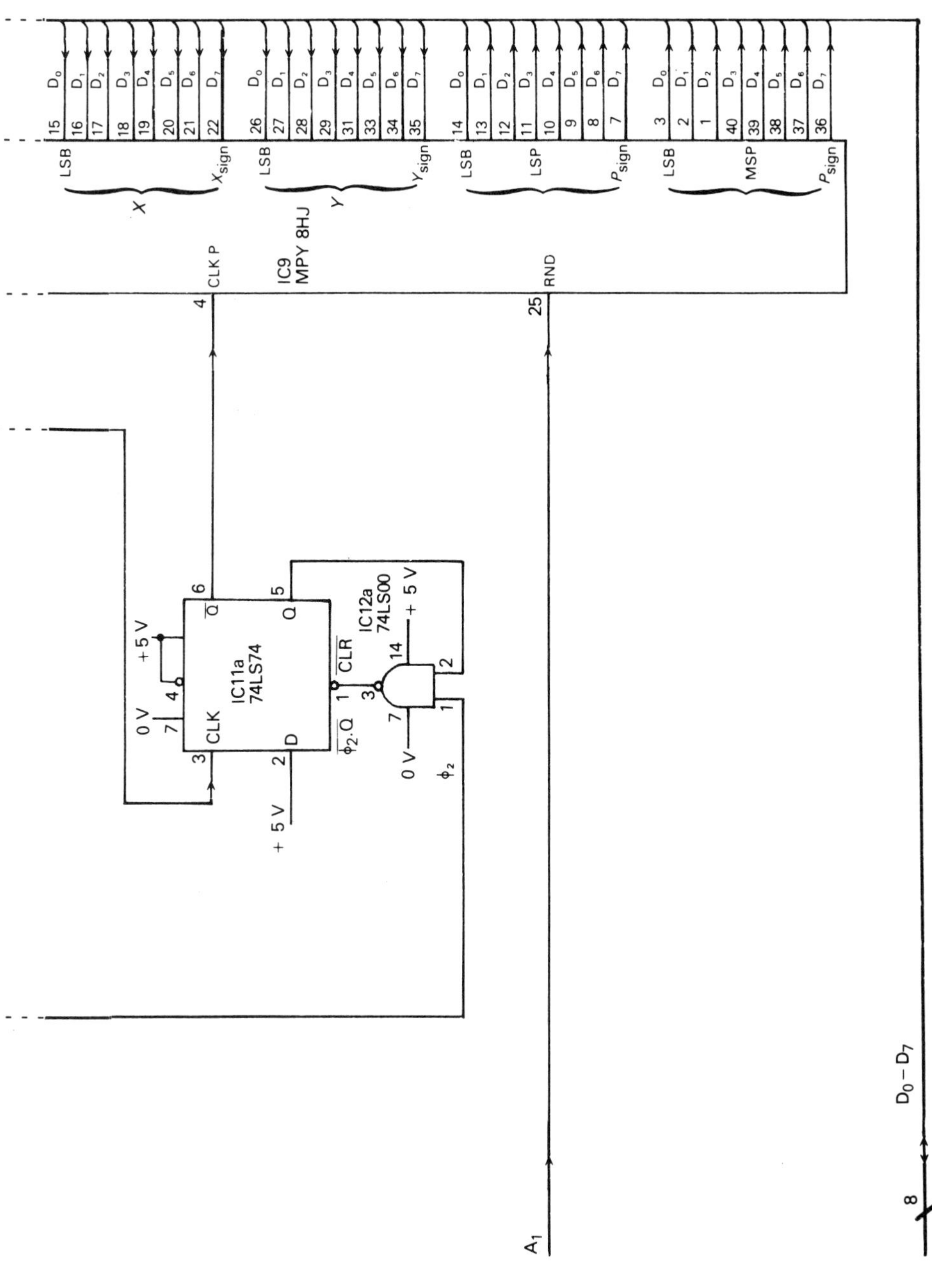
IC9
MPY 8HJ
X
Y
LSB
X_{sign}
Y_{sign}
LSP
MSP
P_{sign}
CLK P
RND
IC11a
74LS74
IC12a
74LS00
CLK
D
Q
$\overline{Q}$
$\overline{CLR}$
$\overline{\phi_2.Q}$
ϕ_2
+ 5 V
0 V
A_1
$D_0 - D_7$
8

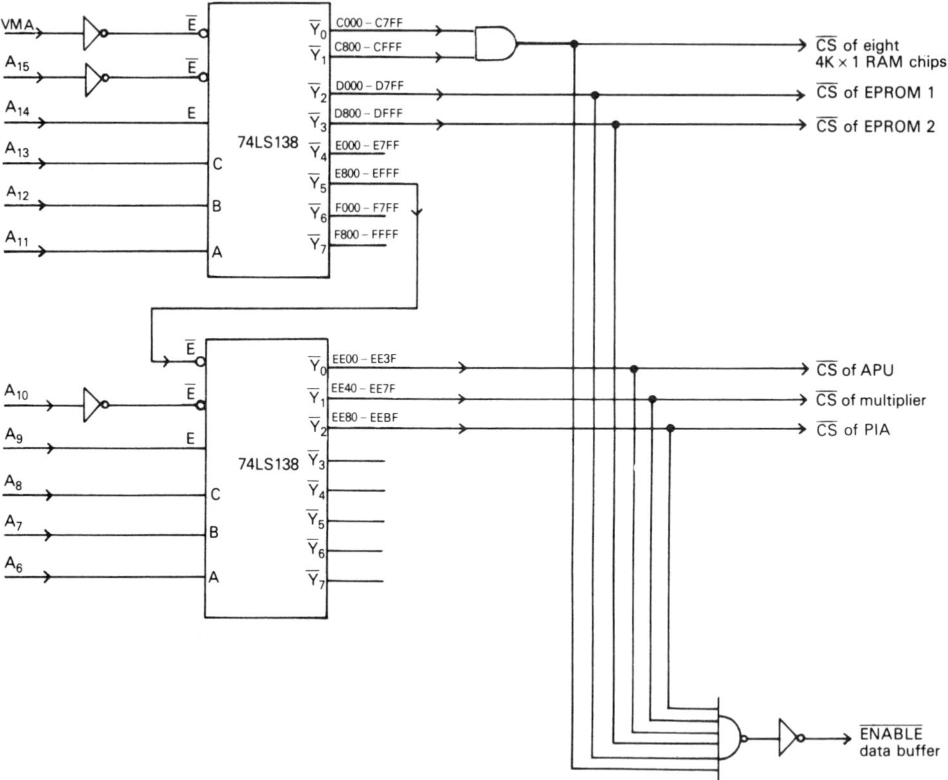

Fig. 6.94 A possible alternative address decoder for the special interface module

of the APU it is highly likely that a series of chained calculations would be carried out, with the APU storing intermediate results on its stack. In the following example, two 32-bit floating-point quantities are added together. The operands are stored in memory starting at $1000.

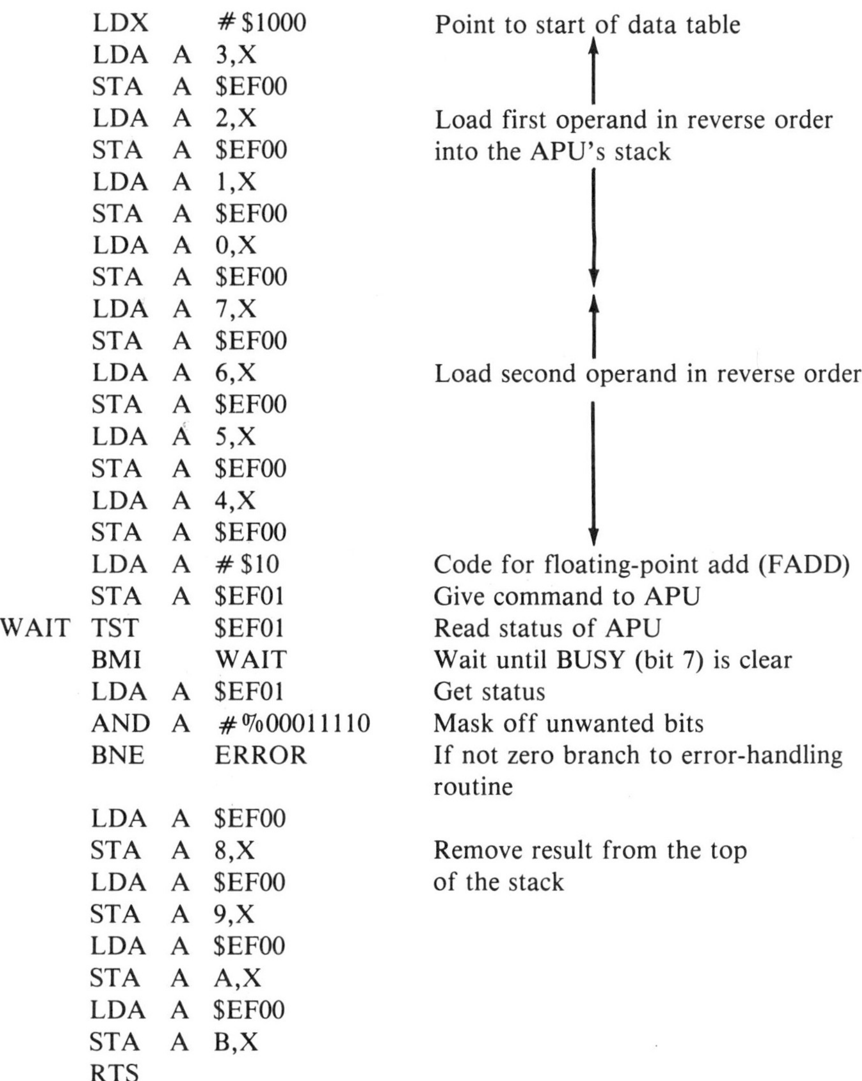

```
        LDX      #$1000         Point to start of data table
        LDA   A  3,X
        STA   A  $EF00
        LDA   A  2,X            Load first operand in reverse order
        STA   A  $EF00          into the APU's stack
        LDA   A  1,X
        STA   A  $EF00
        LDA   A  0,X
        STA   A  $EF00
        LDA   A  7,X
        STA   A  $EF00
        LDA   A  6,X            Load second operand in reverse order
        STA   A  $EF00
        LDA   A  5,X
        STA   A  $EF00
        LDA   A  4,X
        STA   A  $EF00
        LDA   A  #$10           Code for floating-point add (FADD)
        STA   A  $EF01          Give command to APU
WAIT    TST      $EF01          Read status of APU
        BMI      WAIT           Wait until BUSY (bit 7) is clear
        LDA   A  $EF01          Get status
        AND   A  #%00011110     Mask off unwanted bits
        BNE      ERROR          If not zero branch to error-handling
                                routine
        LDA   A  $EF00
        STA   A  8,X            Remove result from the top
        LDA   A  $EF00          of the stack
        STA   A  9,X
        LDA   A  $EF00
        STA   A  A,X
        LDA   A  $EF00
        STA   A  B,X
        RTS
```

In this example the END and SVREQ facilities of the Am9511 have not been used. Instead a polling loop has been entered and bit 7 (BUSY) of the APU's status word has been read until it has cleared, signifying the end of the calculation.

SUMMARY

This chapter has examined many aspects of microprocessor input/output techniques ranging from the serial interface to Teletypes and CRT terminals, to special-purpose (co-processor) hardware designed to handle arithmetic operations.

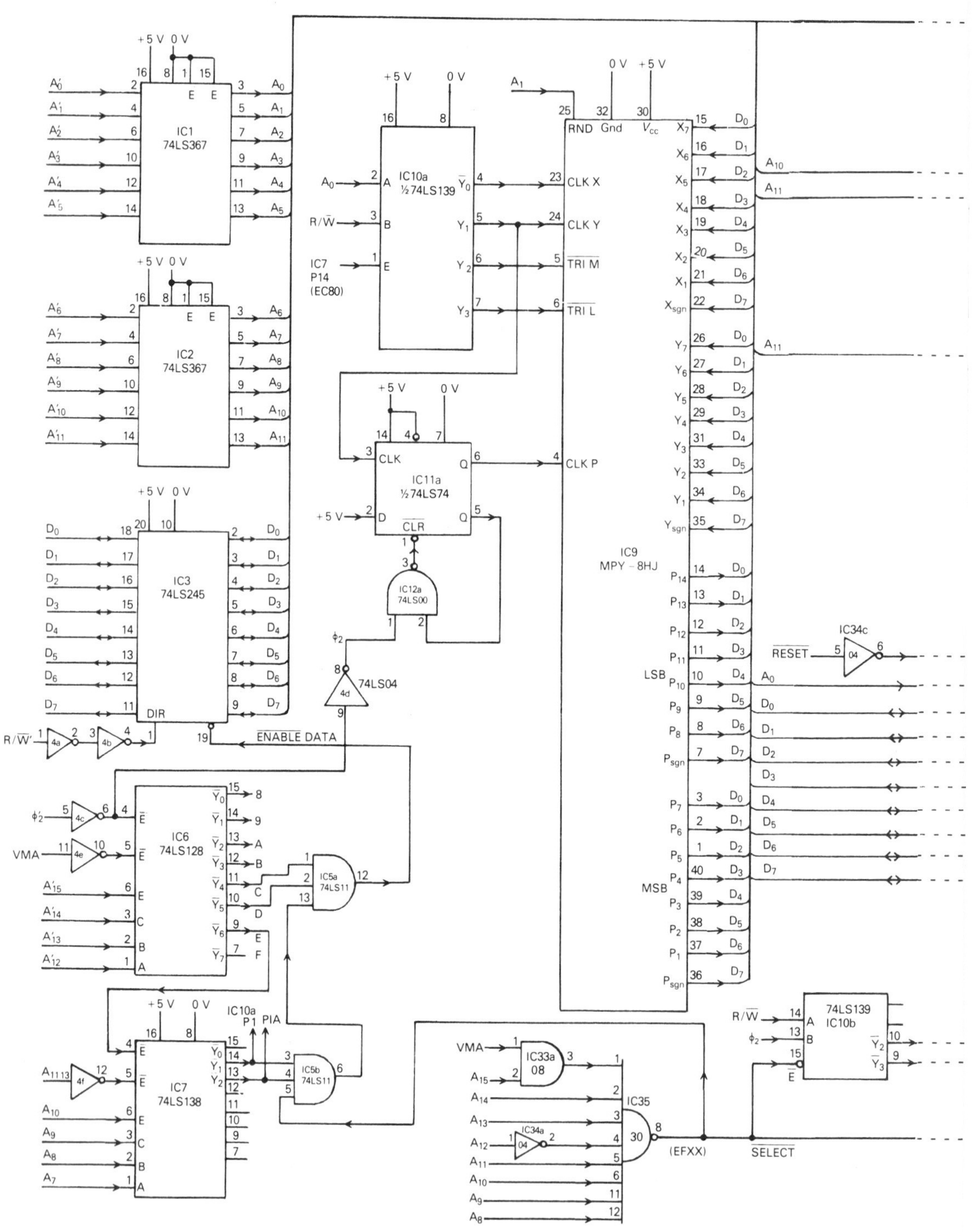
IC1
74LS367
IC2
74LS367
IC3
74LS245
IC10a
½74LS139
IC11a
½74LS74
IC12a
74LS00
74LS04
IC9
MPY – 8HJ
IC6
74LS128
IC5a
74LS11
IC7
74LS138
IC5b
74LS11
IC33a
08
IC34a
04
IC35
IC34c
74LS139
IC10b
RND
Gnd
CLK X
CLK Y
TRI M
TRI L
CLK P
LSB
MSB
ENABLE DATA
RESET
SELECT
(EFXX)
VMA
R/W
DIR
IC7
P14
(EC80)
IC10a
P1
PIA
+5 V
0 V

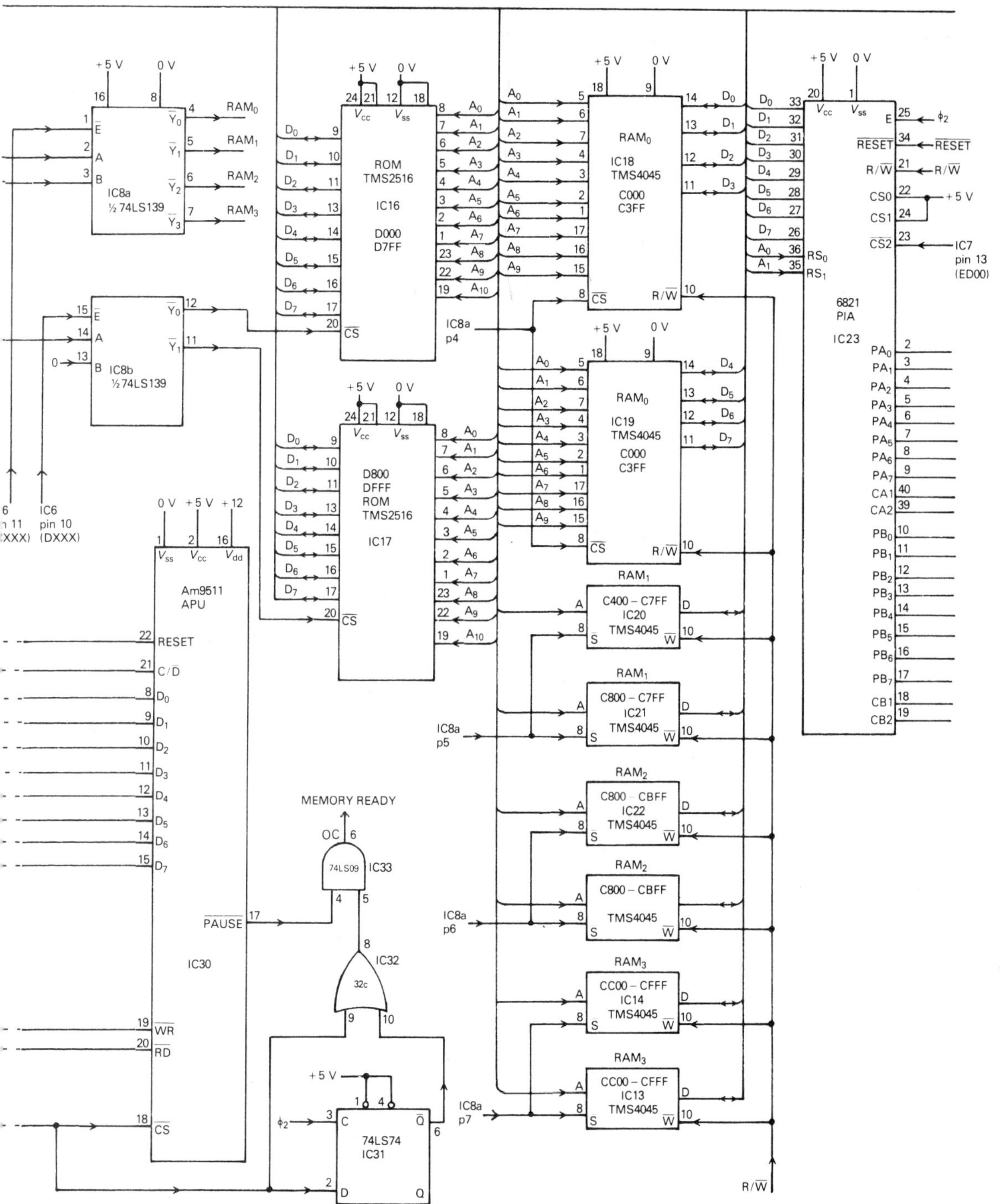

Fig. 6.95 The complete circuit diagram of the special interface module

A wide range of peripheral devices has been created for the 6800 series and the three most popular chips have been described. These are the serial interface, parallel interface, and the timer. It should be apparent that these chips are relatively complex devices and applying them is no easy matter. Indeed some of the newer and more specific interface components (e.g. 6854 ADLC chip) are far more complex than the CPU itself. Part of this difficulty lies in the requirement that the designer should understand intimately the internal operation of the chip. This is to be contrasted with the CPU itself where the designer can program it in an assembly language.

Most general-purpose microprocessor systems have serial data links and a discussion of both the format of the asynchronous serial data and the electrical characteristics of the data link has been included. This leads on to the keyboard which often sits at one end of a serial data line. A description of the popular ASCII code and its control characters is given here.

The next topic dealt with is the CRT terminal, which might appear to be a little out of place in a book on the design of a microprocessor system. While the majority of microprocessor systems will be connected to a commercial display device, many engineers require their own tailor-made display. By showing how a CRT display may be designed I hope that I have enabled the reader to modify it to his own particular specifications.

The concept of microprocessor interfacing may be broadened to include the extension of the system bus to a second system so that additional memory modules and I/O devices may be used. An extender module has been described which allows the TS1 microprocessor system to be linked to a SWTP 6800 system. This module also includes bus termination resistors which reduce some of the noise on the bus caused by reflections.

So far, all I/O has been considered to be digital. In many real applications of a microprocessor it is necessary to read or to generate analog signals. Part of this section has been devoted to the operation of digital-to-analog and analog-to-digital convertors, and practical examples of interfacing D/A and A/D to a 6800 system have been described.

The concluding part of this chapter looked at ways of increasing the power of a microprocessor system by using multiplier circuits or arithmetic processors. Such an approach enables the CPU to deal with data manipulation (at which it is good) and leaves the number of crunching to special-purpose devices. As the number cruncher chosen, the Am9511, was designed to interface to 8080-type CPUs, applying it to a 6800 system provides a useful lesson in reading data sheets and timing diagrams.

PROBLEMS

1 Without the PIA, ACIA, and PTM the interfacing of microprocessors would be very difficult. Sketch out the logic arrangements which would be required to implement each of these devices with TTL.

2 If you were a semiconductor manufacturer what new peripheral devices would you like to create for the microprocessor systems designer?

3 You have been asked to combine the PIA, ACIA and PTM on a single 40-pin chip. What would you do (resignation is not allowed and hitting the bottle is not an acceptable solution)? The basic problem is a lack of pins—would you use an internal pointer register to select other registers, thus avoiding register select lines at the expense of ease of programming?

4 The PIC is able to change the contents of its four address outputs as a function of eight (prioritized) interrupt-request signals. Can this device be used anywhere else in the design of a microprocessor system? Using a device intended for one purpose in an entirely different way can often provide a novel and cost-effective solution to a problem.

5 Some microprocessor systems use a PIA to avoid the cost of an expensive encoded keyboard. Port A puts a pulse on one of its eight lines and port B reads its inputs to see if any one of eight keys has been closed. Write a program to do this, taking account of key bounce (a key closure is not clean but results in a number of short pulses before settling down after a few milliseconds).

6 Simulate the operation of a serial port by programming a PIA to function as an ACIA. The baud rate may be obtained from software timing loops.

7 The circuit designer may avoid the cost of a baud-rate generator by using the output of a PTM to provide a clock input to an ACIA. This approach means that the baud rate may be selected by software. Consider ways of making a system automatically respond to a terminal where the CPU does not know the baud rate of the terminal in advance. One possible approach is to get the operator to hit a given key repeatedly and then allow the CPU to lock onto this character stream.

8 Devise an arrangement whereby the character generator illustrated in Fig. 6.42 (IC6 = MCM66714) may be replaced by a block of programmable RAM, accessible from the CPU bus.

9 How can the memory-mapped display of Fig. 6.42 be modified to allow the display format (rows $\times$ columns) to be made programmable (i.e. under software control of the CPU)?

10 It is possible to operate the Thomson – Efcis CRT controller as the heart of a memory-mapped display by dispensing with its serial input arrangements. Suggest ways of building a memory-mapped display around this device.

11 The ADC of Fig. 6.70 is able to scan 16 channels of analog input. Write a program to sequentially scan these inputs and to display the highest and lowest analog values on the console in a decimal format.

12 Write a program to generate a sinewave at the output of a D/A convertor. To do this it is necessary to consider how a sine function may be synthesized digitally. There are many ways of doing this, from adding together square waves of differing frequency, to evaluating the Taylor series for sin x, to using a look-up table.

13 Write a program to execute 16-bit multiplication by means of the MPY-8HJ 8-bit multiplier.

14 How can the Am9511 APU be used to form the basis of a calculator? The basic problem is that the Am9511 operates on binary numbers, while calculators use BCD arithmetic.

15 Suggest how a light-pen facility may be added to a memory-mapped CRT display.

7

An Introduction to Multiple Microprocessor Systems

The computational power of any given microprocessor is fixed. It is fixed at the time of its conception by the engineers who design its architecture, and by the technology with which the chip is fabricated. A microprocessor user wishing to increase the throughput of his system, or to reduce its response time, cannot add extra instructions or addressing modes to the microprocessor's repertoire. He can, of course, buy a new microprocessor (i.e. a different processor or the same processor fabricated with newer technology permitting a higher clock rate and lower cycle time) which has the power he requires. This course of action may lead to high software costs if an entirely different processor is adopted, or to a system redesign if a faster version of the existing processor is selected. An alternative way of increasing the system's throughput is to emulate the existing microprocessor with bit-slice components. By emulating a microprocessor with high-speed bipolar bit-slice elements it is possible to add new instructions and addressing modes and to speed up the internal operations of the (emulated) microprocessor without incurring large overheads necessitated by either changing all the software or heavily modifying the system's hardware. Bit-slice systems will not be considered further in this book, although bit-slice architectures should not be overlooked by the designer.

Another way of increasing the throughput of a microprocessor system is to employ more than one microprocessor, so that several computations can take place simultaneously. The greatest advantage of a multiple microprocessor system is that a considerable increase in computational power can be attained for a relatively modest increase in the cost of the system over a single processor arrangement. It is the ratio of the cost of the microprocessor to that of the rest of the system (mainly memory) which makes the multiple microprocessor system so attractive. Typically, the cost of the microprocessor is \$3 – 20 which is negligible when compared with the cost of 32K bytes of static RAM—\$300 – 600.

The economic advantages of a multiple microprocessor system stem from the sharing of common resources between several microprocessors. The actual advantages accruing to any given multiple microprocessor system depend very much on the precise arrangement of the system. Unfortunately, when more than one microprocessor share any resource, conflicts arise if two or more microprocessors attempt to access the same resource simultaneously. The greatest drawback of any multiple microprocessor system is the difficulty of coordinating the individual processors which are, paradoxically, cooperating to solve a problem and yet, at the same time, competing for the necessary resources. A multiprocessor system is a general case of the type of arrangement discussed in Section 6.9.

While there is remarkably little variation in the architecture of both microprocessors and mainframe computers, there are many different ways in which microprocessors may be linked together in a multiple microprocessor arrangement. The branch of computer science which deals with such arrangements is relatively new and no standard, universally agreed terminology exists to describe parallel processor systems. Some authorities divide all parallel processor arrangements into two classes—multiprocessor systems and multicomputer systems. In a multiprocessor system the software is integrated and the individual processors work collectively on a single input data stream. The operating system dynamically allocates hardware so that an optimum configuration may be achieved for any given problem. Multiprocessor systems are frequently found in applications where high reliability is required; the operating system is able to reconfigure the architecture of the system if one of the processors fails.

Multicomputer systems operate simultaneously on several input streams (sources of data) with largely independent tasks being distributed between the individual processors. Each processor has its own operating system, unlike the multiprocessor system which has an integrated operating system common to all processors.

In some multicomputer systems each processor is optimized for the function it is to perform, for example number-crunching, I/O processing, or interrupt handling. Multicomputer systems are sometimes called *distributed intelligence* systems, and are often characterized by requiring very little intertask communication. That is, once a task has been passed to a processor, the processor can complete the task without either the intervention of another processor or the need to employ another processor's resources.

Any scheme involving more than one microprocessor (or any other form of computer) must have some form of bus to interconnect the individual processors. The actual bus structure selected in any particular application depends on the requirements of the system: high reliability, expandability, flexibility, or optimized throughput. All bus structures may be divided into either master – master or master – slave arrangements. In a master – master organization each processor has an equal status, while in a master – slave organization all communication between slave processors must go through the master. It is, of course, possible to have hierarchical organizations where a master has a slave and the slave has its own slave, and so on.

Figure 7.1 shows a master – master organization with each processor being able to communicate directly with all the other processors. If there are n processors the total number of interprocessor connections is $\frac{1}{2}n(n-1)$. This bus structure becomes very complex if more than a small number of processors communicate in this way.

In Fig. 7.2 all the processors communicate with each other by means of a ring bus structure. This is less complex than the structure of Fig. 7.1, but because many processors share the same bus there is the possibility of conflict between two or more processors if they try to access the bus simultaneously.

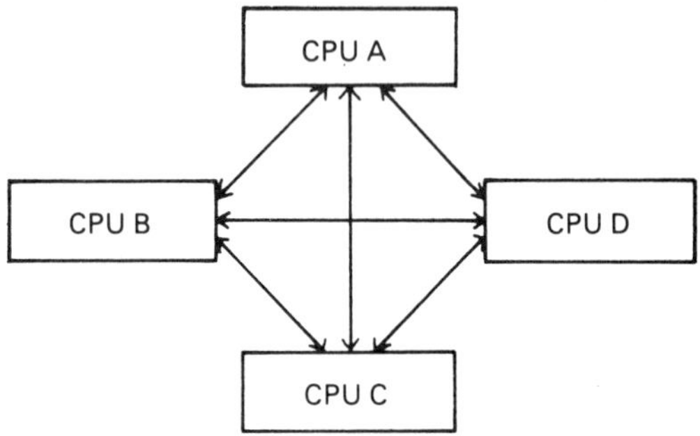

Figure 7.1 Each processor is connected directly to each other processor

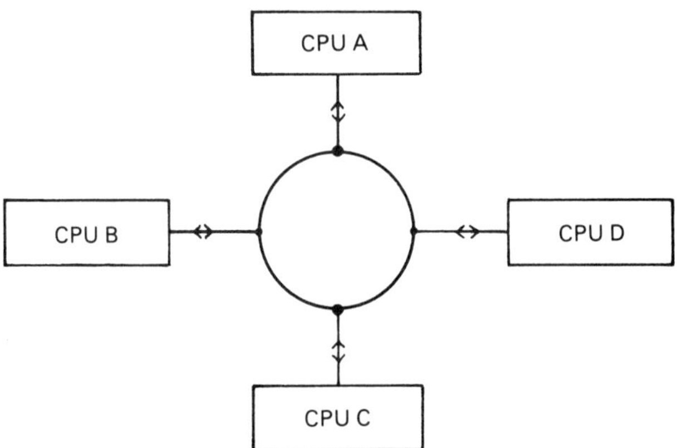

Figure 7.2 Each processor is connected to each other processor by a ring

In Fig. 7.3 and 7.4 two possible arrangements of master – slave systems are illustrated. Figure 7.3 shows a master communicating directly with each of its slaves, and Fig. 7.4 shows a master communicating with each of its slaves by means of a common bus.

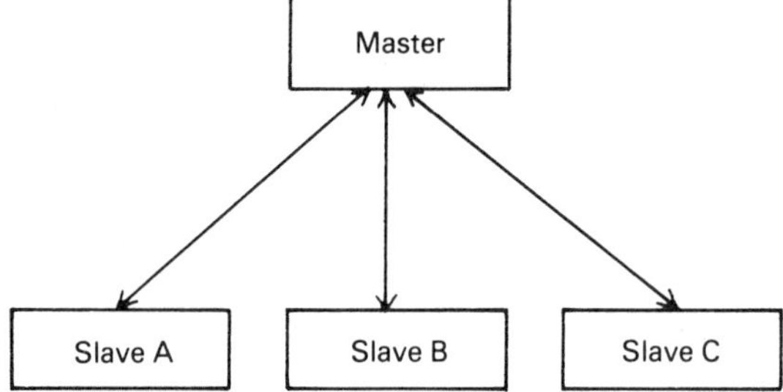

Figure 7.3 Each slave communicates directly with the master

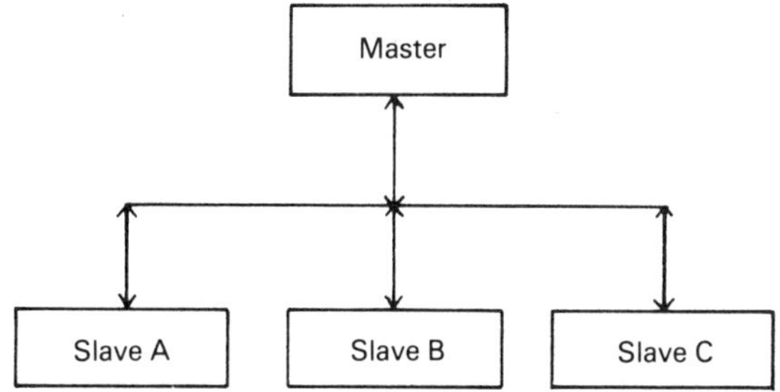

Figure 7.4 Each slave communicates with the master via a common bus

Coupling

Two terms often used to describe parallel processor arrangements are *tightly coupled* and *loosely coupled*. A tightly coupled system passes data between individual processors by means of shared memory. That is, the shared memory is common to more than one processor and may be accessed by more than one processor. Such memory may be thought of as a mailbox where one processor leaves a message for collection by another. A loosely coupled system passes data between processors by shared peripherals or a data link.

The degree of coupling between processors can be expressed in terms of two parameters: the transmission bandwidth, and the latency of the interprocessor link. The transmission bandwidth is the rate at which data is moved between the processors in bits per second, and the latency is the time required to initiate a data transfer. A high degree of coupling is associated with large transmission bandwidths and small latencies. As might be expected, tightly coupled microprocessor systems need more complex hardware than loosely coupled systems.

7.1 LINKING MICROPROCESSORS

Before describing some of the ways in which microprocessors may be linked, it is necessary to consider the difference between a single processor system and a parallel processor system from the designer's point of view. It is easy to design a microprocessor system because the basic circuit configuration is determined largely by the operational requirements of the microprocessor (e.g. reset, interrupt and clock circuits). The designer has little to do other than select suitable ROM, RAM, and interface circuits. The TS1 is a typical general-purpose microprocessor system, and anyone reading this book should have little difficulty in tailoring the TS1 to his own requirements.

Unfortunately, it is just not possible to design a basic multiple microprocessor system which can later be modified to suit any particular application. As we have seen, there are several possible arrangements of multiple microprocessor system. The configuration of any real multiple microprocessor system is determined largely by the purpose for which the system is designed. For example, consider the following two applications of parallel processors: the automatic landing system of an aircraft, and air-traffic control radar. In the former case three microprocessors perform the same function at the same time, while checking the outputs of their neighbors. In this way a high order of reliability is achieved. In the second case, many echoes are received from a number of moving targets, and from these echoes the position, track, and speed of different targets must be calculated in real time. The sheer volume of computing may put this application beyond the capability of any single processor. Dividing the task between a number of processors makes the problem become more tractable. It should now be obvious that, in each of the above cases, the architecture of the system, its bus structure and its interprocessor communications are determined by the application.

The user of small-scale microprocessor systems is likely to employ a parallel processor arrangement for one of three reasons: reliability, increased throughput, or dedicated I/O processing.

Reliability The relatively low cost of microprocessors and their associated components makes a parallel processor arrangement an attractive solution to the problem of obtaining a high order of reliability and system integrity in applications where the cost of a failure may be high. Such applications range from the control of nuclear reactors to the monitoring of a large section railway track (signals, points and traffic). A highly reliable system may be constructed from a series of identical processor modules, each operating on the same input stream (i.e. common data). The outputs of the processors are fed into a majority-logic circuit which accepts as valid the output of the majority of the processors. Although one processor may fail, the chance of two processors failing simultaneously is remote. The design of highly reliable multiple microprocessor systems is not considered further in this book as the topic is of sufficient complexity to merit a book in its own right. An indication of one of the less obvious problems posed by highly reliable multiple microprocessors or systems can be seen from the following example. Suppose that the control system of a chemical plant is triplicated, each microprocessor having its own input devices (temperature and pressure transducers, etc.), and each microprocessor system being identical. Clearly, the outputs of the three microprocessors are identical unless one of the processors fails. Not so! As each of the processors has its own clock and input circuits, an event occurring in the chemical plant will not be recorded simultaneously by all the processors. Consequently the outputs of the processors are not identical—even though no processor has failed. This lack of synchronization between the outputs of the (nominally) identical processors is known as divergence, and steps must be taken in any such system to compensate for this effect.

Increased throughput The most common reason for resorting to parallel processor systems is to increase the throughput of an existing processor without incurring an excessive economic penalty. A suitable candidate for the "multi-micro treatment" is computer chess. Suppose a computer chess game is in progress and it is the computer's turn to move. The computer can calculate, according to some algorithm, a figure of merit for each of the possible moves open to it. The figure of merit is a numerical measure of the goodness (or otherwise) of each move. While a program could be devised to select the computer's next move to be the one which maximizes its figure of merit, such a strategy would be unwise. The weakness of this strategy is that on the next move the computer's opponent will try to optimize his own position—an operation which may reduce (or even negate) the effect of the computer's previous move.

A more suitable strategy from the computer's point of view is firstly to examine all its possible legal moves and then to consider for each of these moves all the possible replies by its opponent. In this way the computer can select for its next move the one which optimizes its position after its opponent has moved. In the majority of computer chess programs, the computer evaluates its position up to several moves ahead. If there are approximately 30 legal moves at any one point in the game, the computer must evaluate 30×30 positions per move and counter move (called a ply). Even if the computer makes a search only three plies deep, a total of $(30 \times 30)^3 = 30^6$ searches must be made. By arranging for several microprocessors to share the task of evaluating different moves, the number of moves which can be evaluated in a given time (i.e. before the player gets bored) is increased, and the strength of the computer's chess is enhanced.

I/O processing In a previous section both input/output and interrupt techniques have been discussed. As the overall complexity of a microprocessor increases with the addition of I/O channels, memory-mapped peripherals, and devices capable of generating interrupts, the CPU has to devote more and more time to handling I/O transactions or servicing interrupts, and less and less time to actual number crunching or data processing. An obvious solution to this predicament is to employ additional microprocessors to deal with I/O and to handle interrupts. A further bonus of this scheme is that by separating the I/O and information handling functions of the computer, the microprocessor dealing with the information handling loses little or none of its memory space to memory-mapped peripherals.

Now let's look at some of the ways in which two or more microprocessors may be linked together to form a multicomputer system. The methods of coupling the processors, in order of the degree of coupling, are:

(1) a serial data link between the processors;
(2) a parallel data link between the processors;
(3) a parallel data link with "first-in – first-out" buffers between the processors;
(4) a DMA link between the processors;
(5) shared memory common to each processor;
(6) a shared bus.

Serial data link Figure 7.5 illustrates a dual processor system with a serial link joining the processors. Each processor sees the other processor as an I/O port. The serial link is simple to implement and is inexpensive. Furthermore, the software needed to control a serial link is also simple; often it is no more complex than that used to operate a VDT or teletype. The transmission bandwidth of this arrangement is very low—assuming a baud rate of 9600 bits/s, and an asynchronous serial link with a start bit, parity bit and stop bit per byte of data, the transmission bandwidth is $9600 \times 8/11 = 6982$ bits/s.

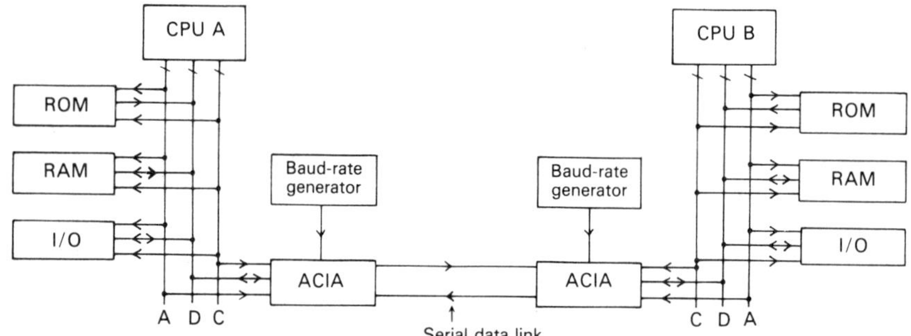

Figure 7.5 Two processors linked by a serial data link

Parallel data link In Fig. 7.6 two microprocessor systems are linked by PIAs. The PIAs are able to transfer data a byte at a time. At a 1 MHz clock rate data can be moved to a PIA at a maximum rate of 1 byte per 21 μs (assuming the use of the index register to move a block of data). This corresponds to a transmission bandwidth of 8/21 MHz= 380 952 bits/s. This is a 55-fold improvement over the serial data link. Unfortunately it is not possible to transmit data at anywhere near this rate in practice as the transmitter must be certain that the receiver has received the data correctly and hence time must be wasted in performing a handshake operation between the transmitting and receiving PIAs.

An additional advantage of the PIA as a parallel data link is that if one of the ports is configured as the data link (remember the PIA port may be configured as an input or an output) the other port may be used to control one of the processors directly. For example, processor A may use one of its PIA lines to reset or interrupt processor B.

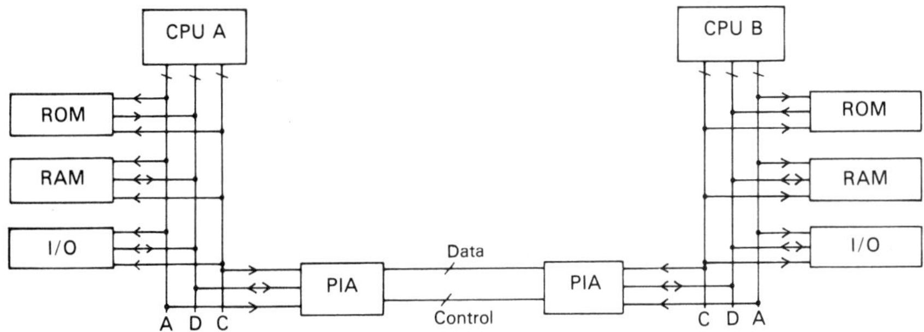

Figure 7.6 Two processors linked by a PIA

Parallel data link with FIFO buffer The FIFO (first-in – first-out) buffer is a special type of memory component which stores its data in the form of a queue. Data enters the FIFO and is stored in the order in which it arrives. When data is read from the FIFO the item at the front of the queue is removed, and the remaining items in the queue move one place forward. Figure 7.7 gives a block diagram of the internal arrangement of a 64×4 FIFO and a brief explanation of its operation. FIFOs can be connected in series to form a buffer of any length.

A parallel data link which removes many of the handshaking procedures required by PIAs is given in Fig. 7.8. A PIA transmits data from CPU A to CPU B. At CPU B the data is received by a FIFO. As each successive byte of data is received at the FIFO it waits in the queue. The PIA belonging to CPU B reads data from the FIFO until it is empty. This technique permits CPU A to transmit a burst of data, say 64 or 128 bytes to CPU B, without any danger of data being lost because CPU B was not ready. Because the FIFO is not bidirectional, two FIFO's must be employed, one to receive data at CPU A and one at CPU B.

DMA link between processors Each of the three above methods of transferring data between two or more processors involves moving data between the processor's accumulators. Consequently, the processors waste time in reading data from RAM and writing it to a peripheral. By using a DMA controller at each processor, data may be moved directly between the memory space of each processor without the active intervention of a CPU. This technique has a high transmission bandwidth and a low latency.

Shared memory Two or more microprocessors may be very lightly coupled by providing a block of RAM which forms part of the address space of each processor. That is, the same block of memory can be directly accessed by more than one processor. Figure 7.9 gives the block diagram of a dual processor system where a single block of RAM is shared by processor A and processor B. The key to the operation of this system is the logic block marked "memory arbiter". Suppose that processor A wishes to access the shared memory and that processor B is currently

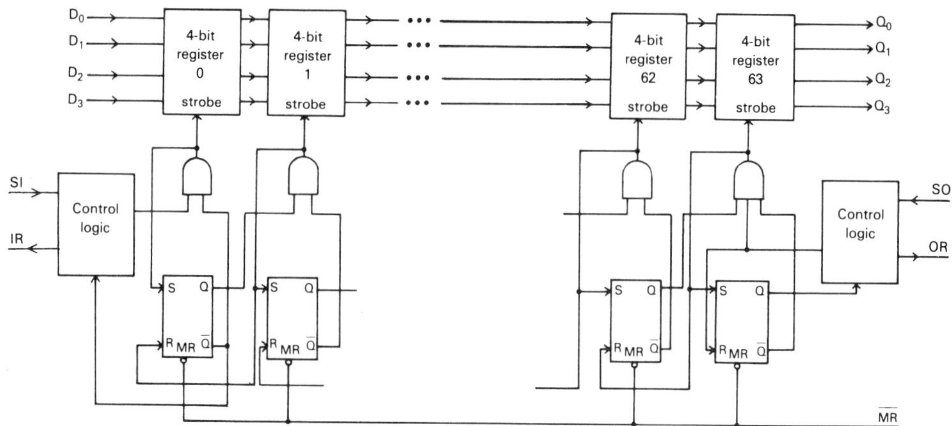

Figure 7.7 The FIFO

In the above diagram data is held in 64 4-bit-wide registers, arranged so that the output of one stage feeds the input of the next. If all 64 registers were clocked simultaneously, the device would behave as a 64-stage shift register. The special properties of the FIFO queue are realized by selectively clocking the registers. Each of the shift registers has a control flip-flop associated with it whose function is to determine whether or not its register contains valid data.

Initially, the FIFO is empty and all control flip-flops are reset to Q = 0. When data is presented to the first stage and "shift-in" (SI) strobed, the corresponding control register is set. The second register has its strobe enabled and data is copied from the first to the second register. The second control flip-flop is set by the strobe signal of shift register one. This process continues until the input has rippled through all 64 stages. Because the setting of a control flip-flop has the effect of clearing the flip-flop on its left, only the last control flip-flop is set. In this way data enters the FIFO and queues up.

When data from the 64th stage is read by strobing "shift-out" (SO) the last control flip-flop is cleared, creating a new "empty" location. The data in the next to the last word is copied into the last stage and the "hole" in the control register moves back towards the input as data words move one place right.

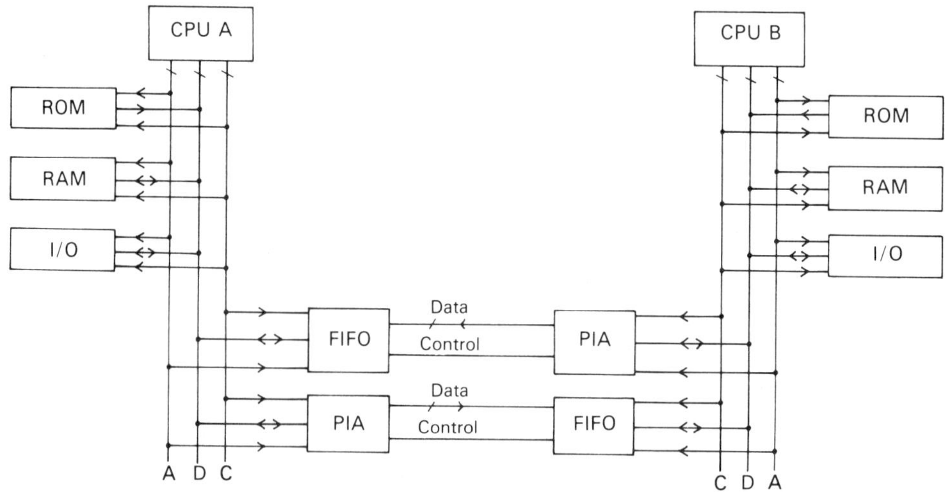

Figure 7.8 Two processors linked by first-in – first-out buffers

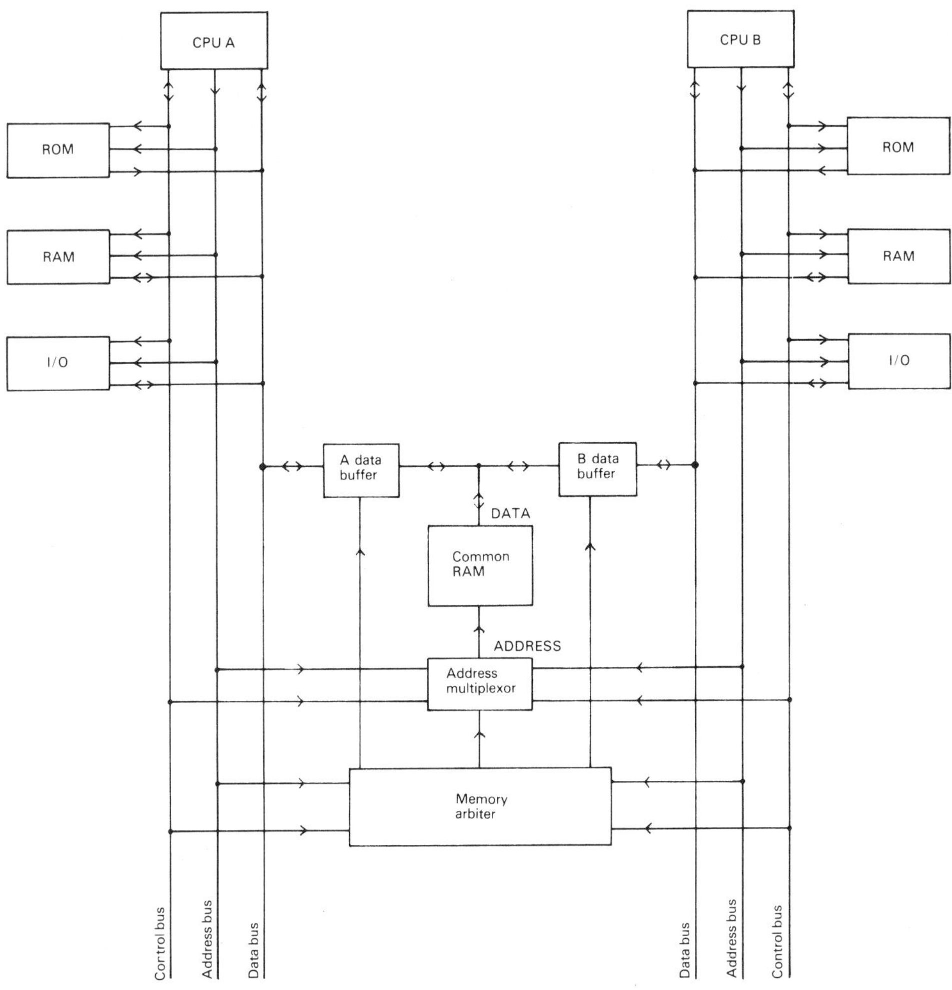

Figure 7.9 A dual processor system employing shared memory

accessing its own local memory. When processor A first accesses the shared memory a memory-select signal is generated about 270 ns after the start of CPU A's ϕ_1 high clock cycle. This signal enables A's data bus buffers and gives CPU A control of the shared RAM's address lines by means of the address bus multiplexers. So far, the shared memory block has behaved as if it were simply a memory module connected to CPU A's bus. As long as CPU A and CPU B do not access the shared memory together, there are no problems. If CPU B tries to access this memory while processor A is busy reading from it or writing to it, then processor B must be prevented from carrying out its access to the shared memory until processor A has relinquished it.

The 6800 CPU is well suited to arrangements of microprocessors with shared memory because the arbiter knows that during a CPU's ϕ_1 clock phase the CPU wishes to access the shared memory in the following ϕ_2 high clock phase. The arbiter can then either give the processor control of the shared memory immediately or hold the ϕ_1 high clock phase high until the other processor has completed its memory-access cycle. This arrangement is best suited to a dual processor system where a common clock may be used to control both processors. Sharing memory between two or more processors leads to a very high transmission bandwidth and a very low latency at the cost of both hardware and software complexities. The hardware complexity is obvious—address and data buffers and the bus control arbiter. The software complexity is less obvious. Although each processor can access the shared memory, it is necessary for one processor to know what its neighbors are up to.

Processor A cannot read data from the shared memory until processor B has put the data there. Some form of software handshaking mechanism must be established between the processors.

Shared bus The 6800 microprocessor is naturally suited to dual processor systems with both processors sharing the same bus. It is, of course, impossible for two systems to share the same bus simultaneously, but there is no reason why a bus cannot be shared between two processors on a time-division multiplex basis. The 6800 does not use the system's address and data bus continuously. During the ϕ_1 active-high clock phase the CPU is busy setting up the state of the address bus which becomes valid approximately 270 ns after the rising edge of ϕ_1. Actual data transfers do not take place until the ϕ_2 active-high portion of the clock cycle. As the majority of 6800-based systems have approximately equal times for which ϕ_1 and ϕ_2 are in the high state, it is relatively easy to arrange for two 6800 CPUs to have their clock so that the ϕ_1 of one CPU is the ϕ_2 of the other CPU, and vice versa.

Consider a dual processor system with a single clock generating two non-overlapping clock pulses ϕ_A and ϕ_B. If ϕ_A and ϕ_B are connected to CPU1's ϕ_1 and ϕ_2 clock inputs, and ϕ_A and ϕ_B are connected to CPU2's ϕ_2 and ϕ_1 clock inputs respectively, the two CPU's will operate on opposite clock phases. But, as data transfers take place only during a CPU's ϕ_2 clock phase both CPU's never need the data and address buses simultaneously. Figure 7.10 shows how two 6800s may be arranged to share the same bus. Each CPU is normally equipped with its own local ROM, RAM and I/O devices which cannot be accessed from the other processor. The bus-control logic determines which CPU currently has access to the address and data bus. The simplest bus-control logic enables a CPU's address and data-bus buffers during the active-high portion of its ϕ_2 clock phase. This arrangement precludes the use of local memory, as the existence of local memory must be taken into account when deciding whether or not to enable the data-bus buffers. Furthermore, in a sophisticated system additional bus-control logic must be included to deal with the following situations:

(1) a memory-ready input to hold a processors's ϕ_1 clock in the high state when slow memory components are accessed;

(2) a DMA request input which freezes ϕ_2 high and relinquishes control of the system bus so that a peripheral may access the memory directly.

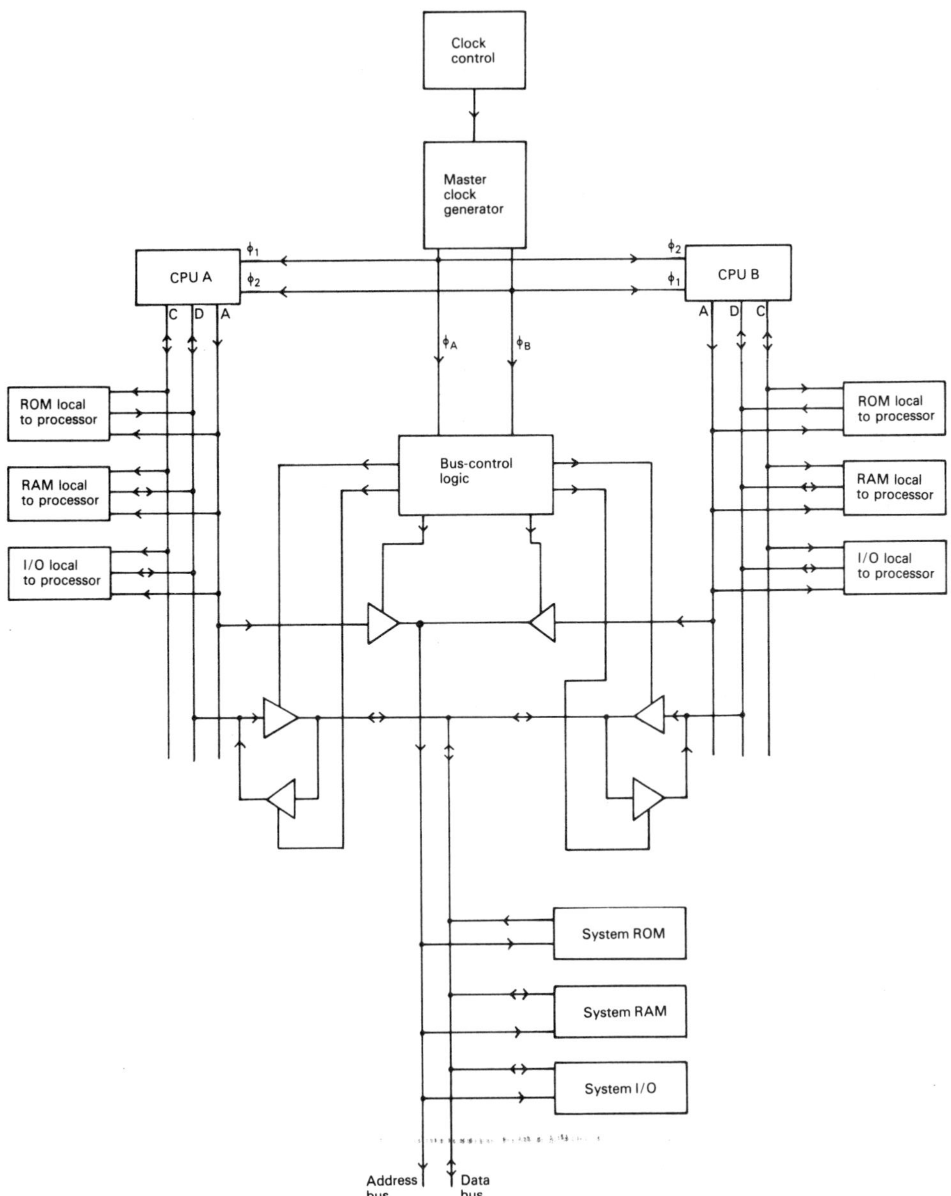

Figure 7.10 Two 6800 CPUs sharing the same bus

Some Problems Associated with Multi-microprocessor Systems

Each microprocessor has a number of control inputs associated with it which influence its normal mode of operation. For example the 6800 has $\overline{\text{IRQ}}$, $\overline{\text{NMI}}$ and

$\overline{\text{RESET}}$ inputs which modify the order in which it executes instructions, and a $\overline{\text{HALT}}$ input which puts the CPU in an idling state and frees the address and data buses. The control of these inputs is relatively straightforward in a single microprocessor system, but in a multiple microprocessor system their control is more complex. How these control inputs are used in any real multiple microprocessor system is, of course, determined by the configuration of the system. The following paragraphs look at some of the considerations which must be borne in mind by anyone attempting to link two or more microprocessors.

Control of reset All microprocessors have to make use of the reset facility even if it is only to start the processor from a known state after the initial power-up. To illustrate some of the factors affecting the control of a microprocessor's $\overline{\text{RESET}}$ input, consider a dual processor arrangement with CPU A and CPU B, and let their respective reset inputs be $\overline{\text{RESET A}}$ and $\overline{\text{RESET B}}$. Five conditions under which one or both processors may be reset are as follows:

(1) power-up (both processors);
(2) manual reset following a program failure (either processor);
(3) automatic reset following a program failure (either processor);
(4) reset of one processor by the other (A by B or B by A);
(5) a master reset of both processors.

Power on reset Both processors must be reset following the initial application of power. Where the dual system operates on a master – slave basis the master processor is reset by a monostable triggered by the rising edge of the power supply. The slave processor may either be reset simultaneously with the master processor or be held in the reset state until it is explicitly released by the intervention of the master.

Manual reset following a program failure Many microprocessor systems have a manual, front panel, reset button which when pushed aborts the execution of a program. In a master – slave arrangement it is probable that any manual reset would reset the master processor or both processors, but it is unlikely that the operator would be allowed to reset the slave processor manually. The fact that a particular system is a dual processor should be transparent to the operator and hence he should not have to concern himself with which processor should be reset following a system collapse or "hang-up".

Automatic reset following a program failure This is a logical extension of the above facility, and may be applied to any computer system—single or multiprocessor. In a well-designed system the detection of program failure should not be left to the operator who is expected to push the reset button after a period of apparent inactivity by the processor. A possible solution to this problem involves the concept of a "watch-dog" circuit which monitors the behavior of the processor. When a program crashes or "hangs up" it either gets stuck in an infinite loop or executes some instruction like "wait for interrupt" or, in the case of the 6800, executes the famous undocumented instruction "halt and catch fire" when it stops processing and cycles through all possible address values. A watchdog circuit operates by resetting (or interrupting) the processor unless the CPU intervenes to stop this happening. Suppose the programmer writes a subroutine to complement one of the output lines of a PIA. If this subroutine is called periodically from the user program (say it is included in each loop in the program) then a square wave appears at the output of the PIA. By rectifying and smoothing this output a constant voltage level may be obtained and fed to a detector. If the program crashes, the subroutine switching the output of the PIA is not called, the square wave disappears and the resulting voltage level at the detector drops. The drop may be employed to trigger a monostable to reset the system. As above, the reset may be applied to the master processor or both processors.

Reset of one processor by the other In a dual processor system operated on a master – slave basis, it is reasonable to expect the master processor to be able to reset the slave processor, but not vice versa (except where the slave processor is acting as a watchdog to the master processor).

Master reset of both processors In general, whenever the master processor is reset, the slave processor is also reset. This is because once the master processor has been reset, and a program aborted, the relationship between the master and slave processors is lost. That is, if the slave is performing a task for the master at the moment the master is reset, it is no longer necessary for the task to be completed as the job from which the task was derived has been abandoned. An exception to this rule occurs when the slave is performing a background task unrelated to the program currently being executed by the master. In such a case it would be unwise to reset the slave automatically following a reset of the master.

Figure 7.11 gives the circuit diagram of one possible reset facility in a dual processor master – slave arrangement. If any of the inputs to gate A (caused by a power-on-reset, manual reset, automatic reset, or an external reset) goes low, the output of gate A goes low, resetting the master processor. Because the output of gate A is an input to gate B the slave is automatically reset every time the master is reset. However, gate B has an additional input which is derived from processor A (e.g. a PIA output line). Consequently, the master can reset the slave under software control.

The control of interrupts The way in which the generation of interrupts is controlled in a multiprocessor system is so heavily influenced by the nature of the system that a short discussion of this topic *in vacuo* is almost impossible. Before we can even begin to consider the design of the interrupt arrangements of the system the following questions must be answered.

(1) Are interrupts dedicated to specific tasks known before the system is designed or is a generalized interrupt structure needed to suit the operator's own requirements?
(2) Are the devices which generate the interrupts to be shared between the processors or are they to be dedicated to specific processors?

(3) Are the interrupts to be "pooled" so that the most lightly loaded processor services the next interrupt?

(4) Can one processor interrupt its neighbor?

In many simple multiprocessor systems the interrupt-handling aspects of the system are the *raison d'être* for employing multiprocessing techniques. As we have already seen, in circumstances where many devices are capable of causing interrupts the time

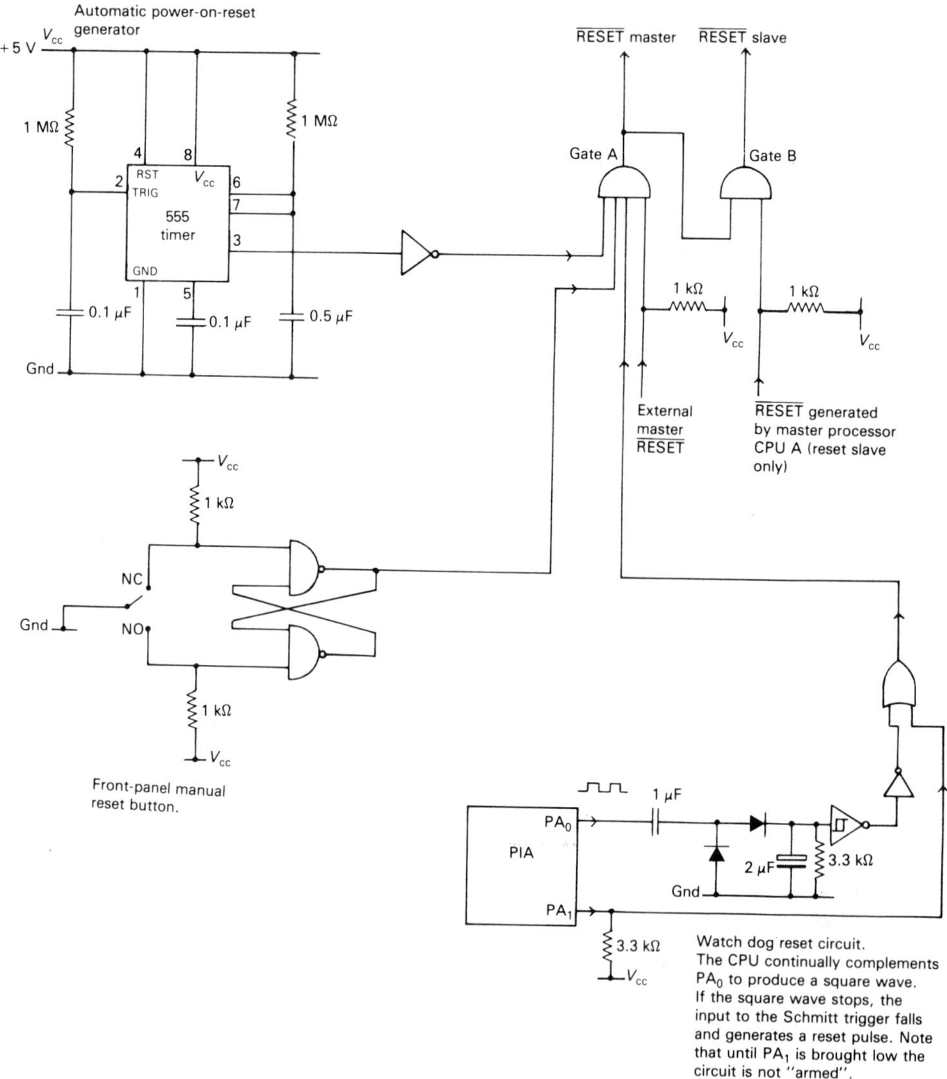

Figure 7.11 A possible arrangement of the reset mechanism of a dual processor system

available to the CPU for number crunching or data processing is rapidly lost to interrupt-handling routines. By dedicating a slave processor to the task of interrupt handling, the master processor can get on with the task for which the processor was originally designed.

The control of $\overline{HALT}$ As in the case of the interrupt mechanism, the way in which a CPU's $\overline{\text{HALT}}$ input is dealt with in a multiprocessor system depends very much on its application. The most likely role of the $\overline{\text{HALT}}$ function of a 6800 in a multiprocessor system is in the implementation of a burst mode of DMA. By halting one processor it is possible for another processor to read or write to its memory space without having to worry about the problems of clock synchronization.

7.2 AN EXAMPLE OF A DUAL PROCESSOR SYSTEM USING THE 6802

In this Section we describe the design of a slave processor which may be linked to the TS1 system to form a dual processor arrangement. Before we can begin to consider a possible design for the slave processor it is necessary to define objectives for the dual processor system. The first objective is to design a slave processor capable of enhancing the power of the TS1 system without the need for any major modifications to either the TS1's existing hardware or software. This approach immediately suggests a loosely coupled system with either a serial or parallel data link joining the processors. The second objective is to make the slave processor a single-board computer which can be operated in a stand-alone mode. That is, the slave processor module must, on a single card, contain the CPU and control, some RAM, ROM, and all necessary I/O devices. The reason for this is purely practical: a single-board computer can be tested independently of the TS1 system. This approach also enables the reader to build the slave processor first, without having to worry about the details of a back plane and external memory modules. These objectives, together with an emphasis on simplicity, have led to the design of a slave processor with the following features:

The Choice of a 6802 CPU

The 6802 is an offspring of the 6800 designed to permit the construction of a microprocessor system with fewer components than are required by a system built around the 6800. The 6802 is entirely software compatible with the 6800, but differs from it in the following four ways:

(1) The 6802 has an on-chip clock circuit.
(2) The 6802 has 128 bytes of on-chip RAM in the region 0000 – 007F.
(3) The 6802 has 32 bytes of RAM (0000 – 001F) which can retain data, when the system is powered down, by means of an auxiliary power supply.
(4) The 6802 does not have provision for TSC and DBE control inputs.

Of the above features, only the on-chip clock is of interest in the present application. The amount of internal RAM is too small to be of any real use and is therefore permanently disabled in favor of external RAM by grounding the 6802's RAM-enable (RE) pin. The lack of TSC and DBE control inputs is unimportant as we do not wish to float the slave processor's address and data buses. The on-chip clock removes the need for any external clock chip. All the 6802 needs is a 4 MHz crystal to be connected between its EXtal and Xtal pins. The 6802 clock generator has an internal divide-by-four circuit so that the effective clock rate is 1 MHz. Of course, the use of an on-chip clock removes some of the provisions for clock control found on the 6875 clock chip. As the slave processor does not need these facilities (e.g. DMA request and DMA grant) no problems arise. The 6802 does have a memory ready (MR) input which, when low, freezes the CPU in a "ϕ_2 high" state. This is not needed in our application. Note that the provision of an on-chip clock dispenses with the need for separate ϕ_1 and ϕ_2 clocks. Instead, the 6802 has a so-called enable (E) output corresponding to the ϕ_2 signal in a conventional 6800 system.

A Serial Data Link Between the TS1 and Slave Processor

The slave processor is designed to communicate with the rest of the TS1 microprocessor system by means of an asynchronous serial data link. A 6850 ACIA at both the TS1 CPU module and the slave processor modules controls the data link. As we have seen, the serial data link provides the loosest form of coupling between the processors. A serial link has been chosen for two reasons. Firstly, it is both inexpensive and simple to implement—the master processor already has the necessary ACIA and baud-rate generator. Secondly, by using a serial link both the master and slave processors see each other as standard serial I/O ports.

Consequently existing I/O routines can be employed to link the processors. In particular, when the slave processor is first built it can be connected to a teletype or VDT, by means of its serial I/O port, and hence tested without reference to the master processor. In practice, the master may communicate with the slave by moving data to it as if the slave were a tape punch or cassette recorder, while the slave may receive data from the master as if the master were a tape reader or cassette recorder. Once data has been passed to the slave, the master may issue the command to execute a program and later read the results of the computations.

The Slave's Monitor Must Be Commercially Available

One of the greatest difficulties facing the first-time designer of a microprocessor system is the writing of a monitor (see Chapter 8) and its transfer to an EPROM. If the designer has access to a cross-assembler and emulator he can develop his software and send a paper-tape disk or cassette dump of the program to anyone with a suitable EPROM programmer. Some designers do not have access to such facilities. The designer needs a system on which to develop software but he cannot build the system until he has designed and programmed his monitor in EPROM—a "Catch 22" situation. One way of breaking the deadlock is to buy a commercially available monitor ROM. Once a prototype system has been built and tested, it can be used to develop a new monitor for other systems. Fortunately, several commercially available monitors exist for incorporation in 6800-based systems. These monitors are often in mask-programmed ROMs and are relatively inexpensive. Many of these monitors are based on the configuration of the MEK 6800D1 kit or the SWTP 6800 system. Consequently, the monitor occupies the range E000 – E3FF, requires scratchpad RAM at A000 and I/O devices at 8004 or 8008. These restrictions do not affect the slave processor, as no more than 4 – 8K bytes of RAM in the region 0000 – 1FFF are to be provided on the slave-processor module. The basic features of some popular monitors are given in Table 7.1.

Table 7.1 The Features of Some of the Commercially Available Monitors for use in 6800-based Systems

Name	*Size and location*	*Location of scratchpad RAM*	*I/O*	*Functions*
MIKBUG	512 bytes E000 – E1FF	A000	PIA at 8004	M, L, P, G, R
MINIBUG 2	1024 bytes E000 – E3FF	A000	ACIA at 8008	M, L, P, G, R
SWTBUG	1024 bytes E000 – E3FF	A000	ACIA or PIA at 8004	M, L, P, G, R, J, C, E, B, D, F
RT68	1024 bytes E000 – E3FF	A000	PIA at 8004 or ACIA at 8000	M, L, P, G, R, H, B, J, S
MSIBUG	1024 bytes E000 – E3FF	A000	ACIA at 8000	M, R, G, L, P

Key to functions (this list is illustrative rather than exhaustive)

M memory examine/change
L load tape
P punch tape
G go (address off the stack)
R examine pseudo registers on the stack
J jump to address
C clear screen
E punch PC and S9 (tape terminator)
B set break point(s)
D disk bootstrap
F find byte in memory
H dump hex to console
S activate multitask operating mode

The Slave Processor Should Have a Simple Address-decoding Network Using Commonly Available Components

As the slave processor does not require full address decoding, a simple form of address decoding is provided on the slave-processor module. An inexpensive 4-line to 16-line decoder is sufficient to perform all the block address decoding for the ROM, RAM, and I/O group of components, and a supplementary 3-line to 8-line decoder serves to distinguish between the memory-mapped peripherals.

The slave processor The block diagram of the slave processor is given in Fig. 7.12,

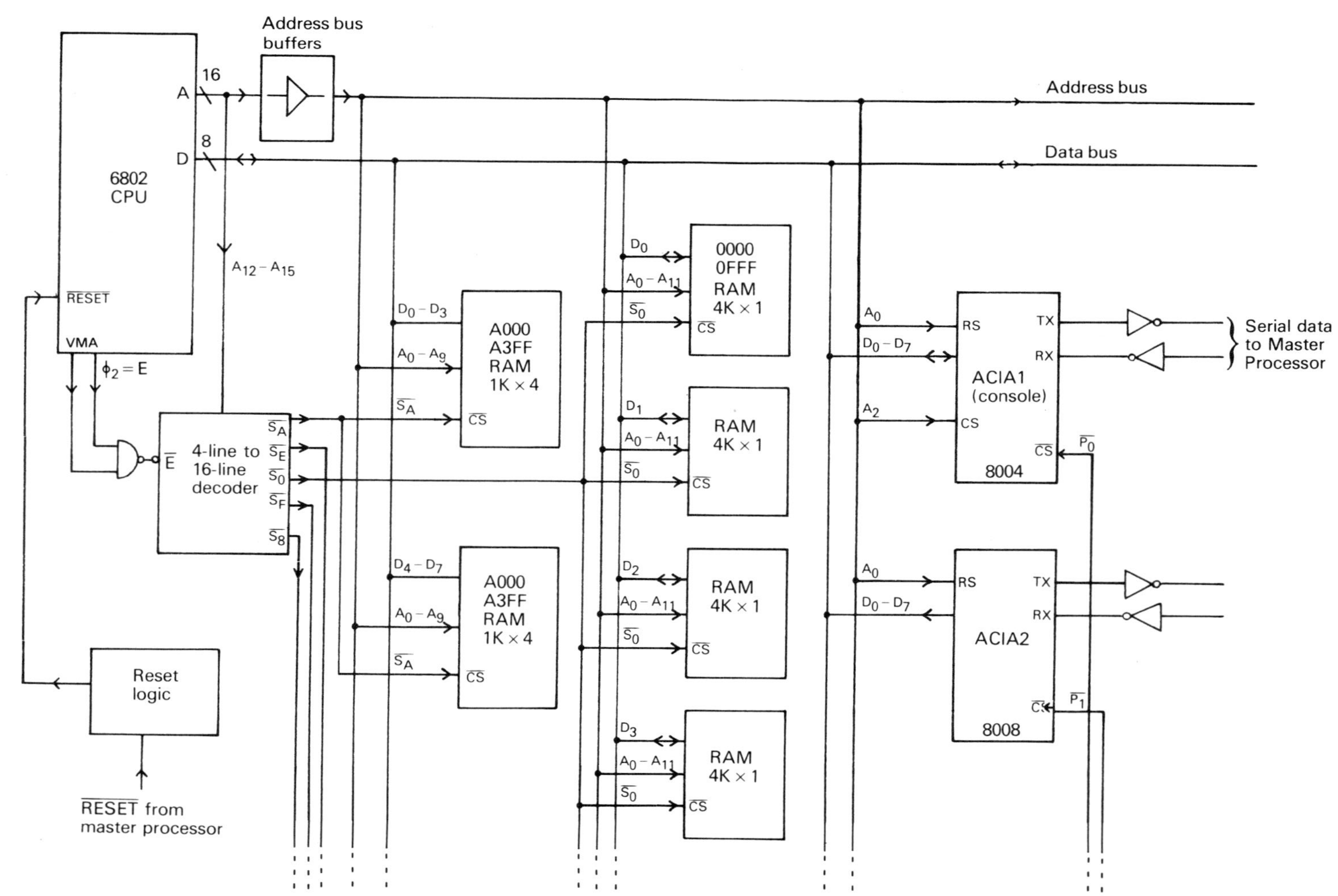
Address bus
Data bus
Serial data to Master Processor
TX
RX
ACIA1 (console)
RS
CS
8004
ACIA2
8008
$\overline{P_0}$
$\overline{P_1}$
A_0
D_0-D_7
A_2
0000 0FFF RAM 4K × 1
RAM 4K × 1
D_0
D_1
D_2
D_3
A_0-A_{11}
$\overline{S_0}$
A000 A3FF RAM 1K × 4
D_0-D_3
D_4-D_7
A_0-A_9
$\overline{S_A}$
Address bus buffers
$A_{12}-A_{15}$
4-line to 16-line decoder
$\overline{S_E}$
$\overline{S_F}$
$\overline{S_8}$
$\overline{E}$
16
8
A
D
6802 CPU
$\overline{RESET}$
VMA
$\phi_2 = E$
Reset logic
$\overline{RESET}$ from master processor

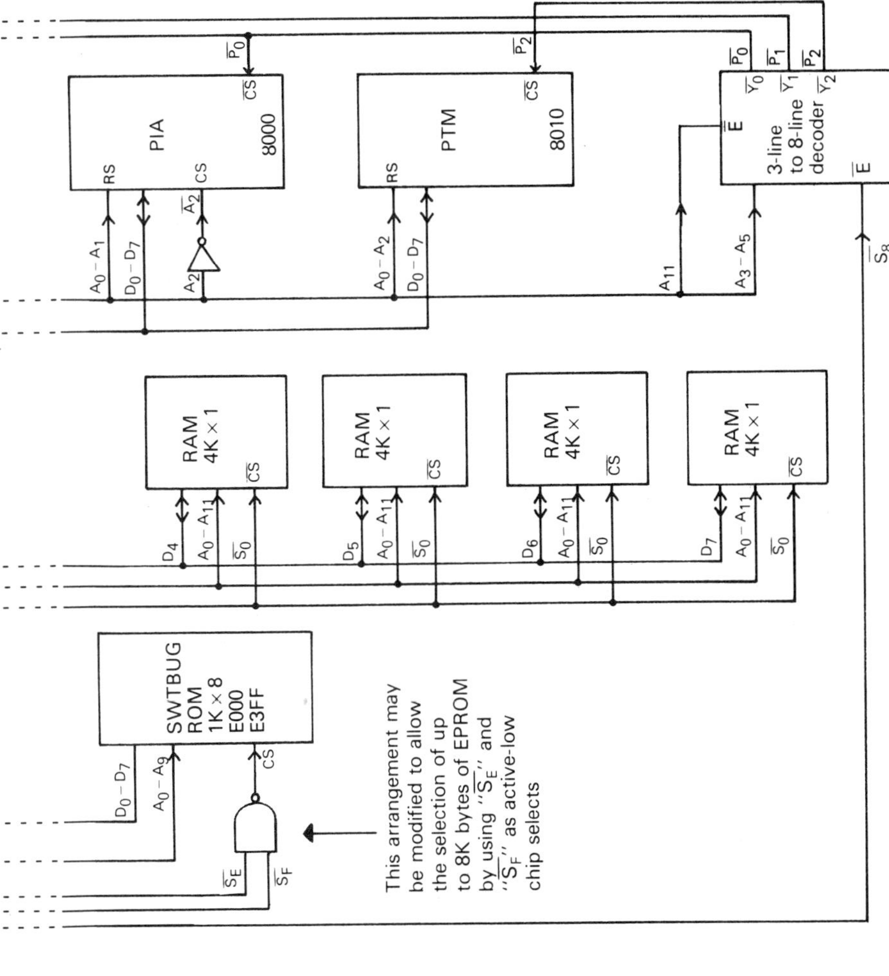

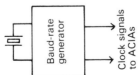

Figure 7.12 ***A block diagram of the slave processor***

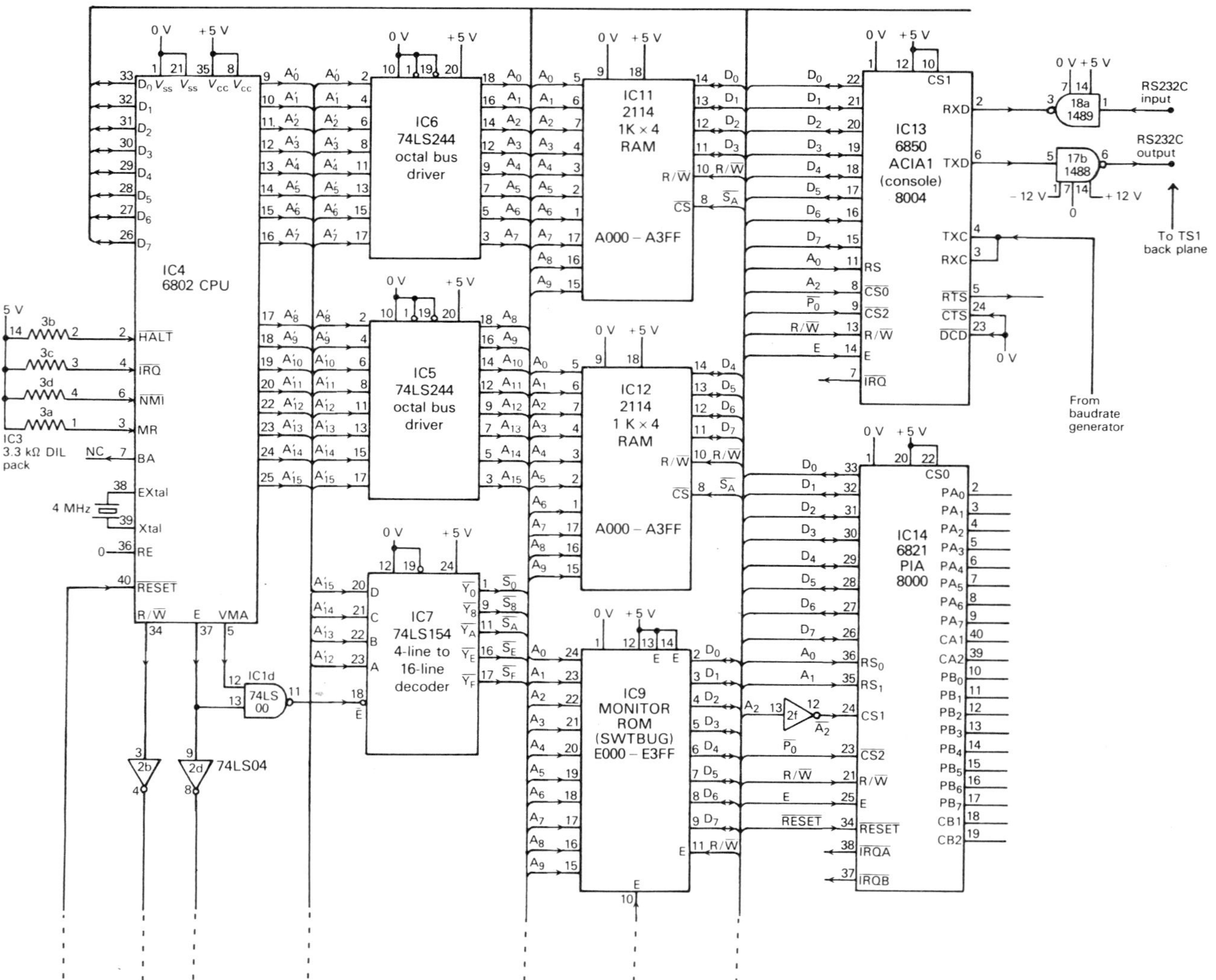
IC4
6802 CPU
IC3
3.3 kΩ DIL
pack
4 MHz
IC6
74LS244
octal bus
driver
IC5
74LS244
octal bus
driver
IC7
74LS154
4-line to
16-line
decoder
IC1d
74LS
00
74LS04
IC11
2114
1K × 4
RAM
A000 – A3FF
IC12
2114
1 K × 4
RAM
A000 – A3FF
IC9
MONITOR
ROM
(SWTBUG)
E000 – E3FF
IC13
6850
ACIA1
(console)
8004
IC14
6821
PIA
8000
RS232C
input
RS232C
output
To TS1
back plane
From
baudrate
generator

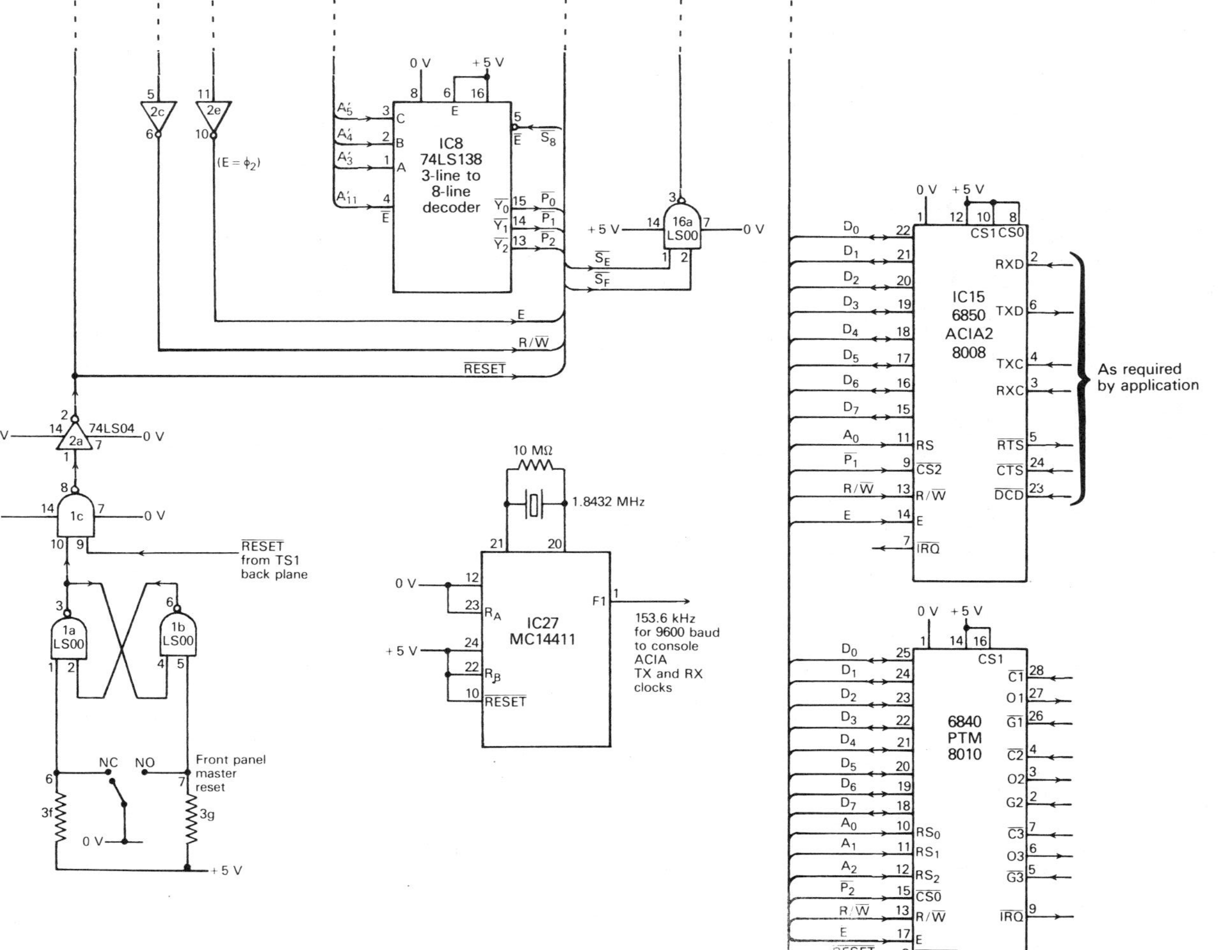

Note: Eight 4096 × 1 RAMs not shown on this diagram. Figure 5.42 shows how TMS4044 RAMs may be used.

Figure 7.13 The slave-processor module

and a full circuit diagram is given in Fig. 7.13. From Fig. 7.12 it can be seen that the structure of the slave processor is relatively simple, because most of the control facilities present on the master CPU module have been omitted. The slave processor may be reset from a front-panel control (necessary if the slave is to be used in a stand-alone mode) or from the master.

The local address bus is buffered by two octal bus drivers because of the relatively high loading on some of the address lines. This loading amounts to 16 NMOS input loads in a 4K system, or 24 loads in an 8K system. No data bus buffering has been included as the load on the data bus is only 8 or 9 NMOS input loads, and is well within the 6802's bus-driving capacity.

A 74LS154 4-line to 16-line decoder provides block address decoding by dividing the 64K memory space into 16 4K blocks. The two lowest blocks, 0XXX and 1XXX, are reserved for the bulk of the system's RAM (more RAM may be added if desired) formed from 4K × 1 static RAM chips. This RAM is fully address decoded. The region of memory space at AXXX is dedicated to a 1K block of static RAM (two 1K × 4 chips) which serves to hold the monitor's stack and temporary variables. The two highest 4K slices of the memory space, EXXX and FXXX, are reserved for up to 8K of system firmware in ROM. This ROM may be implemented as two 4K ROMs or as two 1K ROMs (in which case only 2K of the available 8K of memory space is unique). If a commercial monitor located at E000 – E3FF is used, it is necessary to make this ROM respond to addresses in the range FFF8 – FFFF, otherwise interrupts and resets will not be handled correctly. To do this, the active-low outputs of the 74LS154 corresponding to addresses in the ranges EXXX and FXXX are combined in a NAND gate. The output of the NAND gate (normally low) selects the commercial monitor ROM which has an active-high chip-select input—see Fig. 7.13. Of course, this causes the 1K address space of the ROM to be repeated eight times in the region E000 – FFFF. The memory space at 8XXX is further subdivided by a 74LS138 3-line to 8-line decoder. The I/O devices on the slave processor board are two ACIAs, a PIA and a PTM. Table 7.2 gives the address-decoding table of the slave-processor module. Note the way in which the memory-mapped I/O ports are selected. The 74LS138 is enabled by $A_{15}\overline{A_{14}}\,\overline{A_{13}}\,\overline{A_{12}}$, from the 74LS154, and by $\overline{A_{11}}$ in the selection of the peripherals as full address decoding is not necessary in this application. The case for enabling the 3-line to 8-line decoder by $\overline{A_{11}}$ is that it is free and provides a small advantage. If $\overline{A_{11}}$ is not connected to the $\overline{\text{ENABLE}}$ input of the 74LS138, this input would require grounding. By connecting A_{11} to the $\overline{\text{ENABLE}}$ input the amount of memory space occupied by the peripherals is reduced from 4K to 2K bytes. It is always wise to reduce the amount of memory space occupied by a memory-mapped peripheral, on the grounds that it reduces the chance of the peripheral being accessed during a program crash.

The two ACIAs have almost identical address-decoding arrangements with ACIA1 being selected by $\overline{P_0}$ and ACIA2 by $\overline{P_1}$. By reversing these two connections the functions of ACIA1 and ACIA2 may be reversed. One of the ACIAs is dedicated to the task of communicating with the master processor, and is regarded by the slave's monitor as the console device. The second ACIA is available for duty as a serial link to a cassette system or a VDT.

A baud-rate generator based on the MC14411 is provided on the slave-processor module to control both ACIAs. However, if the slave processor is operated in conjunction with the master CPU module of the TS1, it is possible to obtain clock pulses for the slave processor's ACIAs from the CPU module.

Table 7.2 The Address Decoding Arrangements of the Slave Processor

Memory usage	A_{15}	A_{14}	A_{13}	A_{12}	A_{11}	A_{10}	A_9	A_8	A_7	A_6	A_5	A_4	A_3	A_2	A_1	A_0
4K RAM 0000 – 0FFF	0	0	0	0	×	×	×	×	×	×	×	×	×	×	×	×
4K RAM 1000 – 1FFF	0	0	0	1	×	×	×	×	×	×	×	×	×	×	×	×
↑	0	0	1	0												
24K memory space	0	0	1	1												
not used in this	0	1	0	0												
application	0	1	0	1												
	0	1	1	0												
↓	0	1	1	1												
PIA 8000	1	0	0	0	0						0	0	0	0		×
ACIA 1 8004	1	0	0	0	0						0	0	0	1	×	×
ACIA 2 8008	1	0	0	0	0						0	0	1			×
PTM 8010	1	0	0	0	0						0	1	0	×	×	×
	1	0	0	1												
1K RAM A000 – A3FF	1	0	1	0			×	×	×	×	×	×	×	×	×	×
	1	0	1	1												
	1	1	0	0												
	1	1	0	1												
4K ROM E000 – EFFF	1	1	1	0	×	×	×	×	×	×	×	×	×	×	×	×
4K ROM F000 – FFFF	1	1	1	1	×	×	×	×	×	×	×	×	×	×	×	×

Note: Although the above arrangement allows for two 4K ROMs at E000 – EFFF and F000 – FFFF, the circuit diagram of Fig. 7.13 has the active-low chip selects corresponding to these blocks of memory space NANDed together to create a single active-high chip select for the range E000 – FFFF. A commercial monitor ROM in the range E000 – E3FF with an active-high chip select occupies this block of memory space. In this arrangement $A_{10} - A_{12}$ are don't care conditions.

7.2.1 Linking the Master and Slave Processors

Assuming that the slave and master processors are linked by their ACIAs (the console device in the slave processor and the secondary ACIA located at EC08 in the master processor) it is necessary to devise some software to control the flow of data between the processors. In order to run a program on the slave the following steps must be carried out:

(1) The master passes a program to the slave.
(2) The master causes the slave to execute the program now being held in its memory.
(3) The slave sends the results of its computations to the master.

In this section I intend to sketch out the software requirements of the data link between the slave and master processors. The actual details of such a link depend on the nature of the monitors in both slave and processor, and on how the programmer wishes to use the slave. In order to understand what follows, the reader (if he is not familiar with the details of monitors) should refer to the next section.

To transmit a program to the slave processor is relatively easy. After the initial reset the slave processor is expecting a single character command so that if the master transmits an "L" the slave will enter its loader function and store the following data (if correctly formatted) in its memory. After the master has transmitted the "L" it enters its own "P" function which serves to output data in a suitable format for loading by the slave. The simple loaders operate with absolute data so the program in the master must be located at the same address as it is to be stored in the slave. After the loading has been completed the master must transmit the characters "S9" to terminate the loading sequence in the slave and pass control back to the monitor.

The monitor in the slave processor (in my system it is SWTBUG) has a "GOTO" function which, when invoked by the character "J" followed by a four-character hexadecimal address, causes the execution of a program to begin, starting at that address. Thus to execute the newly loaded program the master must transmit a "J" followed by the entry point of the program.

Having now transferred a program to the slave and caused it to be run, the master must somehow get the results of this computation. One of the difficulties facing the master is how to tell when the slave has completed its task. Of course the master could poll the slave, but such an action would be rather pointless, for if the master has time to poll the slave while it is executing a program the master might as well have executed the program itself.

An alternative approach is to make the master's ACIA interrupt driven so that once the slave has executed its program it can transmit a character to attract the master's attention. When the master has responded to this interrupt it must extricate data from the slave. Two techniques may be used. Firstly, the master may invoke the slave's "P" function to force the slave to transmit a block of data. This has an important disadvantage—the loading process is terminated (at the master) by the reception of the string "S9". As the slave does not provide these characters there is no simple way of terminating the loading—the master just waits for a non-existent S9. The only way round this, apart from operator intervention, is to provide the master with a time-out. That is, a timer is started before the beginning of the loading process. When the timer reaches a given count it interrupts the master, forcing it out of the loading routine.

Possibly the best way of handling the communications between the master and slave processors is to totally bypass the slave's monitor by loading (from the master) a new monitor designed to handle the exchange of data. Thus the master initially uses the slave's own "L" and "J" functions to load and execute the new monitor, but after that a new protocol is established between these processors.

SUMMARY

This section has provided the reader with a brief introduction to the concept of multiple microprocessor systems. As the cost of microprocessors themselves has fallen, it seems quite reasonable to put more than one CPU in a microprocessor system. By doing this the computational tasks may be partitioned between the individual CPUs to increase the effective throughput of the system.

If ever there was an example of the expression "you never get anything for nothing" it is a multiple microprocessor system. Coupling microprocessors so that they can increase the throughput of the system brings with it the problem of interprocessor communication and of coordinating the operation of the processors. We have seen that there are several ways of coupling the processors, varying from the loosest of connections (the serial data link) to the tightest of coupling (shared memory).

The slave-processor module of the TS1 is a simple single-board arrangement, designed both as a stand-alone microcomputer and as a method of demonstrating the operation of multiprocessor systems.

PROBLEMS

1 It is desired to locate two monitors on the slave processor module, one at E000 (MIKBUG-based) and the other at F800 – FFFF. It is desired to make the monitor switchable so that when in normal operation the MIKBUG monitor is selected, but when a line from an external PIA (on the processor module) is made active-low the monitor of F800 is selected. Devise a scheme to do this—bearing in mind the problems imposed by RESET and interrupt vectors.

2 Design programs resident in both the master processor's monitor ROM and the slave processor's monitor to move data between the two CPUs by means of a serial link.

3 Devise a scheme for the transfer of data between the slave and master processors by means of DMA. The slave processor must initiate the transfer by halting the master and providing an address (and $\overline{\text{VMA}}$ E, R/$\overline{\text{W}}$ E) to the system bus. Consider what additional logic would be required on the slave processor and what software would be needed to drive it.

4 To what extent, if any, can the slave processor (as defined in Fig. 7.13) be simplified by reducing the chip count?

8

The Monitor

Introduction

All microprocessor systems, without exception, are composed of two fundamental entities—the hardware and the software. The hardware part of a microprocessor system consists of all the physical components which make up the system, while the software is the program residing in the microprocessor's memory. Although hardware and software are entirely different entities, they are often interchangeable. For example, multiplication may be carried out by means of a special-purpose digital circuit (hardware), or by means of a program (software).

So far, this book has dealt with the hardware aspects of a microprocessor system. In any real application of microprocessors there must be a program somewhere in memory as the only purpose of a microprocessor is to execute the program. This book does not attempt to deal with the subject of software. Indeed the whole area of software is a battlefield of competing ideas. When I applied for my first position as a lecturer in "computer science" I was asked if I had had any experience of a high-level language. When I replied that I had used FORTRAN to simulate digital data-transmission systems as a postgraduate, the interviewer replied curtly, "FORTRAN is banned in this department!"

In recent years not only has the range of hardware components increased, but often the complexity of interface or control chips rivals that of the microprocessor itself. For example, we have already looked at the Thomson – Efcis CRT controller which is almost a VDT-on-a-chip. Possibly the most significant feature of hardware is that components can be bought off-the-shelf at prices which bear little or no relationship to their complexity. Furthermore, hardware components are normally very reliable and come with detailed specification sheets and application notes.

The software components of a microprocessor system cannot, normally, be bought off-the-shelf for three reasons:

(1) Many very different microprocessor systems are built with the same basic hardware components (CPU, buffers, gates, memory components), but for each new application of a microprocessor system new software must be written. For example, consider the following three systems: a point-of-sale

system in a supermarket; a fuel-control system in an automobile designed to optimize the air/fuel mixture to reduce the emission of carbon monoxide; and a small general-purpose computer designed to run programs written in BASIC. Although each of the above systems may have almost identical circuit diagrams, the software must be tailormade for each application. Software cannot yet be mass produced.

(2) Software is highly system-dependent at the machine-code level. Although the same UART can be connected to a 6800 or a Z80 system, the object code executed by a 6800 is entirely different to the object code of a Z80. This makes the use of standard software difficult, unless the source program is written in a high-level language, and a compiler employed to generate the necessary object code for the target microprocessor. As the cost of memory components has fallen, high-level languages have become increasingly popular with microprocessor users at all levels. Perhaps this trend will, one day, make software as easy to obtain as hardware.

(3) It is unfair to compare software and hardware on the same basis. The theory, design and testing of hardware systems has reached a more advanced stage than the theory, design and testing of software.

For the above reasons, the hardware design of a microprocessor system may be relatively straightforward, but the design of the software a costly headache. The hardware designer has, at his fingertips, a whole range of very sophisticated building blocks from which he can put his system together. The programmer is not so lucky, he must construct his program line by line. He cannot, yet, obtain software modules with which to construct his program. Perhaps this view is a little too pessimistic. The science of software is now beginning to emerge from its Dark Ages. Unfortunately, software still belongs to the world of the computer scientist, while the microprocessor belongs to that of the electrical engineer, who often does not know of the latest developments taking place in software engineering.

There are several approaches to the design and testing of a microprocessor's software. One possible approach is to use a time-sharing computer terminal and rent time on some large, central, mainframe computer. In this way a program can be entered, edited, assembled, and then tested by emulating the target microprocessor. This means that the designer can see how his program would behave if it were resident in the memory of his system.

An alternative approach is to develop the software in a microprocessor system which uses the same microprocessor as the final system. The designer is, in effect, building or buying a general-purpose digital computer on which he can develop and test his software. This computer consists of the hardware configuration required by the application for which the microprocessor is intended, plus an interface to a VDT or teletype allowing programs to be entered, tested, modified and stored. The simplest program enabling the designer to perform these functions is called a *monitor*.

A monitor may be thought of as a very simple operating system. If the monitor is a program, resident in the development system and required to allow the designer to create his own special-purpose programs, where does the monitor come from? Major microprocessor manufacturers have been quick to realize that small manufacturers, educational institutions, and hobbyists do not have access to the facilities needed to design and produce their own monitors, and have provided off-the-shelf monitors for use in development systems.

8.1 THE FUNCTION OF A MONITOR

A monitor is a program, resident in ROM, whose minimal function is to enter a program into the microprocessor's RAM and then transfer control to that program. That is, the monitor must be able to read in a program and then run it. Although a monitor can be designed to allow the program to be entered by means of binary switches on a front panel, the availability of teletypes, VDTs and cassette recorder interfaces means that very few monitors are designed to operate in conjunction with a front panel.

Most monitors communicate with the teletype or VDT by means of an asynchronous, serial data link. This places a severe restriction on the input or output device connected to the system. As there are several possible formats for serial data (see Section 6.2.2 on the ACIA), the format selected by the monitor must be compatible with the format of data generated and received by the I/O device. An example of this problem can be seen in the case of a monitor designed to operate on ASCII-coded data, where seven bits represent one of 128 possible characters. Such an arrangement cannot read pure binary data from eight-hole paper tape, or store data on cassette in the efficient form of one byte per character.

Motorola's MIKBUG monitor stores data on paper tape (or cassette) in the form of two ASCII-coded hexadecimal characters for each byte. Such a system is very inefficient because a single byte of data, say 3F, is stored as the two characters "3" and "F", whose ASCII codes are 33 and 46, respectively. Furthermore, if the data is stored on an audio cassette at a density of 10 bits per character (start bit + 7 data + parity + stop bit), then 20 bits are required to store a single 8-bit byte. Some of the more sophisticated monitors allow the programmer to specify the format of the serial data from the keyboard. Of course, the user must have, initially at least, the interface required by the monitor before a new interface can be defined.

All monitors place important restrictions on the design of the microprocessor system. Each monitor resides in a ROM which must occupy some of the available 64K memory space. Furthermore, each monitor needs some RAM to hold its temporary variables. The location of the monitor within the microprocessor's memory space is determined by the way in which the microprocessor starts executing instructions after power is applied, or the reset button is pushed. For example when the 6800 is reset the 16-bit program counter is loaded with the contents of FFFE and FFFF, which means that a ROM must be located so that it will respond to these two addresses. Consequently, many 6800 systems locate their monitor at the top of the memory space in the region FE00 – FFFF for a 1K byte monitor. The location of the scratchpad RAM needed by the monitor can be anywhere within the available memory space. The actual location of this RAM is determined only by the whim of the person who writes the monitor. For example MIKBUG locates its scratchpad RAM in a 128×8 MC6810 at A000. This may be a severe limitation if the programmer requires a large amount of contiguous RAM for his own program (i.e. more than 40K bytes). Yet another restriction introduced by a monitor is the location of memory-mapped I/O ports. If a monitor is designed to access a PIA at 8000 the PIA cannot later be moved to, say, C000 to make room for more RAM at 8000 unless the monitor is rewritten.

Although a monitor is nothing more than a program, it should now be clear that the monitor and the structure of the hardware intimately affect each other. Neither the monitor nor the hardware can be developed in isolation. It is not only necessary to ask what functions a monitor should perform but also in what environment it is going to operate. Possibly the most important question the designer of the monitor should ask is "What limitations will the monitor place on any future development or expansion of the hardware, and how can I prevent this at the time of writing the monitor?"

Before dealing with the design of a monitor for the TS1 microprocessor system, it is worthwhile examining the range of functions provided by many of the commonly available monitors. MIKBUG itself is only 512 bytes long as it occupies a half of an MC6830 mask-programmed ROM. Several manufacturers of 6800-based microprocessor systems aimed at the hobbyist or small business have developed 1K versions of MIKBUG. These MIKBUG replacements are almost always called MIKBUG-compatible because they locate many of their I/O routines at the same address as those in MIKBUG itself. In this way any software written to run in a MIKBUG environment will also run under the MIKBUG replacement.

The range of functions provided by monitors is varied but one function is common to all monitors: a monitor must be able to input the data which forms a program, store it in a specified area of RAM, and then transfer control to the program which has been loaded. The function required to do this is known as a loader. A loader requires that the data is entered in a predetermined format. Figure 8.1 shows the format of the data required by MIKBUG's loader. This data is entered into the microprocessor from either a paper-tape reader or a cassette interface.

The data is broken up into separate blocks called records, where each record is entirely independent of all other records on the tape. A record begins with a header, which is a character, or string of characters, signifying the start of the record. The loader, once engaged, rejects all input until a header is found. This facility enables the user to precede the data block with the name of the program, without the monitor trying to read the name as if it were data.

Immediately following the header is the byte count which informs the loader of the length of the record to be read, i.e. number of bytes = address + data + checksum (that is, three more than the number of bytes in the data field).

The address consists of two bytes which specify where, in memory, the data is to be placed. Two address bytes are required to cover the microprocessor's 64K memory space. In simple loaders, the address is an absolute address (the actual

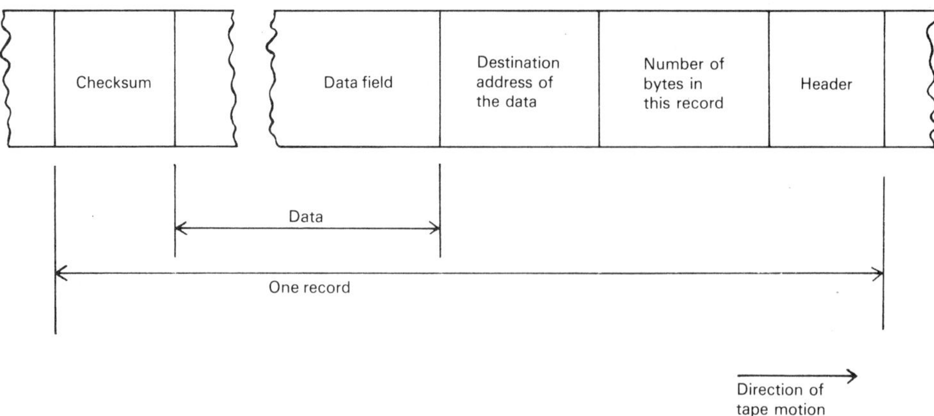

Figure 8.1 The format of data required by MIKBUG's loader

destination of the data) while in more sophisticated loaders the relative address of the data is given. In the latter case, the loader adds an offset to the relative address to obtain the absolute address.

The data following the address is the actual data to be loaded into memory, starting at the specified address and then loading successive bytes of data into consecutive memory locations.

The final piece of information in the record is the checksum, which is the 1s complement of the summation of the 8-bit bytes following the header. That is, when the record is first generated, the checksum is set to zero and each byte, after the header, is added to the checksum. Only the least significant eight bits of the checksum are used in the addition, so that the checksum remains eight bits long no matter how many bytes are added to it. Before the checksum is written on the record, its 1s complement is taken, so that the 0s become 1s and vice versa.

When the record is read by the loader, the sum of all the bytes in the record is formed. The value of this sum should be $FF_{16} = 11111111_2$. If this value is not obtained the record has been incorrectly read, and some action should be taken. The checksum is therefore a means of detecting errors in the reading of a tape. Such a facility is vital when data is stored on a magnetic medium (e.g. cassette).

The loader reads records sequentially until a terminator is encountered. MIKBUG uses S1 as a header and S9 as a terminator. Once the program has been loaded, it may be executed by jumping to its entry point. That is, the program counter is loaded with the address of the first instruction of the program to be executed. MIKBUG transfers control to the user's program by storing the entry point on the stack and then executing a return-from-interrupt instruction. This has the effect of loading all the 6800's registers from the stack. An alternative approach is to create a special record, indicated by a unique header, which contains the entry point of the program. This is often called the *transfer address*. Once the terminator record has been found the loader automatically executes a jump to the transfer address.

Apart from a loader, most monitors contain several other functions which are normally activated by typing a particular letter on the console. The most important of these functions are:

Punch The punch function is the complement of the loader. After a program has been created, or an old program modified, the punch function can be used to store it on paper tape or cassette in the form required by the loader. Almost all monitors include this function.

Examine a memory location This allows the contents of a selected memory location to be examined and, if necessary, modified. This function is provided by all monitors, although its sophistication varies from monitor to monitor.

Move a block of memory This allows a given block of data to be moved from one region of memory to another. More precisely, the data is copied from one region to another. This function is sometimes referred to incorrectly as relocation. True relocation involves not only moving the data but also recalculating the address of jump instructions. The move function is not provided by many monitors as it is of limited use in simple systems. This function is sometimes useful in conjunction with an EPROM programmer—the data is edited in read/write memory and then moved to the EPROM programmer's memory space.

Preset a block of memory locations This instruction allows a block of contiguous memory locations to be set to any given value. Typically, the block of memory locations may be set to zero to clear the memory. This function, although provided by some monitors, is of very limited use. Any locations that require clearing are normally cleared by the program in which they are used. Only a very poor programmer would write a program which required that memory locations were cleared or preset before the program could be run.

Examine registers This function allows the contents of the microprocessor's registers to be displayed on the console. The precise nature of this function varies from monitor to monitor and is largely used to debug programs.

Locate a byte Very few monitors provide this function, which allows the programmer to search through a specified area of memory for a given byte or word (two bytes). This facility is useful when modifying programs, because a particular op-code or address may be speedily located without having to step through memory locations.

Set a breakpoint A breakpoint is a means of halting the execution of a program at some specified address. When the breakpoint is encountered, that is, when the program counter contains the address of the breakpoint, the contents of the microprocessor's registers are displayed on the console. This is a very important facility as it allows the programmer to examine the contents of the microprocessor's registers during the running of a program. Some monitors permit the programmer to set several breakpoints simultaneously.

Trace This function is a close relation of the breakpoint function. When a program runs in the trace mode the contents of all the CPU's working registers are displayed on the console after each op-code is executed. In this way it is possible to follow the execution of a program in minute detail. The trace mode is, therefore, equivalent to the use of a breakpoint which is automatically moved through the program during its execution. The trace facility is provided by very few monitors, and is often implemented in hardware by generating an interrupt after each instruction is executed.

Monitor input/output routines One of the most important considerations in the design of a monitor is the way in which it handles input and output operations. The reason for this stress on the I/O routines is that the programmer often wishes to use these routines for his own I/O transactions rather than writing new I/O routines.

At this point it is worthwhile looking at the operation of MIKBUG's I/O routines. The input routine fetches a character from the console and puts it in accumulator A, and the output subroutine causes the character whose code is represented by the contents of accumulator A to be displayed on the system console. Other useful subroutines within MIKBUG allow data to be entered (or printed) in hexadecimal format, and strings of characters to be displayed on the console. These facilities are very important to the inexperienced programmer because they allow him to write programs without having to worry about the design of his own input/output routines.

The great disadvantage of MIKBUG is its inflexibility. When considering a design for the TS1's monitor, the pitfalls of MIKBUG's I/O should be remembered. The I/O routines of MIKBUG convert the parallel data in accumulator A to a serial format by shifting bits into or out of a PIA, using a hardware timer to determine the interval between successive bits, and hence the bit rate of the serial data. Three disadvantages follow from this arrangement:

(1) The I/O interface is unusual as it employs a PIA as a UART rather than the ACIA. This means that a special PIA-based I/O port must be built into any system using MIKBUG I/O routines. Fortunately, almost all MIKBUG-compatible replacements use an ACIA to input or output data.

(2) Once the output of a character has been initiated the CPU is tied up for the duration of that character. At 300 baud this amounts to approximately 30 000 μs per character. If an ACIA were used instead of a PIA, the ACIA would be able to free the CPU from the time-consuming task of serializing the data. (This time is saved only if the ACIA is operating in an interrupt-driven mode—otherwise the same time is lost in testing the ACIA's Tx status bit.)

(3) While the CPU is outputting a character, bit by bit, MIKBUG's output routine does not check to see if any new data has arrived from the console. This means that input and output cannot take place simultaneously, and that output cannot be interrupted, preventing any break-in.

A further disadvantage of MIKBUG's input routines is that when an error is detected by MIKBUG (i.e. hexadecimal character is expected but a non-hex character is received), control is passed back to MIKBUG. Suppose a programmer has written a program to read data in a hexadecimal format from a cassette system and has used the subroutine BYTE (located at E055) to read the data. No problems occur as long as valid hexadecimal characters are read off the tape. However, as soon as a non-hexadecimal character is detected by BYTE, control is passed back to MIKBUG. This is bad enough (the user program has been aborted), but MIKBUG now regards further input characters coming from the tape as valid MIKBUG commands. A much better approach is to design an input routine which sets a flag (usually the carry bit) whenever an input error is detected. In this way a subroutine need not pass control to a monitor if an invalid character is detected, and the programmer is free to take any action he wishes.

8.2 A MONITOR FOR THE TS1 MICROPROCESSOR SYSTEM

In this section the description and listing of a suitable monitor for the TS1 microprocessor system is given. The monitor is called TS1BUG and occupies the top 1K bytes of memory in the range FC00 – FFFF. Although the address-decoding circuits of TS1 have been designed for a 4K EPROM, TS1BUG has been written to fit into a quarter of this memory space. There are two reasons for this choice. Firstly, a 4K monitor is very large and such a monitor would normally be written for a specific purpose—editor, assembler or disk-operating system. Secondly, by restricting the size of the monitor to 1K, the reader who wishes to build the TS1 can use a 2708 1K × 8 EPROM instead of a 2516 or 2532.

TS1BUG is a typical monitor and has been heavily influenced by MIKBUG which may be thought of as a "prototype" monitor. Unlike some commercial monitors which have been written so that their I/O subroutines have the same address as those of MIKBUG, TS1BUG has no such compatibility with MIKBUG. The basic functions provided by MIKBUG are:

M examine/change the contents of a *M*emory location;
R print the contents of the CPU's *R*egisters;
G execute a program (*G*o);
L *L*oad a formatted paper tape;
P *P*unch a formatted paper tape.

All the above functions are implemented by TS1BUG and several more have been included. Many of MIKBUG's basic weaknesses have been overcome, particularly MIKBUG's poor I/O arrangements. The operating environment of TS1BUG requires scratchpad RAM in the range A000 – A3FF, and an ACIA at EC00 which acts as the console I/O port.

The basic functions provided by TS1BUG are described in Fig. 8.2. Each function is activated by typing a single character on the console. These functions are all subroutines (apart from J, G, and Z) which allows them to be called from user programs. TS1BUG's 12 functions operate in the following way.

(1) Examine memory (M) As this is almost certainly the most frequently used

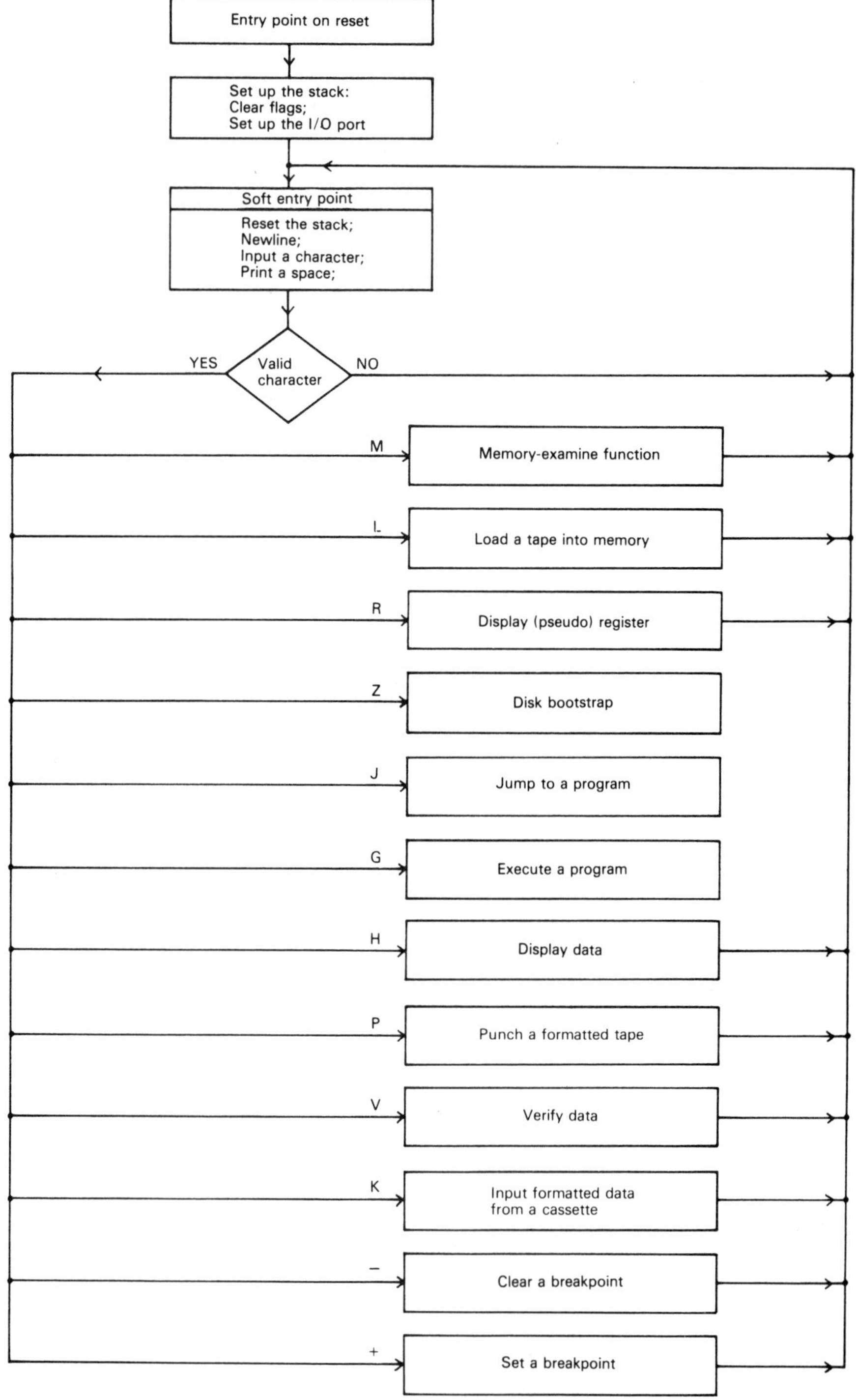

Figure 8.2 The organization of TS1BUG

function, it has been made as versatile as possible. To activate this function an M, followed by the four-character hexadecimal address of the memory location to be displayed, is entered from the console. The monitor then replies by moving to a new line, printing the address and its contents. If the programmer enters any character other than B, N, ., space, or carriage return, the monitor prints the address and contents of the next memory location on a new line. In this way a program may be stepped through, location by location. The behavior of this function is modified by the characters B, N, ., space, and carriage return in the following ways:

If a B is entered after the contents of a memory location have been displayed the monitor steps back to the previous location and prints its address and contents. This allows the correction of errors without resorting to the cumbersome procedure of terminating the M function and re-entering it each time a typing error is made.

When an N is entered (N = new) a new four-character hexadecimal address is expected by the monitor. The programmer types the new address and the monitor examines the contents of this address. This enables the programmer to examine non-consecutive memory locations.

So far we have dealt with ways in which the contents of a given memory location may be displayed but have not considered how the data may be modified. To do this a space is entered after the monitor has displayed the old data. The monitor now expects two hexadecimal characters to replace the old data. When new data has been entered the monitor automatically moves to a new line and prints the address and contents of the next memory location. Whenever new data is entered into a memory location the new data is re-read and compared with the data just stored. If the data has not been correctly stored a question mark is printed, followed by the data actually stored in the memory location. This facility checks for attempts to store data in ROM or in faulty or non-existent memory. TS1BUG's memory examine function uses three no-operations (NOP) between the store operation and the re-read and compare operation. This is because it is possible to store data in non-existent memory and correctly read it back! If memory does not exist at a given address, the data placed on the data bus in a CPU-write cycle applies a charge to the distributed bus capacitance. An immediate read operation to the same address reads the data stored in this capacitance. By inserting the NOP instructions between the store and re-read operations, time is given for the capacitances to discharge (see Question 7 at the end of this chapter). To end the memory-examine sequence a carriage return is entered and control is passed back to the monitor.

A most useful feature of this function is the ability to display data in the form of one instruction per line. This is done by typing a full stop after the contents of a memory location have been displayed. Suppose the current memory location contains the data "BD". Typing a full stop may bring the response

```
@003A BD .FF 0C
@003D A7
```

The code BD represents the three-byte instruction "jump to subroutine". Typing a full stop causes the address to be printed on the same line. Of course, the number of bytes of data printed after the full stop depends on the nature of the op-code. This facility allows a program to be displayed in the form of one instruction per line, making it relatively easy to interpret. The key to this function is the subroutine SIZE which, when called, returns with the number of bytes occupied by an op-code, pointed at by the X register, in accumulator B. Fortunately the machine code of the 6800 is reasonably well-structured and it is possible to extract the size of the op-code with little difficulty.

Figure 8.3 gives an example of the use of the M function; the underlined characters are those entered by the programmer. A flow diagram of the operation of this function is given in Fig. 8.4.

```
@M 0000
@0000 03  11
@0001 76  22
@0002 4A  33
@0003 CF  44
@0004 00 B
@0003 44  55
@0004 00 N 1000
@1000 80 ,
@1001 3F ,
@1002 4C ,
@1003 7E N FC00
@FC00 8E .A0 42
@FC03 CE .EC 00
@FC06 FF .A0 8F
@FC09 FF .A0 91
@FC0C 86 .03
@FC0E A7 .00
@FC10 86
@
```

Figure 8.3 An example of the use of the "M" function

Note: The underlined characters represent the response of the programmer

(2) Register-examine function R The register-examine function has been included to give TS1BUG a measure of functional compatibility with MIKBUG, and because this function is automatically invoked by the "BREAKPOINT" function. The operation of this function is to display the contents of the 6800's registers on the

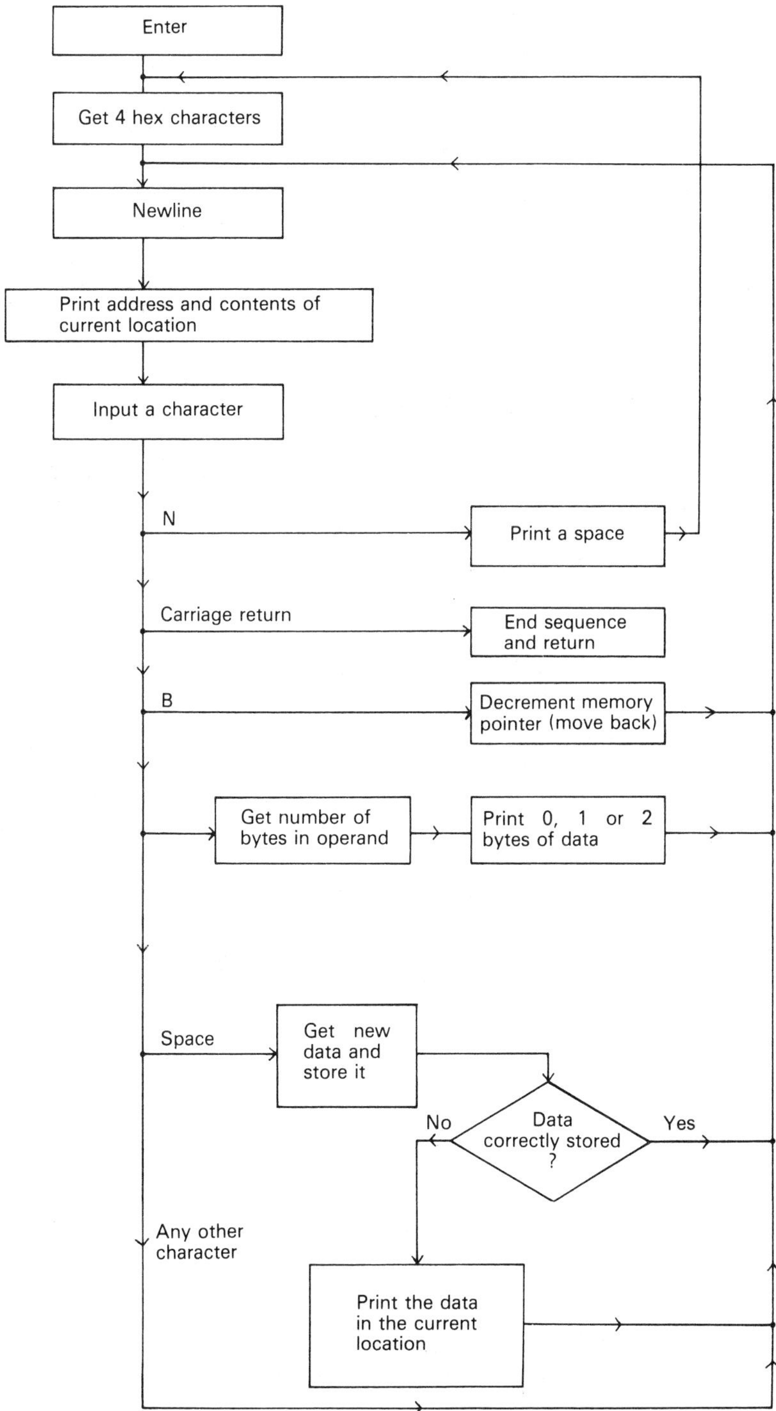

Figure 8.4 The flow diagram of the "M" function

console in the order: condition code register, accumulator B, accumulator A, X register, program counter, and stack pointer. The format of the data is

R 01 AB 34 1000 1489 A061.

The register display function does not actually display the contents of the 6800's internal registers, but instead displays a set of "pseudo registers" located somewhere in RAM. The purpose and operation of this function becomes clear only when the 6800's interrupt mechanism is considered. Immediately after an interrupt (IRQ, NMI, SWI) the 6800 finishes its current operation and deposits the contents of its working registers on the stack. Thus the 7 bytes at the top of the stack are a snapshot of the state of the microprocessor immediately prior to the interrupt. After the interrupt has been serviced an RTI (return from interrupt) instruction has the effect of transferring the data on the stack back into the CPU's registers. The effect of the R function is to display the top 7 bytes of the stack as if they were pseudo registers. Consequently the R function is meaningful only if it is invoked immediately after an interrupt (thus displaying the state of the CPU before the interrupt), or before an RTI instruction (displaying the data about to be loaded into the CPU's registers).

(3) The go function G After a program has been entered into the microprocessor's memory it is often necessary to run it. To execute a program its entry point (starting address) must be loaded into the CPU's program counter. This is normally effected by loading the required address into the index register and executing an indexed jump (i.e. JMP 0,X). MIKBUG implements the G function in a rather interesting way. When a G is entered from the console, an RTI operation is executed. That is, the pseudo registers on the stack are transferred to the CPU's registers. In both MIKBUG and TS1BUG the stack pointer is set to A042 before the TRI is executed. Thus typing a G causes the contents of memory locations A043 to A049 to be transferred to the CPU in the order shown in Fig. 8.5.

Before the G function is invoked it is necessary to load the starting address of the program to be executed into memory locations A048 and A049. Note that any of the CPU's registers can be preset at the start of the program by modifying A043 – A047 as required. Below is an example of the use of the G and R functions.

```
@R 01 AB 0C 3014 AD4F A042
@M A048
@A048 AD  00
@A049 4F  00
@A04A 4A
@R 01 AB 0C 3014 0000 A042
@G
```

There are two drawbacks of the G function. Firstly, it is tedious to set up the contents of A048 and A049 each time a program is to be executed. Secondly, the

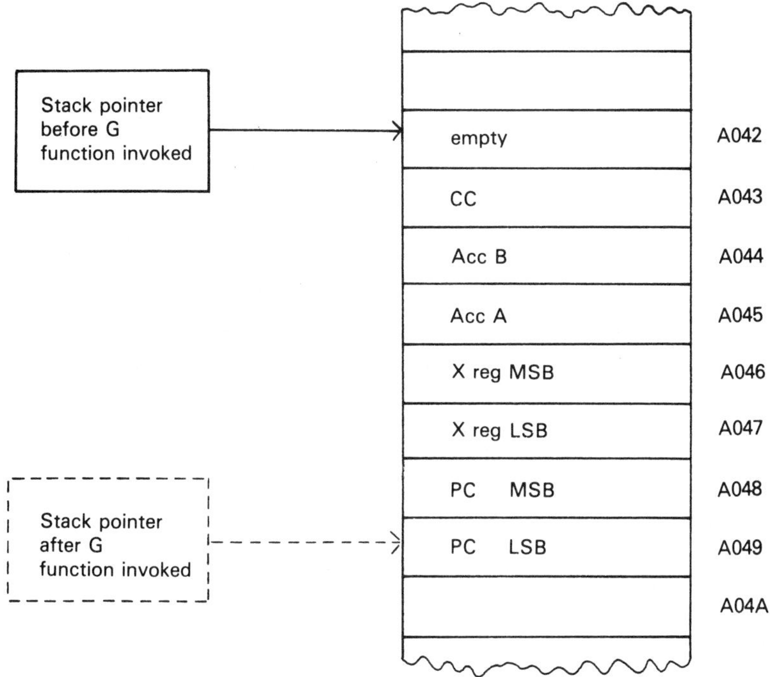

Figure 8.5

contents of A048/49 are often corrupted during the execution of a program so that these locations must be reset every time the program is run.

(4) The jump function J This function, not provided by MIKBUG, provides an alternative way of executing a user program. When a J is entered at the console, followed by a four-hexadecimal character address, control is passed to that address. The address is loaded into the X register and an indexed jump carried out. Control is not passed back to TS1BUG unless an explicit jump is made from the user program.

(5) The loader function L This function is almost identical to MIKBUG's loader and serves to transfer formatted data from a paper tape or cassette interface to TS1's memory. To use this function an L is entered from the console and a paper tape reader or cassette interface is then connected to the console input and switched on. That is, TS1BUG expects data from the console input. The data must have the format shown in Fig. 8.6.

S1 is the header of a data record and is followed by the number of bytes in the record, the address of the first byte of data to be loaded (4 hex chars), the data field, and finally the checksum. All data is in hexadecimal format of two characters per byte. As many records as desired may be loaded from one tape. The loading of data

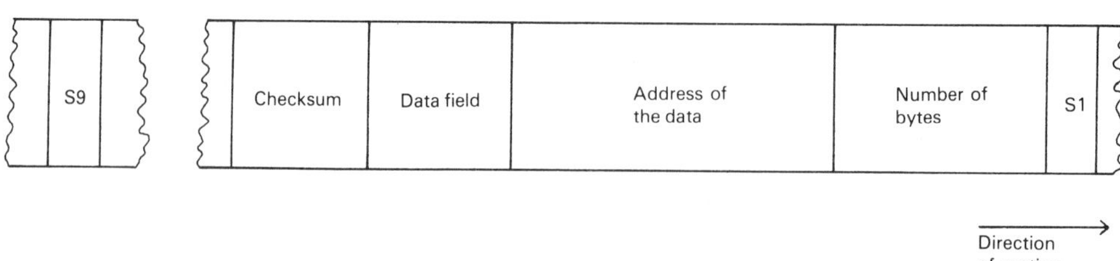

Figure 8.6

is terminated when the header S9 is encountered by the loader. The TS1BUG version of the loader differs from MIKBUG's in two ways:

(a) After data has been loaded into memory it is read back and the loading function is abandoned if an attempt is made to load data into ROM, or faulty RAM.

(b) Each time a loading error occurs (i.e. an incorrect checksum is recorded) an error counter is incremented. At the end of the loading function the number of records in error is printed. In this way loading errors can be detected and the execution of a faulty program avoided.

(6) The punch function P This function is the complement of the load function and serves to create a formatted paper tape or cassette in a form which can later be read back by the L function. The output generated by P function is directed to the console and hence the programmer must either engage a paper-tape punch (if one is fitted to the console output device) or a cassette interface must be connected to the console's serial output line. TS1BUG's P function is an enhanced version of MIKBUG's P function. It was found that when using the MIKBUG loader to read data from a cassette there was no way of determining the starting point of a program.

When the MIKBUG loader function is engaged it is necessary to wind the tape to the starting point of the required program. If several programs are stored on the tape this may be a difficult task. The TS1BUG version of the punch function has been designed to print a header (!!!!) at the start of a program and to print a name before each record. As each record has a name it is very easy to wind the tape to the start of the required program. Because the loader disregards all data not in a record there are no restrictions on the name of the program except that the characters S1 or S9 must not occur in the name. The MIKBUG version of this function requires that the starting address of the data to be punched onto tape is stored in locations A002 and A003, and the end address is stored in locations A004 and A005. To use TS1BUG's P function the following steps must be carried out:

Enter a P to activate the function.
Enter a string of up to 16 characters to name the program.
Terminate the string by a carriage return.
Enter the starting and ending address of the data to be punched.

If the starting address is greater than the ending address a question mark is printed and the function aborted. An example of the use of this function is given below.

```
@P PROGRAM ABC.1
@? 0000 0011  !!!! PROGRAM ABC.1
S113000011223355 00EF3A7F2FEA0BE92AEE2FEC49PROGRAM ABC.1
S10500100FEFEC
@
```

(7) The dump function H This function dumps consecutive bytes of data onto the console display in hexadecimal format. Data is printed in the form of 16 bytes per line. This function is normally used to examine a block of memory. To enter this function an H is typed followed by the starting and ending addresses of the data to be printed. For example,

```
@H 0001 0013
@0001 22 33 55 00 EF 3A 7F 2F EA 0B E9 2A EE 2F EC 0F
@0011 EF 7E EE
@
```

Note that the start and end addresses are not tested for error, so that if the start address were greater than the end address this function would print data from the start address to FFFF and continue from 0000 to the end address. However, the function may be aborted (as we shall see later) by entering a control A character at any time.

(8) The verify function V The verify command is rather unusual and is found in very few other monitors.

When a V is entered from the console all further data from the console input is simply echoed back to the console. The monitor disregards all data until four consecutive exclamation marks (!!!!) are received, when a return to the monitor control is made. The V function has proved helpful in testing input and output devices because it allows data to be input and echoed back as output without the monitor trying to interpret it as a command. Another application of this function is in the positioning of a paper tape. Suppose a paper tape is to be moved to a given position. A V is entered from the console, the paper-tape reader engaged, and the tape moved to the required starting point. Any data read from the tape is displayed on the console. Once the correct point has been located four !'s are entered and control returns to the monitor.

(9) The cassette function K This function serves the same purpose as the L function and is able to load a formatted paper tape into memory. Indeed, the K function actually calls the L function to carry out the loading. The principal purpose of the K function is to load a named program. That is, the loading of a program does not take place until a header followed by the required name is found. To use this function a K is entered followed by a name of up to 16 characters (the same name as used by the P function to generate the tape). A carriage return terminates the entry of the name. The monitor then replies with the prompt "READY" and waits for the operator to engage the tape reader. Data is read from the tape and

ignored until 4 consecutive !'s followed by the same name as that entered after the K are encountered. Control is then passed to the loader function which reads the tape exactly as in the L function. The K function has the advantage (over the L function) that the tape may be wound to a point before the starting point of the required program without any danger of loading part of another program—any data encountered by the K function before the (!!!!) header is ignored.

(10) Set a breakpoint + This function has the effect of setting a breakpoint at some specified address. To activate this function a "+" followed by a four-character hexadecimal address is entered from the console. No further action takes place until the breakpoint is encountered. The breakpoint function has a flag (BREAK) associated with it which indicates when a breakpoint is active. The memory locations BREAK + 1, BREAK + 2 contain the address of the breakpoint, and BREAK + 3 contains the data which was stored at the breakpoint. Note that a breakpoint can be set only in read/write memory. When a breakpoint is active the BREAK flag is set, the contents of the memory location at the breakpoint are stored in BREAK + 3, and the op-code 3F is stored at the breakpoint location. If a program containing the breakpoint is executed a software interrupt is generated when the op-code 3F is encountered. In the software interrupt-handling routine the breakpoint flag is tested. If the flag is clear a user SWI is assumed and a jump to the user SWI interrupt-handling routine is executed. If it is set, a jump to the "print-pseudo registers on the stack" subroutine is executed. In this way, the contents of the registers prior to the interrupt are printed. Control is passed back to TS1BUG after the breakpoint has been dealt with.

One aspect of this function requires a little further explanation. Because the 6800's program counter is incremented after each instruction fetch operation, the value of the program counter saved on the stack is one more than the address of the point at which the breakpoint occurred. To avoid printing an incorrect breakpoint address, the value of the program counter on the stack is decremented before the contents of the pseudo registers are printed. If a breakpoint is already active and an attempt is made to set a new breakpoint (by using the "+" function) the monitor prints a "?" and returns to control. Note that a breakpoint is not cleared automatically after it has been encountered. It is the job of the programmer to clear it.

(11) Clear a breakpoint This function exists to clear a breakpoint after it has been set by the "+" function. Entering a "−" causes the BREAK flag to be cleared. The 3F at the existing breakpoint is replaced by the data which was originally stored at the breakpoint.

(12) Disk bootstrap Z Entering a Z from the console forces an unconditional jump to location 8020 which is the entry point of Smoke Signal Broadcasting (SBC) Inc's disk bootstrap routine. (The SBC disk drive and controller are connected to an SWTP system which is linked to the TS1 by the extender module.) The SBC floppy disk unit includes a PROM containing the program required to load the operating system from a disk. The entry point to the PROM-based routine is 8020. Typing a Z

is equivalent to J 8020. This function may be modified to provide a speedy method of executing a jump to any frequently used program. Some monitors include a "U" function which forces a jump to a location pointed at by the contents of two bytes of RAM. The programmer can then set the two bytes of RAM to the starting point of his program and execute the program by entering a U. ("U" = User defined)

TS1BUG's Input and Output Routines

Possibly the greatest shortcoming of many existing monitors for microprocessor systems is their inflexible I/O routines. Most monitors operate on data in a given format and cannot therefore employ a wide range of I/O devices. For example, MIKBUG operates on 7-bit ASCII-coded data (in fact, MIKBUG employs the 64-character upper-case subset of the ASCII code). If a VDT with both upper- and lower-case characters is connected to the console I/O port of a MIKBUG-based system, the shift key must be pressed each time a letter is entered because MIKBUG ignores lower-case letters. This is an intolerable state of affairs—any reasonably well-written monitor should automatically convert lower-case characters into the corresponding upper-case format whenever necessary.

Another limitation of many monitors is the inability to direct the input or output data stream to more than one peripheral. It would be advantageous, for example, to enter a program from the console, edit it and then dump it on a cassette. Clearly, if there is only one output port, some form of switching between the console display and the cassette interface is required. This has two disadvantages: it is messy, demanding operator intervention, and both the console display and cassette interface must operate at the same baud rate.

TS1BUG's I/O routines, in common with those of other monitors, operate on data in a given format using a particular I/O port. Flexibility has been built into TS1BUG by allowing the programmer to modify the operation of the I/O routines dynamically during the execution of a program. A typical example of the use of these facilities is the control of a cassette interface by an I/O port other than the console. By modifying a status word within the monitor's scratchpad RAM the output (or input) data stream may be directed to the cassette's output port. After a tape has been created or loaded, the status word may be restored to its original value and control passed back to the console. The precise way in which the I/O routines operate is given below.

Input Figure 8.7 gives a flow diagram of TS1BUG's input routine "INCH" (= *in*put a *ch*aracter). The listing of this routine is presented in Fig. 8.8 in the form of a pseudo-code: a structured high-level language for those who do not like spaghetti (an on-going in-joke situation: proper programmers don't use flow charts but rely on structured programming). Although a flow diagram indicates the sequence of operations carried out during the execution of a program, it is possible to get lost in the mass of detail presented in the maze of interconnections (spaghetti) in the diagram. The pseudo-code of Fig. 8.8 has been designed to illustrate the operation of the subroutine in a relatively self-explanatory manner.

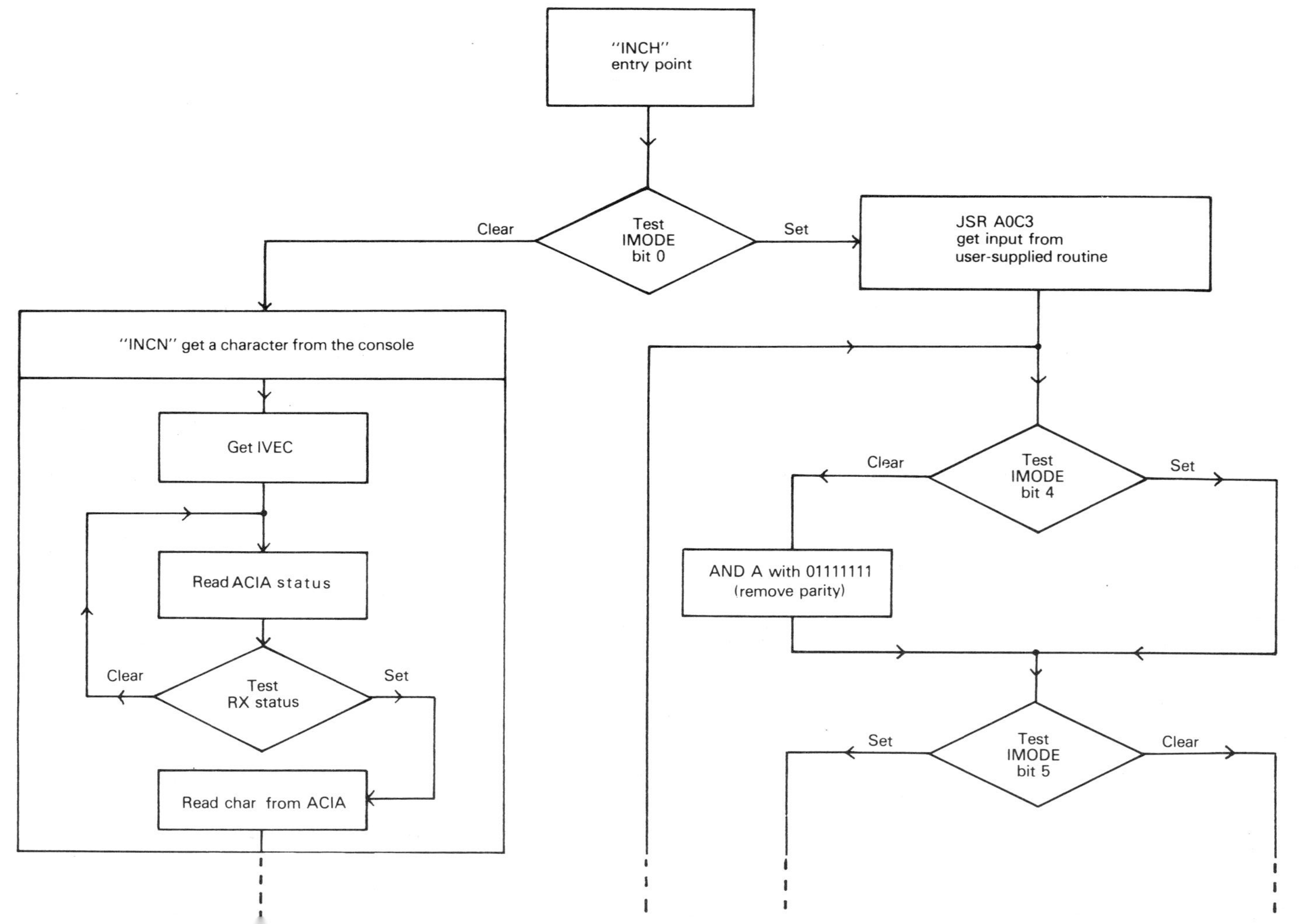
"INCH" entry point
Test IMODE bit 0
Clear
Set
JSR A0C3 get input from user-supplied routine
"INCN" get a character from the console
Get IVEC
Read ACIA status
Test RX status
Clear
Set
Read char from ACIA
Test IMODE bit 4
Clear
Set
AND A with 01111111 (remove parity)
Test IMODE bit 5
Set
Clear

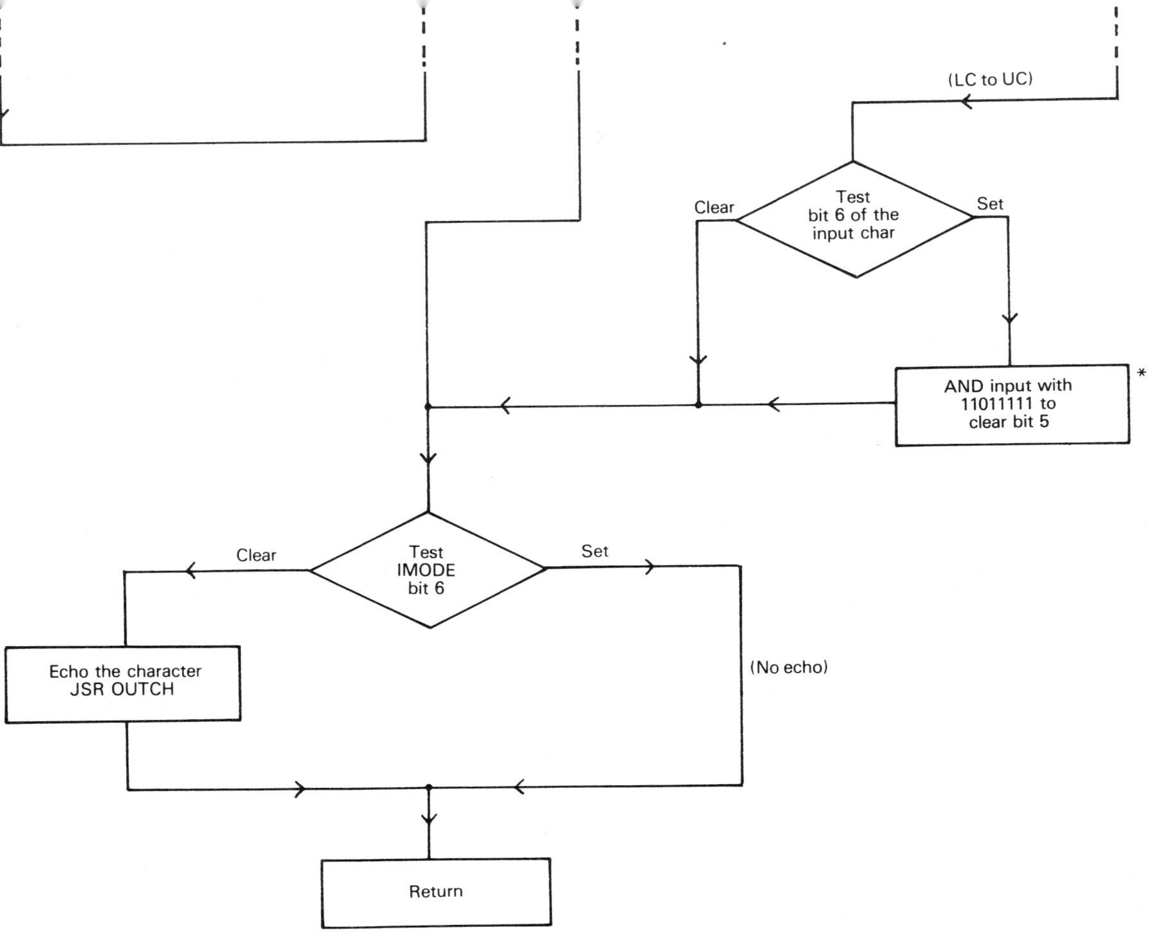

* *Note:* In the actual monitor the input is ANDed with 01011111 which also strips the parity bit.

Figure 8.7 Flow diagram of TS1BUG's input routine

```
BEGIN INCH  {input a character into the A register}

IF imode0 = 0  THEN BEGIN
                    save X register
                    get IVEC pointer to ACIA into X register
                    read ACIA status UNTIL ACIA receiver status set
                    read ACIA data {get the input}
                    restore X register
                    END

               ELSE call user input routine at A0C3

END IF

IF imode4 = 0  THEN strip parity bit from input

IF imode5 = 0  THEN {lower-case to upper-case conversion}
               IF bit 6 of input set THEN clear bit 5 of input

IF imode6 = 0  THEN call OUTCH {echo the character}

END INCH
```

[*Note:* Text enclosed by {} brackets represents a comment.]

Figure 8.8 TS1BUG's input routine expressed in pseudo-code

The key to the operation of the input routine is the status word IMODE which defines the source of the data and its format. When the system is reset and control is first passed to TS1BUG, the bits of IMODE are cleared (i.e. the default value of IMODE = 00000000). IMODE is never directly modified by the monitor, apart from entry following a reset. Consequently, if the programmer modifies IMODE, the modification remains in force until the programmer explicitly rescinds it. The least significant bit of IMODE determines whether the character is obtained by means of TS1BUG's own "input a character from an ACIA" routine (INCN), or by means of a user-supplied routine. If this bit is clear the character is obtained from an ACIA whose address is stored in memory location IVEC. The value of IVEC is initialized, by the monitor on reset, to EC00, the address of the console ACIA. By changing the 16-bit address in IVEC, the programmer may direct the input stream from any memory-mapped ACIA. If the least significant bit of IMODE is set, a jump-to-subroutine (JSR) instruction is executed to the location A0C3. It is now up to the programmer to supply an alternative input routine, anywhere in memory, by providing a JMP USER operation at A0C3. That is, if the user's input routine is at 0100, the code 7E 01 00 must be inserted at A0C3 and bit zero of IMODE set. This arrangement allows data to be input from any source. Data can even by obtained from a disk unit if a jump to the disk handler input routine is stored at A0C3. Because a jump-to-subroutine operation is executed to get data from the user's own input routine, an RTS instruction must end the routine if a return to TS1BUG's INCH routine is required.

Once a character has been obtained by the input routine, bit 4 of IMODE is examined. If it is clear, bit 7 of the input is set to zero, otherwise bit 7 is unaffected. By stripping bit 7 from the input, the parity bit is removed from an ASCII-encoded character. In the TS1 microprocessor system error detection in serial data is not implemented and the parity bit serves no purpose.

Bit 5 of IMODE is tested next, and if clear a lower-case to upper-case character conversion is carried out. If bit 5 is set no action is taken.

This conversion process is necessary when a VDT with a keyboard capable of generating both upper- and lower-case characters is connected to the console input. As TS1BUG operates with the upper-case characters A – F, M, L, R, J, G, H, P, V, K, Z and S, automatic lower-case to upper-case conversion removes the need to operate the shift key whenever these characters are entered. If the operator wishes to read lower-case characters (when editing text), setting bit 5 of IMODE defeats the lower-case to upper-case conversion process.

Bit 6 of IMODE determines whether or not the input character is echoed. If bit 6 is clear the character in the A register is echoed back and printed on the console (or other device depending on the state of OMODE). If bit 6 is set, no data will be displayed on the console when a character is input. This facility is helpful when, for example, a tape is being searched for a given record. By switching off the input echo, irrelevant data is not displayed on the screen until the header is found and bit 6 of IMODE is cleared to resume normal operation.

Table 8.1 summarizes the facilities offered by TS1BUG's input routine.

Table 8.1 Facilities Offered by TS1BUG's Input Routine

Facility	*Activated by*
Select user-supplied input routine	Bit 0 of IMODE
Strip parity bit	Bit 4 of IMODE
Convert L/C to U/C	Bit 5 of IMODE
Echo the input	Bit 6 of IMODE
Select ACIA	IVEC

As an example of the use of the input routine, consider the following program which, when a command "T" is received from the console, inputs 128 bytes of data from a tape reader connected to an ACIA at ED00.

```
TAPE    EQU     $ED00
T1      JSR     INCH            Get a character from the console
        CMP A   #'T             Is it a T?
        BNE     T1              If not try again
        LDX     #TAPE           Address of ACIA for tape reader
        STX     IVEC            Point to "new" ACIA
        LDA A   #% 01110000     No echo, no parity strip, no lower-case
                                to upper-case conversion
```

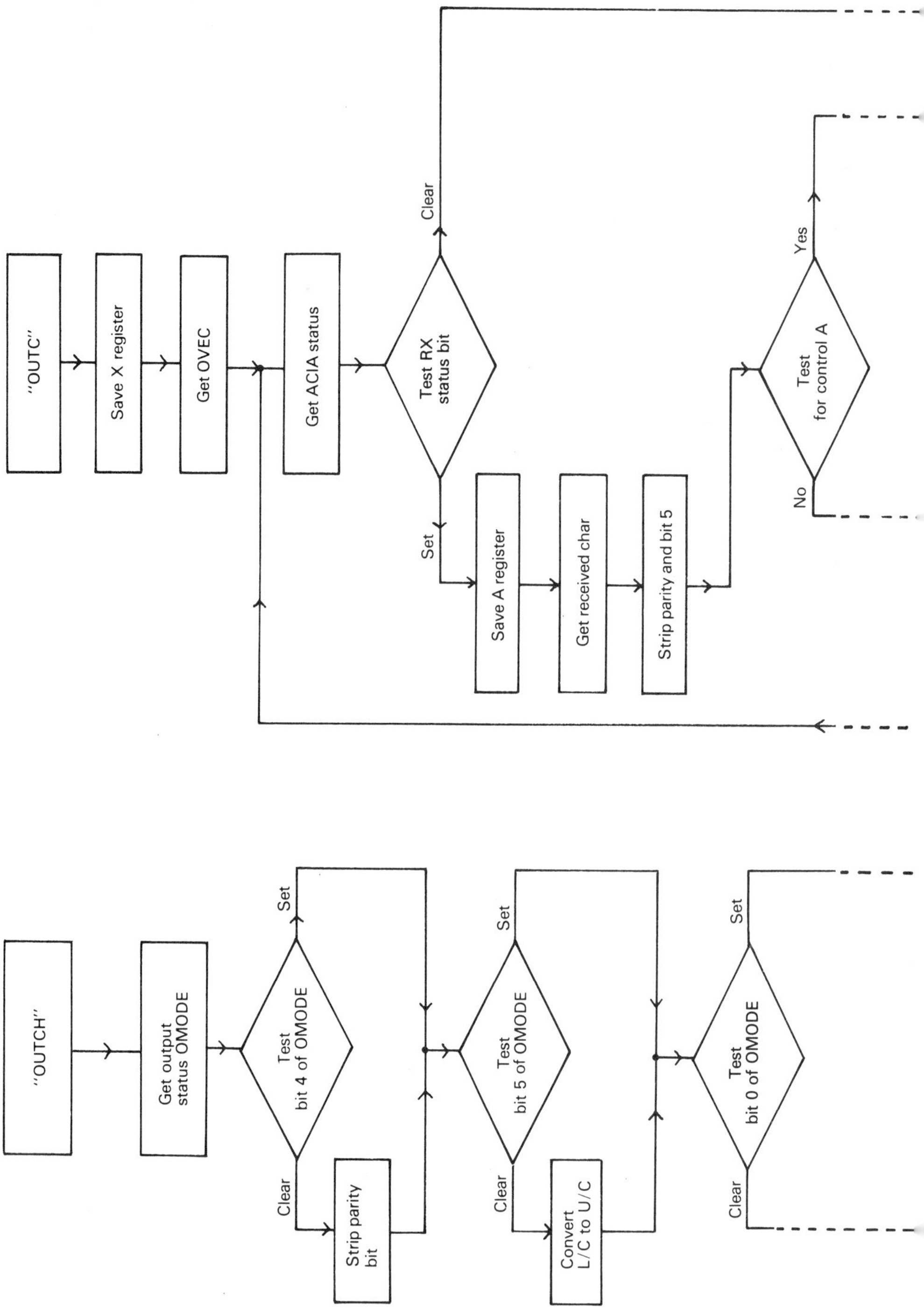

"OUTC"
Save X register
Get OVEC
Get ACIA status
Test RX status bit
Clear
Set
Save A register
Get received char
Strip parity and bit 5
Test for control A
Yes
No
"OUTCH"
Get output status OMODE
Test bit 4 of OMODE
Set
Clear
Strip parity bit
Test bit 5 of OMODE
Set
Clear
Convert L/C to U/C
Test bit 0 of OMODE
Set
Clear

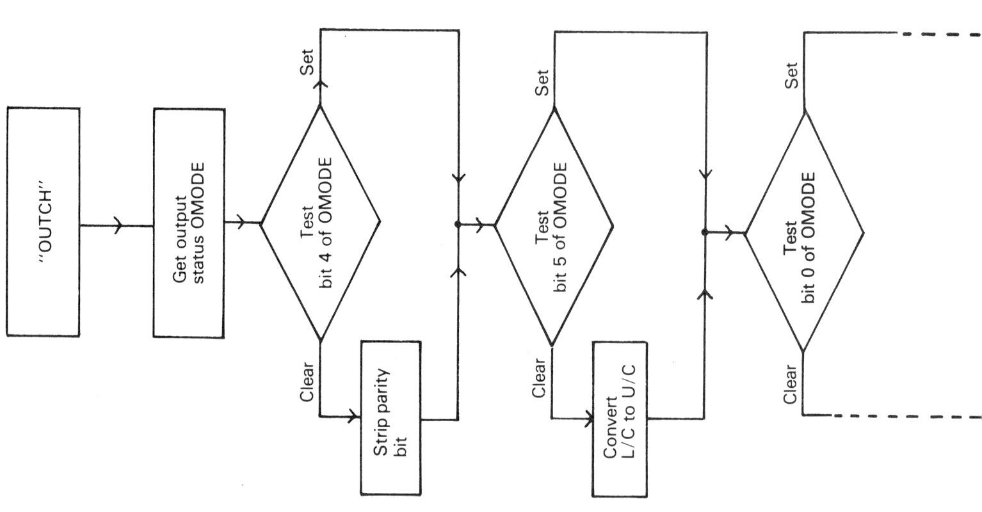

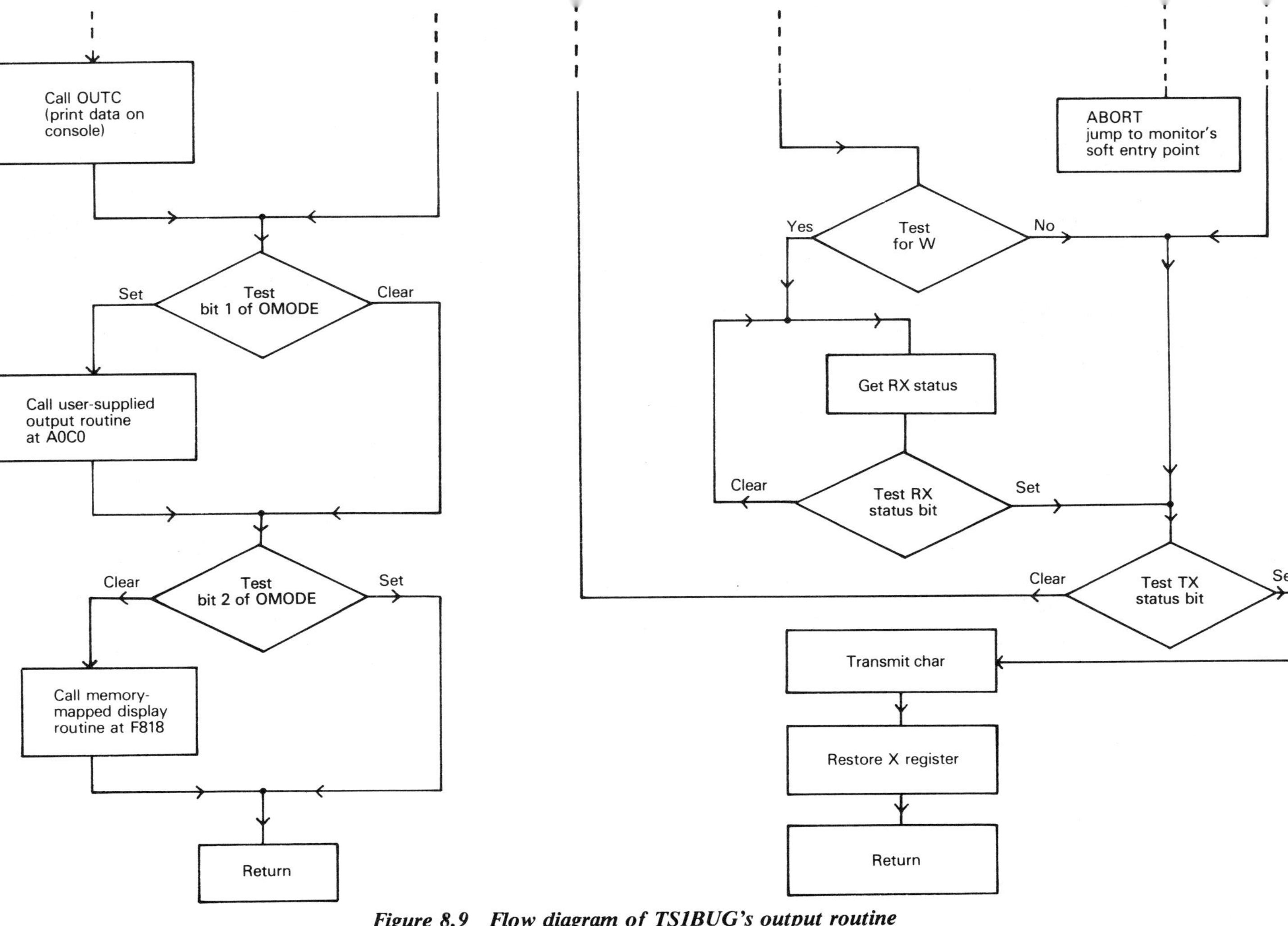

Figure 8.9 Flow diagram of TS1BUG's output routine

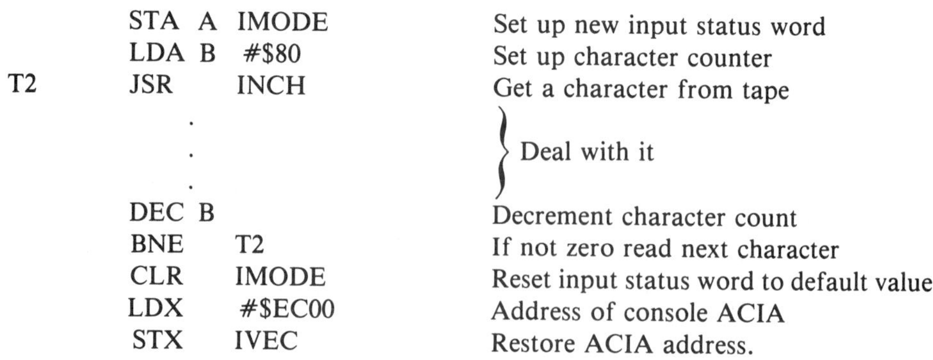

```
         STA A  IMODE       Set up new input status word
         LDA B  #$80        Set up character counter
T2       JSR    INCH        Get a character from tape
          .
          .                 } Deal with it
          .
         DEC B              Decrement character count
         BNE    T2          If not zero read next character
         CLR    IMODE       Reset input status word to default value
         LDX    #$EC00      Address of console ACIA
         STX    IVEC        Restore ACIA address.
```

Output TS1BUG's output routine "OUTCH" has many of the features of the corresponding input routine. The basic features of the output routine are:

(1) The ability to strip a parity bit off the data before printing it.
(2) The ability to convert a character from lower-case to upper-case before printing it.
(3) The ability to select an ACIA as an output device at any memory location.
(4) The ability to substitute a user-supplied output routine instead of or as well as the default routine "OUTC".
(5) The ability to halt or abort a stream of output.
(6) The ability to direct output to the memory-mapped display-handling routines.

The first four attributes of TS1BUG's output routine are identical to those of the corresponding input routine. The fifth facility allows a break-in to be made while data is being printed on the console. Figures 8.9 and 8.10 give the flow diagram and pseudo-code listing of the output routine, respectively. The only aspect of the routine requiring further explanation is the break-in facility. When a character is being output by the ACIA the receiver section of the ACIA is tested for input. If a character has been received from the keyboard it is examined for a "control A" or a "W". If it was a "control A", then whatever data is being output is suspended, and a jump to TS1BUG control is made. Thus, by typing a "control A", any program can be aborted. If the character is a "W" the output function is halted until any character other than a "W" is entered from the keyboard (this character is not echoed). By typing a "W" during the output of data, the operation may be frozen, giving the programmer time to absorb the contents of a VDT screen before it is replaced by further output.

The output routines of TS1BUG automatically display each character on the memory-mapped display. This is done by calling the memory-mapped display routine at F818. To suppress this facility it is necessary to set bit 2 of OMODE. It should now be clear that after power-up TS1BUG directs all output to both the console ACIA at EC00 and the memory-mapped display. By modifying bits 0, 1, and 2 of OMODE it is possible to direct output to the console, any other device by means of user-supplied routines, or the memory-mapped display, respectively. Equally it is possible to switch off any of these modes of display.

```
BEGIN OUTCH   {output a character from the A register}
IF omode4 = 0  THEN strip parity bit from data
IF omode5 = 0  THEN convert L/C characters to U/C format
IF omode0 = 0  THEN call OUTC {print character using ACIA}
IF omode1 = 1  THEN call user output routine at A0C0
IF omode2 = 0  THEN call memory-mapped output routine at F818
END OUTCH

PROCEDURE OUTC
REPEAT
            IF ACIA Rx status = 1  THEN
                                   BEGIN get received character
                                   IF character = 01 THEN ABORT
                                   IF character = "W" THEN WAIT
                                   END

UNTIL ACIA Tx status bit set

transmit data

END OUTC
```

Figure 8.10 TS1BUG's output routine expressed in pseudo-code

Limitations of TS1BUG

The design of TS1BUG, like that of any other monitor of a given size, is a compromise between the number of functions provided and their sophistication. The size of TS1BUG itself has been limited to 1K bytes, even though it resides in a 2K or 4K EPROM. This restriction has been imposed for two reasons. Firstly, a 1K monitor allows TS1BUG to be stored in a relatively inexpensive 1K or 2K EPROM rather than the more costly 4K EPROM in the TS1 microprocessor system. Secondly, the design of a 1K monitor is very much easier than that of a 2K or 4K monitor.

Having decided on a 1K monitor the programmer is confronted with a trade-off between "quantity" and "quality". That is, should a monitor contain many poorly implemented functions or just a few functions of great power and flexibility? TS1BUG could have contained more functions had its I/O routines been simplified to the most basic of ACIA I/O routines. However, the provision of good I/O facilities is considered to be of greater importance than the addition of a few more functions—some of which may be of dubious value. In any case, further functions can always be added by loading them into RAM from cassette or disk as the need arises.

The principal limitations of TS1BUG spring from the fact that it is not an operating system in the normal sense of this expression. An operating system would usually be expected to handle interrupts, implement multiprogramming (more than one program in memory at a time), error handling, resource allocation, and job scheduling. The following list of TS1BUG's limitations has been included to give the reader an idea of the areas of TS1BUG which may be modified to suit his own applications.

(1) Command input The functions provided by TS1BUG are activated by single-character commands entered from the console. After a valid command has been received, TS1BUG prints a space and waits for further data (e.g. an address) if necessary. If an invalid command is entered TS1BUG outputs line feed, carriage return and a prompt character, and then waits for a new command. Should the hexadecimal data required by any of TS1BUG's functions be invalid (say a "G" instead of an "F") a question mark is printed, inviting the re-entry of the incorrect character. This mode of data and command entry is simple and direct. Most reasonably sophisticated system software (operating systems, editors, assemblers, compilers) operate on commands and data stored in a line buffer, rather than from data entered directly from a keyboard. That is, the command is entered as a single entity with any necessary data (its parameters). The command is acted upon (executed) only when a carriage return is entered indicating the completion of the command. Such an arrangement has the following advantages:

(a) An incorrectly typed character may be readily corrected by typing a backspace followed by the desired character. In a direct-entry scheme an incorrect character may be acted upon before it can be corrected. Imagine the effect of accidentally typing a G when operating with TS1BUG.
(b) Several commands may be entered into the line buffer, one after the other. This is analogous to the multiple instruction per line facility of some versions of BASIC.
(c) The command is not lost after its execution as it remains in the line buffer. Consequently the command may be repeated without having to re-type it.
(d) The operation of the monitor, from the programmer's point of view, is brought into line with the operation of other types of system software. This is sensible for ergonomic reasons. The fewer rules the programmer has to remember the easier it is to write effective programs.

(2) Input/output Although TS1BUG has a considerably more flexible I/O arrangement than many other monitors, there are some important limitations. In particular, the I/O routines are not interrupt driven, making a break-in difficult. In a more versatile system the console ACIA is programmed to generated an interrupt whenever a key is pressed on the console. In this mode of input a response is generated no matter what the CPU is doing at the time the key is pressed (unless an IRQ is generated when the CPU's internal mask bit is set). In the current design of the TS1 microprocessor system, TS1BUG responds to the keyboard only if data is expected (i.e. during an ACIA polling loop) or during the outputting of data using

the subroutine OUTCH. In the latter case, the only characters recognized are "W" = wait, and "control A" = abort and return to TS1BUG control.

The outputting of data may also be made to operate in an interrupt-driven mode by programming the ACIA to generate an interrupt whenever a new character is required (i.e. transmitter buffer empty). The advantage of this arrangement is that time is not wasted in dealing with slow output devices. For example, if interrupt-driven output is used to generate a paper tape at 110 baud, the computer can execute another program between successive characters. This facility has not been included as interrupt-driven I/O routines require a more complex operating system with provision for I/O buffering. Furthermore, it is often dangerous to allow interrupts in a 6800 system when dealing with some widely available 6800 software. This is because some programmers have employed the stack as a second index register, and treat it as the location of some data structure. If an interrupt occurs the CPU's registers are pushed on the stack, wiping out part of the data structure. Other limitations of TS1BUG's I/O facilities are:

(a) When output is dealt with by an external user-supplied routine (pointed at by the contents of A0C0) the console is not tested for a break-in or abort unless the programmer supplies the test in his own input routine.
(b) No checking is performed on the ACIA input for parity errors, framing errors, or overrun errors.
(c) If the loader function is employed to read and store data from a tape, a problem exists with the BYTE subroutine. BYTE inputs a byte of data as two successive hexadecimal characters. Whenever BYTE encounters a carriage return, an abort is made and control passed back to TS1BUG. This is intentional and has been included to give a speedy way of aborting a function. However, it can be a problem if a paper tape is being read and a spurious C/R character (i.e. $0D_{16}$) is encountered where a valid hexadecimal character is expected. Fortunately, such an occurrence is relatively unlikely.

(3) Lack of re-entrant code A re-entrant subroutine is one which may be interrupted, used by the interrupting program, and then returned to by the original program after the interrupt has been serviced without any loss or corruption of data. In order to understand the implications of the above definition it is instructive to consider the behavior of the 6800's interrupt mechanism. The 6800 CPU saves the contents of all its working registers on the stack after an interrupt has been signalled, and then restores the registers from the stack after the interrupt has been serviced. The interrupt has no effect on the program being executed apart from the time lost in dealing with it. Now consider what happens when the interrupt-handling routine calls the very program that was interrupted. Such a situation occurs when an output routine moving data to a printer is interrupted and then used to move data to a paper-tape punch. Listing 8.1 provides a copy of the subroutine BADDR in TS1BUG. This subroutine is designed to input four hexadecimal characters from the console into the X register. Suppose BADDR is interrupted after the STA A XTMP instruction has been executed, and then the subroutine is re-entered from the

Listing 8.1 A Subroutine to Input 4 Hexadecimal Characters into the X Register

```
BADDR   PSH A            Save A register
        BSR    BYTE      Get 2 hex characters in A register
        STA  A XTMP      Store the characters in XTMP
        interrupt
        BSR    BYTE      Get next 2 hex characters
        STA  A XTMP+1    Store in location after XTMP
        LDX    XTMP      Put XTMP, XTMP+1 in X register
        PUL  A           Restore A register
        RTS              Return
```

interrupt-handling routine. The old contents of XTMP are over-written during the re-entry process and are *not* restored after the interrupt has been dealt with. Clearly, any subroutine which is interrupted and re-entered loses data if the data is stored in explicitly addressed memory locations. Data which is stored in the CPU's working registers or on the stack is preserved by the stack mechanism and is not lost. To make a subroutine re-entrant all working data must either be held in the CPU's registers or the index register must point to the data somewhere in memory. In the latter case, the X register is saved on the stack during an interrupt, rather than the actual data itself. One method of making the subroutine BADDR of Listing 8.1 re-entrant is given in Listing 8.2. The two pairs of hexadecimal characters input by BYTE are pushed onto the stack, in the reverse order in which they are received. By transferring the stack pointer to the index register the two bytes stored on the stack may be loaded into the index register by means of an LDX 0,X instruction. The stack pointer must then be incremented by two to restore it to its original state. The subroutine is now re-entrant and can be interrupted and re-entered as many times as necessary. Re-entrant code has not been implemented in TS1BUG in order to reduce the size of the monitor. However, wherever possible subroutines have been designed to preserve the values of the A, B and X registers.

Listing 8.2 As Above but in a Re-entrant Form

```
BADDR   PSH A            Save A register
        PSH B            Save B register
        BSR    BYTE      Get 2 hex characters
        TAB              Save them in B register
        BSR    BYTE      Get next 2 hex characters
        PSH A            Push LSB on stack
        PSH B            Push MSB on stack
        TSX              Move stack pointer to X register
        LDX    0,X       Get A and B off stack to X register
        INS              Clean up stack
        INS              Clean up stack
        PUL B            Restore B register
        PUL A            Restore A register
        RTS              Return
```

(4) Limited interrupt-handling facilities TS1BUG does not handle either IRQs or NMIs. Whenever an IRQ is granted by the CPU a jump is executed to A0D0 within TS1BUG's scratchpad RAM. This allows the user to supply a link (i.e. a JMP command) at A0D0 to his own IRQ handling routine. Similarly, an NMI is directed to A0F0. As TS1BUG is designed to operate with the 6828 priority-interrupt controller, provision must be made for interrupts IRQ0 to IRQ7. The 6828 causes IRQ0 to load the program counter with the contents of memory locations FFE8/9. TS1BUG stores the value of its own entry point (i.e. FC00) in FFE8/9. That is, IRQ0 has been programmed to cause a hard reset. In a similar fashion IRQ1 causes a jump to TS1BUG control, IRQ2 causes a jump to the software interrupt-handling routine, IRQ3 causes a jump to location 0000. IRQ4 – IRQ7 cause jumps to memory locations A0DC, A0D9, A0D6, A0D3 respectively. It is, of course, up to the programmer to provide links to his own interrupt-handling routines at the above addresses.

The software interrupt vector at FFFA/B contains the address of TS1BUG's SWI handling routine. This is a simple routine which tests the breakpoint flag. If set, indicating an active breakpoint, the contents of the registers on the stack are printed and a return to TS1BUG's control is made. If the breakpoint flag is clear, a jump to A0E0, where a link to the user's own SWI handling routine is located, is made.

If greater memory space had been available to TS1BUG a more sophisticated interrupt-handling arrangement could have been implemented. (It would be helpful to be able to define an interrupt address from the console in the form (say) "IRQ = A062". A better treatment of the breakpoint routines would include the ability to set multiple breakpoints, and the ability to continue from a breakpoint rather than returning to control. To continue from a breakpoint, the breakpoint flag must be cleared, the SWI code swapped for the data originally held at the breakpoint, the program counter on the stack incremented, and a return from interrupt (RTI) instruction executed.

(5) Limited facilities for expansion The current version of TS1BUG inputs a single letter command and looks through a table (COMTB at FF97) to see if the letter corresponds to a valid command. If it does the command is executed, otherwise a jump is made to F800 where my extension to TS1BUG is located. In the early versions of TS1BUG, if a valid command is not found a return to TS1BUG's soft entry point is made. That is, the instruction at address FC3B was "JMP RESET" instead of "JMP $F800". Suppose that at some later date a new EPROM with additional functions is added to the system, how are the new commands activated? There are only two ways of entering a program in the extended monitor: either a jump to the entry point of the EPROM must be made, or the entry point stored in A048/49 and the G command issued. Both of these alternatives are cumbersome. It would be more satisfying if some method of automatically searching for commands in a second EPROM, whenever the commands are not found in TS1BUG, were implemented. How do we design a monitor which is able to look for a second, extension EPROM? Note that a simple jump from TS1BUG to the second EPROM cannot be made because the second EPROM may not be implemented in

every system. If a command were not found in TS1BUG and an unconditional jump made to a non-existent EPROM, then the system would almost certainly crash. A possible solution to this problem is to let TS1BUG look for an extension EPROM if a command is not found in its own look-up table. If the EPROM is found control is passed to it, otherwise the command is ignored. Assuming that the extension EPROM is to be located in the range C000 – C7FF, consider the effect of the absence of the EPROM. Whenever a memory location in the range C000 – C7FF is accessed, the inputs to the data-bus drivers are floating (no memory component has its chip-select input enabled). Consequently the data inputs to the bus drivers float upwards to a logical one level, or downwards to a logical zero level. If the first (or any other) location of the EPROM is set to 1010 0101 (A5) it is highly unlikely that this combination of bits would exist on the data bus in the absence of the EPROM. Therefore the monitor can now test for the extension EPROM by testing location C000 in the following way:

```
TST     0,X         End of table?           } part of TS1BUG's get
BNE     REST1       If not test next entry  } a command routine
LDA B $C000         Get first byte of extension EPROM
CMP B #$A5          Is it "A5"?(i.e. EPROM located)
BNE     RESET       If not return to TS1BUG command
JMP     $C001       If found jump to it.
```

If the bottom of TS1BUG's own command table is reached (i.e. last entry = 0), location C000 is examined. If it contains "A5" a jump is made to C001 (assumed to be the entry point of the extension EPROM). Otherwise, the command is assumed to be invalid and a return to TS1BUG's soft entry point is made, and a valid command awaited. By employing this technique the designer can build his system without an extension monitor, knowing that it will automatically adapt to a second EPROM at a later date.

The above arrangement can readily be adapted to include commands in RAM. For example, if a command is not found in TS1BUG's command table, TS1BUG can then search for it in a user table, anywhere in RAM. The key to this operation is a flag informing TS1BUG whether or not a user table is active. The following is a possible listing of such an arrangement:

```
        TST     0,X       End of TS1BUG's own table?
        BNE     REST1     If not test then try next entry
        TST     FLAG      Is the extension flag set?
        BEQ     RESET     If clear then get new command
        LDX     USER      Get address of user command table in X register
REST3   CMP A   0,X       Command match?
        BEQ     REST4     If match then get address
        INX               Step past current command
        INX
        INX
```

```
        TST     0,X         End of user table?
        BNE     REST3       If not then examine next entry
        BRA     RESET       If end then return to control
REST4   LDX     1,X         Get jump address from the table
        JSR     0,X         Execute the function
        JMP     RESET       Ready for next command.
```

At the end of TS1BUG's own table, FLAG, a variable somewhere in scratchpad RAM, is examined. If it is clear a return to TS1BUG's soft entry point is made. Otherwise the contents of USER are loaded into the X register. It is the job of the programmer to store the address of his table in USER before setting the FLAG. The user's table is then searched just as TS1BUG's table was searched. In practice, the above routine would not be used because it would be wasteful to write two identical search routines. Instead a subroutine would be called first to search TS1BUG's table and then, if required, to research the user's command table.

8.3 THE LISTING OF TS1BUG

In this section the assembled listing of TS1BUG is given. The preparation of the program was carried out on an earlier version of the TS1 whose monitor has been cross-assembled on an ICL1904 computer. This earlier version of the TS1 was linked to an SWTP 6800 system (without the CPU card) with 28K RAM and a controller card for the Smoke Signal Broadcasting BFD-68 disk unit. The TSC Text Editor and Mnemonic Assembler supplied by SSB were used to prepare TS1BUG.

TS1BUG occupies 1024 bytes of a 2048 byte EPROM and is largely based on Motorola's MIKBUG, a listing of which is given in Motorola's Engineering Note 100.

```
ASMB,TS1BUG.14

                        NAM     TS1BUG
                *                               VERSION OF 30.03.80
A080                    ORG     $A080
A080            XTMP    RMB     2
A082            TMP1    RMB     2
A084            TMP2    RMB     2
A086            TMP3    RMB     2
A088            XSAV    RMB     2
A08A            SP      RMB     2
A08C            DIFF    RMB     3
A08F            IVEC    RMB     2
A091            OVEC    RMB     2
A093            SMODE   RMB     1
A094            IMODE   RMB     1
A095            OMODE   RMB     1
A096            CKSM    RMB     1
```

```
A097                COUNT  RMB    1
A098                ERROR  RMB    1
A099                BREAK  RMB    4
A09D                BUFF   RMB    16
A042                STACK  EQU    $A042      STACK LOCATION
                    *
EC00                ACIAC  EQU    $EC00
EC01                ACIAD  EQU    ACIAC+1
FC00                       ORG    $FC00
                    *
FC00 8E A0 42       ENTRY  LDS    #STACK     SET UP THE STACK
FC03 CE EC 00              LDX    #ACIAC     CONSOLE ACIA
FC06 FF A0 8F              STX    IVEC       SET UP INPUT DEVICE ADDRESS
FC09 FF A0 91              STX    OVEC       SET UP OUTPUT DEVICE ADDRESS
FC0C 86 03                 LDA A  #3         00000011 FOR ACIA RESET
FC0E A7 00                 STA A  0,X
FC10 86 55                 LDA A  #$55       SET CONSOLE ACIA PARAMETERS
FC12 A7 00                 STA A  0,X
FC14 7F A0 94              CLR    IMODE      INPUT CONTROL STATUS
FC17 7F A0 95              CLR    OMODE      OUTPUT CONTROL STATUS
FC1A 7F A0 99              CLR    BREAK      CLEAR BREAKPOINT FLAG
FC1D 8D 61                 BSR    CLEAR      CLEAR THE SCREEN
FC1F                RESET  EQU    *          SOFT ENTRY POINT
FC1F 8E A0 42              LDS    #STACK     RESET THE STACK POINTER
FC22 BF A0 8A              STS    SP
FC25 8D 5E                 BSR    LINES
FC27 BD FE B0              JSR    INCH       GET COMMAND
FC2A BD FF 1F              JSR    OUTS       PRINT A SPACE
FC2D CE FF 97              LDX    #COMTB     POINT TO TABLE OF COMMANDS
FC30 A1 00          REST1  CMP A  0,X        MATCH?
FC32 27 0A                 BEQ    REST2      IF MATCH GO AND GET ADDRESS
FC34 08                    INX               STEP PAST CURRENT COMMAND
FC35 08                    INX
FC36 08                    INX
FC37 6D 00                 TST    0,X        END OF TABLE?
FC39 26 F5                 BNE    REST1      IF NOT TRY NEXT COMMAND
FC3B 7E F8 00              JMP    $F800      TRY EXTENSION
FC3E EE 01          REST2  LDX    1,X        PICK UP ADDRESS FROM TABLE
FC40 AD 00                 JSR    0,X        JUMP TO ADDRESS FROM TABLE
FC42 20 DB                 BRA    RESET      READY FOR NEXT INSTRUCTION
                    *
FC44                JUMP   EQU    *          JUMP TO ADDRESS
FC44 BD FE ED              JSR    ONE        GET ADDRESS
FC47 6E 00                 JMP    0,X        JUMP TO THE ADDRESS
                    *
FC49                GO     EQU    *          LOAD PSEUDO REGISTERS INTO THE CPU
FC49 8E A0 42              LDS    #STACK     RESET THE STACK
FC4C 3B                    RTI               JUMP TO ADDRESS LOADED INTO PC
                    *
FC4D                SWI    EQU    *          SWI CONTROL
```

```
FC4D B6 A0 99          LDA A  BREAK       IS BREAKPOINT SET?
FC50 26 03             BNE    *+5         IF NOT ZERO DEAL WITH BREAKPOINT
FC52 7E A0 E0          JMP    $A0E0       IF SET GO TO SWI HANDLER
FC55 BF A0 8A          STS    SP          SAVE SP
FC58 30                TSX                MOVE SP TO X REG
FC59 6D 06             TST    6,X         EXAMINE PC ON STACK
FC5B 26 02             BNE    *+4
FC5D 6A 05             DEC    5,X         DEC PC MSB
FC5F 6A 06             DEC    6,X         DEC PC LSB
FC61 8D 22             BSR    LINES
FC63 8D 02             BSR    PSR         PRINT THE STACK
FC65 20 B8             BRA    RESET       RETURN TO CONTROL
               *
FC67           PSR     EQU    *           PRINT CONTENTS OF PSEUDO REGISTERS
FC67 FE A0 8A          LDX    SP          GET POINTER TO PSEUDO REGISTERS
FC6A 08                INX                ADJUST POINTER
FC6B BD FF 1D          JSR    OUT2S       PRINT CONDITION CODE
FC6E BD FF 1D          JSR    OUT2S       PRINT ACC B
FC71 BD FF 1D          JSR    OUT2S       PRINT ACC A
FC74 BD FF 1B          JSR    OUT4S       PRINT X REG
FC77 BD FF 1B          JSR    OUT4S       PRINT PROGRAM COUNTER
FC7A CE A0 8A          LDX    #SP         POINT TO STACK
FC7D 7E FF 1B          JMP    OUT4S       PRINT AND RTS
               *
FC80 CE FF C1  CLEAR   LDX    #MES2       FORM FEED CHAR
FC83 20 0C             BRA    TEXT        PRINT AND RTS
               *
FC85           LINES   EQU    *           PRINT A NEW LINE
FC85 36                PSH A
FC86 CE FF BC          LDX    #MES1       CARRIAGE RETURN, LINEFEED, @
FC89 8D 06             BSR    TEXT
FC8B 32                PUL A
FC8C 39                RTS
               *                        TEXT - PRINT DATA POINTED AT BY X REG
FC8D BD FF 3F  TEXT1   JSR    OUTCH
FC90 08                INX
FC91 A6 00     TEXT    LDA A  0,X
FC93 81 04             CMP A  #$04        END OF TEXT?
FC95 26 F6             BNE    TEXT1
FC97 39                RTS
               *
FC98           CLRB    EQU    *           CLEAR BREAKPOINT
FC98 7D A0 99          TST    BREAK       BREAKPOINT SET?
FC9B 27 0B             BEQ    CLRB1       IF CLEAR EXIT
FC9D FE A0 9A          LDX    BREAK+1     GET BREAKPOINT ADDRESS
FCA0 B6 A0 9C          LDA A  BREAK+3     GET DATA
FCA3 A7 00             STA A  0,X         STORE IT
FCA5 7F A0 99          CLR    BREAK       CLEAR BREAKPOINT FLAG
FCA8 39        CLRB1   RTS
               *
```

```
FCA9             SETB   EQU    *          SET A BREAKPOINT
FCA9 7D A0 99           TST    BREAK      BREAKPOINT ALREADY SET?
FCAC 27 03              BEQ    *+5        IF CLEAR SKIP NEXT INSTRUCTION
FCAE 7E FE E5           JMP    QUES       IF SET PRINT "?" AND RETURN
FCB1 BD FE ED           JSR    ONE        GET ADDRESS
FCB4 FF A0 9A           STX    BREAK+1    SAVE BREAKPOINT ADDRESS
FCB7 A6 00              LDA A  0,X        GET DATA AT BREAKPOINT
FCB9 B7 A0 9C           STA A  BREAK+3    SAVE IT
FCBC 86 3F              LDA A  #$3F       SWI OP-CODE
FCBE A7 00              STA A  0,X        STORE IT AT BREAKPOINT ADDRESS
FCC0 7C A0 99           INC    BREAK      SET THE FLAG
FCC3 39                 RTS
                 *
```


```
FCA9             SETB   EQU    *          SET A BREAKPOINT
FCA9 7D A0 99           TST    BREAK      BREAKPOINT ALREADY SET?
FCAC 27 03              BEQ    *+5        IF CLEAR SKIP NEXT INSTRUCTION
FCAE 7E FE E5           JMP    QUES       IF SET PRINT "?" AND RETURN
FCB1 BD FE ED           JSR    ONE        GET ADDRESS
FCB4 FF A0 9A           STX    BREAK+1    SAVE BREAKPOINT ADDRESS
FCB7 A6 00              LDA A  0,X        GET DATA AT BREAKPOINT
FCB9 B7 A0 9C           STA A  BREAK+3    SAVE IT
FCBC 86 3F              LDA A  #$3F       SWI OP-CODE
FCBE A7 00              STA A  0,X        STORE IT AT BREAKPOINT ADDRESS
FCC0 7C A0 99           INC    BREAK      SET THE FLAG
FCC3 39                 RTS
                 *
```


```
FCC4             MEM    EQU    *          DISPLAY CONTENTS OF MEMORY
FCC4 BD FE ED.          JSR    ONE        GET 4 HEX CHARACTERS
FCC7 8D BC       MEM1   BSR    LINES      NEW LINE
FCC9 8D 48              BSR    ADAT       PRINT ADDRESS AND CONTENTS
FCCB 09                 DEX               MOVE POINTER BACK
FCCC BD FE B0    MEM2   JSR    INCH       GET COMMAND
FCCF 81 0D              CMP A  #$0D       TEST FOR C/R = END OF SEQUENCE
FCD1 26 01              BNE    *+3        IF NOT C/R SKIP RETURN
FCD3 39                 RTS
FCD4 81 4E              CMP A  #'N        NEW ADDRESS?
FCD6 26 05              BNE    MEM3
FCD8 BD FF 1F           JSR    OUTS       SPACE
FCDB 20 E7              BRA    MEM        START AGAIN
FCDD 81 42       MEM3   CMP A  #'B        MOVE BACK?
FCDF 26 06              BNE    MEM4
FCE1 09                 DEX
FCE2 FF A0 82           STX    TMP1
FCE5 20 E0              BRA    MEM1       REPEAT
FCE7 81 2E       MEM4   CMP A  #'         FORMATTED DATA?
FCE9 26 0E              BNE    MEM5
FCEB 8D 36              BSR    SIZE       GET NUMBER OF BYTES
FCED 5A                 DEC B
FCEE 27 D7              BEQ    MEM1       ONE BYTE - NEXT INSTRUCTION
FCF0 5A                 DEC B
```

```
FCF1 27 02          BEQ   *+4       SKIP IF TWO-BYTE OP-CODE
FCF3 8D 24          BSR   ADAT1     PRINT TWO HEX CHARS
FCF5 8D 22          BSR   ADAT1     PRINT TWO HEX CHARS
FCF7 20 CE          BRA   MEM1      NEXT OP-CODE
FCF9 81 20    MEM5  CMP A #$20      TEST FOR SPACE (NEW DATA)
FCFB 26 CA          BNE   MEM1      IF NOT SPACE REPEAT
FCFD BD FE 6C       JSR   BYTE      GET NEW DATA
FD00 A7 00          STA A 0,X       STORE THE NEW DATA
FD02 01             NOP             WAIT (DUMMY CYCLES)
FD03 01             NOP
FD04 01             NOP
FD05 A1 00          CMP A 0,X       RE-READ THE DATA
FD07 27 BE          BEQ   MEM1      BRANCH ON CORRECT CHANGE.
FD09 BD FE E5       JSR   QUES      PRINT "?"
FD0C FF A0 82       STX   TMP1
FD0F 8D 02          BSR   ADAT      PRINT ADDRESS AND DATA
FD11 20 B4          BRA   MEM1      REPEAT
              *
FD13          ADAT  EQU   *         PRINT ADDRESS AND DATA
FD13 CE A0 82       LDX   #TMP1     GET POINTER TO ADDRESS
FD16 BD FF 1B       JSR   OUT4S     PRINT ADDRESS AS 4 HEX CHARS
FD19 FE A0 82 ADAT1 LDX   TMP1      GET POINTER TO DATA
FD1C BD FF 1D       JSR   OUT2S     PRINT DATA AS 2 HEX CHARS
FD1F FF A0 82       STX   TMP1
FD22 39             RTS
              *
FD23          SIZE  EQU   *         GET NUMBER OF BYTES IN OP-CODE
FD23 36             PSH A           SAVE A REG
FD24 A6 00          LDA A 0,X       GET DATA
FD26 C6 01          LDA B #1        PRESET TO ONE-BYTE OP-CODE
FD28 81 8C          CMP A #$8C      "CPX"?
FD2A 27 18          BEQ   SIZE3     THREE-BYTE OP-CODE
FD2C 81 8E          CMP A #$8E      "LDS"?
FD2E 27 14          BEQ   SIZE3
FD30 81 CE          CMP A #$CE      "LDX?"
FD32 27 10          BEQ   SIZE3
FD34 84 F0          AND A #$F0      MASK OFF LOWER 4 BITS
FD36 81 20          CMP A #$20      BRANCH?
FD38 27 0B          BEQ   SIZE2
FD3A 81 60          CMP A #$60
FD3C 25 08          BCS   SIZE1
FD3E 84 30          AND A #$30      MASK TO BITS 4 AND 5
FD40 81 30          CMP A #$30
FD42 26 01          BNE   SIZE2
FD44 5C       SIZE3 INC B
FD45 5C       SIZE2 INC B
FD46 32       SIZE1 PUL A
FD47 39             RTS
              *
FD48          LOAD  EQU   *         INPUT FORMATTED DATA (MIKBUG STYLE)
```

```
FD48 7F A0 98         CLR    ERROR      CLEAR ERROR COUNTER
FD4B BD FE B0  LOAD1  JSR    INCH       GET CHAR
FD4E 81 53            CMP A  #'S
FD50 26 F9            BNE    LOAD1      LOOP BACK UNTIL "S" RECEIVED
FD52 BD FE B0         JSR    INCH       GET NEXT CHAR
FD55 81 39            CMP A  #'9        "9" TO END LOADING
FD57 27 33            BEQ    LOAD5
FD59 81 31            CMP A  #'1        "1" TO LOAD DATA
FD5B 26 EE            BNE    LOAD1      IF NOT "S9" OR "S1" START AGAIN
FD5D 7F A0 96         CLR    CKSM       SET CHECKSUM
FD60 BD FE 6C         JSR    BYTE       GET LENGTH OF RECORD
FD63 80 02            SUB A  #2         LENGTH LESS ADDRESS
FD65 B7 A0 97         STA A  COUNT
FD68 BD FE A0         JSR    BADDR      GET DESTINATION OF THE DATA
FD6B BD FE 6C  LOAD2  JSR    BYTE       GET A BYTE OF DATA
FD6E 7A A0 97         DEC    COUNT
FD71 27 0C            BEQ    LOAD3      COUNT=0 MEANS END OF DATA
FD73 A7 00            STA A  0,X        STORE THE DATA
FD75 01               NOP               WAIT
FD76 01               NOP
FD77 01               NOP
FD78 A1 00            CMP A  0,X        TEST FOR FAILURE TO LOAD
FD7A 26 0D            BNE    LOAD4      IF NOT STORED PRINT "?"
FD7C 08               INX
FD7D 20 EC            BRA    LOAD2      GET NEXT BYTE
FD7F 7C A0 96  LOAD3  INC    CKSM
FD82 27 C7            BEQ    LOAD1      IF CHECKSUM ZERO START AGAIN
FD84 7C A0 98         INC    ERROR      BUMP UP ERROR COUNTER
FD87 20 C2            BRA    LOAD1      LOAD NEXT RECORD
FD89 7C A0 98  LOAD4  INC    ERROR      BUMP ERROR COUNT & FALL THROUGH
FD8C CE FF C5  LOAD5  LDX    #MES3      "ERROR"
FD8F BD FC 91         JSR    TEXT
FD92 CE A0 98         LDX    #ERROR     ADDRESS OF ERROR COUNT
FD95 7E FF 1D         JMP    OUT2S      PRINT NUMBER OF ERRORS AND RTS
               *
FD98           DUMP   EQU    *          DUMP 16 BYTES OF DATA PER LINE
FD98 BD FE F4         JSR    TWO        GET START AND END ADDRESS
FD9B BD FC 85  DUMP1  JSR    LINES      NEW LINE
FD9E CE A0 82         LDX    #TMP1      POINTER TO ADDRESS OF DATA
FDA1 BD FF 1B         JSR    OUT4S      PRINT THE ADDRESS
FDA4 C6 10            LDA B  #16        16 BYTES OF DATA PER LINE
FDA6 BD FD 19  DUMP2  JSR    ADAT1      PRINT DATA
FDA9 09               DEX               DEC X REG
FDAA BC A0 84         CPX    TMP2       END OF DATA?
FDAD 27 06            BEQ    DUMP3
FDAF 08               INX               RESTORE X REG
FDB0 5A               DEC B             DECREMENT BYTE COUNT
FDB1 26 F3            BNE    DUMP2      IF NOT ZERO PRINT ANOTHER BYTE
FDB3 20 E6            BRA    DUMP1      PRINT ANOTHER LINE
FDB5 39        DUMP3  RTS
```

```
                  *
FDB6 8D 73     PNCH    BSR     LNBF       GET RECORD NAME
FDB8 BD FC 85          JSR     LINES      NEW LINE
FDBB BD FE E5          JSR     QUES       PROMPT WITH "?"
FDBE BD FE F4          JSR     TWO        GET START AND END ADDRESS
FDC1 7D A0 8E          TST     DIFF+2     LOOK AT TMP2-TMP1 BORROW
FDC4 27 06             BEQ     *+8        IF ZERO OK
FDC6 CE FF C5          LDX     #MES3      "ERROR"
FDC9 7E FC 91          JMP     TEXT       PRINT AND RTS
FDCC CE FF D6          LDX     #MES5      "!!!!"
FDCF BD FC 91          JSR     TEXT       PRINT HEADER
FDD2 B6 A0 85  PNCH1   LDA A   TMP2+1     END ADDRESS LS BYTE
FDD5 B0 A0 83          SUB A   TMP1+1     START ADDRESS LS BYTE
FDD8 F6 A0 84          LDA B   TMP2       END ADDRESS MS BYTE
FDDB F2 A0 82          SBC B   TMP1       START ADDRESS MS BYTE (WITH CARRY)
FDDE 26 04             BNE     PNCH2
FDE0 81 10             CMP A   #16
FDE2 25 02             BCS     PNCH3
FDE4 86 0F     PNCH2   LDA A   #15        15 BYTES OF DATA PER RECORD
FDE6 8B 04     PNCH3   ADD A   #4         PLUS LENGTH+ADDRESS(2)+CHECKSUM
FDE8 B7 A0 97          STA A   COUNT      FRAME COUNT
FDEB 80 03             SUB A   #3         LESS 3 FOR BYTE COUNT+ADDRESS
FDED B7 A0 86          STA A   TMP3       BYTE COUNT
FDF0 CE A0 9D          LDX     #BUFF      POINT TO RECORD HEADER
FDF3 BD FC 91          JSR     TEXT       PRINT HEADER
FDF6 CE FF CE          LDX     #MES4      HEADER - C/R,L/F,NUL,S,1
FDF9 BD FC 91          JSR     TEXT       PRINT THE HEADER
FDFC 5F                CLR B              CLEAR CHECKSUM
FDFD CE A0 97          LDX     #COUNT     X REG POINTS TO BYTE COUNT
FE00 8D 24             BSR     PNCH5      PRINT NO. OF BYTES IN RECORD
FE02 CE A0 82          LDX     #TMP1      X REG POINTS TO START ADDRESS
FE05 8D 1F             BSR     PNCH5      PRINT ADDRESS OF DATA
FE07 8D 1D             BSR     PNCH5
FE09 FE A0 82          LDX     TMP1       ADDRESS OF DATA TO BE PRINTED
FE0C 8D 18     PNCH4   BSR     PNCH5      PRINT THE DATA
FE0E 7A A0 86          DEC     TMP3       ALL DATA PRINTED?
FE11 26 F9             BNE     PNCH4      LOOP BACK AND PRINT MORE DATA
FE13 FF A0 82          STX     TMP1       SAVE DATA POINTER
FE16 53                COM B              COMPLEMENT CHECKSUM
FE17 37                PSH B              PUSH CHECKSUM ON THE STACK
FE18 30                TSX                X REGISTER NOW POINTS TO THE CHECKSUM
FE19 8D 0B             BSR     PNCH5      PRINT CHECKSUM
FE1B 33                PUL B              RESTORE THE STACK
FE1C FE A0 82          LDX     TMP1       GET DATA POINTER
FE1F 09                DEX                MOVE BACK TO LAST BYTE PRINTED
FE20 BC A0 84          CPX     TMP2       ARE WE AT THE END?
FE23 26 AD             BNE     PNCH1      IF NOT GO BACK AND PRINT ANOTHER RECORD
FE25 39                RTS                ALL DATA PRINTED - RETURN
FE26 EB 00     PNCH5   ADD B   0,X        ADD DATA TO THE CHECKSUM
FE28 7E FF 36          JMP     OUT2H      PRINT A BYTE AS 2 HEX AND RTS
```

```
                     *
FE2B              LNBF    EQU     *            INPUT A NAME INTO BUFF
FE2B CE A0 9D             LDX     #BUFF        POINT TO THE BUFFER
FE2E BD FE B0     LNBF1   JSR     INCH         GET CHAR
FE31 81 0D                CMP A   #$0D         C/R?
FE33 27 08                BEQ     LNBF2        IF C/R END
FE35 A7 00                STA A   0,X          STORE IT
FE37 08                   INX
FE38 8C A0 AD             CPX     #BUFF+16     END OF NAME?
FE3B 26 F1                BNE     LNBF1        NEXT CHAR
FE3D 86 04        LNBF2   LDA A   #4           EOT (END OF TEXT)
FE3F A7 00                STA A   0,X          STORE TERMINATOR
FE41 39                   RTS
                  *
FE42              VRFY    EQU     *            INPUT CHARS UNTIL "!!!!"
FE42 C6 04        VRFY1   LDA B   #4           FOUR CHARS TO FIND
FE44 8D 6A        VRFY2   BSR     INCH         GET A CHAR
FE46 81 21                CMP A   #'!          IS IT A "!"?
FE48 26 F8                BNE     VRFY1        IF NOT START AGAIN
FE4A 5A                   DEC B                IF IT IS DEC COUNTER
FE4B 26 F7                BNE     VRFY2        IF COUNT NOT 0 TRY NEXT CHAR
FE4D 39                   RTS
                  *
FE4E              KAS     EQU     *            LOAD A TAPE FROM CASSETTE
FE4E 8D DB                BSR     LNBF         GET NAME
FE50 CE FF DE             LDX     #MES6        "READY"
FE53 BD FC 91             JSR     TEXT
FE56 8D EA                BSR     VRFY         WAIT FOR PROGRAM HEADER "!!!!"
FE58 CE A0 9D     KAS1    LDX     #BUFF        LINE BUFFER POINTER
FE5B E6 00        KAS2    LDA B   0,X          GET CHAR FROM BUFF
FE5D C1 04                CMP B   #4           IS IT EOT?
FE5F 27 08                BEQ     KAS3         IF IT IS END SEQUENCE
FE61 8D 4D                BSR     INCH         GET CHAR
FE63 11                   CBA                  MATCH?
FE64 26 F2                BNE     KAS1         IF NOT START AGAIN
FE66 08                   INX                  MOVE POINTER
FE67 20 F2                BRA     KAS2         TRY NEXT CHAR
FE69 7E FD 48     KAS3    JMP     LOAD         NOW LOAD THE TAPE
                  *
FE6C              BYTE    EQU     *            INPUT 2 HEX CHARS INTO ACC A
FE6C 37                   PSH B                SAVE A REG
FE6D 8D 11                BSR     INHEX        GET FIRST HEX CHAR
FE6F 48                   ASL A                SHIFT IT FOUR PLACES LEFT
FE70 48                   ASL A
FE71 48                   ASL A
FE72 48                   ASL A
FE73 16                   TAB                  SAVE IN ACC B
FE74 8D 0A                BSR     INHEX        GET SECOND HEX CHAR
FE76 1B                   ABA                  CONCATENATE THE TWO CHARS
FE77 16                   TAB                  SAVE IN B
```

```
FE78 FB A0 96          ADD B  CKSM        UPDATE CHECKSUM (FOR PUNCH)
FE7B F7 A0 96          STA B  CKSM
FE7E 33                PUL B              RESTORE B REG
FE7F 39                RTS
                *
FE80            INHEX  EQU    *           INPUT A HEX CHARACTER
FE80 8D 2E             BSR    INCH        GET A CHARACTER
FE82 81 0D             CMP A  #$0D        TEST FOR C/R=ABORT
FE84 27 17             BEQ    INHX3       IF CARRIAGE RETURN THEN ABORT
FE86 80 30             SUB A  #$30        ASCII TO HEX
FE88 2B 0F             BMI    INHX2
FE8A 81 09             CMP A  #$09
FE8C 2F 0A             BLE    INHX1
FE8E 81 11             CMP A  #$11
FE90 2B 07             BMI    INHX2
FE92 81 16             CMP A  #$16
FE94 2E 03             BGT    INHX2
FE96 80 07             SUB A  #$7
FE98 39         INHX1  RTS
FE99 8D 4A      INHX2  BSR    QUES        PRINT "?"
FE9B 20 E3             BRA    INHEX       TRY AGAIN
FE9D 7E FC 1F   INHX3  JMP    RESET       ABORT
                *
FEA0            BADDR  EQU    *           GET 4 HEX CHARS INTO X REG
FEA0 36                PSH A
FEA1 8D C9             BSR    BYTE
FEA3 B7 A0 80          STA A  XTMP
FEA6 8D C4             BSR    BYTE
FEA8 B7 A0 81          STA A  XTMP+1
FEAB FE A0 80          LDX    XTMP
FEAE 32                PUL A
FEAF 39                RTS
                *
FEB0            INCH   EQU    *           INPUT A CHAR INTO ACC A
FEB0 37                PSH B              SAVE B REG
FEB1 F6 A0 94          LDA B  IMODE       GET INPUT CONTROL STATUS
FEB4 C5 01             BIT B  #%00000001  EXAMINE BIT 0
FEB6 27 05             BEQ    INCH1       IF CLEAR GET INPUT FROM CONSOLE
FEB8 BD A0 C3          JSR    $A0C3       IF SET GET CHAR WITH EXT ROUTINE
FEBB 20 02             BRA    *+4         SKIP PAST CONSOLE INPUT ROUTINE
FEBD 8D 15      INCH1  BSR    INCN        CONSOLE INPUT ROUTINE
FEBF C5 10             BIT B  #%00010000  BIT 4 CLEAR TO STRIP BIT 7
FEC1 26 02             BNE    INCH2       IF SET SKIP PARITY STRIP
FEC3 84 7F             AND A  #$7F        REMOVE BIT 7 (PARITY)
FEC5 C5 20      INCH2  BIT B  #%00100000  TEST BIT 5 (CASE CONVERSION) UC
FEC7 26 03             BNE    INCH3       IF SET SKIP CONVERSION
FEC9 BD FF 64          JSR    CONV        PERFORM LOWER TO UPPER CASE CONVERSION
FECC C5 40      INCH3  BIT B  #%01000000  BIT 6 SET TO SUPPRESS ECHO
FECE 26 02             BNE    *+4         IF SET JUMP ECHO ROUTINE
FED0 8D 6D             BSR    OUTCH       ECHO THE INPUT
```

```
FED2 33                 PUL B               RESTORE B REG
FED3 39                 RTS
                *
FED4 FF A0 88   INCN    STX    XSAV         SAVE X REG
FED7 FE A0 8F           LDX    IVEC         GET ACIA ADDRESS
FEDA A6 00      INCN1   LDA A  0,X          GET ACIA STATUS
FEDC 47                 ASR A               LS BIT INTO CARRY
FEDD 24 FB              BCC    INCN1        IF CLEAR RECEIVER NOT READY
FEDF A6 01              LDA A  1,X          GET DATA
FEE1 FE A0 88           LDX    XSAV         RESTORE X REG
FEE4 39                 RTS
                *
FEE5 86 3F      QUES    LDA A  #'?          OUTPUT A "?" AND A SPACE
FEE7 8D 56              BSR    OUTCH
FEE9 86 20              LDA A  #$20         SPACE
FEEB 20 52              BRA    OUTCH        PRINT AND RETURN
                *
FEED            ONE     EQU    *            INPUT 4 HEX INTO X REG AND TMP1
FEED 8D B1              BSR    BADDR        4 HEX IN X REG
FEEF FF A0 82           STX    TMP1         STORE IN TMP1
FEF2 20 2B              BRA    OUTS         PRINT SPACE AND RTS
FEF4            TWO     EQU    *            INPUT 4 HEX INTO TMP2 AND TMP1
FEF4 8D F7              BSR    ONE          FIRST 4 HEX
FEF6 8D A8              BSR    BADDR        GET 4 HEX CHAR
FEF8 FF A0 84           STX    TMP2         SECOND ADDRESS IN TMP2
FEFB 8D 02              BSR    SUB          DIFF=TMP2-TMP1
FEFD 20 20              BRA    OUTS         PRINT A SPACE
                *
FEFF            SUB     EQU    *            SUBTRACT TWO 16-BIT ADDRESSES
FEFF 36                 PSH A
FF00 B6 A0 85           LDA A  TMP2+1       END ADDRESS LS BYTE
FF03 B0 A0 83           SUB A  TMP1+1       START ADDRESS LS BYTE
FF06 B7 A0 8D           STA A  DIFF+1       RESULT IN LS BYTE
FF09 B6 A0 84           LDA A  TMP2         END ADDRESS MS BYTE
FF0C B2 A0 82           SBC A  TMP1         START ADDRESS MS BYTE
FF0F B7 A0 8C           STA A  DIFF         RESULT IN MS BYTE
FF12 86 00              LDA A  #00
FF14 82 00              SBC A  #$00         SUBTRACT ANY BORROW
FF16 B7 A0 8E           STA A  DIFF+2       SAVE ANY BORROW
FF19 32                 PUL A
FF1A 39                 RTS
                *
FF1B 8D 19      OUT4S   BSR    OUT2H        OUTPUT FOUR HEX AND A SPACE
FF1D 8D 17      OUT2S   BSR    OUT2H        OUTPUT TWO HEX AND A SPACE
                *
FF1F            OUTS    EQU    *            PRINT A SPACE
FF1F 36                 PSH A
FF20 86 20              LDA A  #$20         SPACE
FF22 8D 1B              BSR    OUTCH
FF24 32                 PUL A
```

```
FF25 39              RTS
                *
FF26 44        OUTHL  LSR A                OUTPUT LEFT CHAR
FF27 44               LSR A
FF28 44               LSR A
FF29 44               LSR A
FF2A 84 0F     OUTHR  AND A  #$0F          OUTPUT RIGHT CHAR
FF2C 8B 30            ADD A  #$30          HEX TO ASCII CONVERSION
FF2E 81 39            CMP A  #$39          TEST FOR NUMBER>9
FF30 23 02            BLS    *+4           IF<9 OR=9 THEN SKIP TO PRINT
FF32 8B 07            ADD A  #$07          IF>9 THEN ADD 7 TO GET A LETTER
FF34 20 09            BRA    OUTCH         PRINT AND RTS
                *
FF36 A6 00     OUT2H  LDA A  0,X           OUTPUT 2 HEX (POINTED AT BY X)
FF38 8D EC            BSR    OUTHL         PRINT LEFTHAND CHAR
FF3A A6 00            LDA A  0,X           DATA DESTROYED BY OUTHL SO REREAD
FF3C 08               INX                  MOVE POINTER READY FOR NEXT TIME
FF3D 20 EB            BRA    OUTHR         PRINT RIGHT CHAR AND RTS
                *
FF3F           OUTCH  EQU    *             PRINT A CHARACTER
FF3F 36               PSH A                SAVE A REG
FF40 37               PSH B                SAVE B REG
FF41 F6 A0 95         LDA B  OMODE         GET OUTPUT MODE STATUS
FF44 C5 10            BIT B  #%00010000 TEST BIT 4 (PARITY STRIP)
FF46 26 02            BNE    *+4           IF SET THEN SKIP PARITY STRIP
FF48 84 7F            AND A  #$7F          REMOVE BIT 7 (PARITY)
FF4A C5 20            BIT B  #%00100000 TEST BIT 5 (L/C TO U/C CONV)
FF4C 26 02            BNE    *+4           IF SET SKIP CASE CONVERSION
FF4E 8D 14            BSR    CONV          PERFORM L/C TO U/C CONVERSION
FF50 57               ASR B                SHIFT BIT 0 INTO CARRY
FF51 25 02            BCS    *+4           CARRY SET - DON'T PRINT ON CONSOLE
FF53 8D 16            BSR    OUTC          CARRY CLEAR - PRINT ON CONSOLE
FF55 57               ASR B                SHIFT BIT 1 INTO CARRY
FF56 24 03            BCC    *+5           CARRY CLEAR - DON'T PRINT ON EXTERNAL
FF58 BD A0 C0         JSR    $A0C0         EXTERNAL PRINT ADDRESS
FF5B 57               ASR B                SHIFT BIT 2 INTO CARRY
FF5C 25 03            BCS    *+5           IF SET DO NOT USE MEM-MAPPED DISPLAY
FF5E BD F8 18         JSR    $F818         PRINT ON MEMORY-MAPPED DISPLAY
FF61 33               PUL B
FF62 32               PUL A
FF63 39               RTS
                *
FF64           CONV   EQU    *             CONVERT LOWER TO UPPER CASE
FF64 85 40            BIT A  #%01000000 TEST BIT 6
FF66 27 02            BEQ    *+4           IF ZERO NO CHANGE NEEDED
FF68 84 5F            AND A  #%01011111 IF SET REMOVE BIT 5 (AND PARITY)
FF6A 39               RTS
                *
FF6B           OUTC   EQU    *             OUTPUT A CHARACTER USING AN ACIA
FF6B 37               PSH B                SAVE B REG
```

```
FF6C FF A0 88          STX    XSAV       SAVE X REG
FF6F FE A0 91          LDX    OVEC       GET ACIA ADDRESS
FF72 E6 00     OUTC1   LDA B  0,X        GET ACIA STATUS
FF74 57                ASR B             TEST RDRF (BIT 0)
FF75 24 16             BCC    OUTC4      IF CLEAR GO AND CHECK TX STATUS BIT
FF77 36                PSH A             SAVE A REG
FF78 A6 01             LDA A  1,X        GET RECEIVED WORD
FF7A 84 5F             AND A  #%01011111 REMOVE BITS 5 AND 7
FF7C 81 01             CMP A  #$01       TEST FOR "CONTROL A" (BREAK-IN)
FF7E 26 03             BNE    *+5        IF NOT BREAK-IN THEN SKIP RESET
FF80 7E FC 1F          JMP    RESET      ABORT OUTPUT
FF83 81 57             CMP A  #'W        TEST FOR "W" (W=WAIT)
FF85 26 05             BNE    OUTC3      IF NOT WAIT THEN CONTINUE
FF87 A6 00     OUTC2   LDA A  0,X        GET ACIA STATUS (WAIT LOOP)
FF89 47                ASR A             MOVE RX STATUS BIT INTO CARRY
FF8A 24 FB             BCC    OUTC2      IF CLEAR LOOP BACK
FF8C 32        OUTC3   PUL A             RESTORE A REG
FF8D 57        OUTC4   ASR B             TEST TX STATUS BIT
FF8E 24 E2             BCC    OUTC1      IF CLEAR TRY AGAIN
FF90 A7 01             STA A  1,X        TRANSMIT THE CHARACTER
FF92 33                PUL B             RESTORE B REG
FF93 FE A0 88          LDX    XSAV       RESTORE X REG
FF96 39                RTS
               *
FF97 4D        COMTB   FCB    'M         COMMAND TABLE
FF98 FC C4             FDB    MEM
FF9A 4C                FCB    'L
FF9B FD 48             FDB    LOAD
FF9D 52                FCB    'R
FF9E FC 67             FDB    PSR
FFA0 4A                FCB    'J
FFA1 FC 44             FDB    JUMP
FFA3 47                FCB    'G
FFA4 FC 49             FDB    GO
FFA6 48                FCB    'H
FFA7 FD 98             FDB    DUMP
FFA9 50                FCB    'P
FFAA FD B6             FDB    PNCH
FFAC 56                FCB    'V
FFAD FE 42             FDB    VRFY
FFAF 4B                FCB    'K
FFB0 FE 4E             FDB    KAS
FFB2 2D                FCB    '-
FFB3 FC 98             FDB    CLRB
FFB5 2B                FCB    '+
FFB6 FC A9             FDB    SETB
FFB8 5A                FCB    'Z
FFB9 80 20             FDB    $8020      DISK BOOTSTRAP
FFBB 00                FCB    $00        END OF TABLE
               *
```

```
FFBC 00         MES1   FCB    0,$0D,$0A,'@,$04
FFBD 0D 0A
FFBF 40 04
FFC1 0C         MES2   FCB    $0C,0,0,$04
FFC2 00 00
FFC4 04
FFC5 0D         MES3   FCB    $0D,$0A,'E,'R,'R,'O,'R,$20,$04
FFC6 0A 45
FFC8 52 52
FFCA 4F 52
FFCC 20 04
FFCE 0D         MES4   FCB    $0D,$0A,0,0,0,'S,'1,$04
FFCF 0A 00
FFD1 00 00
FFD3 53 31
FFD5 04
FFD6 20         MES5   FCB    $20,'!,'!,'!,'!,$20,0,$04
FFD7 21 21
FFD9 21 21
FFDB 20 00
FFDD 04
FFDE 0D         MES6   FCB    $0D,$0A,'R,'E,'A,'D,'Y,$0D,$0A,$04
FFDF 0A 52
FFE1 45 41
FFE3 44 59
FFE5 0D 0A
FFE7 04
                *                            INTERRUPT VECTORS
FFE8 FC 00             FDB    ENTRY          IRQ0
FFEA FC 1F             FDB    RESET          IRQ1
FFEC FC 4D             FDB    SWI            IRQ2
FFEE 00 00             FDB    $0000          IRQ3
FFF0 A0 DC             FDB    $A0DC          IRQ4
FFF2 A0 D9             FDB    $A0D9          IRQ5
FFF4 A0 D6             FDB    $A0D6          IRQ6
FFF6 A0 D3             FDB    $A0D3          IRQ7
FFF8 A0 D0             FDB    $A0D0          IRQ
FFFA FC 4D             FDB    SWI            SWI
FFFC A0 F0             FDB    $A0F0          NMI
FFFE FC 00             FDB    ENTRY          ENTRY POINT
                       END
    NO ERROR(S) DETECTED
```

```
SYMBOL TABLE:
ACIAC  EC00    ACIAD  EC01    ADAT   FD13    ADAT1  FD19
BADDR  FEA0    BREAK  A099    BUFF   A09D    BYTE   FE6C
CKSM   A096    CLEAR  FC80    CLRB   FC98    CLRB1  FCA8
COMTB  FF97    CONV   FF64    COUNT  A097    DIFF   A08C
DUMP   FD98    DUMP1  FD9B    DUMP2  FDA6    DUMP3  FDB5
ENTRY  FC00    ERROR  A098    GO     FC49    IMODE  A094
INCH   FEB0    INCH1  FEBD    INCH2  FEC5    INCH3  FECC
INCN   FED4    INCN1  FEDA    INHEX  FE80    INHX1  FE98
INHX2  FE99    INHX3  FE9D    IVEC   A08F    JUMP   FC44
KAS    FE4E    KAS1   FE58    KAS2   FE5B    KAS3   FE69
LINES  FC85    LNBF   FE2B    LNBF1  FE2E    LNBF2  FE3D
LOAD   FD48    LOAD1  FD4B    LOAD2  FD6B    LOAD3  FD7F
LOAD4  FD89    LOAD5  FD8C    MEM    FCC4    MEM1   FCC7
MEM2   FCCC    MEM3   FCDD    MEM4   FCE7    MEM5   FCF9
MES1   FFBC    MES2   FFC1    MES3   FFC5    MES4   FFCE
MES5   FFD6    MES6   FFDE    OMODE  A095    ONE    FEED
OUT2H  FF36    OUT2S  FF1D    OUT4S  FF1B    OUTC   FF6B
OUTC1  FF72    OUTC2  FF87    OUTC3  FF8C    OUTC4  FF8D
OUTCH  FF3F    OUTHL  FF26    OUTHR  FF2A    OUTS   FF1F
OVEC   A091    PNCH   FDB6    PNCH1  FDD2    PNCH2  FDE4
PNCH3  FDE6    PNCH4  FE0C    PNCH5  FE26    PSR    FC67
QUES   FEE5    RESET  FC1F    REST1  FC30    REST2  FC3E
SETB   FCA9    SIZE   FD23    SIZE1  FD46    SIZE2  FD45
SIZE3  FD44    SMODE  A093    SP     A08A    STACK  A042
SUB    FEFF    SWI    FC4D    TEXT   FC91    TEXT1  FC8D
TMP1   A082    TMP2   A084    TMP3   A086    TWO    FEF4
VRFY   FE42    VRFY1  FE42    VRFY2  FE44    XSAV   A088
XTMP   A080
```

Some Details of TS1BUG's Most Important Memory Locations and Subroutines

In order to avoid time-consuming cross references to TS1BUG's listing, a number of subroutines which may be called from user programs are given together with their entry points and the registers which they modify (i.e. those registers that may be changed on returning from the subroutine). This list is headed by some of the more significant memory locations used by TS1BUG.

Name	*Bytes*	*Address*	*Function*
TMP1	2	A082	Used by BADDR to hold the first 4-character hex address
TMP2	2	A084	Used by BADDR to hold the second 4-character hex address
IVEC	2	A08F	Location of the ACIA for input (initialized to EC00)

Name	*Bytes*	*Address*	*Function*
OVEC	2	A091	Location of the ACIA for output (initialized to EC00)
IMODE	1	A094	Character input mode control
OMODE	1	A095	Character output mode control
ACIAC	1	EC00	Console ACIA control/status
ACIAD	1	EC01	Console ACIA data
		A0C0	Address of optional user character output routine
		A0C3	Address of optional user character input routine
		A0DC	IRQ4 vector (lowest priority)
		A0D9	IRQ3 vector
		A0D6	IRQ2 vector
		A0D3	IRQ1 vector (highest priority)
		A0D0	IRQ vector
		A0F0	NMI vector
		A0E0	SWI vector if breakpoint inactive

Note: IRQ1 – IRQ4 above are back-plane designations and correspond to inputs IRQ7 – IRQ4 of the 6828 PIC, respectively.

ENTRY	(FC00)	This is the entry point of TS1BUG following a system reset (i.e. $\overline{\text{RESET}}$ goes low), and causes all flags and vectors to be reset and the screen to be cleared.
RESET	(FC1F)	This is the soft entry point of TS1BUG which resets the system stack but does not affect any flags, vectors or ACIA parameters.
LINES X	(FC85)	Calling LINES has the effect of printing a carriage return line feed and the prompt character "@".
TEXT A,X	(FC91)	This subroutine prints the string of characters, the location of the first of which is pointed at by the contents of the index register prior to entering TEXT. The string must be terminated by 04.
ADAT A,X	(FD13)	ADAT has the effect of printing the 4-character hex address stored in TMP1 and the contents of that address as two hex characters.
SIZE B	(FD23)	This subroutine is called with the address of an op-code in the X register and a return is made with the number of bytes minus 1 taken up by the op-code in accumulator B. That is, B contains the number of bytes of data following the op-code: 0, 1, or 2.
VRFY A,B	(FE42)	When called, VRFY inputs characters from the active input device. A return is not made until four consecutive !s have been received.

BYTE A	(FE6C)	BYTE inputs two hex characters and combines them into a single byte in accumulator A. Each byte is added (modulo 256) to the variable CKSM which is employed by the load facility to generate a checksum.
INHEX A	(FE80)	This subroutine is called by BYTE and has the effect of inputting a single hex character into accumulator A. The hex character (i.e. ASCII coded) is converted into its binary equivalent. If a non-hex character is received, a question mark is printed and a valid hex character awaited. Should a carriage return (OD_{16}) be input, a return to TS1BUG's soft entry point is made.
BADDR X	(FEA0)	BADDR calls BYTE twice and has the effect of inputting four hex characters and putting their binary equivalent into the X register.
INCH A	(FEB0)	This subroutine inputs a character into accumulator A. The operation of INCH is controlled by the bits of IMODE in the following way:

Bit	*Clear*	*Set*
0	Get char from ACIA	Get char from routine at A0C3
4	Strip parity bit	Do not strip parity bit
5	L/C to U/C conversion	No L/C to U/C conversion
6	Echo character	Suppress echo

INCN A	(FED4)	This subroutine is called by INCH if bit 0 of IMODE is clear. INCN gets a character from the ACIA pointed at by the address in IVEC, which is initialized to the console ACIA at EC00.
ONE X	(FEED)	Inputs four characters by means of BADDR into the X register and TMP1 and outputs a space.
TWO X	(FEF4)	Inputs two groups of four hex characters with a space following each group. The first group is loaded into TMP1 and the second group into TMP2. The arithmetic difference between these two 16-bit numbers is calculated and stored in DIFF.
OUT4S A,X	(FF1B)	Prints the two bytes pointed at by the X register as four hex characters followed by a space.
OUT2S A,X	(FF1D)	As OUT4S except that only two hex characters are printed.
OUTS	(FF1F)	Calling OUTS prints a single space.
OUT2H A,X	(FF36)	This subroutine outputs the two hex characters pointed at by the X register. That is, it is equivalent to OUT2S but without the space character.
OUTCH	(FF3F)	OUTCH prints the value of the character in accumulator A. Its operation is controlled by the bits of OMODE as follows:

		Bit	*Clear*	*Set*
		0	Print on console	Do not print on console
		1	Do not call user O/P routine	Call user O/P routine at A0C0
		2	Print on memory-mapped display	Do not print on memory-mapped display
		4	Strip parity	Do not strip parity
		5	Convert L/C to U/C	Do not convert L/C to U/C

CONV A (FF64) When called, the lower-case character in accumulator A is converted into its upper-case equivalent. The parity bit is also stripped by this subroutine.

OUTC (FF6B) This subroutine is called by OUTCH if bit 0 of OMODE is clear. OUTC outputs the character in the accumulator A to an ACIA which on initialization is set to the console device at EC00. This subroutine tests for input immediately before the character is printed. Inputting a "W" halts output until another character is received while inputting a "control A" aborts the output and forces a jump to TS1BUG's soft entry point.

SUMMARY

This section has departed from the hardware orientation of the rest of the book and has examined the software requirements of a basic microprocessor system. After taking a brief look at some of the facilities found in typical commercial monitors, TS1's own monitor is described. This monitor, TS1BUG, follows the general trend of other monitors, but has an extended input/output facility. By modifying various flags it is possible to change the format of the I/O stream or even to divert it to devices other than the console.

Some of the limitations of TS1BUG have been included to give the reader a starting point for the extension of this monitor. In particular it is suggested that a line buffer be used to hold input commands, rather than relying on a simple single letter followed by an address (if necessary).

The final part of this section has been devoted to a listing of TS1BUG. This should provide a firm foundation for those who wish to write their own monitors.

PROBLEMS

1. Are you happy with the set of functions I have chosen for TS1BUG? What functions would you modify and what new functions would you add?

2 Implement a trace function. This may be done by planting a breakpoint after the current instruction. After the breakpoint has been 'hit' it is necessary to remove it and plant it after the next instruction. Note that when tracing a program care must be taken with instructions which modify the flow of the program (branch and jump).

3 TS1BUG deals with I/O operations by means of flags (IMODE and OMODE). An alternative technique involves the concept of the "device control block" (DCB) where a short block of memory is associated with an I/O device. The successive locations of this block contain the address of the subroutine which actually handles the I/O transaction, and the various parameters controlling the way in which the transaction takes place. Write subroutines to implement this form of I/O control. Note that during the initialization process, the monitor normally sets up a DCB in RAM for the system console.

4 Design part of a monitor to operate with a line buffer so that commands may be entered and edited (by backspace, cancel, etc.). When the command is complete a carriage return passes control to a routine which analyzes the contents of the buffer.

5 Examine the listing of TS1BUG. Can it be simplified (i.e. made more compact)? The answer is almost certainly yes; I stopped compressing TS1BUG and removing unnecessary op-codes when the effort involved became less than cost-effective. In some circumstances I did not simplify the code because it would lead to difficulty in understanding the operation of the program.

6 Is a monitor of the complexity of TS1BUG required? Would it not be better to have a tiny bootstrap loader routine and to load an operating system from tape or disk into RAM?

7 In the first version of my memory examine function (M) I stored new data in a location and then read it back on the next instruction to see if it had been correctly stored. The purpose of this test was to detect writes to: (a) ROM, (b) faulty RAM, (c) non-existent memory. The scheme worked perfectly in the first two cases but failed on (c). That is, data could be stored at a location where no read/write memory had been implemented and read back! On placing several no-operation (NOPs) between the store and read instructions the problem was solved. I argued that writing data to a non-existent location caused the address bus to become charged so that reading the data back immediately gave the correct value. The data-bus distributed capacitance was acting as a "one-cell dynamic memory". My colleague argued that this could not be the case because after writing the data to the non-existent memory a fetch instruction operation is performed, obliterating the data held as a charge. Therefore, my explanation could not be correct. I said my explanation was indeed correct. What did I tell my colleague?

9

Building a Microprocessor System

Having decided to construct a microprocessor system, there are three practical considerations to be taken into account: the circuit of the system, the physical construction of the circuit, and the housing of the circuit. The design of the microprocessor's circuit has been considered elsewhere in this book, leaving two questions to be answered—'How do I build it?' and 'What do I put it in?'

The choice of method of construction was limited in the case of the TS1 by two constraints—the system had to be capable of being built at home with few tools, and it had to be modular, enabling new units to be added to the existing system without difficulty. These constraints led to the use of 203 mm (8 in) square circuit boards plugging into a series of slots in a cardframe. The circuit boards (or cards) are manufactured by the same company which produces the cardframe and the metal case (rack) into which the cards fit. The components mounted on each module are connected together by means of a technique known as wire wrapping. This technique, described later in this section, enables complex digital circuits to be produced remarkably rapidly with no more than three specialized tools. Moreover, wire wrapping is one of the few construction techniques which permits easy modification of the circuit at a later date. Plate 9.1 illustrates the TS1 and Plate 9.2 shows one of the eight cards (modules) which make up the TS1.

The Construction of the Modules

Here we look at the reasons for choosing the particular type of card for the TS1's modules and consider alternative forms of construction. In the 1940s and 1950s the construction of electronic equipment was largely metal work (or "metal bashing") involving the machining of a metal chassis. In those days electronic apparatus was largely composed of a relatively small number of components of widely differing physical characteristics (e.g. the valve, transformer, resistor, and capacitor). Today the situation has changed dramatically. The advent of digital electronics has led to systems made up of large numbers of components, each of which falls into three of four basic physical sizes. In general, the size and shape of digital integrated circuits are totally divorced from their functions. Typically, a digital system is fabricated almost entirely from 14-, 16-, 18-, 22-, 28-, or 40-pin dual-in-line (DIL) packages, with a 2.54 mm (0.1 in) spacing between adjacent pins,

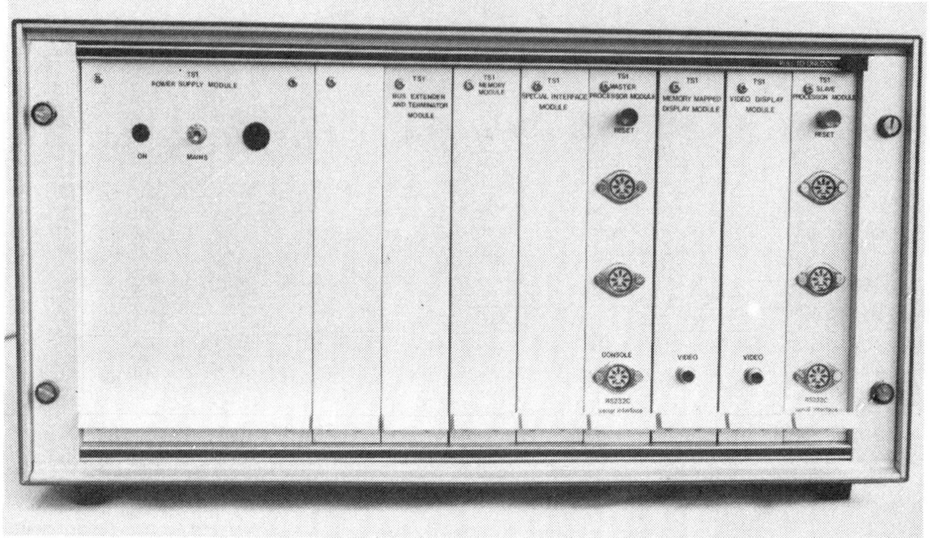

Plate 9.1 The TS1 microprocessor system

and a 7.62 mm (0.3 in) or 15.24 mm (0.6 in) spacing between adjacent rows of pins. The trend to DIL packages has been so great that even resistor networks and reed relays are now available in DIL packages. In cases where discrete components (transistors, diodes, etc.) are not available in DIL packages it is possible to mount them on a DIL header—a flat insulating plate with two rows of terminals which plugs into a DIL socket. As time passes and the "realm of things digital" encroaches more and more into the analog world, the trend to standardize packages will continue.

Today circuit boards are constructed in one of two different ways. The DIL components may be mounted on a "customized" circuit board which has been specially manufactured for one given application, or they may be mounted on a general-purpose, perforated board with a matrix of holes, spaced at 2.5 mm (0.1 in) intervals in both the vertical and horizontal planes. The special-purpose board is called a printed circuit board (PCB), and consists of a flat sheet of insulating material with copper tracks running between the pins of integrated circuits which are to be connected together electrically. This form of construction has great advantages. Once the board has been produced and holes drilled to receive the components, it is necessary only to mount the components and solder their terminal pins to the copper tracks. Soldering may be done by hand or by means of a flow-solder process whereby the entire copper-side of the board comes into contact with a bath of molten solder, soldering all components into place in a single step.

The PCB has two important advantages. Once it is made it takes little time to mount the components and solder them in place. The leads of the components on the PCB need to project through the copper-covered side by approximately 1.2 mm (1/20 in)—enough to make a good contact. This leads to slim circuit boards. The

Plate 9.2 The CPU module

snag with the PCB lies in its production. While it is not difficult to knock off a small PCB for a simple analog circuit, it is not so easy to create a PCB for a complex digital circuit involving 30 or more DIL packages. The professional manufacturing of PCBs involves a photographic process followed by the etching of unwanted copper. Furthermore, complex circuits often have tracks on both sides of the PCB to facilitate the crossing of tracks. Such boards normally have plated-through holes to link tracks on opposite sides of the board. The production of double-sided PCBs with plated-through holes requires high technology and is not open to the designer of a single prototype system. Of course, in mass production the PCB is still the most economic form of circuit mounting and construction.

One of the most popular forms of circuit board is called Veroboard after its main supplier, and consists of an insulating board punched with a matrix of holes. On one side there is a series of parallel strips of copper. Circuits are built on this board by pushing components through the holes from the non-copper side and then soldering the leads to the copper strips. The copper tracks may be broken, where necessary, by means of a simple low-cost tool called a spot face cutter. Parallel tracks may be linked by means of wires on the component side of the board. This construction medium is popular in University and Polytechnic laboratories, and with amateurs, particularly for analog circuitry. A version of Veroboard with horizontal tracks on one side and vertical tracks on the other is available for use with more complex digital circuits requiring large numbers of interconnections. Interconnection between horizontal and vertical copper strips can be made by means of shorting pins pushed through the holes. This form of construction has not been adopted for the TS1 because it requires the soldering of components to the tracks. This makes it difficult to modify the board, as repeated soldering can damage the tracks.

An alternative form of circuit board is called DIP board and has been specially designed for mounting DIL sockets. These boards have copper conductors on both sides. On one side there are two power rails arranged in the form of "fingers", one for each row of ICs. On the other side there are also power rails, plus individual mounting pads for the ICs. Figure 9.1 illustrates this form of circuit board. Note that the power-supply rails run in parallel on opposite sides of the boards and may be connected together to increase their current-carrying capacities. Along the length of the V_{cc} and ground tracks "miniwrap terminals" are inserted and soldered to the tracks. Connections may then be made from these pins to the power supply pins of the integrated circuits. These connections are made by wire-wrapping (see later). The

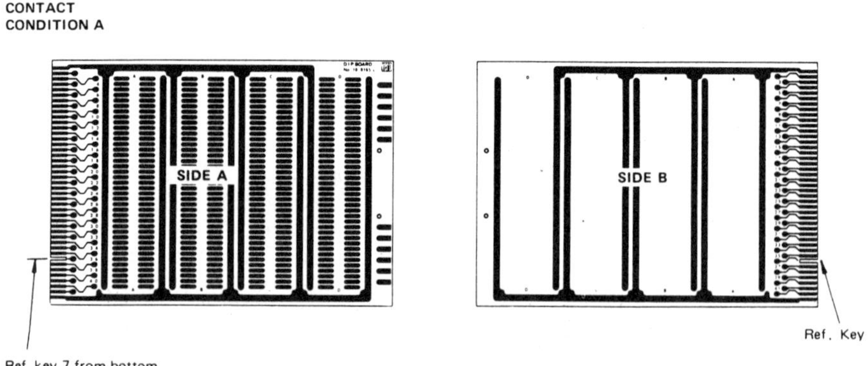

Figure 9.1 The DIP plug-in board

base material of these boards (and of almost all other circuit boards) is either epoxy glass based or paper phenolic based. The epoxy glass boards have superior mechanical and electrical qualities but are substantially more expensive than the paper phenolic boards.

The circuit modules of the TS1 microprocessor system are constructed on 203.20 mm × 203.20 mm DIP boards. These boards are able to hold up to 45 14-pin DIL sockets in five rows. One edge of the board is designed to plug into a 77-way connector (actually a 78-way connector but one slot is cut out and serves as an index or reference). On each side of this edge are 77 gold-plated contacts allowing up to

Figure 9.2 The wire wrapped joint

154 connections to the board. In the TS1 system single-sided edge connectors are used so that only the 77 contacts on one side of the board are available.

The individual integrated circuits may have their pins connected to each other by conventional soldered joints or by means of a technique called wire wrapping which does not involve solder. Wire wrapping was developed in the 1950s in the telephone industry and allows a wire to be attached to a terminal pin without solder, heat, or any other special treatment. In wire wrapping a wire is wrapped in the form of a closed helix round a rigid terminal, which has at least two (normally four) sharp edges. The pressure of the wire at the edges of the terminal (radius of curvature <0.08 mm (0.003 in)) crushes the oxide layer on both the terminal and the wire to form a clean, oxide-free metal-to-metal contact. In fact, the pressure is so high that a cold weld is formed. Figure 9.2 illustrates a wire wrapped joint.

The wire used in wire wrapping is often a single stranded 0.25 mm (0.01 in)(30 AWG) silver-plated copper conductor with Kynar insulation. This wire has a maximum current rating of 0.4 A at 25°C and is suited only to systems whose working voltage is less than 150.

To carry out wire wrapping three tools are required.

(1) A rotating tool, which may be a battery-powered gun, pneumatically powered gun, or a simple, inexpensive hand tool which fits over a terminal and wraps the wire round it.
(2) A stripping tool which removes the insulation from one end of the wire.
(3) An unwrapping tool which is used to remove incorrect wraps. This is often a simple hand-held tool.

There are basically three reasons why wire wrapping has been adopted for the construction of the TS1 microprocessor system. Firstly, it is relatively inexpensive once the above three tools have been purchased. The only major expense is the cost of DIL sockets with wire wrapping terminals which are more expensive than the corresponding DIL sockets with solder tags. Secondly, wire wrapping is fast. Once the circuit has been designed and the DIL sockets attached to the DIP board, a wire wrapped joint requires no preparation and can be made in a few seconds. Thirdly, all wire wrap components are re-usable (there is no solder and its attendant heat to cause damage). Furthermore, it is very easy to correct a mistake, the offending joint is simply unwrapped and a new wrap made.

Possibly the only disadvantages of wire wrapping are the additional width taken up by a wire wrapped module because of the terminal pins (typically 14 mm), and the "bird's nest" appearance of the end result. The former disadvantage limits the spacing between adjacent modules in a rack, while the second disadvantage is less important. At worst the bird's nest effect makes debugging difficult because following individual wires is not easy. This problem may be alleviated by choosing different colored wires for each type of connection. For example, in the construction of the TS1 the following convention has been chosen:

red	+5 V power supplies and points strapped to a logical 1;
blue	ground and points strapped to a logical 0;
yellow	lines carrying data;
orange	lines carrying addresses;
black	lines carrying control signals.

There is no room in this book to consider the details of wire wrapping technology and the techniques required to implement it. Figure 9.3 gives some examples of wire wrapping techniques.

One of the most significant ways in which professional and amateur constructors differ is in their documentation standards. The amateur often designs his circuit on a scrap of paper (marked "to be lost at the first opportunity"). Furthermore, he often modifies the circuit at a later date without recording the nature of the modification. When the system fails or needs further modification he is lost. While working to high documentation standards may seem tedious and unnecessary to the amateur it is mandatory in any professional activity. Table 9.1 gives the wiring schedule of one integrated circuit—the 6802 microprocessor in the slave-processor module. In this table (there is one per IC in the module) the pin function, its total electrical loading, its connections to other pins, and any notes are given for each of the CPU's 40 pins. For example, pin 22 is A_{12} and is connected to pin 11 of IC5 and to pin 23 of IC7. Both IC1 and IC7 are low-power Schottky TTL circuits so that pin 22 is loaded by two LSTTL inputs. Of course, in the wiring schedule for IC5 the entry corresponding to pin 11 should show a connection to pin 22 of IC4 (the 6802). When wire wrapping a module it is often helpful to tick off the connections as they are made so that an interruption (coffee break) does not cause missed connections.

Power supply decoupling When the transistors in the integrated circuits change state they often cause a high-speed current spike to appear at the power supply pins of the DIL package. Because of the finite resistance of the wire-wrap wires (or tracks on a PCB) a pulse may be propagated along the power distribution lines and may even affect the operation of adjacent ICs. To combat this problem it is good practice to decouple the power lines to ICs by connecting a small capacitor (typically 0.1 μF) between ground and V_{cc} as close to an IC's power supply pins as possible. It is not necessary to decouple the power supply of every IC—one capacitor per four ICs is regarded as adequate.

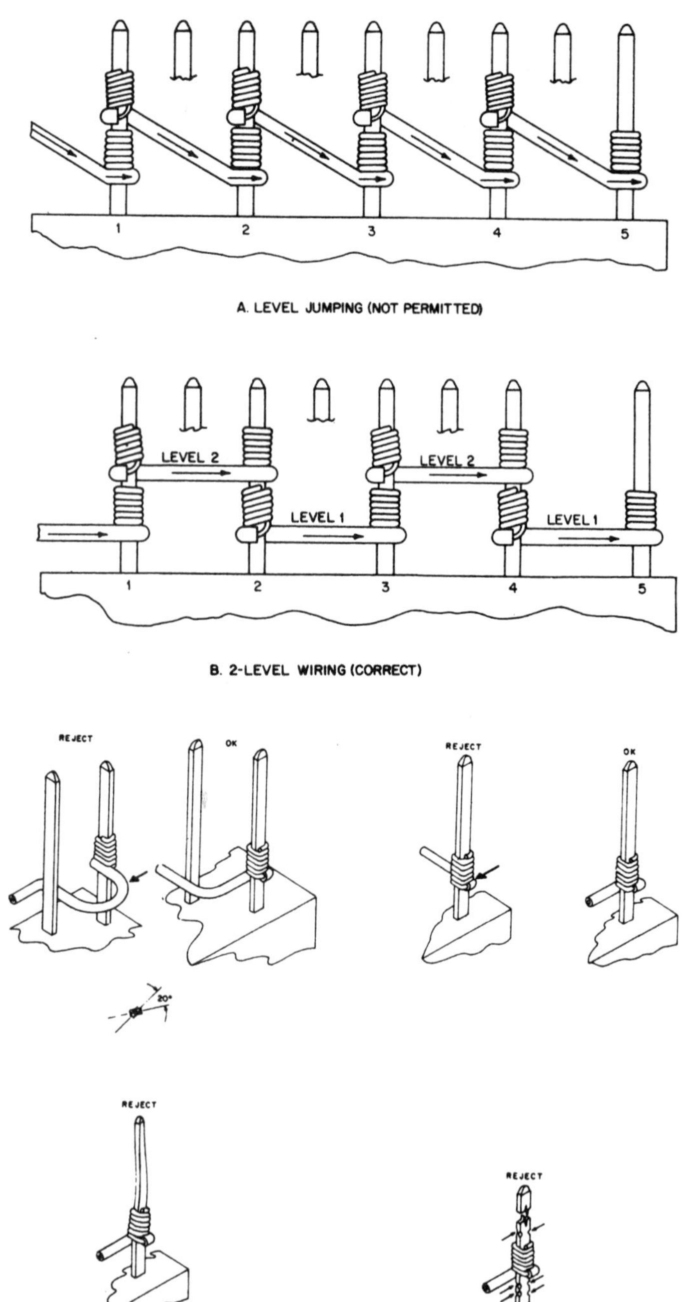

Figure 9.3 Some wire-wrapping techniques

(reproduced by permission of the Digital Equipment Corporation)

Table 9.1 The Wiring Schedule for IC4 in the Slave-processor Module

PIN	IC4 6802 CPU Function	Loading	Connections		Notes
1	V_{ss}		Ground		
2	$\overline{HALT}$	3.3 kΩ pull-up	IC3p2		
3	$\overline{MR}$	3.3 kΩ pull-up	IC3p1		
4	$\overline{IRQ}$	3.3 kΩ pull-up	IC3p3		
5	VMA	1 × LS	IC1p12		
6	$\overline{NMI}$	3.3 kΩ pull-up	IC3p4		
7	BA	NC	Not used		
8	V_{cc}	-	+5 V		
9	A_0	1 × LS	IC6p2		
10	A_1	1 × LS	IC6p4		
11	A_2	1 × LS	IC6p6		
12	A_3	2 × LS	IC6p8	IC8p1	
13	A_4	2 × LS	IC6p11	IC8p2	
14	A_5	2 × LS	IC6p13	IC8p3	
15	A_6	1 × LS	IC6p15		
16	A_7	1 × LS	IC6p17		
17	A_8	1 × LS	IC5p2		
18	A_9	1 × LS	IC5p4		
19	A_{10}	1 × LS	IC5p6		
20	A_{11}	2 × LS	IC5p8	IC8p4	
21	V_{ss}	-			
22	A_{12}	2 × LS	IC5p11	IC7p23	
23	A_{13}	2 × LS	IC5p13	IC7p22	
24	A_{14}	2 × LS	IC5p15	IC7p21	
25	A_{15}	2 × LS	IC5p17	IC7p20	
26	D_7	7 × NMOS	IC12p11	IC9p9	
27	D_6	7 × NMOS	IC12p12	IC9p8	
28	D_5	7 × NMOS	IC12p13	IC9p7	
29	D_4	7 × NMOS	IC12p14	IC9p6	
30	D_3	7 × NMOS	IC11p11	IC9p5	
31	D_2	7 × NMOS	IC11p12	IC9p4	
32	D_1	7 × NMOS	IC11p13	IC9p3	
33	D_0	7 × NMOS	IC11p14	IC9p2	
34	$R/\overline{W}$	1 × LS	IC2p3		
35	V_{cc} (standby)		+5 V		
36	RE		0 V		
37	E	2 × LS	IC1p13	IC2p9	
38	EXtal	Xtal	Xtal		
39	Xtal	Xtal	Xtal		
40	$\overline{RESET}$		IC2p2	IC14p34	

The Housing of the TS1 Microprocessor System

The housing chosen for the cards which make up the microprocessor system is intimately connected with the size of the cards themselves. That is, the cards and their housing, the card frame, are produced for each other. Consequently, once a card size has been selected, there is little freedom in the choice of the card frame. The card frame chosen for the TS1's modules is a Vero Electronics System 3E card frame. This frame, or rack, is able to house either modules (e.g. the power supply)* or 203.20×203.20 mm cards. Figure 9.4 gives the details of this card frame and Table 9.2 gives the list of components used in the TS1's housing. The card frame is housed in a 482.60 mm (19 in) wide case. Plate 9.1 gives an impression of the overall system.

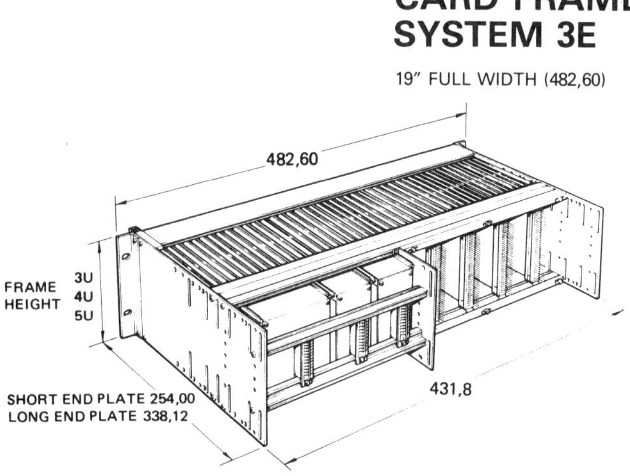

Figure 9.4 The card frame used for the TS1

The module housing the power supply does not plug into the back of the rack but has 4 mm sockets for the +12 V, −12 V, ground, and +5 V power supplies. Connections between the back plane and the power supply module are made by means of 4 mm plugs on flying leads.

The cards slot into the card frame at intervals of 38.10 mm (1½ in). This horizontal spacing permits a total of eight cards together with the power supply module. Each card plugs into a single-sided 77-way edge connector. The back plane may be formed by wire wrapping the pins of the connectors together. An alternative approach is to use a MEKTRON strip bus, a strip of metal with holes at 2.54 mm (0.1 in) intervals, which may be laid across the pins of the card connectors and soldered into place. Figure 9.5 gives an illustration of the installation of the strip bus. Note that it is possible to obtain the strip bus with alternate large holes which do not make contact with wire wrap terminals passing through the holes. In this way double-sided edge connectors may be handled as in Fig. 9.5(b). The advantage of the

* Here "module" refers to a subsection which may be mounted in an aluminum box and slotted into the card frame.

strip bus over wire wrapping is that the strip bus has a lower inductance than wire wrapping wire because it is flat. As the TS1 is built around cards with 77-way, single-sided edge connectors, the strip bus of Fig. 9.5(a) has been selected to form the back plane.

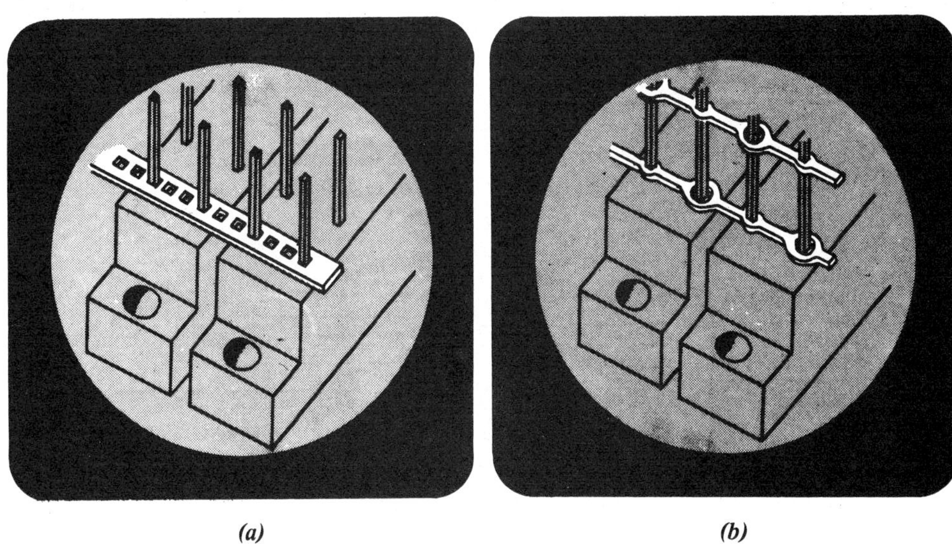

(a) *(b)*

Figure 9.5 The Mektron strip bus

Since this project was started Vero Electronics have decided to phase out the cards and card frame used in the construction of the TS1. In their place KM4A and KM6A systems have been introduced. These systems are compatible with the industry standard "Eurocards" which are available as small Eurocards (100 × 160 mm) or large Eurocards (223.4 × 160 mm).

Table 9.2 The Component Parts of the TS1 Card Frame and Housing

Quantity	*Description*	*Vero part number*
6	203.20 × 203.20 mm DIP board	10-0155F
2	3-Plane high-density DIP board	06-3462C
8	Edge connector 77-way	14-0998G
16	End bracket (to hold edge connector)	41-0213E
8	Card mounting front panel (38.10 mm; 1½ in)	37-7782C
1	Card frame System 3E	37-8303L 37-8026E
1	Module (for power supply)(127 mm; 5 in wide)	37-2969A
1	Base plate for module	37-0661A
1	Top plate for module	37-0686H
2	Side plate for module	37-0669E

Note: The slave processor and memory module are built on high-density DIP boards, allowing more ICs to be located on the board than on a normal DIP board.

9.1 TESTING THE TS1

It would be rather nice to design a microprocessor system, construct it, burn a monitor into EPROM, switch it on, and then use it without further ado. Such a scenario is no more probable than dropping a piece of toast and seeing it land buttered side upwards. There are many potential sources of trouble lying in wait for the designer and constructor of a microprocessor system. Some of the most likely danger spots are:

Incorrect Design

A faulty circuit design may result from one of two sources: the blunder and the subtlety. A blunder results from the designer's carelessness—he simply makes a gross error (say putting a NAND gate where a NOR gate is required) which is not in keeping with his own ability. The subtle design error results from some second-order effect which may not be apparent until the specification sheets of the components have been read several times. Typical types of subtle error are caused by pin 5 of the IC having a lower fan-out than all the other output pins, or by the delay in an address-decoding network violating the chip-select set-up time of a memory component. The subtle fault can often give rise to intermittent faults or erratic behavior and may be very difficult to trace.

Faulty Construction

Because of the "bird's nest" appearance of a wire wrapped system it is very difficult indeed to trace connections visually. For this reason it is easy to connect a wire to the wrong pin. Only by means of a meticulous procedure is it possible to reduce wire wrapping errors to a vanishingly small number. Once a system has been wire wrapped it should be tested (before any ICs are inserted into their sockets) by means of a continuity checker or ohmmeter.

Faulty Components

Even in a correctly designed and constructed system it is possible to encounter problems due to malfunctioning components. Fortunately, at least in my own experience, the vast majority of ICs are highly reliable. However, when a faulty component does find its way into a system it may be difficult to detect, particularly if it is a complex device (e.g. CPU) and only part of it is not functioning as it should.

Faulty Software

Because a microprocessor system is an intimate combination of hardware and software, it is possible that a programming error may appear to be a hardware error. For example, if the 6800's reset vector is incorrectly programmed in EPROM, a random jump to a WAI instruction may be made, giving the designer the impression that the system is dead.

Some Equipment Used to Debug Microprocessor Systems

The nature of the test equipment available to the microprocessor system's constructor depends very much on his circumstances: whether he is working at home, in a University or Polytechnic, or in industry. The minimum equipment available to the home constructor is the multimeter (analog or digital) and the pulse detector (a latch which detects short-lived digital pulses). Such equipment is really suited only to continuity checking, the examining of the state of lines at a constant signal level, and the detection of streams of pulses. A much more useful piece of equipment is the oscilloscope whose price starts at that of a disk drive. Most oscilloscopes allow one or two channels of high-speed repetitive data to be displayed on a CRT. Even the most modest of oscilloscopes can handle clock waveforms at a frequency of 1 MHz. The TS1 was constructed with little more than a single-beam 15 MHz oscilloscope. The chief drawbacks of the oscilloscope are its limited number of channels (it would be nice to see traces corresponding to all sixteen address lines) and its inability to deal with non-repetitive waveforms. As long as the input to the oscilloscope is repeated cyclically a stable display is obtained. The practical effect of this is that data and address lines can be examined only if the CPU is in a software loop.

A new aid to debugging has recently appeared, called the logic analyzer. This may be thought of as a multi-channel oscilloscope operating in the digital domain rather than the time domain. A number of probes monitor up to 32 points* in a digital system and store their inputs in digital form (0 or 1) in successive locations in RAM which is arranged as a shift register. The rate at which the inputs to the probes are sampled is controlled by either an internal clock or a clock derived from the system under test.

The data stored in the RAM is read periodically and displayed on a CRT. Thus transient information from the probes may be recorded and displayed continually. The logic analyzer may display the data as a number of waveforms rather like an oscilloscope (although the trace is derived from the contents of the RAM and therefore does not show the rise time or any other electrical attribute of the signal at the input to the probes). Data may also be displayed in tabular form either as 1s or 0s or in hexadecimal format, or in the case of some logic analyzers, the data may even be disassembled and displayed in mnemonic form.

Yet another way of displaying data is to treat the display as a map. In this form of display the MSB bits of the input data (say channels 8 – 15 in a 16-channel system) determine the vertical deflection of the beam on the CRT, and the LSB bits determine the horizontal deflection. Hence each of the 65 536 possible data values is associated with a spot on the screen with 0000_{16} being displayed in the upper left-hand corner of the display, and $FFFF_{16}$ in the lower right-hand corner. When a stream of data words is displayed in this format, the CRT looks like a bad case of measles and the pattern of dots represents the signature of the data. Interpreting this type of display requires some experience.

One of the most important facilities of the logic analyzer is its ability to trigger off a given data word, or after a certain delay preceding or following this trigger word. Such a facility would, for example, enable the interrupt address (FFF8) in a 6800 system to cause the contents of the address and data buses to be recorded for the next, say, 256 clock pulses.

* At least one logic analyzer is equipped with multiplexing probes and can deal with 96 channels.

The logic analyzer is a very powerful debugging tool, particularly when dealing with dynamic or intermittent problems in a microprocessor system. Logic analyzers are relatively expensive, ranging from \$1000 to over \$20 000.

Debugging the TS1

There are few things worse than being confronted by a dead microprocessor system. Solving the riddles of the defunct microprocessor system has much in common with tackling a crossword puzzle. Both activities need a considerable amount of previous experience, each involves clues whose relevance may not be immediately apparent, and, finally, a measure of luck is necessary to reach a successful conclusion. To demonstrate these points it is necessary to consider one of my earlier encounters with a faulty microprocessor system.

A friend had an MEK 6800D1 board which did not produce anything on the console device when the reset button was pushed. By examining the data, address and clock lines with an oscilloscope it was found that the CPU was functioning because digital data appeared on these lines. However, the VMA line was discovered to be permanently at a logical zero level. Changing the CPU had no effect on the state of the VMA line. On looking at the state of the VMA line very carefully on the screen a certain amount of noise could be seen. When the gain of the oscilloscope was increased, it became apparent that the VMA line contained a square wave at a few millivolts amplitude. The CPU chip was removed from the board, its VMA pin bent through 90° so that it stuck out from the side and then it was replaced. Now it was found that the CPU's VMA pin put out a perfectly healthy signal. The source of all this difficulty was a tiny blob of solder underneath an IC socket shorting the VMA line to ground.

When a relatively straightforward microprocessor system is first built and refuses to work the most probable source of the problem is almost certainly a blunder. An IC may have been inserted upside-down, or two address lines crossed over. The first stage of debugging is to get the CPU operating at a minimal level (CPU, monitor, scratchpad RAM, and I/O device) and then to use the CPU itself, under software control, to debug the remainder of the system. Getting the CPU module going can be achieved with remarkably little test equipment if some common sense is applied at an early enough stage.

My own way of testing a CPU module is as follows, although the details vary in any actual case. Firstly the wiring is tested with a continuity tester. In particular the paths of the data bus and address buses to the monitor, RAM and I/O chips are scrutinized. The module is then inserted into its card frame and the potential of those points which should be at ground or V_{cc} level is measured. The clock generator, CPU and any necessary control ICs (e.g. reset control) are inserted and an oscilloscope used to monitor the clock signals and the state of the $\overline{\text{IRQ}}$, $\overline{\text{NMI}}$, $\overline{\text{HALT}}$, $\overline{\text{RESET}}$ and BA pins. If the reset button is pushed $\overline{\text{RESET}}$ should go high and the contents of the address bus display FFFE.

If the $\overline{\text{RESET}}$ pin is allowed to return high and the address lines monitored, it should be found that the CPU is cyclically and continuously stepping through all addresses from 0000 to FFFF. As there is no signal on the data bus, whenever the

CPU performs a "read op-code" it sees 00 (00_{16} is interpreted by the 6800 as NOP) on the data bus (unlike TTL, floating NMOS gates often assume a logical zero level). Some authorities suggest that instead of letting the data bus float, resistors should be wired between the appropriate data pins and V_{cc} or ground to force the NOP code onto the data bus.

At this point it is worth looking at the memory decoders. If the CPU is cycling through all possible addresses, then each memory space corresponding to ROM, RAM, I/O should occasionally be "hit". The oscilloscope probe should be attached to the chip-select input of each block of decoded memory. The waveform observed should be bursts of pulses (because most chip selects are enabled by ϕ_2) whose duty cycle (ratio of pulses to no pulses) should be in the same proportion as the size of the decoded memory to the whole 64K memory.

The next step is to insert the monitor ROM and its scratchpad RAM. When this has been done the system should display patterns on the data and address buses of a cyclic nature and the chip-select input of the appropriate ACIA should periodically go low as the ACIA is accessed. Now ACIA, baud-rate generator and RS232C buffers may be inserted and the system wired to a console. When the CPU is reset the console should respond by displaying the prompt character. If it does all is well and the rest of the module may be built up and the CPU used to monitor each new function as it is added.

If a prompt character does not appear the first step is to take a valium, sit down and think. Finding the fault now becomes a real piece of detective work that even Holmes would not find elementary. If things get really difficult, it may be necessary to remove the CPU and inject into its socket values for $A_0 - A_{15}$, VMA and other necessary signals, from pull-up or pull-down resistors. For example, by squirting in FFFE on the address bus, the most significant byte of the reset vector should appear on the data bus. If this does not happen the most probable causes are an incorrectly wired address or data bus, an incorrectly programmed EPROM, or faulty address decoding circuitry.

While a totally dead system may, at least initially, prove very infuriating, there is nothing worse than an intermittent fault. I once had a camera which when used in the Sahara desert at noon told me that the lighting conditions were equivalent to dark night. When I took it back to the camera shop the manager observed the fault and sent it back to the manufacturer. Alas, at the manufacturer's it performed perfectly, leading them to the conclusion that I was either an idiot or a con-man. A totally dead computer is nearly always indicative of a blunder, while an intermittent fault usually points to a subtlety.

One of my microprocessor systems worked normally for a few minutes after switching on but later produced pages of gibberish on the console device in situations where a simple line-feed carriage-return and prompt character was expected. This behavior pointed to the possibility of a temperature-related fault so I squirted the contents of a freezer aerosol at various parts of the circuit. When the monitor EPROM was cooled, everything functioned perfectly. The EPROM had either not been properly erased or programmed so that one of its bits was close to the threshold level with a small change in temperature moving it from one side of the threshold to the other. This particular bit just happened to fall in the "04" terminator byte at the end of the character string containing the prompt. Each time the string was printed the 04 was missed and all the characters until the next 04 was encountered were printed on the console.

One source of intermittent faults is mains-borne transients. These tend to be correlated with external events—switching on an oscilloscope or a vacuum cleaner in the next room. The only way of combating this problem (apart from resorting to battery-driven microprocessor systems) is to fit RF suppressors in the mains supply and provide decoupling capacitors on the modules themselves.

Yet another source of intermittent fault is poor mechanical construction. A soldered joint may be loose or a piece of wire or solder intermittently bridging the gap between two pins of a socket or tracks on a printed circuit. Fortunately, the intermittent mechanical fault is often easy to find because it may be observed by gently tapping the region in which the fault lies.

10

Epilogue

It has taken me two years to complete this book and it is only reasonable that I should comment on what I have written. I began writing because I felt that no book on the practical aspects of the design of a microprocessor system had been written. My original intention was to produce a compendium of "advanced microprocessor design techniques". This was not to be, partly because the first reviewer of my draft manuscript thought that the book should be of a more introductory nature and partly because the sheer volume of practical work made this approach untenable.

In its final form this book has turned out almost as a diary cataloging the construction of the TS1. My main aim as set out in the statement of the book's objective (Section 1.2) has been to try and give the reader an insight into the design of a microprocessor system. While I feel I have achieved this to a certain extent, since starting my book I have come across a new breed of student. A few years ago almost anybody using a microprocessor had some experience of electronics. Today students are being churned out of Computer Science Departments with knowledge of a wide range of Computer Science subjects from assembly language to compilers and operating systems but with no understanding of electronics whatsoever. Such a student must read an elementary primer in electronics before contemplating the design and construction of a microprocessor system.

I have just two regrets about the design of the TS1. Firstly, although I tried to employ the most up-to-date components in its construction, two years after its inception these components are commonplace or are even becoming dated. This is inevitable in a world where radically new components are appearing every day and components that were once monstrously expensive suddenly become cost effective.

My most serious regret about the TS1 is that it has been designed on an *ad hoc* basis with each of its sections designed to demonstrate some particular principle. Perhaps if Sigmund Freud were alive he would tell me that by designing a machine so unworthy of emulation I have subconsciously tried to stop people building it and hence avoid the wrath of those who do not like my design. Were I to repeat this exercise I would design the TS1 as a complete system and try to integrate the various modules better. Some of the points I would consider if I were designing a "TS2" are:

Ease of testing It is possible to divert some of the power of the microprocessor into the self-testing of the system. I once heard of a salesman who was trying to sell a microprocessor-controlled oxyacetylene cutting machine to an engineer. The salesman explained that not only was the cutting head controlled by a complex program which precisely calculated all the forces necessary to move the head from place to place, but that the microprocessor continually tested all parts of the system whenever it was not actually in use. ''I don't want it,'' said the engineer, ''all this testing will wear it out.'' Self-testing can be carried out in many ways from a superficial check of the major functions of a system to a relatively thorough battery of tests. It would be easy to devote part of the monitor to routine testing of the hardware and software of the system; special data patterns could be written into memory and read back, sample programs testing all the op-codes could be executed and so on. In a similar way the hardware sections could also be designed with testability in mind. For example, in the TS1 some of the unused gates in the FPGA address decoder have been programmed to decode the address map of the MEK 6800D1 kit. When the CPU module was first constructed, these outputs were employed to select a MIKBUG-compatible ROM and its associated ACIA. In this way the TS1 was tested with a monitor known to be working and so TS1BUG was then substituted safe in the knowledge that the hardware was functioning correctly.

Memory As the cost of memory components has declined so rapidly some of the following possibilities are well worth considering:

(1) Dynamic RAM is becoming easier to use now that dynamic RAM controller chips are available.

(2) CMOS RAM is still relatively expensive but a 1K×4 CMOS chip may be obtained for little more than the cost of a similar NMOS RAM three years ago. The advantage of CMOS memory is its remarkably tiny power requirements. Blocks of CMOS memory could be made (effectively) non-volatile by means of rechargeable nickel – cadmium batteries which provide power when the rest of the system is switched off.

(3) Error detecting and correcting memories have become more attractive as the cost of memory components has declined. By adding an extra four check bits to each byte of data stored it is possible to detect and correct single errors by means of the Hamming code. Such an arrangement requires little more than a few MSI parity trees. By means of error-correcting codes the mean time between crashes in a system can be radically increased.

Of course, the addition of error-correcting memory increases the cost of the system by approximately 50% as the basic memory data word has grown from eight bits to twelve bits. Instead of providing error-correcting memory it is possible to add one extra parity bit to detect single-bit (or an odd number) errors. By detecting an error it is possible to avoid the danger of executing an erroneous instruction or using faulty data. In both cases the detection of an error would be used to force an interrupt and the execution of a ''recovery-from-error'' routine.

The VDT When I started writing this book the 6845 CRT controller chip had only recently appeared, leaving me too little time to investigate its properties. This chip is able to generate a wide range of display formats under software control. Two other useful additions to any display system are graphics and color. A graphics facility could be added to the TS1 memory-mapped display generator by multiplexing the video data between the character generator ROM and a block of random-access read/write memory.

Real-time clock A most useful addition to the TS1 would be a real-time clock keeping the time of day and, if possible, the calendar date. Such a circuit could be based on one of the popular, low cost, clock chips. Unfortunately, these chips tend to run off non-TTL compatible power supplies and are designed to work with multiplexed seven-segment displays. A better approach is to use a special purpose, microprocessor-bus compatible clock such as the MM58176. This chip is fabricated with CMOS technology which means that its power consumption is very low indeed, allowing a small battery to provide a back-up power supply when the rest of the system is switched off. The MM58176 uses a low-cost 32.768 kHz quartz crystal as its source of timing information.

The master – slave link One of the greatest shortcomings of the TS1 is the slave processor and its link to the master. I created the slave processor to illustrate the design of a simple, no-frills microcomputer, and to show how it could be connected to the main processor to form a master – slave arrangement. Unfortunately, by choosing a commercially available MIKBUG-like monitor for the slave processor, the software needed to drive the master – slave link becomes unnecessarily complex and cumbersome. A far better approach would have been to provide the slave with an electronically switchable monitor. That is, the master processor, by changing the status of a line, could switch off the slave's MIKBUG-like monitor and select a second EPROM-based monitor containing the link protocol.

Bulk storage devices The reader may be puzzled by the lack of any form of bulk storage device in this book. I decided that to do justice to the floppy disk, sections on the disk drive, disk controller and the disk operating system would be needed. These topics cannot be included in this book as to deal with them at length would require a very considerable amount of space. My own solution to the problem of bulk storage has been to link the TS1 to an SBC disk-controller board by means of the bus extender. The absence of a cassette interface is due to lack of time needed to develop a suitable system. It would have been easy enough to design a Kansas City standard interface operating at 300 baud, but as there is a plethora of such interfaces within the pages of the popular magazines, I decided such a project was not worthwhile. My objection to the Kansas City system is its ludicrously low data rate, taking approximately five minutes to load an 8K program. If it is assumed that recording data on a cassette is equivalent to transmitting the data over a channel with the same bandwidth and signal-to-noise ratio as the cassette system, then the maximum theoretical transmission rate may be obtained from Shannon's theorem. This states that the maximum capacity of a channel in bits per second is given by

$$C = W \log_2 (1 + S/N),$$

where W is the bandwidth of the channel and S/N is signal to noise ratio. For a cassette recorder with a bandwidth of 5 kHz and a signal-to-noise ratio of 40 dB, the upper limit to the transmission rate is 65 000 bits/s. This is over 200 times faster than the Kansas City rate. By devising suitable modulation and demodulation techniques, there is no reason why the average cassette recorder should not handle data at rates of up to 20 000 bits/s.

DMA Although facilities have been included in the TS1 to allow the address, data, $R/\overline{W}$, and VMA buses to be controlled by an external device during a DMA operation, no DMA controller has been described. As in the case of the disk controller, the DMA controller is a complex device and cannot be dealt with in isolation but needs to be treated as part of a, say, high-speed disk interface. In a future version of the TS1 it may even be worthwhile considering the application of DMA to the master – slave link.

A note on PIA timing

While checking the draft version of this book I noticed that I had made a design error in the address decoding circuitry of the PIAs on the memory module and the special interface modules. Both of these PIAs use ϕ_2 in their address decoding networks.

According to the data sheet of the 6821, the chip select, $R/\overline{W}$ and register select lines of the PIA should be valid at least 160 ns before the rising edge of the E input (i.e. ϕ_2). This condition is satisfied for $R/\overline{W}$ and the register select inputs but not for the chip select. This error was not detected because the circuit works quite happily with the PIA's chip select strobed by the ϕ_2 clock. It is, of course, possible that the timing diagram of the 6821 and other 6800-series peripherals is excessively conservative. However, the timing diagram should always be complied with and ϕ_2 should not take part in the address decoding of a PIA or any other peripheral with a similar timing restriction.

Appendix A1 Designing the Power Supply

In this appendix the operation of a power supply is described and criteria for the selection of the components which make up the power supply are given.

The Transformer, Rectifier and Smoothing Circuit

Three arrangements of transformer and rectifier are commonly used to provide a basic unsmoothed d.c. power supply. These are the half-wave rectifier circuit, the full-wave rectifier circuit with a centre-tapped transformer, and the full-wave rectifier circuit with a bridge rectifier. The circuit diagrams of these three arrangements are given in Fig. A1.1 together with graphs of their respective outputs as functions of time. In practice the half-wave rectifier circuit is almost never used

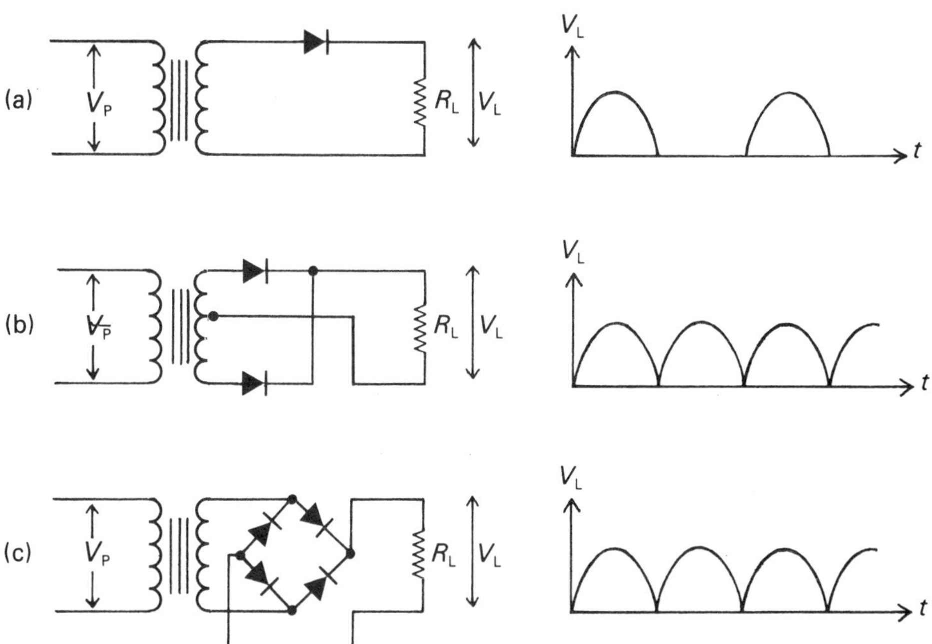

Figure A1.1 Three rectifier circuits and their outputs: (a) half-wave rectifier circuit; (b) full-wave centre-tapped rectifier circuit; (c) full-wave bridge rectifier circuit

(at least in microprocessor applications) because the rectifier conducts for only half a cycle, a very inefficient arrangement. Furthermore, the half-wave rectifier circuit puts a very heavy demand on the smoothing circuit, which must provide an output current to the load during the half-cycle when the rectifier is not conducting. The two full-wave rectifier arrangements of Fig. A1.1 make use of both half-cycles of the mains input so that the output of the rectifier consists of a series of pulses at a repetition rate twice that of the mains frequency.

Both the centre-tapped transformer circuit and bridge rectifier circuit are widely used in power supplies. An additional advantage of these circuits over the half-wave rectifier circuit is that no net d.c. component of the output current flows through the transformer, magnetizing the core and increasing the power loss. The bridge rectifier configuration is most widely used for two reasons:

(1) Transformers are costly components and the bridge rectifier requires only one winding with two terminals which is cheaper to manufacture.
(2) The bridge circuit requires a transformer with a lower volt-ampère rating than the corresponding centre-tapped transformer circuit, and therefore makes more efficient use of the transformer.

The chief disadvantage of the bridge rectifier configuration is the need to use four rectifiers. It is not the additional cost of a bridge rectifier that causes problems, but the power dissipated by it. Unlike Hi-Fi amplifiers or radio transmitters, with power supplies in the region of 60 V in the former case and possibly 1000 V in the latter case, a microprocessor system has a power supply of 5 V. Clearly, if the voltage drop across a rectifier is approximately 1 V, the power dissipated by the bridge rectifier is an appreciable fraction of the power consumed by the microprocessor system.

The pulses of current at the output of a full-wave rectifier circuit must be smoothed or averaged to produce an approximately constant voltage. The process of smoothing may be thought of as that of integration or low-pass filtering. A wide variety of smoothing or filtering circuits exist, but the simplest and most common circuit uses a capacitor connected across the output of the rectifier circuit. Figure A1.2 illustrates the effect of a smoothing capacitor (sometimes called a reservoir capacitor), and gives a graph of the voltage across the capacitor as a function of time.

Assuming that the power is first applied at a zero crossing, the smoothing capacitor charges up during the first half-cycle. After the peak of the cycle, point B, the voltage across the capacitor is greater than that across the transformer secondary, resulting in the rectifier becoming reverse biased and therefore non-conducting. Between points B and C the capacitor discharges exponentially into the load. (As the load, in most cases, is a voltage regulator with a constant current output, the smoothing capacitor discharges linearly into the load.) At point C the transformer secondary voltage, which is now rising in the next half-cycle, reaches the falling voltage across the capacitor, and the rectifier once more becomes forward biased. Current now flows through the rectifier to charge the capacitor to the next peak at D, and the process repeats itself every half cycle.

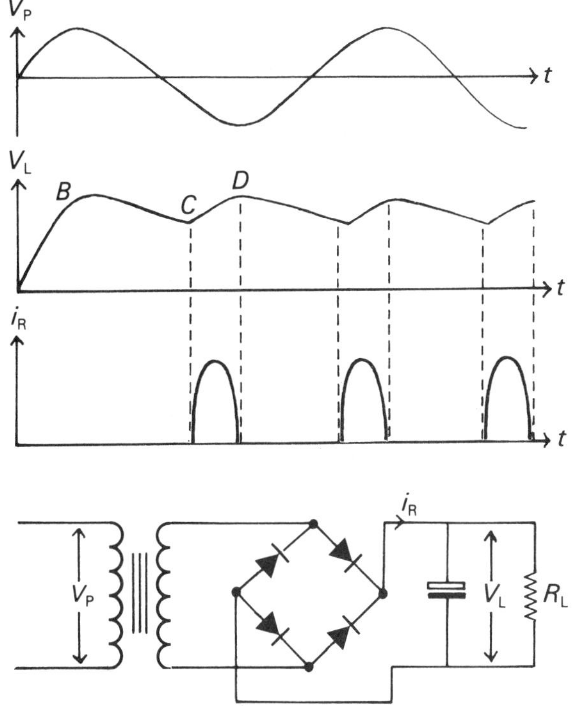

Figure A1.2 The effect of a smoothing capacitor

In Fig. A1.2 it can be seen that the rectifiers conduct for only a part of each half-cycle, and that the rectifier current consists of a series of pulses. The amplitude of these pulses plays an important role in the selection of the rectifier and smoothing capacitor. Clearly, the effect of increasing the value of the smoothing capacitor is to reduce the ripple voltage superimposed on the average d.c. output of the power supply—a good thing. However, as the capacitance increases, the period of conduction of the rectifiers is reduced, resulting in an increase in the amplitude of the current pulses through the rectifiers—a bad thing. The amplitude of these pulses must not exceed the maximum surge rating of the rectifiers. To avoid excessive rectifier currents it is usual to limit the amount of smoothing to a peak-to-peak ripple voltage of 10 – 30% of the mean voltage across the capacitor.

There are three ways in which the value of the smoothing capacitor may be calculated: by an analysis of the equivalent circuit of the transformer, rectifier, capacitor and load arrangement; by a simple rule-of-thumb calculation; or by the use of graphical techniques. The first method, employing analytical techniques, is not normally used because it requires a knowledge of the leakage inductance of the transformer, and of the effective series resistance of the rectifier plus the transformer secondary winding. Analytical techniques are normally employed only in critical applications, or in cases where the large-scale production of a power supply makes the economies achieved by choosing cost-effective components worthwhile.

The simplest way of obtaining a value for the smoothing capacitor is to apply the formula $Q=CV$ to Fig. A1.3, a linearized version of Fig. A1.2:

$$Q=CV,$$

so that

$$i=C\frac{dv}{dt}$$

or

$$C=i/\frac{dv}{dt}$$

The value of dv/dt is given by the slope of BC in Fig. A1.3. For example, for a 60 Hz power supply with a peak to peak ripple (V_R) of 5 V and a mean output ($V_M+V_R/2$) of 20 V, the slope of BC is 5 V in 1/120 s. If the mean load current is 6 A, then C is given by

$$C=i/\frac{dv}{dt} = 6/\frac{5}{1/120} = \frac{6}{600}$$

$$=\frac{1}{100}\text{F} = 10\,000\ \mu\text{F}.$$

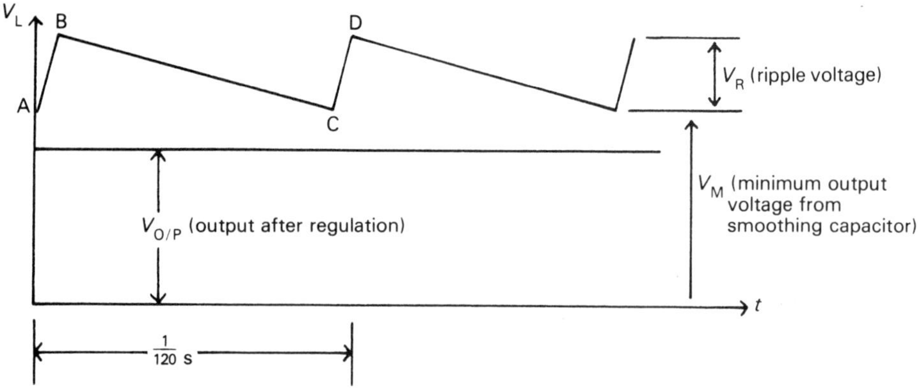

Figure A1.3 A linearized representation of the voltage V_L across the load of a bridge rectifier circuit with a smoothing capacitor

Another popular procedure for the design of a power supply with a reservoir capacitor connected directly to the output of the rectifier (i.e. capacitor-input filter), is based on the use of tables of graphs. O. H. Schade, *Proc. IRE* **31**, 356 (1943), presents a set of graphs in which the relationships between the parameters of a capacitor-input filter are displayed. Of particular interest is the relationship between the peak alternating voltage at the output of the transformer secondary and the output voltage across the smoothing capacitor, as a function of ωCR_L. Figure A1.4 shows such a set of curves for a full-wave rectifier circuit, from which it can be seen that the output voltage is not greatly increased when ωCR_L is greater than about 10. Other graphs presented by Schade include the relationship between the peak rectifier current and the value of the smoothing capacitor. For a full-wave rectifier circuit with $\omega CR_L = 10$, the peak rectifier current is approximately seven times the average rectifier current.

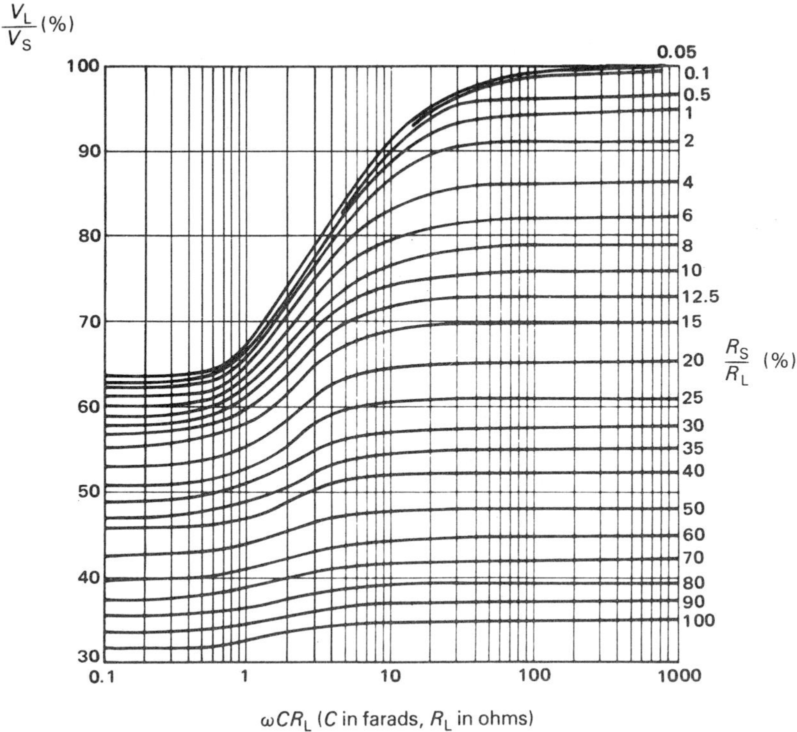

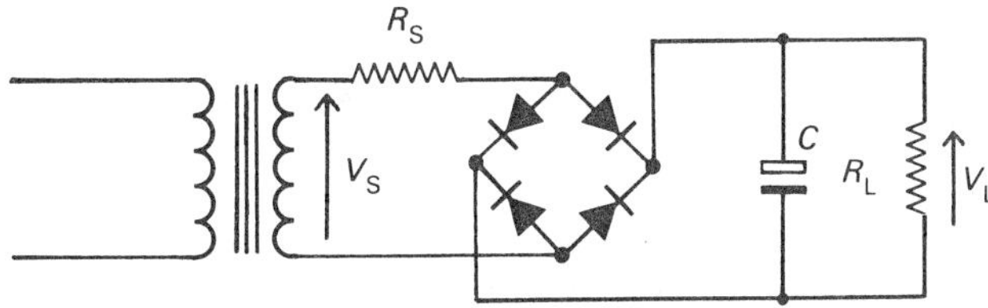

Figure A1.4 The relationship between V_s and V_L in a bridge rectifier circuit with a capacitor-input filter

Selecting the Transformer

In many manufacturers' catalogs four parameters are used to characterize transformers: the primary RMS voltage, the secondary RMS voltage, the volt-ampère (VA) rating, and the regulation. The regulation of a transformer is defined as

$$\frac{\text{off-load voltage} - \text{full-load voltage}}{\text{off-load voltage}} \times 100\%$$

The maximum voltage across the smoothing capacitor under no-load conditions is given by:

$$V_C = V_S \times 1.41$$

where V_S is the r.m.s. secondary voltage of the transformer. From Fig. A1.4 it can be seen that this value of V_C can, in practice, be approached only when ωCR_L is greater than 100 and the effective series resistance is less than $\frac{1}{2}\%$ of the load resistance.

The largest mean direct current which can be drawn by the load in a bridge rectifier current is given by:

$$I_L = I_{AC} \times 0.62 = \frac{VA}{V_S} \times 0.62;$$

where VA is the volt-ampère rating of the secondary.

Selecting the Rectifier

The most popular form of rectifier is the relatively inexpensive silicon junction diode. Bridge rectifiers, containing four silicon diodes mounted in epoxy plastic, can readily be obtained and are widely found in full-wave rectifier circuits. Rectifiers are usually characterized by four parameters: the peak inverse voltage, the maximum average forward current, the maximum forward current, and the voltage drop across the rectifier when it is conducting.

The maximum peak inverse voltage of a rectifier is the largest voltage that can safely be applied across the rectifier when it is reverse biased. In a half-wave rectifier circuit the maximum voltage across the rectifier occurs at the peak of the half-cycle when it is non-conducting. The total voltage across the rectifier is the transformer secondary voltage plus the voltage across the capacitor, i.e. $2V_C = 2 \times 1.41\,V_S$, or nearly three times the r.m.s. rating of the transformer secondary. In a bridge rectifier circuit two diodes are connected in series, so it might be thought that the PIV rating of each diode need be only half that of the equivalent half-wave rectifier circuit, i.e. $1.41\,V_S$. Unfortunately, when the diodes are reverse biased, their series resistance is indeterminate and there is no guarantee that the voltage will be distributed equally across the diodes. Hence both diodes in series in a bridge rectifier should have PIVs three times the value of V_S, or PIVs only $1\frac{1}{2}$ times V_S if voltage equalizing resistors are connected in parallel with them.

The maximum current which flows through the rectifiers is governed by the value of the smoothing capacitor. In a bridge rectifier circuit the maximum rectifier current is approximately seven times the average forward current at $\omega CR_L = 10$, and twenty times the average forward current at $\omega CR_L = 100$ ($R_S/R_L = 0.02\%$).

When a rectifier is forward biased there is a voltage drop between its anode and cathode, consisting of the voltage drop across the rectifying junction plus a voltage drop due to the ohmic resistance of the rectifier. A typical voltage drop across a bridge rectifier, at 10 A, is 1.88 V. The forward voltage drop across silicon diodes is of little importance in high-voltage power supplies, but in low-voltage power supplies, producing the high currents required by large memories, the forward voltage drop is an appreciable fraction of the voltage across the smoothing capacitor. Conventional silicon junction diodes lower the rectification efficiency of the circuit and waste a large amount of power. Possible alternatives to silicon junction diodes are Schottky diodes with their lower forward voltage drop, or synchronous rectifiers using transistors which have a collector – emitter saturation voltage of approximately 0.3 V.

Selecting the Capacitor

The choice of an electrolytic capacitor in a filter circuit is determined by three parameters: the capacitance, the maximum applied voltage, and the maximum ripple current. The capacitance may be calculated as described earlier in this section, and the voltage rating of the capacitor must be greater than the peak secondary voltage plus an amount large enough to allow for increases in the primary voltage due to line overloads. Capacitors also have a maximum surge voltage rating which is the maximum instantaneous voltage which may be applied across the capacitor. Unfortunately the surge voltage of an electrolytic capacitor is often not appreciably greater than the maximum working voltage.

The ripple rating of the smoothing capacitor is very important, but is sometimes neglected by inexperienced designers. As we have seen, the voltage across the smoothing capacitor is composed of a constant voltage plus a ripple component. The ripple voltage causes a current, the ripple current, to flow through the capacitor. If we assume that the ripple voltage is approximately sinusoidal, the ripple current is given by

$$I_{\text{ripple}} = \frac{V_R}{2\sqrt{2}}\,\frac{1}{X_C} = \frac{V_R(2\pi fC)}{2\sqrt{2}} = 267\,V_R C.$$

I_{ripple} is given by $267\,V_R C$ for a 60 Hz supply and by $222\ V_R C$ for a 50 Hz supply. The effective ripple frequency is twice the line frequency. In the above example, $V_R = 5$ V and $C = 0.01$ F, so that $I_{\text{ripple}} = 13.3$ A. Failure to choose a capacitor with an adequate ripple current rating leads to high internal temperatures and a reduced capacitor life. Note that the maximum ripple current rating of a capacitor is temperature dependent.

The Regulator

The smoothed voltage across the reservoir capacitor is far from the constant voltage required by most digital integrated circuits, i.e. 5 V±5%. In order to create a true constant voltage source an electronic regulator must be used. Electronic regulators can have very complex circuits, and several books have been written on the subject of their design. Fortunately, the designer of a small to medium-size microprocessor system has been freed of the relatively complex task of designing his own regulator by the availability of monolithic regulators. Monolithic regulators are high-performance integrated circuits which provide a constant voltage output from an unregulated input. Their advantage is twofold: they are very cheap; and they are easy to use, having only three terminals. Table A1.1 gives the parameters of four monolithic regulators, each of which has a 5 V output, and Fig. A1.5 shows how a regulator is used. Note that most monolithic regulators have internal protection circuitry, saving the regulator from the effects of short-circuiting their output. Some regulators (e.g. 78H05) also include protection against thermal overload—the device is shut down when the junction temperature rises above a predetermined limit.

Table A1.1 The Characteristics of Five Monolithic Regulators

Characteristic	*7805*	*L005*	*LM309K*	*LM323K*	*78H05K*
Output current (A)	1	0.6	1.2	3	5
Input voltage range (V)	7–25	7.5–20	7–35	7.5–20	8–25
Load regulation	0.2%	0.3%	1%	0.3%	10 mV
Ripple rejection (dB)	70	62	70	58	60
Output resistance (mΩ)	30	15	50	—	2
Line regulation	0.2%	0.1%	0.1%	0.1%	10 mV
Output noise voltage (mV)	0.04	0.07	0.04	0.04	0.04
Short-circuit current (A)	0.75	0.190	—	—	7
Case	Plastic	T03	T03	T03	T03

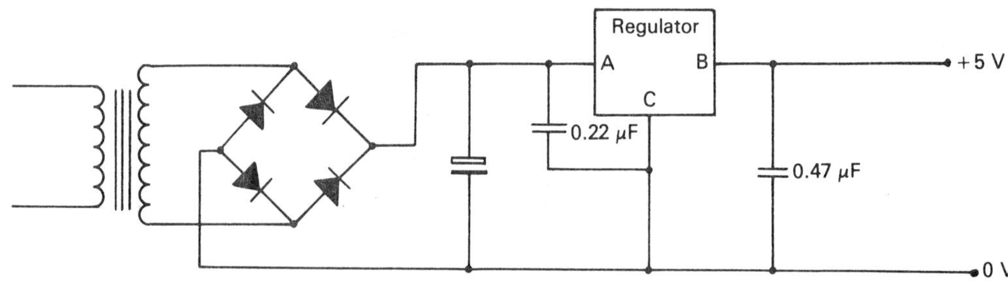

Figure A1.5 A stabilized power supply using a monolithic voltage regulator

Monolithic regulators suffer from two important disadvantages. They are sometimes prone to instability and may oscillate in the megahertz region, superimposing a high-frequency waveform with an amplitude of several volts on the 5 V output. Such oscillations are normally prevented by connecting two capacitors between the regulator input and ground, and between the regulator output and ground, as shown in Fig. A1.5. These capacitors should be located as close as possible to the pins of the regulator. It may seem strange that a 0.22 μF capacitor is used to bypass a smoothing capacitor of 10 000 μF, but the reactance of an electrolytic capacitor rises rapidly above 10 kHz. The effect of this is to prevent the capacitor from bypassing high-frequency noise.

A second limitation of the monolithic regulator is its inability to pass really large currents (above 10 A). This forces the designer to seek one of two alternatives: to design a regulator circuit with discrete high-power transistors, or to distribute the unregulated power supply to each module in the microprocessor system and use on-board regulators to provide a local stabilized 5 V supply. It is difficult to choose between these alternatives because both have their advantages and disadvantages. The SS50 bus and the S100 bus both have a power-supply rail carrying an unstabilized (approximately 8 V) power supply plus on-board regulation on all memory, CPU, and peripheral cards.

The principal advantages of a multiregulator power supply are:

(1) Simple, inexpensive, 1 A regulators may be used instead of a complex, and possibly expensive, high-current regulator.
(2) A very low-impedance power-supply bus need not be used to distribute the stabilized power between individual cards—this can simplify the design of the system and save money.
(3) The regulators provide additional isolation between the various modules.
(4) The failure of a single monolithic regulator will not damage more than one module.

The principal disadvantages of a multi-regulator power supply are:

(1) The power dissipation of the regulators is put on the modules where it is least wanted. On some large memory boards using the older 1 K chips, up to four 1 A regulators are used, considerably increasing the waste heat generated by the board. When a single regulator is employed it is normally located in an enclosure, away from the more delicate modules.
(2) Although the use of several regulators reduces the total damage done if a regulator fails, the chance of failure is increased because there are more regulators to fail.
(3) Regulators with their associated bypass capacitors and heat sinks take up valuable space on the cards where they are located. Furthermore, they often limit the minimum spacing between adjacent cards.

Power-supply Protection

An ideal power supply and a.c. mains to which it is connected should have the following characteristics:

(1) The mains supply is a perfectly sinusoidal voltage of constant amplitude and frequency.

(2) The mains should have always been connected to the power supply, and should always be connected to it. That is, the power is never turned on or off, thus avoiding switching transients.
(3) The components which make up the power supply are perfect: they never age, (i.e. change their properties) or fail.

Unfortunately the above situation does not exist. Because the mains supply has a non-zero impedance (typically $0.4 + 0.25j\ \Omega$ at 50 Hz*), the waveform at the power-supply transformer primary contains components due to the effects of other loads connected to the mains. Common sources of mains-borne interference are:

(1) switched inductive loads—motors, solenoids, relays, etc.;
(2) lightning strikes to, or near, the power distribution networks;
(3) alternating-current switching circuits—e.g., SCR phase control circuits;
(4) energizing or de-energizing transformer primaries.

It is not uncommon for transients of the order of 1000 V to be superimposed on the mains supply, although most transients have an amplitude of less than 200 V and a duration of tens of microseconds. Transients usually have the form of an exponentially damped sine wave with a very rapid rise time. Why are the designers of power supplies so concerned about transients? A transient can, occasionally, have enough energy to destroy components inside the power supply or within the microprocessor system itself. More commonly, a transient may be large enough to affect a logic level on the system bus, causing a logical one to be interpreted as a logical zero by some device (or vice versa). This can cause a program to crash—especially if an address is corrupted and a random jump executed.

A common technique of removing some of the effects of mains-borne interference involves the insertion of filter networks between the mains and the power supply. A typical commercially available filter has an attenuation of 35 dB between 150 kHz and 30 MHz, and its circuit diagram is given in Fig. A1.6.

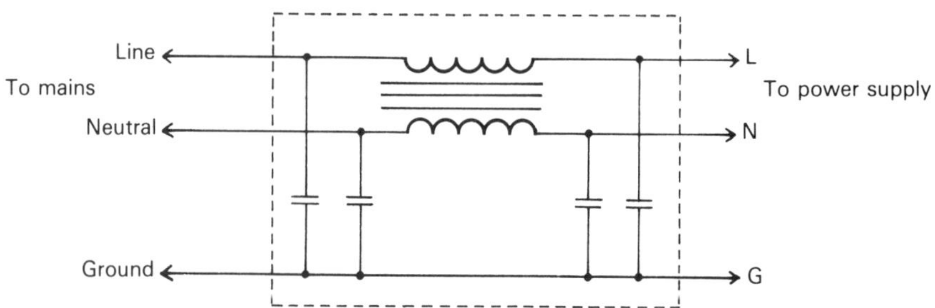

Figure A1.6 The circuit diagram of a mains filter

* A value suggested by the Comité Européen des Normes Électriques (CENELEC) for European power supplies. The corresponding EIA value is $0.4 + 15.7j\ \Omega$ at 100 kHz.

Another type of transient suppressor is the zinc oxide voltage-dependent resistor (VDR) which has a highly non-linear voltage – current characteristic. The *V/I* curve of a typical zinc oxide VDR is given in Fig. A1.7. A power supply is protected from mains-borne transients by connecting the VDR across the mains terminals at the input to the power supply. When a transient appears across the VDR, its resistance falls, causing a current to flow through the VDR. In this way a large fraction of the energy of the transient is dissipated within the body of the VDR. A tenfold increase in the current through a VDR corresponds to an approximately 8% increase in the voltage across it.

In addition to protecting the power supply from mains-borne transients it is usual to provide protection against excessive load current and load voltages. To protect the power supply from excessive load currents, a current sensor must detect an overload condition and then take action to stop any further increase in output

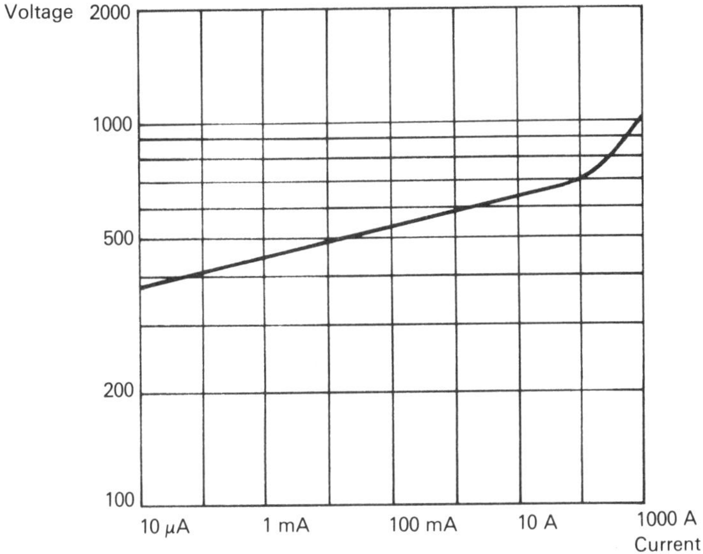

Figure A1.7 Typical V/I characteristics of a zinc oxide VDR for use with a 240 V r.m.s. mains supply

current. This is done in one of two ways, by holding the output current constant, or by fold-back current limiting, which reduces the current to a very low value until the cause of the overload is removed. As many microprocessor systems use monolithic regulators, the power-supply designer must choose the regulator with the type of current limiting best suited to his application.

It is advisable to add over-voltage protection to the output of a power supply. A widely used method of over-voltage protection is the crowbar circuit. The crowbar circuit is so-named because of its "brute force and ignorance" technique of putting an almost dead-short across the power supply terminals in the event of an overload.

The effect of the short circuit switches off the drive to the regulator either by means of a resettable electronic switch or by a simple fuse.

The circuit diagram of a crowbar circuit is given in Fig. A1.8. The silicon-controlled rectifier (SCR) placed across the output terminals of the power supply is normally in the non-conducting state. When a positive-going pulse appears at its gate the SCR conducts and remains conducting until it is reset by turning off the power supply. The gate voltage required to turn on the SCR is provided by sampling the power-supply output with a zener diode which is non-conducting until the reverse bias voltage across its anode – cathode terminals reaches its zener point. The crowbar circuit does not always give complete protection of the system because the SCR takes about a microsecond to turn on, and there is a further delay of several microseconds in the zener diode trigger circuit. During the delay it is still possible for a large over-voltage transient to cause some damage to MOS and TTL devices.

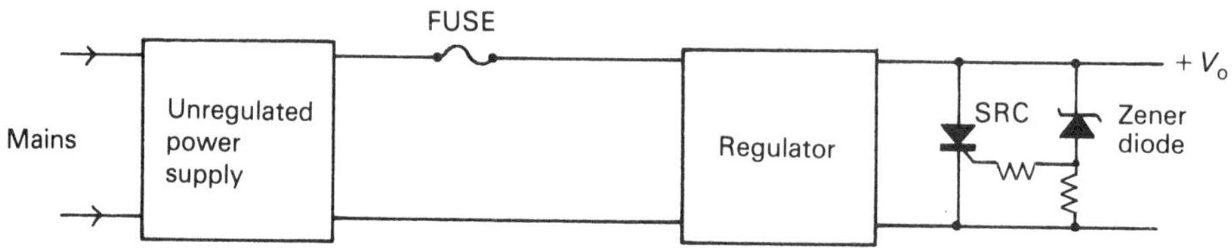

Figure A1.8 A simple crowbar overvoltage protection circuit

The zinc oxide voltage-dependent resistor is usually used to suppress high-voltage transients at the mains input. General Semiconductor Industries produce a device called the *TransZorb*, which is able to suppress transients on low-voltage lines. A TransZorb is a silicon PN avalanche device for suppressing transients above a predetermined level, at which the PN junction breaks down (reversibly) and conducts—in other words a TransZorb is a special type of zener diode. TransZorbs have relatively low breakdown voltages and are designed to protect the outputs of power supplies, or even the MOS and bipolar TTL circuits themselves. A TransZorb is simply connected across the output of a power supply.

Three parameters define the breakdown of the TransZorb: reverse stand-off voltage, clamping voltage, and breakdown voltage. The reverse stand-off voltage is less than the voltage at which the avalanche* effect occurs and is a point where there is essentially no conduction through the TransZorb. The breakdown voltage is the level at which clipping begins, just above the avalanche voltage. The maximum clamping voltage is the maximum voltage across the TransZorb under peak pulse current conditions. Table A1.2 gives the characteristics of some TransZorbs.

* The avalanche effect occurs when the voltage across a reverse-biased PN junction causes some of the electrons, which form the reverse leakage current, to collide with valence electrons of the atoms in the crystal lattice, thus creating additional free electrons. Some of these new electrons collide with other atoms, freeing more electrons. This process builds up rapidly, resulting in a very large reverse-biased current.

Table A1.2 The Characteristics of Six General Semiconductor Industries' TransZorb Transient Suppressors

Type number	*Stand-off voltage* V_R (V)	*Maximum reverse leakage @* V_R (μA)	*Minimum breakdown voltage @ 1 mA* (V)	*Maximum clamping voltage @ Ipp = 1 A* (V)	*Maximum clamping voltage @ Ipp = 10 A* (V)	*Maximum peak pulse current* (A)
MPTE-5	5.0	300	6.0	7.1	7.5	160
MPTE-8	8.0	25	9.4	11.3	11.5	100
MPTE-10	10.0	2	11.7	13.7	14.1	90
MPTE-12	12.0	2	14.1	16.1	16.5	70
MPTE-15	15.0	2	17.6	20.1	20.6	60
MPTE-18	18.0	2	21.2	24.2	25.2	50

To select a TransZorb for a given application it is necessary to determine the maximum continuous voltage to which it will be subjected. This voltage is the rated voltage of the power supply plus the tolerance in the rated voltage. The TransZorb must have a reverse stand-off voltage equal to or greater than the maximum circuit voltage, defined above. The TransZorbs described in Table A1.2 each have a maximum peak pulse power dissipation of 150 W at 25°C, and may be used to provide transient voltage protection either before or after the regulator. The cost of TransZorbs is low enough (≈\$2) to allow a TransZorb to be used to protect each circuit module.

Switching Regulators

A section on power supplies for digital computers would not be complete without a mention of switching regulators. The type of stabilized power supply dealt with so far is very inefficient; the TS1 power-supply module has an input to the smoothing capacitor of approximately 12 V, and an output from the regulator of 5 V corresponding to an efficiency of only 42%. When operating at a current of 6 A this power supply dissipates in the region of 42 W of potentially harmful heat. The switching regulator operates at an efficiency of 70 – 80% (or more) and is normally smaller than an equivalent linear regulator.

Figure A1.9 illustrates the basic principles of the switching regulator. When the switching transistor is turned on, a current flows into the inductor and thence to the load and output capacitor. If the transistor is turned off a current continues to flow in the inductor because of its energy storage property. This current flows through the load and returns via the diode, D. As the load takes current, the voltage across C drops, causing the control circuit to switch on the series transistor once more. Consequently the series transistor is turned on and off at a high rate (tens of kHz). Because this transistor is turned hard on or fully off, little heat is dissipated in it. Furthermore, as the switching frequency is so high the smoothing capacitor need be

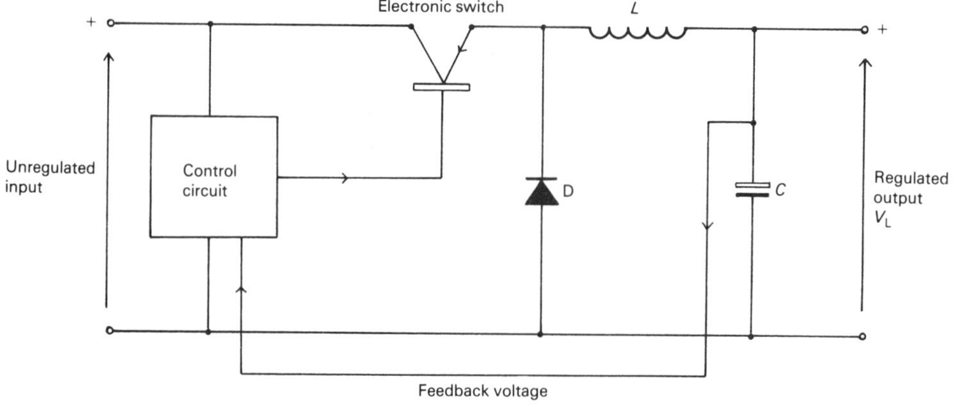

Figure A1.9 The switching regulator

only a small fraction of the size of the smoothing capacitor following the bridge rectifier. The output voltage of the circuit is given by

$$V_{out} = V_{in}\left(\frac{t_{on}}{t_{on} + t_{off}}\right),$$

where t_{on} and t_{off} are the times for which the switching transistor is turned on and off, respectively.

The switching regulator is not treated in detail in this book because of its much greater complexity than the monolithic linear regulator. However, a commercial switching regulator power supply should always be considered as an alternative to the more conventional form of power supply.

Appendix A2
The Hardware Section of the 6800 Data Sheet

This appendix has been included to provide the reader with a quick reference to some of the finer points of the 6800 CPU. A data sheet for the 6802 has not been included because it is electrically very similar to the 6800 and is identical from a software point of view.

MC6800
(1.0 MHz)
MC68A00
(1.5 MHz)
MC68B00
(2.0 MHz)

8-BIT MICROPROCESSING UNIT (MPU)

The MC6800 is a monolithic 8-bit microprocessor forming the central control function for Motorola's M6800 family. Compatible with TTL, the MC6800, as with all M6800 system parts, requires only one +5.0-volt power supply, and no external TTL devices for bus interface.

The MC6800 is capable of addressing 65K bytes of memory with its 16-bit address lines. The 8-bit data bus is bidirectional as well as 3-state, making direct memory addressing and multiprocessing applications realizable.

- Eight-Bit Parallel Processing
- Bidirectional Data Bus
- Sixteen-Bit Address Bus – 65K Bytes of Addressing
- 72 Instructions – Variable Length
- Seven Addressing Modes – Direct, Relative, Immediate, Indexed, Extended, Implied and Accumulator
- Variable Length Stack
- Vectored Restart
- Maskable Interrupt Vector
- Separate Non-Maskable Interrupt – Internal Registers Saved in Stack
- Six Internal Registers – Two Accumulators, Index Register, Program Counter, Stack Pointer and Condition Code Register
- Direct Memory Addressing (DMA) and Multiple Processor Capability
- Simplified Clocking Characteristics
- Clock Rates as High as 2.0 MHz
- Simple Bus Interface Without TTL
- Halt and Single Instruction Execution Capability

MOS

(N-CHANNEL, SILICON-GATE, DEPLETION LOAD)

MICROPROCESSOR

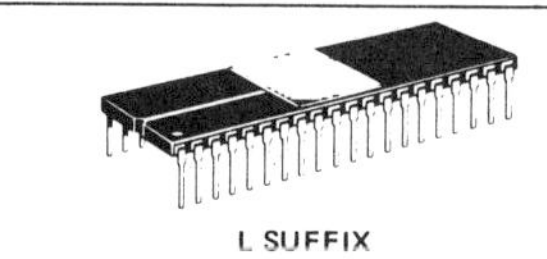

L SUFFIX
CERAMIC PACKAGE
CASE 715

P SUFFIX
PLASTIC PACKAGE
CASE 711

ORDERING INFORMATION

Speed	Device	Temperature Range
1.0 MHz	MC6800P, L	0 to 70°C
	MC6800CP, CL	−40 to +85°C
MIL-STD-883B	MC6800BQCS	−55 to +125°C
MIL-STD-883C	MC6800CQCS	
1.5 MHz	MC68A00P, L	0 to +70°C
	MC68A00CP, CL	−40 to +85°C
2.0 MHz	MC68B00P, L	0 to +70°C

PIN ASSIGNMENT

Pin	Signal	Signal	Pin
1	V_{SS}	$\overline{Reset}$	40
2	$\overline{Halt}$	TSC	39
3	φ1	N.C.	38
4	$\overline{IRQ}$	φ2	37
5	VMA	DBE	36
6	$\overline{NMI}$	N.C.	35
7	BA	R/W	34
8	V_{CC}	D0	33
9	A0	D1	32
10	A1	D2	31
11	A2	D3	30
12	A3	D4	29
13	A4	D5	28
14	A5	D6	27
15	A6	D7	26
16	A7	A15	25
17	A8	A14	24
18	A9	A13	23
19	A10	A12	22
20	A11	V_{SS}	21

TABLE 1 — MAXIMUM RATINGS

Rating	Symbol	Value	Unit
Supply Voltage	V_{CC}	-0.3 to +7.0	Vdc
Input Voltage	V_{in}	-0.3 to +7.0	Vdc
Operating Temperature Range—T_L to T_H	T_A		^oC
MC6800, MC68A00, MC68B00		0 to +70	
MC6800C, MC68A00C		-40 to +85	
MC6800BQCS, MC6800CQCS		-55 to +125	
Storage Temperature Range	T_{stg}	-55 to +150	^oC
Thermal Resistance	θ_{JA}		$^oC/W$
Plastic Package		70	
Ceramic Package		50	

This device contains circuitry to protect the inputs against damage due to high static voltages or electric fields; however, it is advised that normal precautions be taken to avoid application of any voltage higher than maximum rated voltages to this high impedance circuit.

TABLE 2 — ELECTRICAL CHARACTERISTICS (V_{CC} = 5.0 V, ± 5%, V_{SS} = 0, T_A = T_L to T_H unless otherwise noted)

Characteristic		Symbol	Min	Typ	Max	Unit
Input High Voltage	Logic	V_{IH}	V_{SS} + 2.0	–	V_{CC}	Vdc
	φ1, φ2	V_{IHC}	V_{CC} – 0.6	–	V_{CC} + 0.3	
Input Low Voltage	Logic	V_{IL}	V_{SS} – 0.3	–	V_{SS} + 0.8	Vdc
	φ1, φ2	V_{ILC}	V_{SS} – 0.3	–	V_{SS} + 0.4	
Input Leakage Current		I_{in}				μAdc
(V_{in} = 0 to 5.25 V, V_{CC} = max)	Logic*		–	1.0	2.5	
(V_{in} = 0 to 5.25 V, V_{CC} = 0.0 V)	φ1, φ2		–	–	100	
Three-State (Off State) Input Current	D0-D7	I_{TSI}	–	2.0	10	μAdc
(V_{in} = 0.4 to 2.4 V, V_{CC} = max)	A0-A15, R/$\overline{W}$		–	–	100	
Output High Voltage		V_{OH}				Vdc
(I_{Load} = -205 μAdc, V_{CC} = min)	D0-D7		V_{SS} + 2.4	–	–	
(I_{Load} = -145 μAdc, V_{CC} = min)	A0-A15, R/$\overline{W}$, VMA		V_{SS} + 2.4	–	–	
(I_{Load} = -100 μAdc, V_{CC} = min)	BA		V_{SS} + 2.4	–	–	
Output Low Voltage (I_{Load} = 1.6 mAdc, V_{CC} = min)		V_{OL}	–	–	V_{SS} + 0.4	Vdc
Power Dissipation		P_D	–	0.5	1.0	W
Capacitance		C_{in}				pF
(V_{in} = 0, T_A = 25°C, f = 1.0 MHz)	φ1		–	25	35	
	φ2		–	45	70	
	D0-D7		–	10	12.5	
	Logic Inputs		–	6.5	10	
	A0-A15, R/$\overline{W}$, VMA	C_{out}	–	–	12	pF

TABLE 3 — CLOCK TIMING (V_{CC} = 5.0 V, ± 5%, V_{SS} = 0, T_A = T_L to T_H unless otherwise noted)

Characteristics		Symbol	Min	Typ	Max	Unit
Frequency of Operation	MC6800	f	0.1	–	1.0	MHz
	MC68A00		0.1	–	1.5	
	MC68B00		0.1	–	2.0	
Cycle Time (Figure 1)	MC6800	t_{cyc}	1.000	–	10	μs
	MC68A00		0.666	–	10	
	MC68B00		0.500	–	10	
Clock Pulse Width	φ1, φ2 – MC6800	$PW_{\phi H}$	400	–	9500	ns
(Measured at V_{CC} – 0.6 V)	φ1, φ2 – MC68A00		230	–	9500	
	φ1, φ2 – MC68B00		180	–	9500	
Total φ1 and φ2 Up Time	MC6800	t_{ut}	900	–	–	ns
	MC68A00		600	–	–	
	MC68B00		440	–	–	
Rise and Fall Times (Measured between V_{SS} + 0.4 and V_{CC} – 0.6)		$t_{\phi r}$, $t_{\phi f}$	–	–	100	ns
Delay Time or Clock Separation (Figure 1)		t_d				ns
(Measured at V_{OV} = V_{SS} + 0.6 V @ t_r = t_f ≤ 100 ns)			0	–	9100	
(Measured at V_{OV} = V_{SS} + 1.0 V @ t_r = t_f ≤ 35 ns)			0	–	9100	

TABLE 4 – READ/WRITE TIMING (Reference Figures 2 through 6)

Characteristic	Symbol	MC6800			MC68A00			MC68B00			Unit
		Min	Typ	Max	Min	Typ	Max	Min	Typ	Max	
Address Delay C = 90 pF C = 30 pF	t_{AD}	 – –	 – –	 270 250	 – –	 – –	 180 165	 – –	 – –	 150 135	ns
Peripheral Read Access Time $t_{ac} = t_{ut} - (t_{AD} + t_{DSR})$	t_{acc}	–	–	530	–	–	360	–	–	250	ns
Data Setup Time (Read)	t_{DSR}	100	–	–	60	–	–	40	–	–	ns
Input Data Hold Time	t_H	10	–	–	10	–	–	10	–	–	ns
Output Data Hold Time	t_H	10	25	–	10	25	–	10	25	–	ns
Address Hold Time (Address, R/$\overline{W}$, VMA)	t_{AH}	30	50	–	30	50	–	30	50	–	ns
Enable High Time for DBE Input	t_{EH}	450	–	–	280	–	–	220	–	–	ns
Data Delay Time (Write)	t_{DDW}	–	–	225	–	–	200	–	–	160	ns
Processor Controls											
Processor Control Setup Time	t_{PCS}	200	–	–	140	–	–	110	–	–	ns
Processor Control Rise and Fall Time	t_{PCr}, t_{PCf}	–	–	100	–	–	100	–	–	100	ns
Bus Available Delay	t_{BA}	–	–	250	–	–	165	–	–	135	ns
Three-State Delay	t_{TSD}	–	–	270	–	–	270	–	–	220	ns
Data Bus Enable Down Time During ϕ1 Up Time	$t_{\overline{DBE}}$	150	–	–	120	–	–	75	–	–	ns
Data Bus Enable Rise and Fall Times	t_{DBEr}, t_{DBEf}	–	–	25	–	–	25	–	–	25	ns

FIGURE 1 – CLOCK TIMING WAVEFORM

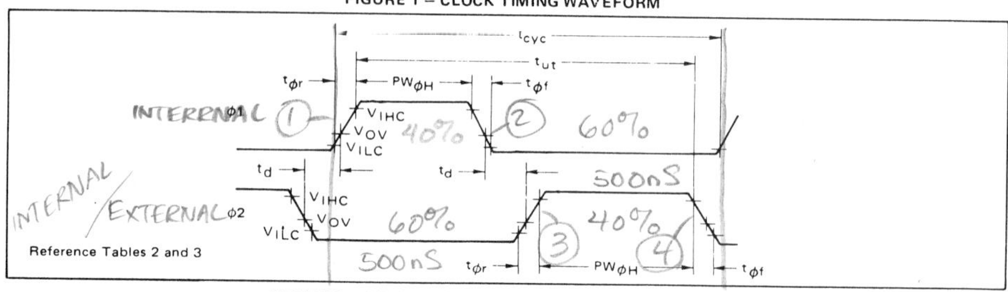

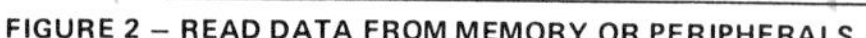

FIGURE 2 – READ DATA FROM MEMORY OR PERIPHERALS

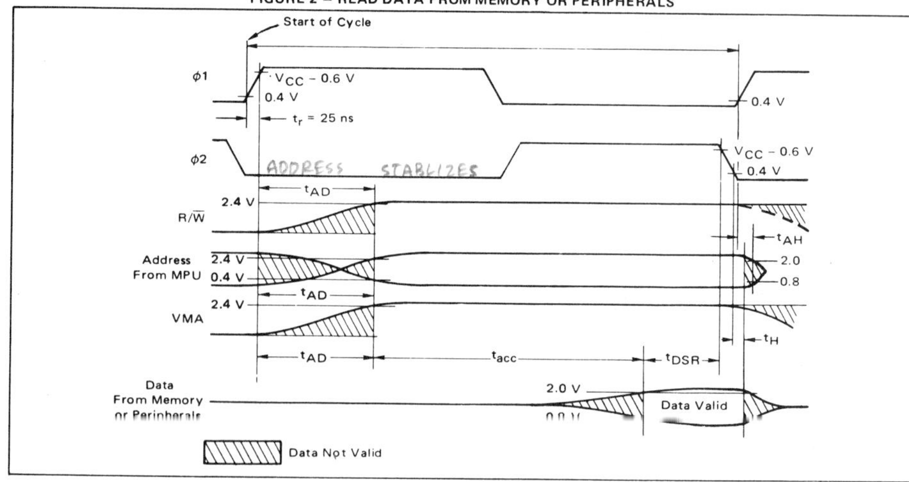

FIGURE 3 – WRITE IN MEMORY OR PERIPHERALS

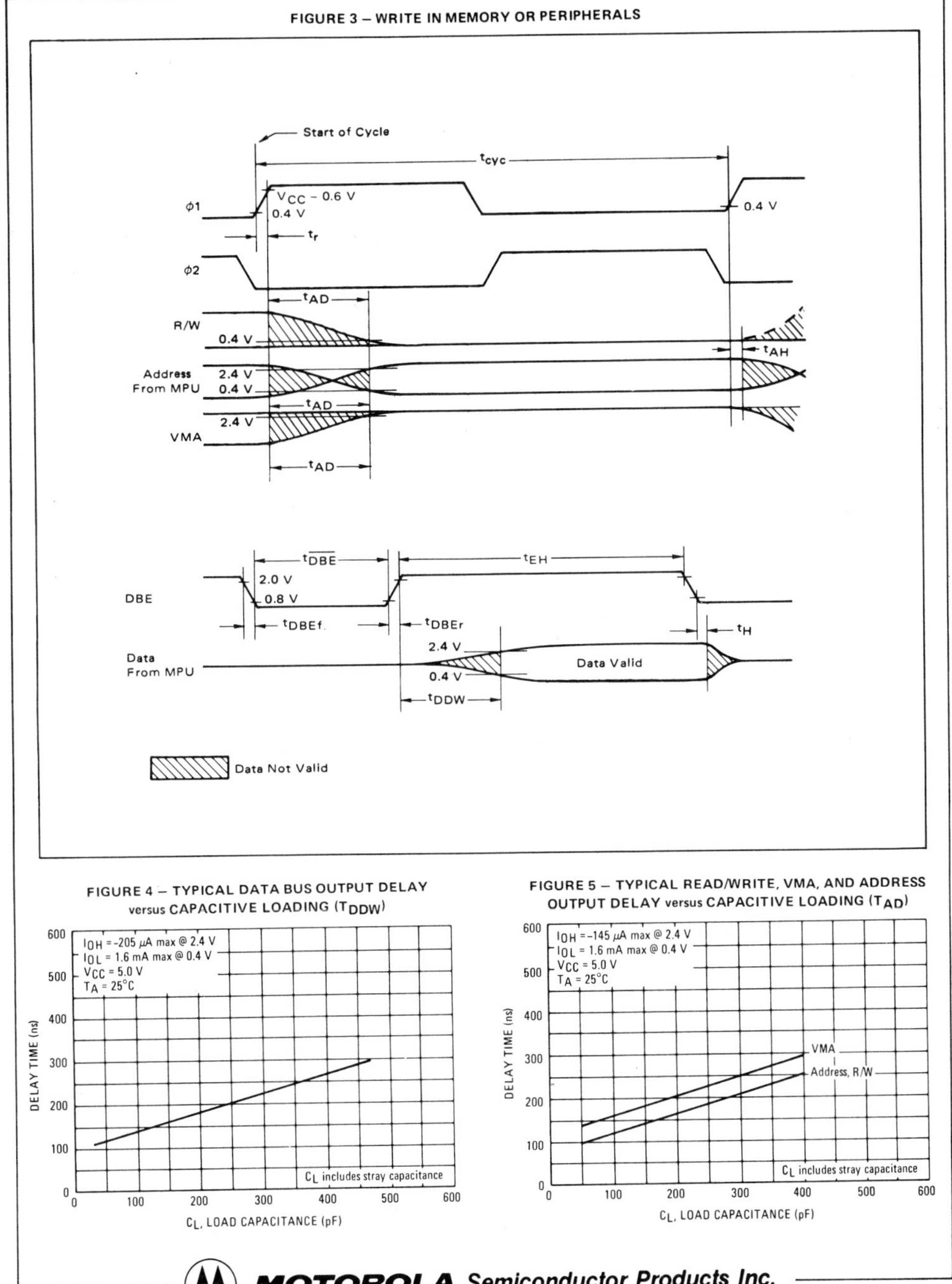

FIGURE 4 – TYPICAL DATA BUS OUTPUT DELAY versus CAPACITIVE LOADING (T_{DDW})

FIGURE 5 – TYPICAL READ/WRITE, VMA, AND ADDRESS OUTPUT DELAY versus CAPACITIVE LOADING (T_{AD})

FIGURE 6 – BUS TIMING TEST LOADS

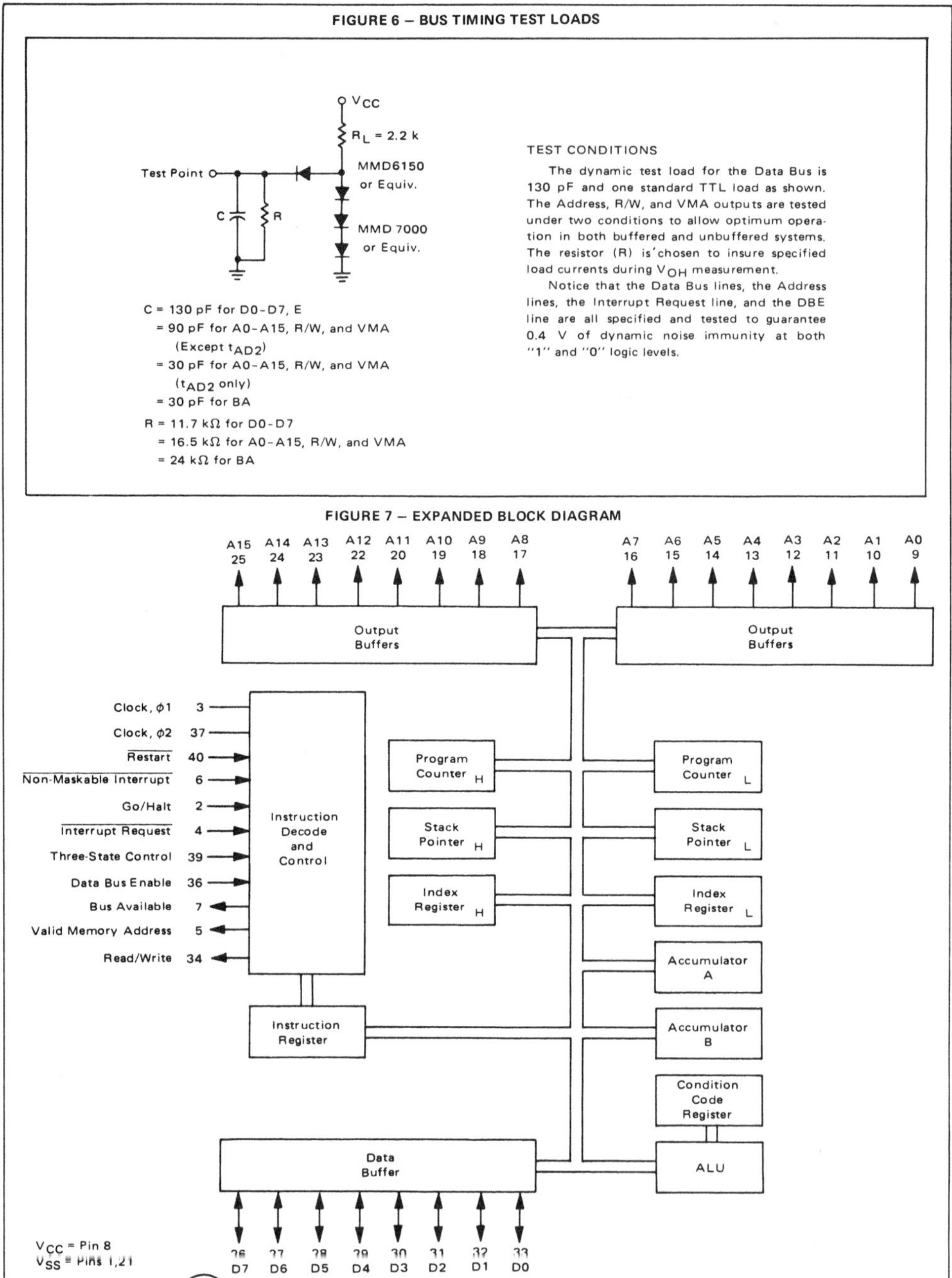

VCC
RL = 2.2 k
Test Point
MMD6150
or Equiv.
C
R
MMD 7000
or Equiv.
C = 130 pF for D0-D7, E
= 90 pF for A0-A15, R/W, and VMA
(Except tAD2)
= 30 pF for A0-A15, R/W, and VMA
(tAD2 only)
= 30 pF for BA
R = 11.7 kΩ for D0-D7
= 16.5 kΩ for A0-A15, R/W, and VMA
= 24 kΩ for BA
TEST CONDITIONS
The dynamic test load for the Data Bus is 130 pF and one standard TTL load as shown. The Address, R/W, and VMA outputs are tested under two conditions to allow optimum operation in both buffered and unbuffered systems. The resistor (R) is chosen to insure specified load currents during VOH measurement.
Notice that the Data Bus lines, the Address lines, the Interrupt Request line, and the DBE line are all specified and tested to guarantee 0.4 V of dynamic noise immunity at both "1" and "0" logic levels.
FIGURE 7 – EXPANDED BLOCK DIAGRAM
A15 25
A14 24
A13 23
A12 22
A11 20
A10 19
A9 18
A8 17
A7 16
A6 15
A5 14
A4 13
A3 12
A2 11
A1 10
A0 9
Output Buffers
Output Buffers
Clock, φ1 3
Clock, φ2 37
Restart 40
Non-Maskable Interrupt 6
Go/Halt 2
Interrupt Request 4
Three-State Control 39
Data Bus Enable 36
Bus Available 7
Valid Memory Address 5
Read/Write 34
Instruction Decode and Control
Program Counter H
Program Counter L
Stack Pointer H
Stack Pointer L
Index Register H
Index Register L
Accumulator A
Accumulator B
Instruction Register
Condition Code Register
Data Buffer
ALU
VCC = Pin 8
VSS = Pins 1,21
26 D7
27 D6
28 D5
29 D4
30 D3
31 D2
32 D1
33 D0

MPU SIGNAL DESCRIPTION

Proper operation of the MPU requires that certain control and timing signals be provided to accomplish specific functions and that other signal lines be monitored to determine the state of the processor.

Clocks Phase One and Phase Two ($\phi1,\phi2$) – Two pins are used for a two-phase non-overlapping clock that runs at the V_{CC} voltage level.

Figure 1 shows the microprocessor clocks, and Table 3 shows the static and dynamic clock specifications. The high level is specified at V_{IHC} and the low level is specified at V_{ILC}. The allowable clock frequency is specified by f (frequency). The minimum $\phi1$ and $\phi2$ high level pulse widths are specified by $PW_{\phi H}$ (pulse width high time). To guarantee the required access time for the peripherals, the clock up time, t_{ut}, is specified. Clock separation, t_d, is measured at a maximum voltage of V_{OV} (overlap voltage). This allows for a multitude of clock variations at the system frequency rate.

Address Bus (A0-A15) – Sixteen pins are used for the address bus. The outputs are three-state bus drivers capable of driving one standard TTL load and 90 pF. When the output is turned off, it is essentially an open circuit. This permits the MPU to be used in DMA applications. Putting TSC in its high state forces the Address bus to go into the three-state mode.

Data Bus (D0-D7) – Eight pins are used for the data bus. It is bidirectional, transferring data to and from the memory and peripheral devices. It also has three-state output buffers capable of driving one standard TTL load and 130 pF. Data Bus is placed in the three-state mode when DBE is low.

Data Bus Enable (DBE) – This input is the three-state control signal for the MPU data bus and will enable the bus drivers when in the high state. This input is TTL compatible; however in normal operation, it would be driven by the phase two clock. During an MPU read cycle, the data bus drivers will be disabled internally. When it is desired that another device control the data bus such as in Direct Memory Access (DMA) applications, DBE should be held low.

If additional data setup or hold time is required on an MPU write, the DBE down time can be decreased as shown in Figure 3 (DBE $\neq \phi2$). The minimum down time for DBE is $t_{\overline{DBE}}$ as shown and must occur within $\phi1$ up time. The minimum delay from the trailing edge of DBE to the trailing edge of $\phi1$ is t_{DBED}. By skewing DBE with respect to E in this manner, data setup or hold time can be increased.

Bus Available (BA) – The Bus Available signal will normally be in the low state; when activated, it will go to the high state indicating that the microprocessor has stopped and that the address bus is available. This will occur if the $\overline{\text{Halt}}$ line is in the low state or the processor is in the WAIT state as a result of the execution of a WAIT instruction. At such time, all three-state output drivers will go to their off state and other outputs to their normally inactive level. The processor is removed from the WAIT state by the occurrence of a maskable (mask bit I = 0) or nonmaskable interrupt. This output is capable of driving one standard TTL load and 30 pF. If TSC is in the high state, Bus Available will be low.

Read/$\overline{\text{Write}}$ (R/$\overline{\text{W}}$) – This TTL compatible output signals the peripherals and memory devices whether the MPU is in a Read (high) or Write (low) state. The normal standby state of this signal is Read (high). Three-State Control going high will turn Read/$\overline{\text{Write}}$ to the off (high impedance) state. Also, when the processor is halted, it will be in the off state. This output is capable of driving one standard TTL load and 90 pF.

$\overline{\text{Reset}}$ – The $\overline{\text{Reset}}$ input is used to reset and start the MPU from a power down condition resulting from a power failure or initial start-up of the processor. This input can also be used to reinitialize the machine at any time after start-up.

If a high level is detected in this input, this will signal the MPU to begin the reset sequence. During the reset sequence, the contents of the last two locations (FFFE, FFFF) in memory will be loaded into the Program Counter to point to the beginning of the reset routine. During the reset routine, the interrupt mask bit is set and must be cleared under program control before the MPU can be interrupted by $\overline{\text{IRQ}}$. While $\overline{\text{Reset}}$ is low (assuming a minimum of 8 clock cycles have occurred) the MPU output signals will be in the following states: VMA = low, BA = low, Data Bus = high impedance, R/$\overline{\text{W}}$ = high (read state), and the Address Bus will contain the reset address FFFE. Figure 8 illustrates a power up sequence using the $\overline{\text{Reset}}$ control line. After the power supply reaches 4.75 V a minimum of eight clock cycles are required for the processor to stabilize in preparation for restarting. During these eight cycles, VMA will be in an indeterminate state so any devices that are enabled by VMA which could accept a false write during this time (such as a battery-backed RAM) must be disabled until VMA is forced low after eight cycles. $\overline{\text{Reset}}$ can go high asynchronously with the system clock any time after the eighth cycle.

$\overline{\text{Reset}}$ timing is shown in Figure 8 and Table 4. The maximum rise and fall transition times are specified by t_{PCr} and t_{PCf}. If $\overline{\text{Reset}}$ is high at t_{PCS} (processor control setup time) as shown in Figure 8 in any given cycle, then the restart sequence will begin on the next cycle as shown. The $\overline{\text{Reset}}$ control line may also be used to reinitialize the MPU system at any time during its operation. This is accomplished by pulsing $\overline{\text{Reset}}$ low for the duration of a minimum of three complete $\phi2$ cycles. The $\overline{\text{Reset}}$ pulse can be completely asynchronous with the MPU system clock and will be recognized during $\phi2$ if setup time t_{PCS} is met.

FIGURE 8 – RESET TIMING

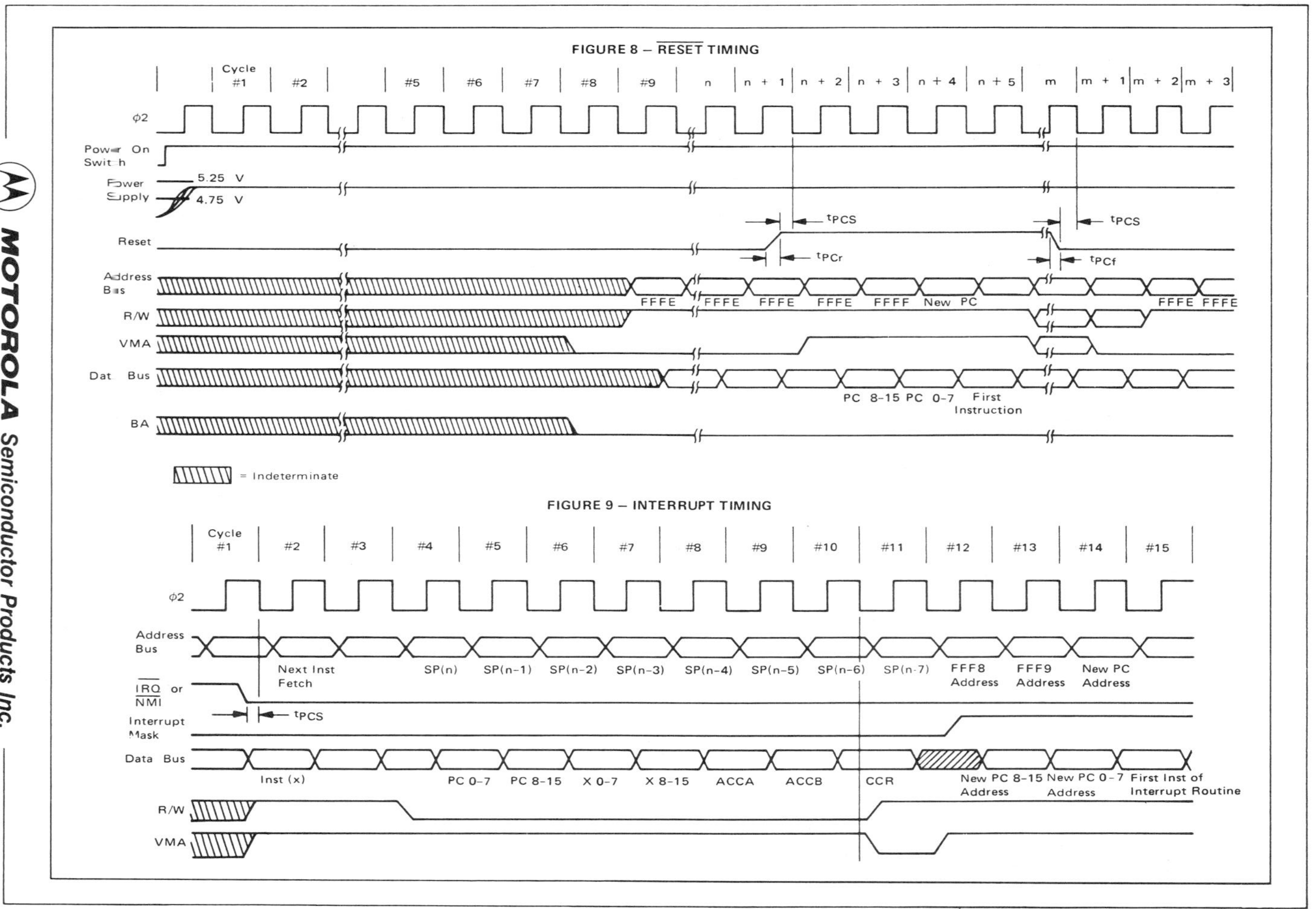

FIGURE 9 – INTERRUPT TIMING

Interrupt Request ($\overline{IRQ}$) – This level sensitive input requests that an interrupt sequence be generated within the machine. The processor will wait until it completes the current instruction that is being executed before it recognizes the request. At that time, if the interrupt mask bit in the Condition Code Register is not set, the machine will begin an interrupt sequence. The Index Register, Program Counter, Accumulators, and Condition Code Register are stored away on the stack. Next the MPU will respond to the interrupt request by setting the interrupt mask bit high so that no further interrupts may occur. At the end of the cycle, a 16-bit address will be loaded that points to a vectoring address which is located in memory locations FFF8 and FFF9. An address loaded at these locations causes the MPU to branch to an interrupt routine in memory. Interrupt timing is shown in Figure 9.

The $\overline{Halt}$ line must be in the high state for interrupts to be serviced. Interrupts will be latched internally while $\overline{Halt}$ is low.

The $\overline{IRQ}$ has a high impedance pullup device internal to the chip; however a 3 kΩ external resistor to V_{CC} should be used for wire-OR and optimum control of interrupts.

Non-Maskable Interrupt ($\overline{NMI}$) and Wait for Interrupt (WAI) – The MC6800 is capable of handling two types of interrupts: maskable ($\overline{IRQ}$) as described earlier, and non-maskable ($\overline{NMI}$). $\overline{IRQ}$ is maskable by the interrupt mask in the condition code register while $\overline{NMI}$ is not maskable. The handling of these interrupts by the MPU is the same except that each has its own vector address. The behavior of the MPU when interrupted is shown in Figure 9 which details the MPU response to an interrupt while the MPU is executing the control program. The interrupt shown could be either $\overline{IRQ}$ or $\overline{NMI}$ and can be asynchronous with respect to $\phi 2$. The interrupt is shown going low at time t_{PCS} in cycle #1 which precedes the first cycle of an instruction (OP code fetch). This instruction is not executed but instead the Program Counter (PC), Index Register (IX), Accumulators (ACCX), and the Condition Code Register (CCR) are pushed onto the stack.

The Interrupt Mask bit is set to prevent further interrupts. The address of the interrupt service routine is then fetched from FFFC, FFFD for an $\overline{NMI}$ interrupt and from FFF8, FFF9 for an $\overline{IRQ}$ interrupt. Upon completion of the interrupt service routine, the execution of RTI will pull the PC, IX, ACCX, and CCR off of the stack; the Interrupt Mask bit is restored to its condition prior to Interrupts.

Figure 11 is a similar interrupt sequence, except in this case, a WAIT instruction has been executed in preparation for the interrupt. This technique speeds up the MPU's response to the interrupt because the stacking of the PC, IX, ACCX, and the CCR is already done. While the MPU is waiting for the interrupt, Bus Available will go high indicating the following states of the control lines: VMA is low, and the Address Bus, R/$\overline{W}$ and Data Bus are all in the high impedance state. After the interrupt occurs, it is serviced as previously described.

TABLE 1 – MEMORY MAP FOR INTERRUPT VECTORS

Vector		Description
MS	LS	
FFFE	FFFF	Restart
FFFC	FFFD	Non-maskable Interrupt
FFFA	FFFB	Software Interrupt
FFF8	FFF9	Interrupt Request

Refer to Figure 11 for program flow for Interrupts.

Three State Control (TSC) – When the Three-State Control (TSC) line is a logic "1", the Address Bus and the R/$\overline{W}$ line are placed in a high impedance state. VMA and BA are forced low when TSC = "1" to prevent false reads or writes on any device enabled by VMA. It Is necessary to delay program execution while TSC is held high. This is done by insuring that no transitions of $\phi 1$ (or $\phi 2$) occur during this period. (Logic levels of the clocks are irrelevant so long as they do not change.) Since the MPU is a dynamic device, the $\phi 1$ clock can be stopped for a maximum time $PW_{\phi H}$ without destroying data within the MPU. TSC then can be used in a short Direct Memory Access (DMA) application.

Figure 12 shows the effect of TSC on the MPU. TSC must have its transitions at t_{TSE} (three-state enable) while holding $\phi 1$ high and $\phi 2$ low as shown. The Address Bus and R/$\overline{W}$ line will reach the high impedance state at t_{TSD} (three-state delay), with VMA being forced low. In this example, the Data Bus is also in the high impedance state while $\phi 2$ is being held low since DBE = $\phi 2$. At this point in time, a DMA transfer could occur on cycles #3 and #4. When TSC is returned low, the MPU Address and R/$\overline{W}$ lines return to the bus. Because it is too late in cycle #5 to access memory, this cycle is dead and used for synchronization. Program execution resumes in cycle #6.

Valid Memory Address (VMA) – This output indicates to peripheral devices that there is a valid address on the address bus. In normal operation, this signal should be utilized for enabling peripheral interfaces such as the PIA and ACIA. This signal is not three-state. One standard TTL load and 90 pF may be directly driven by this active high signal.

$\overline{Halt}$ – When this input is in the low state, all activity in the machine will be halted. This input is level sensitive.

The $\overline{Halt}$ line provides an input to the MPU to allow control of program execution by an outside source. If $\overline{Halt}$ is high, the MPU will execute the instructions; if it is low, the MPU will go to a halted or idle mode. A response signal, Bus Available (BA) provides an indication of the current MPU status. When BA is low, the MPU is in the process of executing the control program; if BA is high, the MPU has halted and all internal activity has stopped.

When BA is high, the Address Bus, Data Bus, and R/$\overline{W}$ line will be in a high impedance state, effectively removing the MPU from the system bus. VMA is forced low so that the floating system bus will not activate any device on the bus that is enabled by VMA.

FIGURE 10 – MPU FLOW CHART

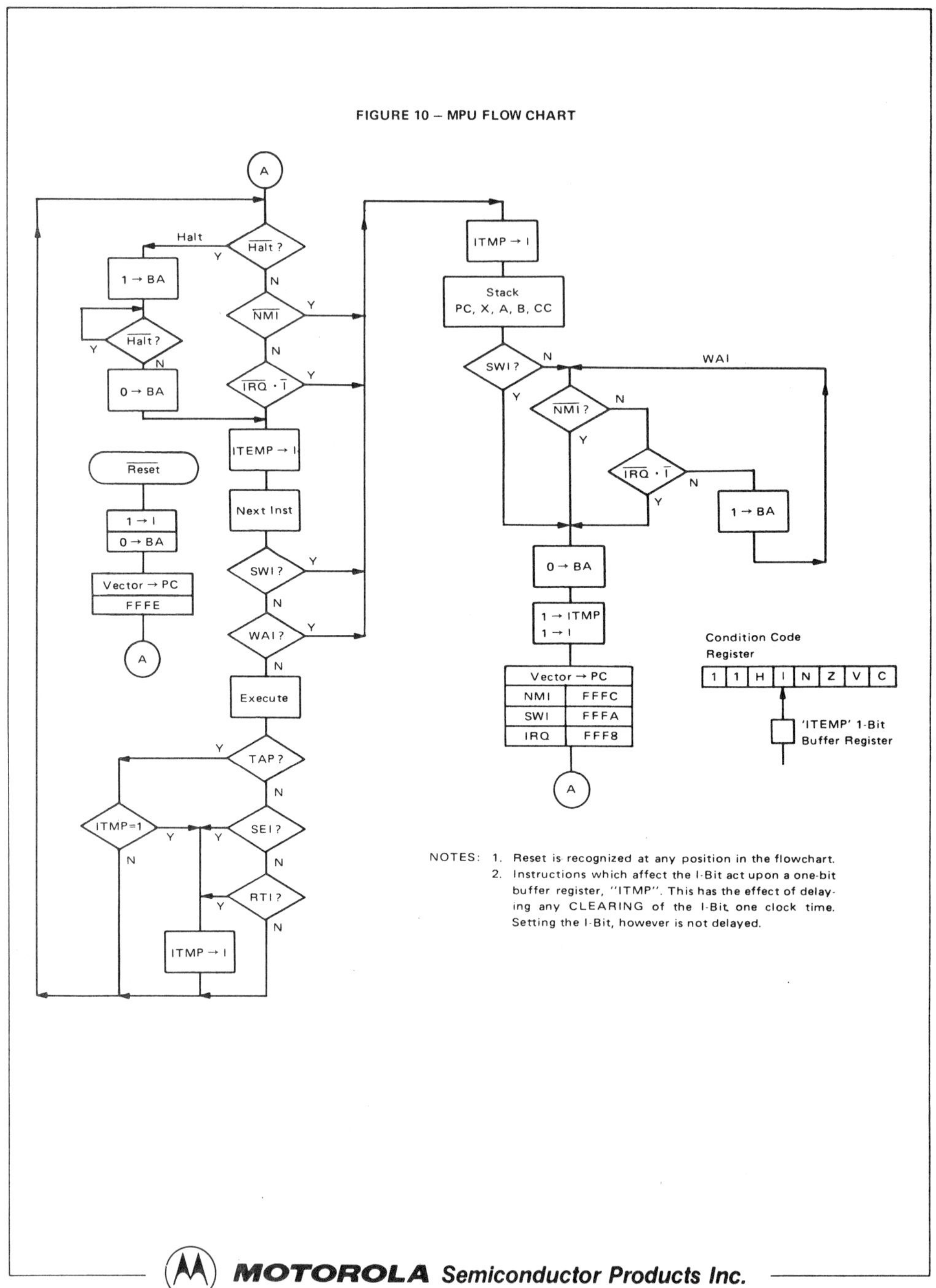

NOTES: 1. Reset is recognized at any position in the flowchart.
2. Instructions which affect the I-Bit act upon a one-bit buffer register, "ITMP". This has the effect of delaying any CLEARING of the I-Bit one clock time. Setting the I-Bit, however is not delayed.

While the MPU is halted, all program activity is stopped, and if either an $\overline{NMI}$ or $\overline{IRQ}$ interrupt occurs, it will be latched into the MPU and acted on as soon as the MPU is taken out of the halted mode. If a $\overline{Reset}$ command occurs while the MPU is halted, the following states occur: VMA = low, BA = low, Data Bus = high impedance, R/$\overline{W}$ = high (read state), and the Address Bus will contain address FFFE as long as $\overline{Reset}$ is low. As soon as the Halt line goes high, the MPU will go to locations FFFE and FFFF for the address of the reset routine.

Figure13 shows the timing relationships involved when halting the MPU. The instruction illustrated is a one byte, 2 cycle instruction such as CLRA. When $\overline{Halt}$ goes low, the MPU will halt after completing execution of the current instruction: The transition of $\overline{Halt}$ must occur t_{PCS} before the trailing edge of $\phi 1$ of the last cycle of an instruction (point A of Figure 13). $\overline{Halt}$ must not go low any time later than the minimum t_{PCS} specified.

The fetch of the OP code by the MPU is the first cycle of the instruction. If $\overline{Halt}$ had not been low at Point A but went low during $\phi 2$ of that cycle, the MPU would have halted after completion of the following instruction. BA will go high by time t_{BA} (bus available delay time) after the last instruction cycle. At this point in time, VMA is low and R/$\overline{W}$, Address Bus, and the Data Bus are in the high impedance state.

To debug programs it is advantageous to step through programs instruction by instruction. To do this, $\overline{Halt}$ must be brought high for one MPU cycle and then returned low as shown at point B of Figure 13. Again, the transitions of $\overline{Halt}$ must occur t_{PCS} before the trailing edge of $\phi 1$. BA will go low at t_{BA} after the leading edge of the next $\phi 1$, indicating that the Address Bus, Data Bus, VMA and R/$\overline{W}$ lines are back on the bus. A single byte, 2 cycle instruction such as LSR is used for this example also. During the first cycle, the instruction Y is fetched from address M + 1. BA returns high at t_{BA} on the last cycle of the instruction indicating the MPU is off the bus. If instruction Y had been three cycles, the width of the BA low time would have been increased by one cycle.

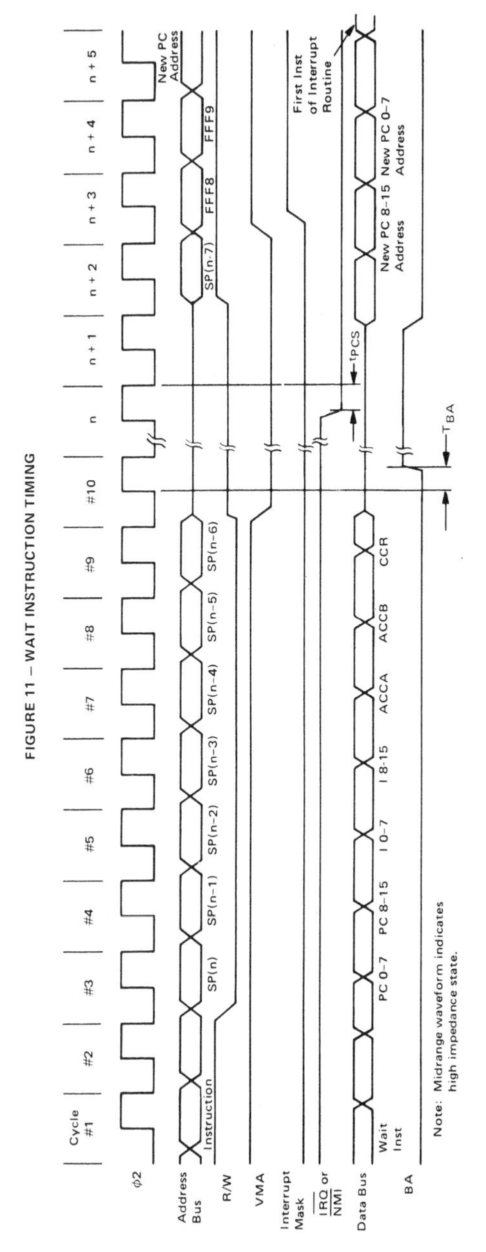

FIGURE 11 – WAIT INSTRUCTION TIMING

FIGURE 12 – THREE STATE CONTROL TIMING

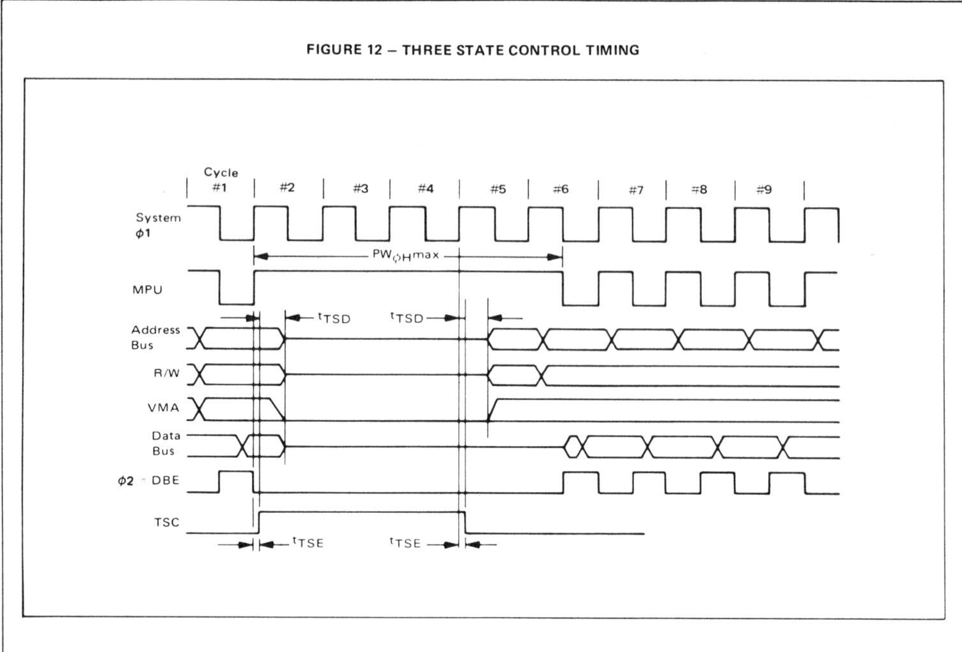

FIGURE 13 – $\overline{\text{HALT}}$ AND SINGLE INSTRUCTION EXECUTION FOR SYSTEM DEBUG

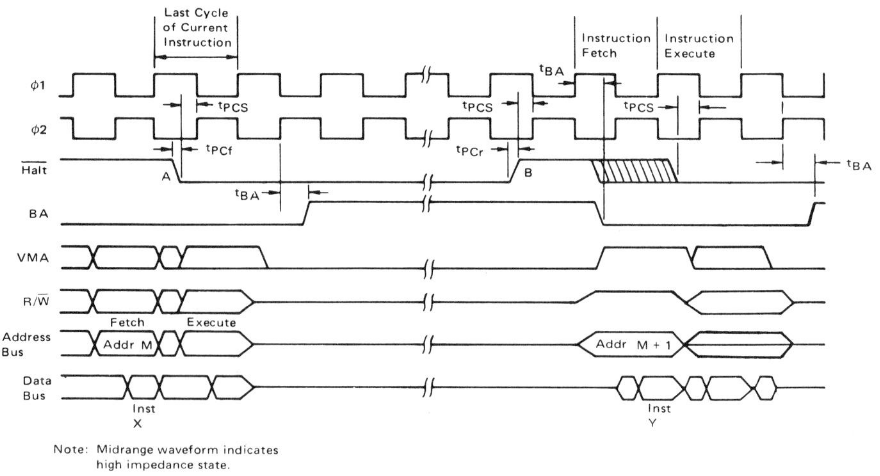

Note: Midrange waveform indicates high impedance state.

Appendix A3
Data on the 1488, 1489 and MC14411

These three devices have been included as an appendix because of their great importance in the design of interface circuits and because even though many other works give considerable details about ROMs, RAMs, CPUs, UARTs, etc., details of these important devices are often omitted.

Am1488

Quad RS-232C Line Driver

FUNCTIONAL DESCRIPTION

The Am1488 is a quad line driver that conforms to EIA specification RS-232C. Each driver accepts one or two TTL/DTL inputs and produces a high-level logic signal on its output. The HIGH and LOW logic levels on the output are defined by the positive and negative power supplies to the drivers. For power supplies of plus and minus nine volts, the output levels are guaranteed to meet the ±6-volt specification with a 3kΩ load. There is an internal 300Ω resistor in series with the output to provide current limiting in both the HIGH and LOW logic levels. The Am1488 driver is intended for use with the Am1489 or Am1489A quad line receivers.

LOGIC SYMBOL

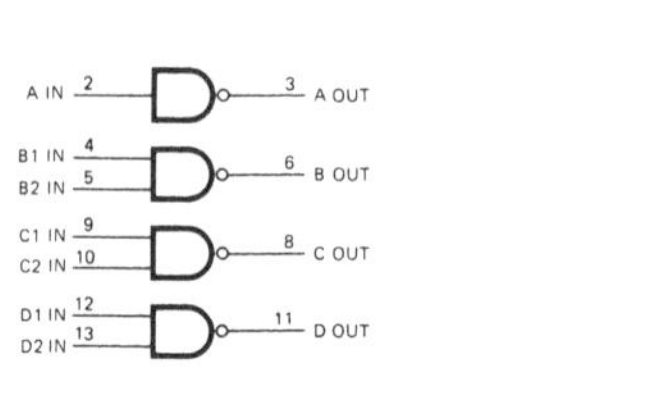

V− = Pin 1
V+ = Pin 14
GND = Pin 7

CIRCUIT DIAGRAM
(one driver shown)

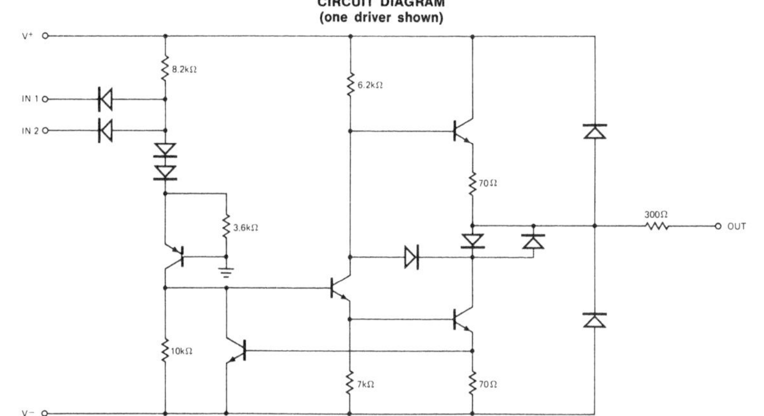

CONNECTION DIAGRAM
Top View

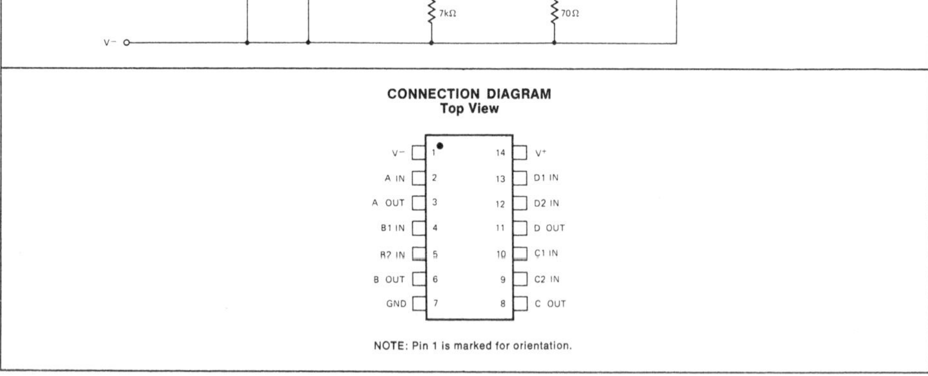

NOTE: Pin 1 is marked for orientation.

ELECTRICAL CHARACTERISTICS OVER OPERATING TEMPERATURE RANGE (Unless Otherwise Noted)

T_A = 0°C to +75°C V^+ = +9.0 V V^- = −9.0 V

Parameters	Description	Test Conditions		Min	Typ	Max	Units
V_{OH}	Output HIGH Voltage	R_L = 3 kΩ V_{IN} = 0.8 V		+6.0	+7.0		Volts
V_{OL}	Output LOW Voltage	R_L = 3 kΩ V_{IN} = 1.9 V			−7.0	−6.0	Volts
V_{IH}	Input HIGH Level	Guaranteed input logical HIGH voltage		1.9			Volts
V_{IL}	Input LOW Level	Guaranteed input logical LOW voltage				0.8	Volts
I_{IL}	Input LOW Current	V_{IN} = 0 V			−1.0	−1.3	mA
I_{IH}	Input HIGH Current	V_{IN} = 5.0 V				10	μA
I_{SC}	Output Short Circuit Current	V_{OUT} = 0.0 V	V_{in} = 0.8 V		−8.0	−10.0	mA
			V_{in} = 1.9 V		+8.0	+10.0	
I_{CC}	Positive Power Supply Current	V_{IN} = 1.9 V	V^+ = 9.0 V		15	20	mA
			V^+ = 12.0 V		19	25	
I_{EE}	Negative Power Supply Current	V_{IN} = 1.9 V	V^- = −9.0 V		−13	−17	
			V^- = −12.0 V		−18	−23	
R_O	Output Resistance	$V^+ = V^-$ = 0.0 V, V_{OUT} = ±2.0 V		300			Ω

Switching Characteristics (T_A = 25°C, V^+ = +9.0V, V^- = −9.0V)

Parameters	Definition	Test Conditions	Min	Typ	Max	Units
t_{pd+}	Delay from input LOW to output HIGH	Z_L = 3.0 kΩ and 15 pF		150	200	ns
t_{pd-}	Delay from input HIGH to output LOW			65	120	ns
t_r	Output rise time			55	100	ns
t_f	Output fall time			45	75	ns

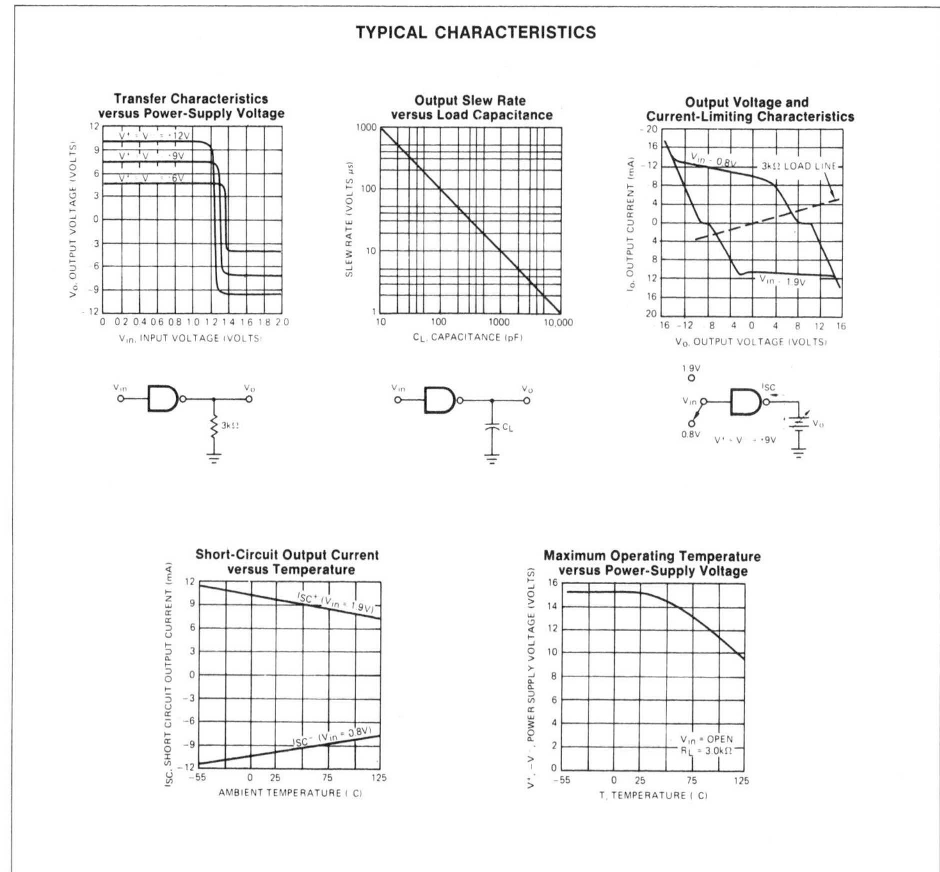
TYPICAL CHARACTERISTICS
Transfer Characteristics versus Power-Supply Voltage
Vo, OUTPUT VOLTAGE (VOLTS)
Vin, INPUT VOLTAGE (VOLTS)
Output Slew Rate versus Load Capacitance
SLEW RATE (VOLTS/μs)
CL, CAPACITANCE (pF)
Output Voltage and Current-Limiting Characteristics
3kΩ LOAD LINE
Io, OUTPUT CURRENT (mA)
Vo, OUTPUT VOLTAGE (VOLTS)
Short-Circuit Output Current versus Temperature
ISC, SHORT CIRCUIT OUTPUT CURRENT (mA)
AMBIENT TEMPERATURE (°C)
Maximum Operating Temperature versus Power-Supply Voltage
Vin = OPEN
RL = 3.0kΩ
T, TEMPERATURE (°C)

Am1489 • Am1489A

Quad RS-232C Line Receivers

FUNCTIONAL DESCRIPTION:

The Am1489 and Am1489A are quad line receivers whose electrical characteristics conform to EIA specification RS-232C. Each receiver has a single data input that can accept signal swings of up to ±30 V. The output of each receiver is TTL/DTL compatible, and includes a 2kΩ resistor pull-up to V_{CC}. An internal feedback resistor causes the input to exhibit hysterisis so that AC noise immunity is maintained at a high level even near the switching thresholds. For both devices, when a driver is in a LOW state on the output, the input may drop as LOW as 1.25 volts without affecting the output. Both devices are guaranteed to switch to the HIGH state when the input voltage is below 0.75 V. Once the output has switched to the HIGH state, the input may rise to 1.0 V for the Am1489 or 1.75 V for the Am1489A without causing a change in the output. The Am1489 is guaranteed to switch to a LOW output when its input reaches 1.5 V and, the Am1489A is guaranteed to switch to a LOW output when its input reaches 2.25 V. Because of this hysterisis in switching thresholds, the devices can receive signals with superimposed noise or with slow rise and fall times without generating oscillations on the output. The threshold levels may be offset by a constant voltage by applying a DC bias to the response control input. A capacitor added to the response control input will reduce the frequency response of the receiver for applications in the presence of high frequency noise spikes. The companion line driver is the Am1488.

LOGIC SYMBOL

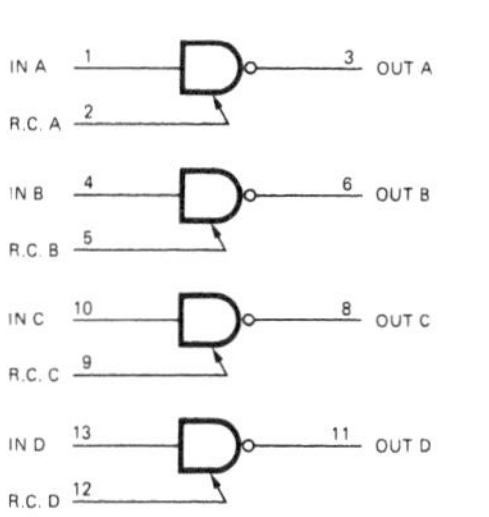

CIRCUIT DIAGRAM (one receiver)

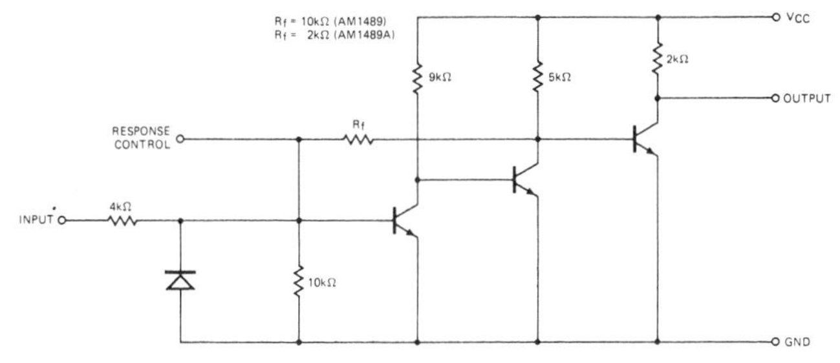

CONNECTION DIAGRAM Top View

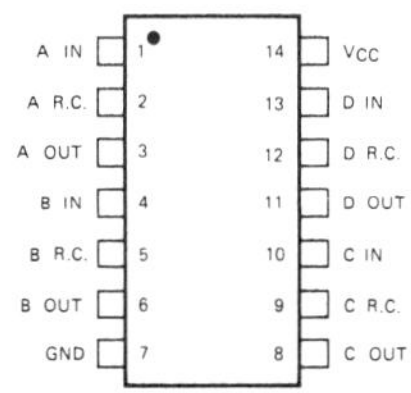

NOTE: PIN 1 is marked for orientation.

ELECTRICAL CHARACTERISTICS OVER OPERATING TEMPERATURE RANGE (Unless Otherwise Noted)

$T_A = 0°C$ to $+75°C$ $V_{CC} = 5.0\ V \pm 1\%$ Response control pin open

Parameters	Description	Test Conditions		Min	Typ (Note 1)	Max	Units
V_{OH}	Output HIGH Voltage	$I_{OH} = -0.5$ mA $V_{IN} = +0.75$ V or open		2.6	4.0		Volts
V_{OL}	Output LOW Voltage	$I_{OL} = 10$ mA $V_{IN} = 1.5$ V			0.2	0.45	Volts
V_{IH}	Input HIGH Level Threshold	$T_A = 25°C$ $V_{OL} = 0.45$ V	Am1489	1.0	1.25	1.5	Volts
			Am1489A	1.75	1.95	2.25	
V_{IL}	Input LOW Level Threshold	$T_A = 25°C$, $V_{OH} = +2.5$ V		0.75		1.25	Volts
I_{IL}	Input LOW Current	$V_{IN} = -3.0$ V		−0.43			mA
		$V_{IN} = -25$ V		−3.6		−8.3	
I_{IH}	Input HIGH Current	$V_{IN} = +3.0$ V		0.43			mA
		$V_{IN} = +25$ V		3.6		8.3	
I_{SC}	Output Short Circuit Current	$V_{IN} = 0.0$ V $V_{OUT} = 0.0$ V			3.0		mA
I_{CC}	Power Supply Current	$V_{CC} =$ MAX.			20	26	mA

Note: 1) Typical Limits are at $V_{CC} = 5.0$ V, 25°C ambient and maximum loading.

Switching Characteristics ($T_A = 25°C$, response control pin open, $C_L = 15$ pF)

Parameters	Definition	Test Conditions	Min	Typ	Max	Units
t_{pd+}	Delay from Input LOW to Output HIGH	$R_L = 3.9\ k\Omega$		25	85	ns
t_{pd-}	Delay from Input HIGH to output LOW	$R_L = 390\ \Omega$		25	50	ns
t_r	Output Rise Time (10% to 90%)	$R_L = 3.9\ k\Omega$		120	175	ns
t_f	Output Fall Time (90% to 10%)	$R_L = 390\ \Omega$		10	20	ns

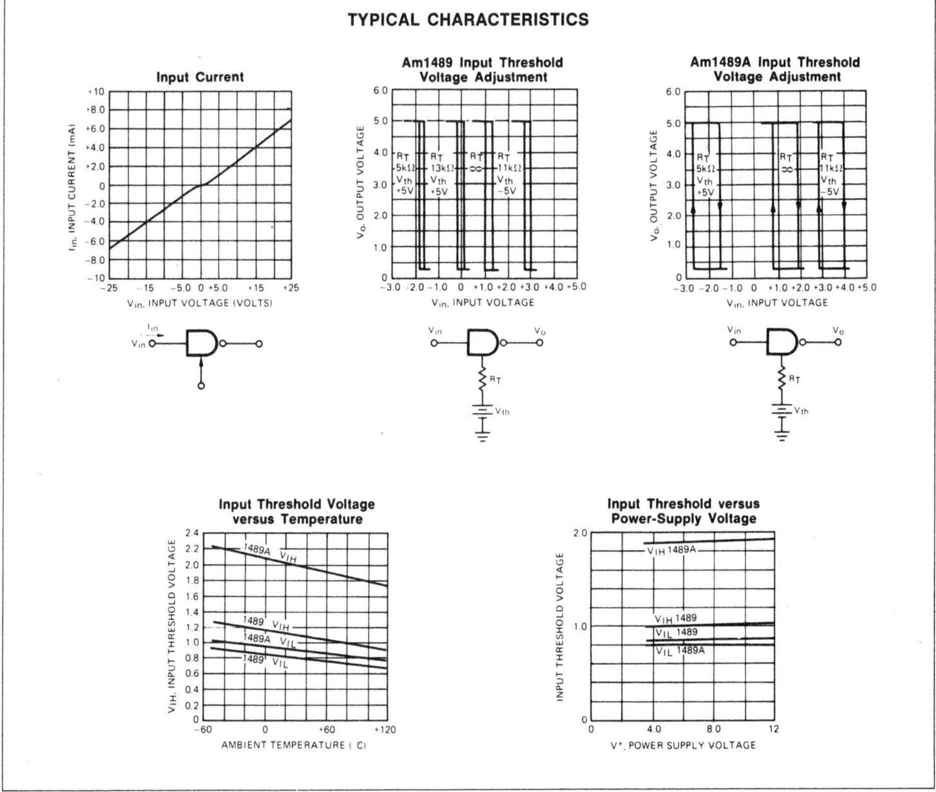
TYPICAL CHARACTERISTICS
Input Current
Am1489 Input Threshold Voltage Adjustment
Am1489A Input Threshold Voltage Adjustment
I_in, INPUT CURRENT (mA)
V_in, INPUT VOLTAGE (VOLTS)
V_O, OUTPUT VOLTAGE
V_in, INPUT VOLTAGE
Input Threshold Voltage versus Temperature
Input Threshold versus Power-Supply Voltage
V_IH, INPUT THRESHOLD VOLTAGE
AMBIENT TEMPERATURE (°C)
INPUT THRESHOLD VOLTAGE
V+, POWER SUPPLY VOLTAGE

MC14411L
MC14411P

BIT RATE GENERATOR

The MC14411 bit rate generator is constructed with complementary MOS enhancement mode devices. It utilizes a frequency divider network to provide a wide range of output frequencies.

A crystal controlled oscillator is the clock source for the network. A two-bit address is provided to select one of four multiple output clock rates.

- Single 5.0 Vdc (± 5%) Power Supply
- Internal Oscillator Crystal Controlled for Stability (1.8432 MHz)
- Sixteen Different Output Clock Rates
- 50% Output Duty Cycle
- Programmable Time Bases for One of Four Multiple Output Rates
- Buffered Outputs Compatible with Low Power TTL
- Noise Immunity = 45% of V_{DD} Typical
- Diode Protection on All Inputs

MAXIMUM RATINGS (Voltages referenced to V_{SS}, Pin 12.)

Rating	Symbol	Value	Unit
DC Supply Voltage Range	V_{DD}	5.25 to −0.5	Vdc
Input Voltage, All Inputs	V_{in}	V_{DD} + 0.5 to V_{SS} −0.5	Vdc
DC Current Drain per Pin	I	10	mAdc
Operating Temperature Range	T_A	−40 to +85	°C
Storage Temperature Range	T_{stg}	−65 to +150	°C

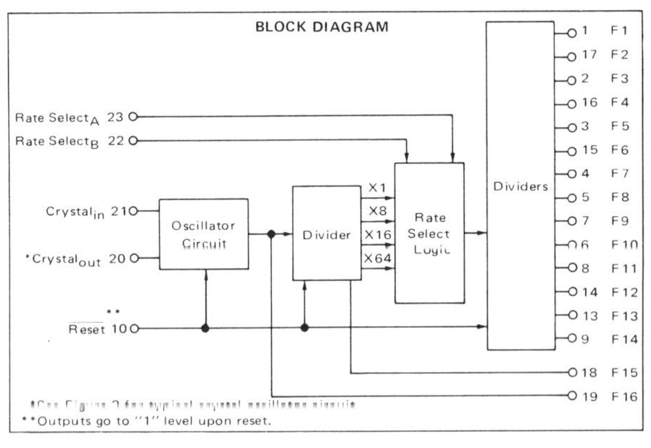

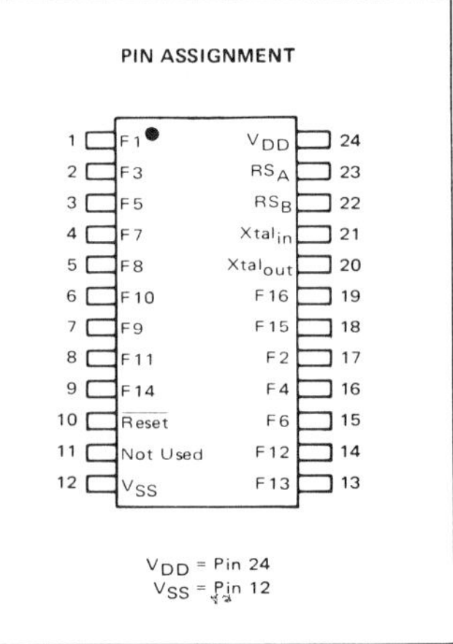

ELECTRICAL CHARACTERISTICS

Characteristic	Symbol	V_{DD} Vdc	-40°C Min	-40°C Max	25°C Min	25°C Typ	25°C Max	+85°C Min	+85°C Max	Unit
Supply Voltage	V_{DD}	—	4.75	5.25	4.75	5.0	5.25	4.75	5.25	Vdc
Output Voltage "0" Level	V_{out}	5.0	—	0.01	—	0	0.01	—	0.05	Vdc
"1" Level		5.0	4.99	—	4.99	5.0	—	4.95	—	Vdc
Noise Immunity ($\Delta V_{out} \leq 1.5$ Vdc)	V_{NL}	5.0	1.5	—	1.5	2.25	—	1.4	—	Vdc
($\Delta V_{out} \leq 1.5$ Vdc)	V_{NH}	5.0	1.4	—	1.5	2.25	—	1.5	—	Vdc
Output Drive Current (V_{OH} = 2.5 Vdc) Source	I_{OH}	5.0	-0.23	—	-0.20	-1.7	—	-0.16	—	mAdc
(V_{OL} = 0.4 Vdc) Sink	I_{OL}	5.0	0.23	—	0.20	0.78	—	0.16	—	mAdc
Input Current	I_{in}	—	—	—	—	10	—	—	—	pAdc
Input Capacitance (V_{in} = 0)	C_{in}	—	—	—	—	5.0	—	—	—	pF
Quiescent Dissipation	P_Q	5.0	—	2.5	—	0.015	2.5	—	15	mW
Power Dissipation**† (Dynamic plus Quiescent) (C_L = 15 pF)	P_D	5.0	(P_D = (7.5 mW/MHz) f + P_Q)							mW
Output Rise Time** t_r = (3.0 ns/pF) C_L + 25 ns	t_r	5.0	—	—	—	70	200	—	—	ns
Output Fall Time** t_f = (1.5 ns/pF) C_L + 47 ns	t_f	5.0	—	—	—	70	200	—	—	ns
Maximum Input Clock Frequency	f_{max}	5.0	—	—	—	1.8432	—	1.85	—	MHz

† For dissipation at different external load capacitance (C_L) refer to corresponding formula:

$$P_T(C_L) = P_D + 2.6 \times 10^{-3} (C_L - 15\text{ pF})\, V_{DD}{}^2 f$$

where: P_T, P_D in mW, C_L in pF, V_{DD} in Vdc, and f in MHz.

**The formula given is for the typical characteristics only.

TABLE 1 – OUTPUT CLOCK RATES

Rate Select B	Rate Select A	Rate
0	0	X1
0	1	X8
1	0	X16
1	1	X64

Output Number	Output Rates (Hz) X64	X16	X8	X1
F1	614.4 k	153.6 k	76.8 k	9600
F2	460.8 k	115.2 k	57.6 k	7200
F3	307.2 k	76.8 k	38.4 k	4800
F4	230.4 k	57.6 k	28.8 k	3600
F5	153.6 k	38.4 k	19.2 k	2400
F6	115.2 k	28.8 k	14.4 k	1800
F7	76.8 k	19.2 k	9600	1200
F8	38.4 k	9600	4800	600
F9	19.2 k	4800	2400	300
F10	12.8 k	3200	1600	200
F11	9600	2400	1200	150
F12	8613.2	2153.3	1076.6	134.5
F13	7035.5	1758.8	879.4	109.9
F14	4800	1200	600	75
F15	921.6 k	921.6 k	921.6 k	921.6 k
F16*	1.843M	1.843M	1.843M	1.843M

*F16 is buffered oscillator output.

FIGURE 1 – DYNAMIC SIGNAL WAVEFORMS

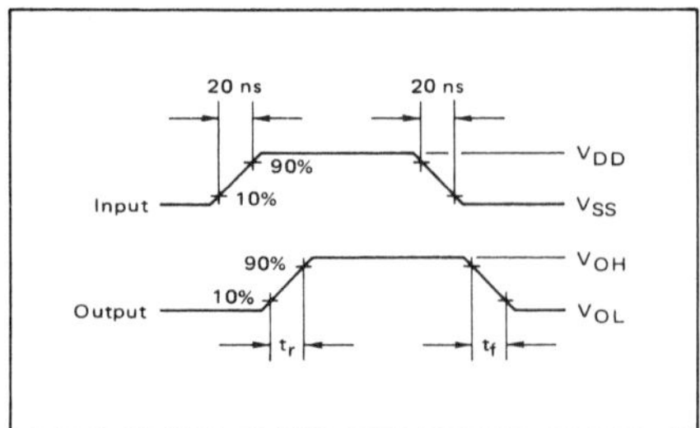

FIGURE 2 – TYPICAL CRYSTAL OSCILLATOR CIRCUIT

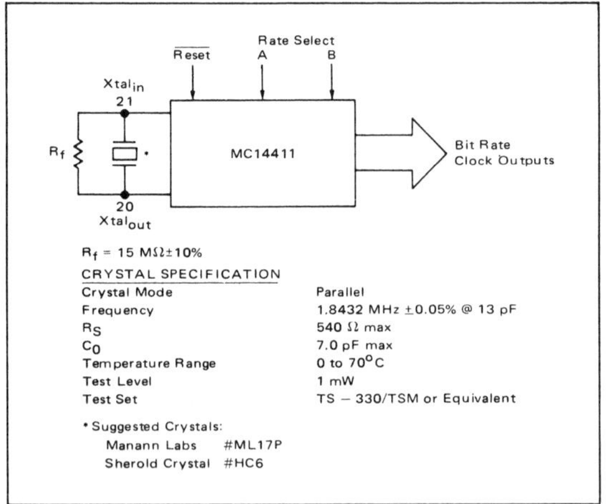

R_f = 15 MΩ±10%

CRYSTAL SPECIFICATION

Crystal Mode	Parallel
Frequency	1.8432 MHz ±0.05% @ 13 pF
R_S	540 Ω max
C_O	7.0 pF max
Temperature Range	0 to 70°C
Test Level	1 mW
Test Set	TS – 330/TSM or Equivalent

* Suggested Crystals:
  - Manann Labs #ML17P
  - Sherold Crystal #HC6

Appendix A4
A Program to Drive a Memory-mapped Display

This program has been included as an example of a program to control a memory-mapped display. The program resides from F800 to F9A9 in the lower half of the 2516 EPROM holding TS1BUG. In addition to the display driver, new commands to TS1BUG's repertoire have been included. The first "Q", causes ASCII characters with codes $20_{16} - 7F_{16}$ to be continually printed on the system console, providing a simple test of the operation of the system. The second function "X" provides a link to an assembler held in a 2516 EPROM on the special interface module at D000.

The actual memory-mapped display program extends from F818 (also its entry point) to F975. The basic design of the program is heavily influenced by an article by A. I. Anderson in *Byte* (see Bibliography for Chapter 6). On entering the subroutine INPUT, bit 7 of OMODE is tested. If clear all the flags used by this routine are set up and if set the initialization procedure is bypassed. Once initialization has taken place, $OMODE_7$ is set. Two flags used by the display routines are of special interest: AUTOC when clear generates an automatic carriage return following a linefeed, and SPECL when set causes the ASCII control characters $00_{16} - 1F_{16}$ to be displayed as the Greek letters and special symbols stored in the MCM66174 character generator.

The initial part of the display program deals with the normal set of control characters and implements them by modifying the relevant line and row column counters, etc. It is interesting to note that this section of the program is the software equivalent of the hardware in Fig. 6.37. The display of a character is performed by INPT1 (F8BC) which also deals with the cursor control. A cursor is generated by writing a "_" ($5F_{16}$) in the location of the next character to be displayed.

Following INPT1 are a number of subroutines which perform various tasks in the display process, including scrolling the display.

```
1:ASEMB,EBUG.15

                      NAM    EXMON
                *     EXTENSION MONITOR FOR TS1BUG
                *     VERSION OF 30.03.80
                *     NOTE: THIS VERSION WAS WRITTEN TO ALLOW THE USE
                *     OF THE MEMORY-MAPPED DISPLAY AND HAS NOT BEEN
                *     OPTIMIZED. THIS PROGRAM MAY BE EXTENDED TO OTHER
                *     FORMATS BUT NOTE THAT THE MULTIPLICATION ROUTINE
                *     IN "DISP" MUST BE CHANGED UNLESS 64 CHARS PER
                *     LINE ARE USED.
A0B0                  ORG    $A0B0
A0B0            COL   RMB    1          POINTER TO COLUMN
A0B1            ROW   RMB    1          POINTER TO ROW
A0B2            OLD   RMB    1          HOLDS THE CHAR OBSCURED BY CURSOR
A0B3            SPECL RMB    1          DISPLAY CONTROL FLAG
A0B4            AUTOC RMB    1          AUTO CARRIAGE RETURN FLAG
A0B5            BASE  RMB    2          START OF DISPLAY IN MEMORY
A0B7            TOP   RMB    2          END OF DISPLAY
A0B9            POINT RMB    2          POINTER TO CURRENT ACTIVE CHAR POS
A0BB            CURSR RMB    2          CURSOR ADDRESS
A0BD            XSAVE RMB    2          TEMP STORE FOR X REG
A094            IMODE EQU    $A094
A095            OMODE EQU    $A095
E400            MAP   EQU    $E400      LOCATION OF MEMORY-MAPPED DISP
0040            MAXCL EQU    64         64 CHARACTERS PER ROW
0010            MAXRW EQU    16         16 ROWS PER SCREEN
003F            LASCL EQU    MAXCL-1    NUMBER OF LEFTMOST COLUMN
000F            LASRW EQU    MAXRW-1    NUMBER OF BOTTOM ROW
0400            CHARS EQU    MAXCL*MAXRW TOTAL CHARACTERS IN DISPLAY
E7C0            LIMIT EQU    MAP+CHARS-MAXCL LIMIT OF DISPLAY FOR SCROLLING
FC1F            RESET EQU    $FC1F      TS1BUG SOFT ENTRY POINT
FF3F            OUTCH EQU    $FF3F      TS1BUG OUTPUT ROUTINE
FEB0            INCH  EQU    $FEB0      TS1BUG INPUT ROUTINE
FC85            LINES EQU    $FC85      TS1BUG NEWLINE ROUTINE
                *
                *
F800                  ORG    $F800      EXTENSION MONITOR ENTRY POINT
                *     EXTENDED SEARCH FOR CONTROL CHARACTER
F800 CE F9 A3         LDX    #XTAB      EXTENSION TABLE ADDRESS
F803 A1 00      REST1 CMP A  0,X        MATCH?
F805 27 0A            BEQ    REST2      IF MATCH THEN FIND ADDRESS OF COMMAND
F807 08               INX               STEP PAST COMMAND
F808 08               INX
F809 08               INX
F80A 6D 00            TST    0,X        END OF TABLE?
F80C 26 F5            BNE    REST1      IF NOT END THEN TRY AGAIN
F80E 7E FC 1F         JMP    RESET      IF END THEN RETURN TO MONITOR
F811 EE 01      REST2 LDX    1,X        GET COMMAND ADDRESS
F813 AD 00            JSR    0,X        JUMP TO IT
F815 7E FC 1F         JMP    RESET      RETURN TO TS1BUG
                *
F818            INPUT EQU    *          ENTRY POINT TO MM DISPLAY
F818 36               PSH A             SAVE A REG
F819 37               PSH B             SAVE B REG
```

```
F81A FF A0 BD         STX   XSAVE       SAVE X REG (NOT REENTRANT)
                 *    TEST FOR FIRST TIME ENTRY
F81D F6 A0 95         LDA B OMODE       GET OUTPUT STATUS WORD
F820 2B 22            BMI   INPTO       IF MS BIT SET THEN IGNORE SETUP
F822 CA 80            ORA B #%10000000 SET MSB
F824 F7 A0 95         STA B OMODE       SAVE IT
F827 7F A0 B3         CLR   SPECL       DEFAULT TO ASCII CHARS
F82A 7F A0 B4         CLR   AUTOC       DEFAULT TO AUTO C/R MODE
F82D CE E4 00         LDX   #MAP        GET STARTING ADDRESS (TOP LH)
F830 FF A0 BB         STX   CURSR       SET UP CURSOR
F833 FF A0 B5         STX   BASE        SET UP BASE ADDRESS
F836 CE E7 C0         LDX   #LIMIT      GET END ADDRESS (FOR SCROLLING)
F839 FF A0 B7         STX   TOP         SET UP END ADDRESS
F83C BD F9 4D         JSR   CLRS        CLEAR SCREEN
F83F 86 20            LDA A #$20        GENERATE A SPACE
F841 B7 A0 B2         STA A OLD         PUT IT IN OLD (CHAR AT CURSOR)
                 *    NORMAL ENTRY POINT TO DISPLAY ROUTINES
F844 FE A0 BB    INPTO LDX  CURSR       GET CURSOR
F847 F6 A0 B2         LDA B OLD         GET CHAR BLOTTED OUT BY CURSOR
F84A E7 00            STA B 0,X         RESTORE THIS CHAR
F84C 7D A0 B3         TST   SPECL       SPECIAL CHAR MODE?
F84F 26 73            BNE   INPT2       IF SPECIAL MODE THEN IGNORE CONTROL
F851 81 0D            CMP A #$0D        TEST FOR CARRIAGE RETURN
F853 26 05            BNE   LF          IF NOT C/R THEN TRY LINEFEED
F855 7F A0 B0         CLR   COL         IF C/R THEN RESET COL COUNT
F858 20 62            BRA   INPT1       EXIT TO DISPLAY
F85A 81 0A       LF   CMP A #$0A        LINEFEED?
F85C 26 19            BNE   BS          IF NOT L/F THEN TRY BACKSPACE
F85E 7D A0 B4         TST   AUTOC       TEST FOR AUTOMATIC C/R AFTER LINE FEED
F861 26 03            BNE   *+5         IF NOT AUTO C/R THEN SKIP C/R
F863 7F A0 B0         CLR   COL         DO C/R (BY RESETTING COL COUNT)
F866 F6 A0 B1         LDA B ROW         EXAMINE ROW COUNT
F869 C1 0F            CMP B #LASRW      ARE WE ON THE LAST LINE?
F86B 27 05            BEQ   *+7         IF SO SKIP TO SCROLL THE DISP
F86D 7C A0 B1         INC   ROW         IF NOT THEN INC LINE COUNT
F870 20 4A            BRA   INPT1       EXIT TO DISPLAY
F872 BD F9 01         JSR   SCRL        GO AND SCROLL THE DISPLAY
F875 20 45            BRA   INPT1       EXIT TO DISPLAY
F877 81 08       BS   CMP A #$08        BACK SPACE?
F879 26 0A            BNE   HT          IF NOT B/S THEN TRY HORIZONTAL TAB
F87B F6 A0 B0         LDA B COL         GET COLUMN COUNT
F87E 27 03            BEQ   *+5         IF ZERO THEN FORGET BACKSPACE
F880 7A A0 B0         DEC   COL         IF NOT ZERO DEC COLUMN COUNT
F883 20 37            BRA   INPT1       EXIT TO DISPLAY
F885 81 09       HT   CMP A #$09        HORIZONTAL TAB? (MOVE 1 PLACE RIGHT)
F887 26 0C            BNE   VT          IF NOT HT THEN TRY VERTICAL TAB
F889 F6 A0 B0         LDA B COL         GET COLUMN COUNT
F88C C1 3F            CMP B #LASCL      ARE WE AT THE END OF A LINE?
F88E 27 03            BEQ   *+5         IF SO THEN SKIP HT
F890 7C A0 B0         INC   COL         MOVE CURSOR ONE COL RIGHT
F893 20 27            BRA   INPT1       EXIT TO DISPLAY
F895 81 0B       VT   CMP A #$0B        VERTICAL TAB? (MOVE UP A LINE)
F897 26 0A            BNE   FF          IF NOT VT THEN TRY CLEAR SCREEN
F899 F6 A0 B1         LDA B ROW         GET ROW COUNT
F89C 27 03            BEQ   *+5         IF ZERO THEN WE ARE ALREADY AT THE TOP
```

```
F89E 7A A0 B1          DEC    ROW        MOVE UP A LINE
F8A1 20 19             BRA    INPT1      EXIT TO DISPLAY
F8A3 81 0C     FF      CMP A  #$0C       FORMFEED (CLEAR SCREEN)?
F8A5 26 05             BNE    EOR        IF NOT FF THEN TRY ERASE TO END OF LINE
F8A7 BD F9 4D          JSR    CLRS       GO AND CLEAR THE SCREEN
F8AA 20 10             BRA    INPT1      EXIT TO DISPLAY
F8AC 81 1C     EOR     CMP A  #$1C       TEST FOR ERASE TO END OF LINE
F8AE 26 05             BNE    HM         IF NOT EOR THEN TRY HOME
F8B0 BD F9 63          JSR    ETER       IF EOR THEN GO AND DO IT
F8B3 20 07             BRA    INPT1      EXIT TO DISPLAY
F8B5 81 1A     HM      CMP A  #$1A       TEST FOR HOME (CURSOR TO TOP LH)
F8B7 26 03             BNE    *+5        IF NOT HOME THEN EXIT TO DISPLAY
F8B9 BD F9 5C          JSR    HOME       IF HOME THEN DO IT
               *
F8BC           INPT1   EQU    *          DEAL WITH CURSOR AND CHAR DISPLAY
F8BC 81 20             CMP A  #$20       TEST FOR CONTROL CHARS (<20)
F8BE 24 04             BCC    INPT2      IF NOT CONTROL THEN SKIP TO INPT2
F8C0 8D 5E             BSR    CHAP       CALC CHAR POSITION (IN X REG)
F8C2 20 06             BRA    INPT3      DO NOT DISPLAY A CONTROL CHAR
F8C4 8D 16     INPT2   BSR    DISP       DISPLAY CHAR
F8C6 FE A0 B9          LDX    POINT      GET CHAR POSITION POINTER
F8C9 08                INX               POINT TO NEXT POSITION
F8CA A6 00     INPT3   LDA A  0,X        GET CHAR CURRENTLY AT THIS POINT
F8CC B7 A0 B2          STA A  OLD        SAVE IT
F8CF 86 5F             LDA A  #$5F       LOAD CODE OF CURSOR CHARACTER
F8D1 A7 00             STA A  0,X        DISPLAY THE CURSOR
F8D3 FF A0 BB          STX    CURSR      SAVE THE CURSOR POINTER
F8D6 33                PUL B             RESTORE B REG
F8D7 32                PUL A             RESTORE A REG
F8D8 FE A0 BD          LDX    XSAVE      RESTORE X REG
F8DB 39                RTS               RETURN FROM THE DISPLAY
               *
F8DC           DISP    EQU    *          DISPLAY A CHARACTER
F8DC 37                PSH B             SAVE B REG
F8DD 36                PSH A             SAVE A REG (CHAR TO BE DISPLAYED)
F8DE F6 A0 B0          LDA B  COL        GET COL COUNT
F8E1 C1 3F             CMP B  #LASCL     ARE WE AT THE END OF A LINE?
F8E3 2F 06             BLE    *+8        IF NOT THEN SKIP NEWLINE PROCEDURE
F8E5 7F A0 B0          CLR    COL        IF AT END THEN MOVE BACK TO LH MARGIN
F8E8 7C A0 B1          INC    ROW        MOVE TO NEXT ROW
F8EB B6 A0 B1          LDA A  ROW        GET ROW COUNT
F8EE 80 0F             SUB A  #LASRW     TEST FOR LAST ROW
F8F0 2F 05             BLE    *+7        IF NOT LAST ROW THEN DO NOT SCROLL
F8F2 8D 0D             BSR    SCRL       IF LAST ROW THEN SCROLL THE DISPLAY
F8F4 7A A0 B1          DEC    ROW        NOW MOVE BACK A ROW
F8F7 8D 27             BSR    CHAP       CALCULATE THE CURRENT CHAR POSITON
F8F9 32                PUL A             RESTORE THE CHAR TO BE DISPLAYED
F8FA A7 00             STA A  0,X        DISPLAY IT
F8FC 7C A0 B0          INC    COL        MOVE COLUMN COUNTER ONE PLACE RIGHT
F8FF 33                PUL B             RESTORE B REG
F900 39                RTS
               *
F901           SCRL    EQU    *          SCROLL THE DISPLAY
F901 36                PSH A             SAVE A REG
F902 FE A0 B5          LDX    BASE       GET POINTER TO START OF DISPLAY
F905 A6 40     SCRL1   LDA A  MAXCL,X    GET A CHAR ONE ROW ONWARDS
```

```
F907 A7 00           STA A  0,X         MOVE IT UP ONE ROW
F909 08              INX                INC POINTER
F90A BC A0 B7        CPX    TOP         HAVE WE MOVED UP THE ENTIRE DISPLAY?
F90D 26 F6           BNE    SCRL1       IF NOT THEN CONTINUE
F90F 8D 52           BSR    ETER        NOW CLEAR THE BOTTOM ROW
F911 32              PUL A              RESTORE A REG
F912 39              RTS
               *
F913           EROW  EQU    *           ERASE A ROW
F913 8D 0B           BSR    CHAP        CALC THE POSITION OF THE CURRENT CHAR
F915 C6 40           LDA B  #MAXCL      SET UP A COLUMN COUNTER
F917 86 20           LDA A  #$20        SET UP A SPACE
F919 A7 00     EROW1 STA A  0,X         ERASE ONE CHAR BY STORING A SPACE
F91B 08              INX                MOVE TO NEXT CHAR
F91C 5A              DEC B              DEC COLUMN COUNTER
F91D 26 FA           BNE    EROW1       REPEAT UNTIL ALL COLS ERASED
F91F 39              RTS
               *
F920           CHAP  EQU    *           CALC THE POS OF THE ACTIVE CHAR
F920 B6 A0 B1        LDA A  ROW         GET THE ROW COUNT
F923 7F A0 B9        CLR    POINT       CLEAR THE POINTER MS BYTE
F926 B7 A0 BA        STA A  POINT+1     LS BYTE HOLDS ROW COUNT
F929 C6 06           LDA B  #6          MULTIPLY BY 64 BY DOUBLING 6 TIMES
F92B 78 A0 BA  POSN1 ASL    POINT+1     SHIFT LS BYTE LEFT
F92E 79 A0 B9        ROL    POINT       SHIFT MS BYTE LEFT (WITH CARRY)
F931 5A              DEC B              DEC SHIFT COUNT
F932 26 F7           BNE    POSN1       CONTINUE FOR 6 SHIFTS
F934 F6 A0 B0        LDA B  COL         NOW GET COL COUNT
F937 FB A0 BA        ADD B  POINT+1     ADD IN POINTER LS BYTE
F93A FB A0 B6        ADD B  BASE+1      ADD IN BASE LS BYTE
F93D F7 A0 BA        STA B  POINT+1     SAVE LS BYTE OF POINTER
F940 B6 A0 B9        LDA A  POINT       GET MS BYTE OF POINTER
F943 B9 A0 B5        ADC A  BASE        ADD IN BASE MS BYTE
F946 B7 A0 B9        STA A  POINT       SAVE MS BYTE OF POINTER
F949 FE A0 B9        LDX    POINT       RETURN WITH ADDRESS IN X REG
F94C 39              RTS
               *
F94D           CLRS  EQU    *           CLEAR THE SCREEN
F94D 86 0F           LDA A  #LASRW      GET BOTTOM ROW
F94F B7 A0 B1        STA A  ROW         SAVE IT
F952 7F A0 B0        CLR    COL         CLEAR COL COUNTER
F955 8D BC     CLRS1 BSR    EROW        ERASE A ROW
F957 7A A0 B1        DEC    ROW         DEC ROW COUNTER
F95A 2C F9           BGE    CLRS1       CONTINUE UNTIL ALL ROWS ERASED
F95C 7F A0 B1  HOME  CLR    ROW         CLEAR ROW COUNT TO MOVE TO TOP
F95F 7F A0 B0        CLR    COL         CLEAR COL COUNT TO MOVE TO LEFT
F962 39              RTS
               *
F963           ETER  EQU    *           ERASE TO END OF ROW
F963 B6 A0 B0        LDA A  COL         GET COLUMN COUNT
F966 81 3E           CMP A  #LASCL-1    AT END OR PENULTIMATE COLUMN?
F968 2C 0B           BGE    ETER2       IF SO THEN RETURN
F96A 4C              INC A              INC COL COUNT
F96B C6 20           LDA B  #$20        SPACE CODE
F96D E7 00     ETER1 STA B  0,X         CLEAR A CHARACTER
F96F 08              INX                MOVE POINTER TO NEXT CHAR
```

```
F970 4C                  INC A                 INC COLUMN COUNTER
F971 81 41               CMP A   #MAXCL+1      ARE WE AT THE END OF A ROW?
F973 26 F8               BNE     ETER1         IF NOT THEN REPEAT
F975 39         ETER2    RTS
                *
F976            PRNT     EQU     *             DISPLAY ASCII SET (CONTINUALLY)
F976 BD FC 85            JSR     LINES         NEWLINE
F979 86 20               LDA A   #$20          START WITH A SPACE
F97B BD FF 3F   PRNT1    JSR     OUTCH         OUTPUT A CHARACTER
F97E 4C                  INC A                 MOVE TO NEXT CHAR IN ASCII SET
F97F 81 80               CMP A   #$80          DISPLAY FROM 20 TO 7F
F981 26 F8               BNE     PRNT1         NEXT CHAR
F983 20 F1               BRA     PRNT          REPEAT WITHOUT END
                *
                *
                *
                *       ASEM                  ASSEMBLE/DISASSEMBLE
F985 86 7E      ASEM     LDA A   #$7E          SET UP LINKS TO TS1BUG I/O
F987 97 00               STA A   00
F989 97 03               STA A   03
F98B CE FE B0            LDX     #INCH
F98E DF 01               STX     0001
F990 CE FF 3F            LDX     #OUTCH
F993 DF 04               STX     0004
F995 7F 00 06            CLR     06
F998 B6 A0 94            LDA A   IMODE
F99B 8A 40               ORA A   #%01000000 SUPPRESS ECHO
F99D B7 A0 94            STA A   IMODE
F9A0 7E D0 00            JMP     $D000         ENTRY POINT OF ASSEM/DISASSEM
                *
                *       EXTENDED COMMAND TABLE
F9A3 51         XTAB     FCB     'Q
F9A4 F9 76               FDB     PRNT
F9A6 58                  FCB     'X
F9A7 F9 85               FDB     ASEM
F9A9 00                  FCB     $00           END OF TABLE
                         END
      NO ERROR(S) DETECTED


   SYMBOL TABLE:
ASEM     F985     AUTOC    A0B4     BASE     A0B5     BS       F877
CHAP     F920     CHARS    0400     CLRS     F94D     CLRS1    F955
COL      A0B0     CURSR    A0BB     DISP     F8DC     EOR      F8AC
EROW     F913     EROW1    F919     ETER     F963     ETER1    F96D
ETER2    F975     FF       F8A3     HM       F8B5     HOME     F95C
HT       F885     IMODE    A094     INCH     FEB0     INPT0    F844
INPT1    F8BC     INPT2    F8C4     INPT3    F8CA     INPUT    F818
LASCL    003F     LASRW    000F     LF       F85A     LIMIT    E7C0
LINES    FC85     MAP      E400     MAXCL    0040     MAXRW    0010
OLD      A0B2     OMODE    A095     OUTCH    FF3F     POINT    A0B9
POSN1    F92B     PRNT     F976     PRNT1    F97B     RESET    FC1F
REST1    F803     REST2    F811     ROW      A0B1     SCRL     F901
SCRL1    F905     SPECL    A0B3     TOP      A0B7     VT       F895
XSAVE    A0BD     XTAB     F9A3
```

Bibliography

Some of the most important source material used in the preparation of this book is listed here. A brief comment on the content of each item is provided.

Chapter 1

Doerr, J., Low-cost microcomputing: The personal computer and single-board computer revolutions. *Proc. IEEE*, **66** (2), 117 – 30 (February 1978).
A review and history of the early days of personal computing.

Chapter 2

Morrow, G. and Fullmer, H., Proposed standard for the S100 bus. *Computer*, 84 – 90 (May 1978).
This article provides a specification of the popular S100 bus including its timing diagrams.

Patchett, G. N., *Electronic Power Supplies*. Pitman Publishing, 1970.
A well-written and easy to understand book on the analysis, design and characteristics of power supplies. It is now slightly dated with little on modern high-power monolithic regulators.

McNulty, J. F., Power supply systems for computer-based applications. *Digital Design*, 32 – 46 (March 1979).
A wide-ranging article dealing with all the aspects of power supplies—in particular reliability.

Pope, T., Designing with high current regulators. *Electronics Industry*, 21 – 7 (March 1979).
This article gives two worked examples of designing 5 V power supplies with high-current monolithic regulators. The problem of power dissipation is dealt with.

Adair, R. P., Transient-voltage suppressors suit pc-board protection needs. *EDN*, 105 – 9 (20 August 1979).
A short note on the application of Zener-type transient voltage suppressors in electronic circuits.

Chapter 3

Ferguson, B., This 6800 system handles clock stealing. *Digital Design,* 60–8 (October 1978).
This describes the use of the 6875 clock generator in a 6800 system with a 6844 DMA controller and a 6854 ADLC chip.

Bookout, S. R., *M6800 Systems Utilizing the MC6875 Clock Generator/Driver.* Motorola Inc. application note AN-775.
A detailed description of the 6875 clock generator chip and its applications to slow memory, DMA, and multiple processors.

Chapter 4

The E78 Microcomputer Bus Specification.
The E78 Microcomputer Bus Standards Committee, Avante House, 9 Bridge Street, Pinner, Middlesex, HA5 3HR, England, 1979.
This booklet deals with the specification of the E78, a general-purpose microprocessor bus. Anybody wishing to design a microprocessor bus will find this an excellent introduction to the electrical, mechanical, logical, and timing aspects of bus design.

Cergel, L., *Interfacing MPU-MC6800 with CMOS Systems.*
Motorola Inc. Application note AN-320.
This note looks at the electrical characteristics of NMOS devices (e.g. ACIA, PIA) and examines how they may be connected to CMOS devices. Voltage-level shifting and the noise immunity of such arrangements is considered.

Harrington, W., *MEK6800D2 Microcomputer Kit System Expansion Techniques.* Motorola Inc. Application note AN-771 (1977).
A very useful note on how to expand a microprocessor kit. Included is the ability to select one of two monitor ROMs, and the addition of a serial port to this kit.

United Technical Publications Inc., *Modern Guide to Digital Logic.* Foulsham-Tab (1977).
This book deals with the electrical characteristics of a wide variety of logic families from CMOS to MECL, and is particularly useful to anyone interfacing these designs with each other. The problems of noise and reflections are also dealt with.

Chapter 5

Hnatek, E. R., Semiconductor memory update. *Computer Design*, 67–77 (December 1979); 119-31 (January 1980); 147-59 (February 1980).
These three articles deal with ROMs, RAMs, and high-density memory technologies, respectively. They provide an excellent overview of the state-of-the-art of memory devices and consider likely developments in the next few years.

Hauck, L. T., Who's afraid of dynamic memories? *Byte*, **3** (7), 42 – 6, 140 – 50 (July 1978).
This is a primer on dynamic memories intended for those who wish to design a system using them. The MK4116 16K dynamic RAM is described, and its timing and power-supply considerations are considered.

Mullard Ltd., *Field Programmable Logic Arrays*. Mullard Technical Information Bulletin 62, TPI652, 1977.
A 47-page booklet on FPLAs with examples of their applications.

Ciarcia, S., Add nonvolatile memory to your computer. *Byte*, **4** (12), 36 – 53 (December 1979).
An article describing the operation of General Instrument Corp's EAROMs, complete with practical circuits.

Chapter 6

Binder, R. F., Designing a microprocessor driven multipurpose peripheral controller. *Computer Design*, 83 – 91 (April 1979).
An overview of the requirements and design of an "intelligent" peripheral controller based on the Z80.

Fronheiser, K. *Device Operation and System Implementation of the Asynchronous Communications Interface Adaptor (MC6850)*. Motorola Inc. Application Note AN-754.
This application note deals with the theory, operation and applications of the 6850 ACIA.

Motorola Inc., *Programmable Timer Fundamentals and Applications*. Motorola publication MC6840UM (AD), 1979.
This is an approximately 60-page booklet dealing with the operation of the 6840 PTM and its applications. Several examples of the use of the PTM are given including a digital thermometer, real-time clock, and an automobile engine analyzer. The last application is treated at length.

Uebelhor, M., Programmable CRT-Controller ICs adapt easily to μC display needs. *EDN*, 145 – 51 (20 June, 1979).
This article gives the full circuit diagram of a 6800-based VDT using the 6845 CRT controller and a dynamic memory.

Anderson, A. I., Build this video display terminal. *Byte*, **1** (11), 106 – 18 (November 1976).
An excellent article giving full details of the hardware design of a memory-mapped display plus a full complement of subroutines in 6800 assembly language to drive the display. Also included is a set of photographs of waveforms at various parts of the circuit.

Haas, B., Single chip video controller. *Byte*, **4** (5), 52 – 75 (May 1979).
This lengthy article is a detailed description of the 6845 CRTC together with the circuit and software of a VDT built round the 6845.

Weinstein, L., A programmable character generator. *Byte,* **3** (5), 79–90 (May 1978); **3** (6), 14–22 (June 1978).
Part one of this two part series deals with the construction of a programmable character generator which enables the character set of a VDT to be modified dynamically under software control. Essentially, the character generator "ROM" is mapped into part of the CPU's memory space. The second part of this article deals with the software requirements of the programmable character generator. No program listings are given and hence the discussion is processor independent.

Lancaster, D., *TV Typewriter Cookbook.* Howard Sams (1976).
This is the definitive "how to build a VDT" book and deals with all aspects of a raster-scan display at a thoroughly practical level. Keyboard and cassette interfaces are also included. Although the book is now dated by its lack of LSI VDT controllers it contains much valuable information.

Loos, T., Use your television set as a video monitor. *Byte,* **4** (2), 46–54 (February 1979).
A short article on interfacing the video stages of a TV to the composite video output of a VDT. This bypasses the IF amplifier, increasing the bandwidth and resolution of the display.

Catt, I., Davidson, M. F. and Walton, D. S., Interconnection of logic elements. *Wireless World,* **84** (1510), 61–3 (June 1978).
A short but interesting note on some of the properties of transmission lines, TTL and tri-state logic. This note might be subtitled "Tri-state logic considered as harmful."

Smith, D., Flat cables for digital circuits. *New Electronics*, 96–100 (22 January 1980).
This article takes a look at the electrical properties of ribbon cable and considers how these properties may be derived from its physical dimensions. The effect of the cable on pulse distortion and crosstalk is also examined.

Ogdin, C. A., Some simple hardware techniques allow fail-safe LSI interfacing. *EDN,* 117–20 (20 February 1979).
A short but extremely interesting article on connecting two digital systems (each with their own power supply) together. It considers the horrors of poorly designed systems which kill ICs if the power supplies are switched off in the wrong order. A worked example of a fail-safe interconnection is given.

Zuch, E. L., Interpretation of data converter accuracy specifications. *Computer Design,* 113–21 (September 1978).
A useful guide to the factors affecting the selection of an ADC or DAC. Transfer functions, quantization noise, offset, gain, linearity errors, and temperature effects are all considered in this article.

Milojkovic, D., *Data Conversion with Companding DAC Devices.* Advanced Micro Devices Application Note (February 1978).
This 36 page application note deals with the principles and applications of the non-linear DAC. The companding DAC permits the dynamic range of speech to be compressed into 8 bits.

Bylanski, P. and Ingram, D. G. W., *Digital Transmission Systems.* Peter Peregrinus, 1976.
A very readable book dealing with digital data transmission systems from a practical point of view. A section is devoted to transmission-line theory.

Bryant, J. and Swasdee, M., How to multiply in a wet climate. *Byte*, **3** (4), 28 – 35, 100 – 10 (April 1978); **3** (5), 104 – 14 (May 1978).
Despite the strange title, this is an excellent article on the MPY-8AJ 8-bit multiplier. A practical circuit for a 6800 system is given. Much of this article is taken up by a discussion of signed and unsigned binary multiplication.

Nelson, P., The number crunching processor. *Byte*, **3** (8), 64 – 74 (August 1978).
In this article the MM57109 number cruncher is described and a practical circuit for its interface to an 8080 CPU is given. The necessary software control routines are also included.

Adams, J. H., A scientific computer. *Wireless World*, **85** (1520), 44 – 8 (April 1979); **85** (1521), 89 – 93 (May 1979); **85** (1522), 85 – 8 (June 1979); **85** (1523) 81 – 4 (July 1979; **85** (1524), 79 – 82 (August 1979); **85** (1525), 61 – 3 (September 1979).
This series of articles presents the full design of a Z80 based microprocessor system and its interface to an MM57109 number cruncher chip. The circuits of both a cassette interface and a VDT are also included in this series.

Bregoli, L., The MM57109 number cruncher. *Kilobaud*, 38 – 46 (September 1979).
This article describes the MM57109 and gives a circuit diagram of its interface with a 1802 microprocessor together with the software (in flow chart form) to drive the number cruncher.

Osborne, A., Number crunching—two hardware solutions. *Kilobaud*, 84 – 8 (May 1978).
An article which compares and contrasts the MM57109 and the Am9511.

Gupta, B. K., Arithmetic processor chips enhance microprocessor system performance. *Computer Design*, 85 – 94 (July 1980).
This article describes the interfacing requirements of both the Am9511 and the MM57109 to 8080-type CPUs.

Chapter 7

Searle, B. C. and Freberg, D. E., Tutorial: Microprocessor applications in multiple processor systems. *Computer*, **8** (10), 22 – 30 (October 1975).
A paper outlining the terminology associated with multiple processor systems and giving the reader a general introduction to this topic. An extensive bibliography covering 1963 – 75 is included.

Loewer, B., The Z-80 in parallel. *Byte*, **3** (7), 60 – 3, 174 – 6 (July 1978).
This article deals with a dual processor system where two Z80s share a common block of 32K RAM and each CPU has its own dedicated block of 32K memory. Included in this article is a discussion of memory arbitration logic, and system timing requirements are given.

Castleman, K. R., The intelligent memory block. *Byte*, **3** (3), 186 – 92 (March 1978).
In this article multiple processor systems based on CPUs with two-phase clocks (i.e. 6800, 6502) are considered. The arrangement described is a master – slave system where each slave has a 4K block of memory which is common to the master processor's memory space. The slaves are transparent to the master processor.

Boyd, M., Two systems sharing the same bus. *Kilobaud,* 92 – 8 (June 1978).
An interesting article dealing with the practical aspects of the interface between two different (commercial) 6800 based systems. The effects of driving ribbon cables are also examined.

Schmidt, R. W., Asynchronous-sampling method simplifies dual-port memories. *EDN*, 201 – 4 (20 April 1980).
A short note describing how a block of RAM may be multiplexed between two ports without prioritization logic. This article is useful to anyone designing memory-mapped VDTs or dual processor systems.

Chapter 8

Motorola Inc., *Engineering Note 100.* Motorola Inc.
This engineering note gives a fully assembled and commented listing of MIKBUG, the prototype 6800 monitor. Included in this note is a description of the interface and the operating environment required by this monitor.

Microware Systems Corporation, *RT/68MX Systems Manual.* Microware Systems Corporation.
This is a manual for the RT/68MX ROM supplied as an alternative to MIKBUG. The manual includes an excellent introduction to the operation of a real-time, multitasking operating system. A fully commented assembly language listing of the monitor is provided. This manual should be regarded as essential reading for those attempting to produce their first real-time operating system.

Hemenway, J., EDN software systems design course. *EDN*, 252 – 312 (20 November 1978).
An extended article in seven chapters covering the design of a disk-based operating system for the 6800. The article is written at a tutorial level and includes the listing of a disk operating system.

Osborne, A., *6800 Programming for Logic Design.* Adam Osborne and Associates (1977).
This book deals with the assembly language of the 6800 and its application as a controller.

General References

Morris, R. L. and Miller, J. R., *Designing with TTL Integrated Circuits.* McGraw-Hill Kogakusha (1971).

This is a book written by members of Texas Instruments Ltd., and deals with all aspects of TTL logic—operation, characteristics, and application. It is good both as a practical handbook and as a logic primer.

Peatman, J. B., *Microcomputer-based Design*. McGraw-Hill Kogakusha (1977).
A general-purpose introduction to microprocessors with much useful information on interfacing them.

Motorola Inc., *M6800 Microprocessor Applications Manual*. Motorola Inc. (1975).
This is the basic source of information on the 6800, and is effectively a collection of application reports. The book is now considerably dated—especially the section on floppy disks. Clock circuits are rather basic (discrete components), and when it was written the only peripheral devices were the PIA and ACIA. In spite of this, there is much useful information in this publication.

Bishop, R., *Basic Microprocessors and the 6800*. Hayden Book Company (1979).
An elementary introduction to microprocessors based on the 6800.

Tanenbaum, A. S., *Structured Computer Organization*. Prentice-Hall (1976).
This is not a microprocessor book as such but is probably one of the very best general-purpose books on computer science ever written. Tanenbaum deals with a wide range of important topics (from machine code to self-virtualizing machines) at a tutorial level. At the end of each chapter are some very interesting questions providing food for thought. This is a vital book for any serious computer scientist or enthusiast who wishes to understand what modern computing is all about.

Blakeslee, T. R., *Digital Design with Standard MSI and LSI*. (2nd edn, 1979). Wiley.
This book deals with a wide range of topics from TTL logic and Boolean algebra to microprocessors. Some useful topics for the microprocessor systems' designer are dealt with in this book (e.g. reflections on transmission lines).

Ballard, D. R., Designing fail-safe microprocessor systems. *Electronics*, 139 – 43 (4 January 1979).
A short article taking a look at some of the considerations involved in the design of a highly reliable system. For example, a one-at-a-time address decoder detector is given which detects the simultaneous selection of two or more memory devices, and signals an error condition.

Wakerly, J. F., The Intel MCS-48 microcomputer family: A critique. *Computer*, 22 – 31 (February 1979).
This article gives the reader some idea of how to go about judging a microprocessor.

Leventhal, L. A., *Introduction to Microprocessors—Software, Hardware, Programming*. Prentice-Hall (1979).
A good general-purpose microprocessor handbook. It is well written and compares and contrasts the 6800 and 8080.

Klingman, E. E., *Microprocessor Systems Design*. Prentice-Hall (1977).
An excellent book on the design of microprocessor systems written in a very interesting style. The illustrations are particularly well done.

Index

A

W

Z

Integrated Circuits